MODERN
MANUFACTURING
PROCESSES

MODERN
MANUFACTURING
PROCESSES

DAVID L. GOETSCH

DELMAR PUBLISHERS INC.

NOTICE TO THE READER

DELMAR STAFF

Senior Administrative Editor: Michael McDermott
Developmental Editor: Lisa Reale
Project Editor: Christopher Chien
Production Coordinator: Helen Yackel
Art Manager: John Lent
Design Supervisor: Susan C. Mathews

All cover photos courtesy of Cincinnati Milacron

Printed in the United States of America
Published simultaneously in Canada
by Nelson Canada,
a division of The Thomson Corporation

10 9 8 7 6 5 4 3 2 1

Library of Congress Cataloging-in-Publication Data:

Goetsch, David L.
     Modern manufacturing processes/by David L. Goetsch and the Society of Manufacturing Engineers.
          p.   cm.

     Includes bibliographical references and index.
     ISBN 0-8273-2928-8
     1. Manufacturing processes.   I. Society of Manufacturing Engineers.   II. Title.
TS183.G65 1991
670.42—dc20

90-43917
CIP

Contents

PREFACE

Manufacturing is the enterprise through which materials are converted into products. Over the years, the materials used in manufacturing have evolved and changed. Metals are still a widely used material and the variety of metals available has expanded greatly over the years. But modern manufacturing materials also include plastics, ceramics, elastomers, and composites. Some of the processes used to convert materials into products have been used for years. Others are relatively new. Many of the traditional processes, though still used, have changed over the years.

MODERN MANUFACTURING PROCESSES was written in response to the need for a text that accomplishes the following purposes:

1. Provides comprehensive, up-to-date coverage of the materials used in a modern manufacturing setting.
2. Provides comprehensive, up-to-date coverage of the processes used in a modern manufacturing setting.
3. Provides comprehensive, up-to-date coverage of concepts that are shaping the future of manufacturing (i.e., computer control, artificial intelligence, adaptive control, automation, integration, machine vision, etc.)

MODERN MANUFACTURING PROCESSES was also written to fill a void that exists for a text that provides the appropriate breadth and depth of coverage for a survey course covering modern manufacturing materials and processes. Although there are several textbooks in this market, there is no middle ground between those in which the coverage is too extensive and those in which the coverage is too restricted for a one-semester survey course. *MODERN MANUFACTURING PROCESSES* was written to fill this void.

Persons undertaking a course in which this book is used should come away with a thorough understanding of modern manufacturing materials and the various processes used to convert them into useable products.

Intended Audience

MODERN MANUFACTURING PROCESSES is intended for use primarily in survey courses covering manufacturing materials and processes. It is appropriate for use in universities, community colleges, and technical colleges by students in such programs as:

- Industrial Engineering
- Mechanical Engineering
- Manufacturing Engineering
- Engineering Technology
- Industrial Technology
- Manufacturing Technology
- Drafting and Design Technology
- Machining Technology
- Quality Control Technology
- Production Control Technology
- Industrial Supervision and Management
- Technology Teacher Education
- Industrial Arts Teacher Education

Special Features of This Book

MODERN MANUFACTURING PROCESSES has a number of special features that enhance its usefulness as a learning aid. The most important of these are the following:

1. Complex technical material is presented in a simple, easy-to-understand format and in easily readable language.
2. Each chapter is a complete learning package that includes comprehensive coverage of the subject matter accompanied by:
   - Up-to-date illustrations and photographs
   - Comprehensive list of key terms and phrases
   - Comprehensive list of questions for additional study and review
3. Comprehensive glossary of terms and phrases.
4. Comprehensive index for easy access to specific material.

About the Authors

Dr. David L. Goetsch is Dean of Technical Education at Okaloosa-Walton Community College (OWCC) and Director of Florida's Center for Manufacturing Competitiveness (CMC), which is a technology transfer center for advanced manufacturing technologies. Dr. Goetsch and other CMC personnel work with manufacturing firms to help them stay competitive through the adoption and optimum use of appropriate advanced manufacturing technologies. The services provided to manufacturing firms by the CMC include updating and retraining of manufacturing personnel, updating of management personnel and key decision makers on new and emerging manufacturing technologies, selection and pilot testing of new technological systems and equipment, and setup and optimization of advanced manufacturing processes. The CMC is the State of Florida's representative in the Southern Technology Council's Consortium of Manufacturing Competitiveness, a twelve-state consortium of community colleges, universities, and technical colleges whose main purpose is technology transfer in the manufacturing arena.

The Society of Manufacturing Engineers, or SME, is a nonprofit technical society dedicated to the advancement of scientific knowledge in the field of manufacturing and to applying its resources to research, writing, publishing, and disseminating information. Founded in 1932, SME has its world headquarters in Dearborn, Michigan.

Education is one of the key activities of SME. The society produces curriculum materials, textbooks, training aids, and videotapes. As a member of the Accreditation Board for Engineering and Technology (ABET), SME has responsibilities for the accreditation criteria in manufacturing engineering, manufacturing engineering technology, and related degree areas.

SME's Manufacturing Engineering Education Foundation, through partnerships with industry, stimulates development of new and existing manufacturing engineering and technology through funding for capital equipment, research, awards, and student, faculty, and curriculum development. Further information about SME is available from the society's headquarters:

Society of Manufacturing Engineers
One SME Drive
P.O. Box 930
Dearborn, Michigan 48121-0930

Acknowledgements

The author wishes to thank the following people for their valuable input in reviewing this book.

Mike Kozak
North Texas State University
Denton, Texas

James R. Drake
Cuyahoga Community College
Cleveland, Ohio

Antoine F. Kassab
Northern Virginia Community College
Annandale, Virginia

Peter Fricano
Triton College
River Grove, Illinois

Gerald Post
Harrisburg Area Community College
Harrisburg, Pennsylvania

Howard A. Johnson
Monroe County Community College
Monroe, Michigan

Richard F. Morris
Grosse Pointe Park, Michigan

The author also acknowledges the invaluable assistance of Faye Crawford and Nancy Henderson in helping prepare the manuscript.

Chapter Opener Photos

Chapter 1 photos courtesy of Cincinnati Milacron Marketing Company

Chapter 2 photo courtesy of WESGO Division, GTE Products Corporation

Chapter 3 photo courtesy of WESGO Division, GTE Products Corporation

Chapter 4 photo courtesy of Van Dorn Plastic Machinery Company

Chapter 5 photo courtesy of Waukesha Foundry, Inc.

Chapter 6 photo courtesy of Protective Metal Alloys Inc.

Chapter 7 photo courtesy of Thermolyne Corporation

Chapter 8 photo courtesy of DoAll Company

Chapter 9 photo courtesy of The Olofsson Corporation

Chapter 10 photo courtesy of SKF & Dormer Tools Group

Chapter 11 photo courtesy of Cincinnati Milacron

Chapter 12 photo courtesy of Precision Laser Services

Chapter 13 photo courtesy of The Olofsson Corporation

Chapter 14 photo courtesy of Lincoln Electric Company

Chapter 15 photo courtesy of Fusion Inc.

Chapter 16 photo courtesy of Toyota Motor Manufacturing, USA Inc.

Chapter 17 photo courtesy of The L. S. Starrett Company

Chapter 18 photo courtesy of Cincinnati Milacron Marketing Company

Chapter 19 photo courtesy of Cincinnati Milacron Marketing Company

SOCIETY OF MANUFACTURING ENGINEERS & DELMAR PUBLISHERS INC.

A PARTNERSHIP IN EDUCATIONAL EXCELLENCE

SME and DELMAR have proudly joined forces to form a partnership dedicated to educational excellence. We believe that quality manufacturing education is the key to keeping America competitive in the years ahead.

The Society of Manufacturing Engineers is an international technical society dedicated to advancing scientific knowledge in the field of manufacturing. SME has more than 80,000 members in 70 countries and serves as a forum for engineers and managers to share ideas, information, and accomplishments.

To be successful, today's engineers and technicians must keep pace with the torrent of information that appears each day. To meet this need, SME provides, in addition to the publication of books, many opportunities in continuing education for its members. These opportunities include: monthly meetings through five associations and more than 300 chapters; educational programs including seminars, clinics, and videotapes, as well as conferences and expositions.

Today's manufacturing technology students represent our future. Our goal is to provide these students with the finest manufacturing technology educational products. By pooling our many resources, SME and DELMAR are going to help teachers get the job done.

Together SME and DELMAR will provide outstanding educational materials to prepare students to enter the real world of manufacturing.

Thomas J. Drozda
Director of Publications
Society of Manufacturing Engineers

Gregory C. Spatz
President
Delmar Publishers Inc.

Introduction

The title of this book, **MODERN MANUFACTURING PROCESSES**, was chosen to indicate that the book focuses on the most modern engineering materials and the most modern processes used to convert them into useful products. After completing **MODERN MANUFACTURING PROCESSES**, the reader should have a thorough understanding of the materials and processes he or she will confront in a modern manufacturing setting.

Manufacturing Defined

Manufacturing is that enterprise concerned with converting raw material into finished products. There are three distinct phases in manufacturing (see Fig. 1-1). These phases are as follows:

- Input
- Processing
- Output

The first phase includes all of the elements necessary to create a marketable product. First, there must be a demand or need for the product. The necessary materials must be available. Also needed are such resources as energy, time, human knowledge, and human skills. Finally, it takes capital to obtain all of the other resources.

Input resources are channeled through the various processes in Phase Two. These are the processes used to convert raw materials into finished products. A design is developed. Based on the design, various types of planning are accomplished. Plans are put into action through various production processes. The various resources and processes are managed to

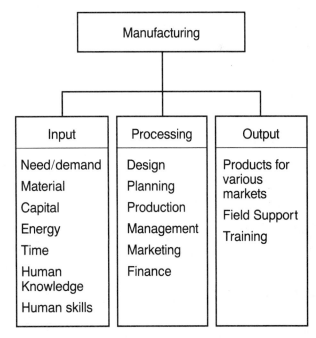

Manufacturing		
Input	**Processing**	**Output**
Need/demand	Design	Products for various markets
Material	Planning	
Capital	Production	Field Support
Energy	Management	Training
Time	Marketing	
Human Knowledge	Finance	
Human skills		

Figure 1-1 Three phases in manufacturing

1

ensure efficiency and productivity. For example, capital resources must be carefully managed to ensure they are used prudently. Finally, the product in question is marketed.

The final phase is the output or finished product. Once the finished product has been purchased it must be transported to users. Depending on the nature of the product, installation and ongoing field support may be required. In addition, with some products, particularly those of a highly complex nature, training is necessary. **MODERN MANUFACTURING PROCESSES** is primarily concerned with the material component of Phase One and the production component of Phase Two.

Materials and Processes in Manufacturing

Engineering materials covered herein are divided into two broad categories: **metals** and **nonmetals**. Metals are subdivided into ferrous metals, nonferrous metals, high-performance alloys, and powdered metals. Nonmetals are subdivided into plastics, elastomers, composites, and ceramics, Fig. 1-2.

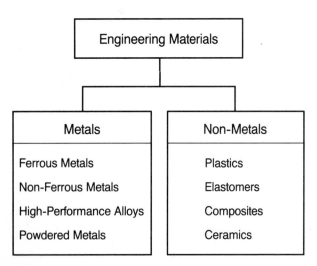

Figure 1-2   Two broad categories of engineering materials

Production processes covered herein are divided into several broad categories including forming, forging, casting/molding, heat treatment, fastening/joining, metrology/quality control, and material removal, Fig. 1-3. Each of these is subdivided into several other processes so that the book covers all of the materials and production processes that are the most widely used in the world of modern manufacturing. Also covered are a variety of new technologies that are emerging and will be widely used in the future.

Stages in the Development of Manufacturing

Over the years, manufacturing processes have gone through four distinct, although overlapping, stages of development, Fig. 1-4. These stages are as follows:

Stage 1 .... Manual
Stage 2 .... Mechanized
Stage 3 .... Automated
Stage 4 .... Integrated

When people first began converting raw materials into finished products, they used manual processes. Everything was accomplished using human hands and manually operated tools. This was a very rudimentary form of fully integrated manufacturing. A person identified the need, collected materials, designed a product to meet the need, produced the product, and used it. Everything from start to finish was integrated within the mind of the person who did all the work.

Then during the industrial revolution mechanized processes were introduced and humans began using machines to accomplish work previously accomplished manually. This led to work specialization which, in turn, eliminated the integrated aspect of manufacturing. In this stage of development, manufacturing workers might see only that part of an overall manufacturing operation represented by that specific

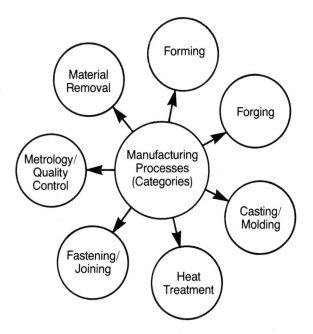

Figure 1-3   Categories of manufacturing processes

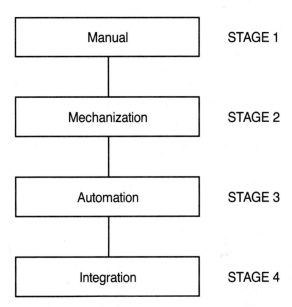

Figure 1-4   Stages in the development of manufacturing

piece on which they worked. There was no way to tell how their efforts fit into the larger picture or their workpiece into the finished product.

The next stage in the development of manufacturing processes involved the automation of selected processes. This amounted to computer control of machines and processes. During this phase, *islands of automation* began to spring up on the shop floor. Each island represented a distinct process or group of processes used in the production of a product. Although these islands of automation did tend to enhance the productivity of the individual processes within the islands, overall productivity often was unchanged. This was because the islands were sandwiched in among other processes that were not automated and were not synchronized with them.

The net result was that workpieces would move quickly and efficiently through the automated processes only to back up at manual stations and create bottlenecks. To understand this problem, think of yourself driving from stoplight to stoplight in rush hour traffic. Occasionally you find an opening and are able to rush ahead of the other cars that are creeping along, only to find yourself backed up at the next light. The net effect of your brief moment of speeding ahead is canceled out by the bottleneck at the next stoplight. Better progress would be made if you and the other drivers could synchronize your speed to the changing of the stoplights. Then all cars would move steadily and consistently along and everyone would make better progress in the long run.

This need for steady, consistent flow on the shop floor led to the development of integrated manufacturing, a process that is still emerging. In fully integrated settings, machines and processes are computer controlled and integration is accomplished through computers. In the analogy used in the previous paragraph, computers would synchronize the rate of movement of all cars with the changing of the stoplights so that everyone moved steadily and consistently along. Computer integrated manufacturing, or CIM, is covered in Chapter 19.

Significant Developments in Manufacturing

Over the years since people first converted clay from the earth into bowls, dishes, and various other containers, there have been many significant developments in manufacturing materials and processes. Some of the more important of these are presented on the timeline in Fig. 1-5. There have been too many developments to summarize on one timeline. Those shown represent only selected highlights.

Organization of a Manufacturing Company

The CASA/SME's **CIM Wheel** in Fig. 1-6 illustrates the various components of a manufacturing company.

All of these components are involved in one or more of the three broad categories of manufacturing processes: **input, processing,** and **output**. The outer ring summarizes the input and output processes. The inner ring is devoted to the design, production planning and control, and production processes. Viewing the organization of a manufacturing company as a wheel as opposed to the traditional block diagram gives a better picture of the interrelationships of the various components in a modern manufacturing company.

Organization of this Book

MODERN MANUFACTURING PROCESSES consists of 19 chapters, an extensive glossary, and an appendix. Chapters 2 and 3 cover the materials most widely used in a modern manufacturing setting. Chapter 4 covers the various forming processes used for changing the shape of these materials.

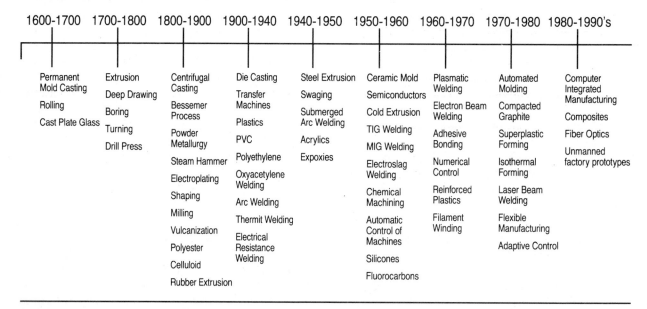

1600-1700	1700-1800	1800-1900	1900-1940	1940-1950	1950-1960	1960-1970	1970-1980	1980-1990's
Permanent Mold Casting	Extrusion	Centrifugal Casting	Die Casting	Steel Extrusion	Ceramic Mold	Plasmatic Welding	Automated Molding	Computer Integrated Manufacturing
Rolling	Deep Drawing	Bessemer Process	Transfer Machines	Swaging	Semiconductors	Electron Beam Welding	Compacted Graphite	Composites
Cast Plate Glass	Boring	Powder Metallurgy	Plastics	Submerged Arc Welding	Cold Extrusion	Adhesive Bonding	Superplastic Forming	Fiber Optics
	Turning	Steam Hammer	PVC	Acrylics	TIG Welding	Numerical Control	Isothermal Forming	Unmanned factory prototypes
	Drill Press	Electroplating	Polyethylene	Expoxies	MIG Welding	Reinforced Plastics	Laser Beam Welding	
		Shaping	Oxyacetylene Welding		Electroslag Welding	Filament Winding	Flexible Manufacturing	
		Milling	Arc Welding		Chemical Machining		Adaptive Control	
		Vulcanization	Thermit Welding		Automatic Control of Machines			
		Polyester	Electrical Resistance Welding		Silicones			
		Celluloid			Fluorocarbons			
		Rubber Extrusion						

Figure 1-5   Timeline of significant developments in manufacturing

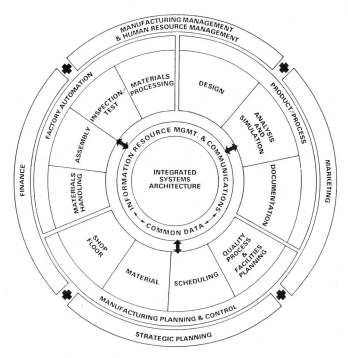

Figure 1-6 Organization of a manufacturing company as depicted by the SME/CASA's "CIM wheel"

Chapters 5 and 6 cover forging, casting, and molding processes. Those covered in Chapter 5 are the traditional processes that are still widely used. Those covered in Chapter 6 are the more contemporary processes. Heat treatment processes are covered in Chapter 7. Chapter 8 is devoted to broaching and sawing. Turning and boring are covered in Chapter 9.

Drilling and various related processes are covered in Chapter 10. Milling and grinding are covered in Chapter 11. Chapter 12 is devoted to a variety of machining processes known collectively in the language of manufacturing as **nontraditional** machining processes. Chapter 13 covers the various ways in which manufacturing machines and processes are controlled, giving particular attention to the various types of computer control.

Chapters 14 and 15 cover the various fastening and joining processes used in modern manufacturing settings. Chapter 16 explains how these and other assembly operations are automated. Chapter 17

covers metrology and the various processes used to control and assure quality.

Chapter 18 provides an in-depth treatment of flexible manufacturing which leads into computer-integrated manufacturing (CIM), covered in Chapter 19.

Although there are separate chapters devoted entirely to the advanced manufacturing concepts of flexible manufacturing and CIM, up-to-date information is also integrated where appropriate in other chapters. For example, Chapter 17 covers the various traditional metrology and quality control processes and procedures that are still widely used, but it also covers the more modern processes such as statistical process control (SPC). All other chapters follow this same format. Contemporary and emerging manufacturing technologies covered in various chapters include just-in-time (JIT), numerical control (CNC and DNC), group technology, adaptive control, laser applications, industrial robots, artificial intelligence, machine vision, sensor technology, manufacturing resources planning (MRP), and many others.

CHAPTER 2

Engineering Materials: Metals

MAJOR TOPICS COVERED

- Carbon Steels
- Alloy Steels
- High-Strength Low-Alloy Steels
- Stainless Steels
- Maraging Steels
- Cast Steels
- Cast Irons
- High Performance Alloys
- Tungsten, Molybdenum, and Titanium
- Aluminum, Copper, and Magnesium
- Lead, Tin, and Zinc
- Powdered Metals

Metal is still a widely used engineering material in the modern manufacturing setting. There is an almost infinite number of products made of a wide variety of metals (see Fig. 2-1). The metals most commonly used in modern manufacturing are covered in this chapter.

Carbon Steels

Iron and carbon are the predominant elements in steels. Carbon content ranges from a few hundredths to about one percent. The amount of additional alloying elements determines whether the steel is considered to be a carbon or an alloy steel.

Steel is considered a carbon steel when no minimum content is specified or required for aluminum (except for oxidation or to control grain size), chromium, cobalt, columbium, molybdenum, nickel, titanium, tungsten, vanadium, zirconium, or any other

Figure 2-1 A variety of products produced of metal *(Courtesy of Zagar Incorporated)*

element to obtain a desired alloying effect; when the specified minimum for copper does not exceed 0.40%; or when the addition of manganese, silicon, and copper is limited to a maximum of 1.65%, 0.60%, and 0.60%, respectively.

On the basis of carbon content, carbon steels can be divided into three groups. The first group contains 0.001-0.30% carbon and is considered low-carbon steel. The second group contains 0.30-0.70% carbon and is considered medium-carbon steel. The third group contains 0.70-1.30% carbon and is considered high-carbon steel.

Certain grades may also specify the addition of boron to improve hardenability and aluminum for deoxidation and to control grain size. Carbon steels also contain small quantities of residual elements or impurities from the raw material such as copper, nickel, molybdenum, chromium, phosphorus, and sulfur, which are considered incidental.

Carbon steels may be classified according to chemical composition, deoxidation practice, quality, and end-product forms. Common end-product forms include bar, sheet/strip, plate, wire, tubing, and structural shapes. Carbon steel may also be classified as hot rolled or cold drawn (cold rolled when referring to sheets). Cold finished steels are produced from hot rolled steel by several cold finishing processes, resulting in improved surface finishes, dimensional accuracy, alignment, or machinability; elongation and yield and tensile strengths are increased. Cold rolled sheets are available in different tempers and can be precoated with zinc, aluminum, terne (lead-tin alloy), tin, and organic coatings.

Types of Steel

The principal reaction in steelmaking is the removal of excess carbon by the combination of carbon and oxygen to form a gas. If the extra oxygen remaining after this reaction is not removed prior to or during casting, the gaseous products continue to evolve during solidification. The type of steel produced is determined by the amount of deoxidation that takes place before casting. The four types of carbon steels produced are killed, semikilled, rimmed, and capped.

Grades of Steel

Grade usually denotes the chemical composition of a particular steel. The grades may vary in chemical composition from almost pure iron to a material of complex constitution. A particular grade of carbon steel usually has specified limits for various elements, but the properties of products made from that grade can be diverse.

Lists of standard steels designed to serve the needs of fabricators and users of steel products are published by the American Iron and Steel Institute (AISI) and the Society of Automotive Engineers (SAE). The general acceptance and use of standard steels since their inception in 1941 have demonstrated that these steels have, in most cases, successfully replaced the many steels of specialized compositions previously used. The list is altered from time to time to accommodate steels of proven merit and to provide for changes that develop in industry. There are still specialized steels being produced, however, for particular applications.

Grade Designation: A four-numeral series, adopted by the AISI and the SAE, is used to designate standard carbon steels specified to chemical composition ranges. It is important to note that these designations do not indicate specifications. The prefix M is used to designate a series of merchant-quality steels and the suffix H designates standard hardenability steels.

The first two digits indicate the steel type and identifying elements as shown in Fig. 2-2. The last

Series Designation*	Type and Approximate Percentages of Identifying Elements
10XX	Nonresulfurized, 1.00% manganese maximum
11XX	Resulfurized
12XX	Rephosphorized and resulfurized
15XX	Nonresulfurized, over 1.00% manganese

* XX indicates carbon content in hundredths of a percent.

Figure 2-2   Grade designations of standard carbon steels

two digits indicate the approximate mean of the carbon range. For example, in the grade designation 1035, 35 represents a carbon range of 0.32 to 0.38%. It is necessary to deviate from this system and to interpolate numbers in the case of some carbon ranges and for variations in manganese, phosphorus, or sulfur with the same range. Special-purpose elements such as lead and boron are designated by inserting the letter L or B, respectively, between the second and third numerals.

In 1975, the Unified Numbering System (UNS) for Metals and Alloys was established by the American Society for Testing and Materials (ASTM) and the SAE. The UNS number consists of a single letter prefix followed by five digits. The letter G indicates standard carbon steels, and H indicates standard hardenability steels. The first four digits usually correspond to standard AISI, ASTM, or SAE steel designations, and the last digit usually indicates that an additional element such as lead or boron is specified. The number four indicates that lead is added, the number one indicates boron, and the number six indicates that an electric furnace is used for melting.

Mechanical Properties

Mechanical properties are those properties of the material that are associated with the material's reaction when a force is applied. Mechanical properties are usually determined from tension, bend, and hardness tests. The properties most commonly specified are tensile and yield strengths, total elongation, reduction in area, and hardness.

Hot rolled and cold drawn bars are usually produced to meet mechanical property requirements as well as limited compositional requirements. The tensile characteristics of hot rolled bars are mainly influenced by chemical composition, thickness or cross-sectional area, and variables in hot rolling and cooling practices. The effect of cold working on cold drawn bars depends on chemical composition, cross-sectional area, amount of cold reduction, and thermal treatment. During cold working, the yield strength of a material increases more than the tensile strength.

Data from tension tests are used to determine the mechanical properties of sheet steel that influence drawing and stretching. The two main properties are the plastic strain ratio (r) and the work-hardening exponent (n).

The plastic strain ratio is indicative of the ability of a sheet to resist thinning during drawing and is defined as the ratio of width strain to thickness strain in the tensile test. Since the properties of the sheet are different in different directions, the average strain ratio ($\overline{r}$) is given. As the $\overline{r}$ value increases, the depth of permissible draw increases.

The work-hardening exponent (n) is a measure of the ability of the sheet to resist localized straining and thus increase uniform deformation. A metal with a high n value tends to strain uniformly even under nonuniform stress conditions. Typical n values for low-carbon steels are 0.20-0.22.

Alloy Steels

Simply stated, an alloy steel is a steel that has one or more alloying elements added to it to obtain properties not obtainable in carbon steels. Steel is considered to be an alloy steel when the maximum range for manganese, silicon, or copper exceeds 1.65, 0.60, and 0.60%, respectively. A steel is also considered an alloy when a definite range or a minimum quantity is specified or required for aluminum, chromium (up to 3.99%), cobalt, columbium, molybdenum, nickel, titanium, tungsten, vanadium, zirconium, or any other alloying element.

The alloy steels discussed in this section are the low-alloy steels. These steels may be divided into the structural grades and those listed by the AISI and the SAE. In the structural grades, the alloying elements are the principal means of strengthening the ferrite matrix. The structural grade alloy steels are generally used in the as-rolled condition, the quenched and tempered condition, and in the normalized or annealed condition. In the AISI/SAE grades, the alloying elements serve primarily to improve the mechanical properties over equivalent carbon steel and to enhance the response of the steel to heat treatment.

Grade Designation: As with low-carbon steels, a four-numeral series designates alloy steels specified to chemical composition ranges. For certain grades, a five-numeral series is used.

The last two digits of the four-numeral series indicate the approximate middle of the carbon range; for example, 20 represents a range of 0.18 to 0.23% carbon. In the five-numeral series, the last three digits represent the carbon range. The first two digits of both the four- and five-numeral series indicate the primary alloying elements used in the grade, along with their approximate percentages.

The prefix letter E is used to designate steels normally made by the basic electric furnace practice. Steels without the prefix are normally manufactured by the basic open-hearth or basic oxygen processes.

The UNS for metals and alloys designates the various alloy steel grades using a single letter prefix followed by five digits. The letter G indicates standard alloy or carbon steels, and the first four digits usually correspond to the AISI/SAE steel designations. The fifth digit indicates an additional element, such as boron (indicated by the number one), or a particular manufacturing practice.

Hardenability Grades: As a result of cooperative work done by the SAE and the AISI, hardenability bands have been developed for many of the constructional alloy steels. The hardenability limits were determined from data obtained by conducting standard 1″ (25.4 mm) Jominy end-quench hardenability tests (ASTM Standard A 256) on many heats of each composition.

As a means of identifying steels specified to hardenability requirements, the suffix letter H has been added to the conventional series number. The UNS designates these steels with the prefix letter H instead of G which is used to designate standard alloy or carbon steels.

Alloy Steel Quality

Alloy steels are made with more than ordinary care throughout their manufacture. They are more sensitive to thermal and mechanical operations, the control of which is complicated by the varying effects of different chemical combinations.

The quality characteristics of alloy steel include, among others, internal soundness, uniformity of chemical composition, and freedom from injurious surface imperfections. The degree to which these characteristics can be obtained is limited by existing raw materials, manufacturing methods, and the technological nature of the alloy steel. Quality characteristics are related to the suitability of the steel to make a particular part (see Fig. 2-3).

Alloying Elements

Alloying elements are added to ordinary steels for the purpose of modifying their behavior during heat treatment, which in turn results in improvement of the mechanical and physical properties. Specifically, the additions are made for one or more of the following reasons:

- Improve tensile strength without lowering material ductility.
- Improve toughness.
- Increase hardenability, which permits the hardening of larger sections than possible with plain carbon steels or allows successful quenching with less drastic cooling rates, reducing the hazard of distortion and quench cracking.
- Retain physical properties at elevated temperatures.
- Obtain better corrosion resistance.
- Improve wear resistance.
- Impart a fine grain size to the steel.
- Improve surface (case) hardening characteristics.

Mechanical Properties

Alloy steels are not directly produced to specific mechanical properties, but are usually heat treated to achieve desired properties. Cold finished alloy steel bars usually require thermal treatments in order to meet definite limitations for tensile or hardness values. Alloy steels in the annealed and cold finished condition can be produced to specified maximum hardness limits. For steels in the normalized and cold

Quality Designations	Characteristics	Applications
Regular quality	Basic or standard quality for alloy steel. These steels are killed and are produced as fine grain. May contain surface imperfections.	Used for regular constructional applications.
Axle shaft quality	Special rolling practices, special billet and bar conditioning, and selective inspection are employed to minimize surface imperfections.	Used for power-driven axle shafts for automobiles and trucks.
Ball and roller bearing quality	Subjected to restricted melting and special teeming, rolling, cooling, and conditioning practices. Thorough examinations for internal imperfections are performed.	Used for antifriction bearings.
Cold heading quality	Bars are supplied from steel produced by closely controlled steelmaking practices and are subject to testing and inspection to determine internal soundness, uniformity of chemical composition, and freedom from detrimental surface imperfections. Hardness and microstructure controlled by heat treatment.	Used in the production of fasteners, studs, anchor pins, bearing rollers, and cap screws by cold plastic deformation.
Special cold heading quality	Produced by closely controlled steelmaking practices to provide uniform chemical composition and internal soundness. Surface imperfections removed at intermediate stages by grinding or equivalent surface preparation. Hardness and microstructure controlled by heat treatment.	Used for applications requiring severe, cold plastic deformation such as for front suspension studs, socket screws, and valves.
Aircraft quality	Produced using exacting steelmaking, rolling, and testing practices. Phosphorus and sulfur limited to 0.025% maximum.	Used for highly stressed aircraft, missile, and rocket parts.

Figure 2-3   Summary of quality designations for hot and cold rolled alloy steel bars

finished condition, minimum hardness or minimum tensile strength may be specified. If the steels are normalized and tempered before cold finishing, either maximum and minimum hardnesses or maximum and minimum tensile values can be produced to a range that varies with the tensile strength level and is equivalent to a Brinell indentation diameter range of four-tenths of a millimeter (e.g., 4.0 to 4.4) at any specified location. If the steels are quenched and tempered before cold finishing, either maximum and minimum hardnesses or maximum and minimum tensile strength values can be produced to a range that varies with the tensile strength level and is equivalent to a Brinell indentation diameter range of three-tenths of a millimeter (e.g., 3.6 to 3.9) at any specified location.

When both hardness and tensile values are specified at the same position, the limits should be consistent with each other. In many cases, when the Brinell limits are specified as surface values, the tensile test results, which are of necessity obtained below the surface, and the surface hardness results will not be consistent because they vary according to the size of bar and the hardenability of the steel involved. For that reason the purchaser should recognize inconsistencies between the two and specify limits accordingly. In either case, it is essential that the position at which Brinell hardness values are taken be specified by the purchaser.

Generally the yield, elongation, and reduction of area are specified as minimums for steel in the quenched and tempered or normalized and tempered conditions, and they should be consistent with the tensile strength or Brinell hardness.

High-Strength Low-Alloy Steels

High-strength low-alloy (HSLA) steels are a group of steels that exhibit and develop strengths significantly higher than carbon steels owing to the addition of small amounts of alloying elements, coupled with special steel processing methods. The carbon content of these steels is usually less than 0.30% by weight. Small amounts of manganese, silicon, phosphorus, copper, aluminum, chromium, niobium, vanadium, titanium, molybdenum, nickel, zirconium, nitrogen, calcium, and rare earth elements are used singly or in combination to increase strength, toughness, formability, and corrosion resistance.

The total alloy content of a few grades of HSLA steel is high enough to qualify them as alloy steels. However, HSLA steels are considered distinct from traditional alloy steels, such as constructional alloy steels, since, with a few exceptions, they achieve their high strength without separate heat treatment after finishing.

Types of HSLA Steels

High-strength low-alloy steels have been categorized or grouped largely on composition. Several

types can often achieve a given strength level, but with varying degrees of toughness, formability, weldability, and corrosion resistance. In addition, the strength, toughness, and formability of a given type of HSLA steel can vary depending on the rolling and finishing practices used during production.

HSLA steels are typified by a high strength-to-weight ratio, and, as a result, yield strength is an important consideration. Hot rolled grades exhibit yield strengths ranging from 42 to 90 ksi (290 to 620 MPa). Cold rolled sheet and strip grades develop yield strengths from 40 to 140 ksi (276 to 965 MPa).

Stainless Steels

Stainless steels are iron-based alloys containing 10.50% or more chromium. These steels achieve their "stainless" characteristics as a result of the invisible and adherent, chromium-rich oxide film that forms on the material's surface. The oxide film is self-forming and self-healing in the presence of oxygen. Other elements added to improve corrosion resistance, fabricating and machining characteristics, or strength include nickel, molybdenum, copper, titanium, silicon, manganese, columbium, aluminum, nitrogen, and sulfur. Carbon is normally present in amounts from 0.03% to over 1.00% in certain martensitic grades, which contributes to improvements in the alloy's strength.

The selection of stainless steels is based on corrosion or heat resistance, mechanical properties, fabrication characteristics, availability, and the total product cost. Generally, corrosion resistance and mechanical properties are the predominant factors in selecting the appropriate grade of stainless steel for a given application.

Types of Stainless Steels

Stainless steels possess resistance to attack by many corrosive media at room and elevated temperatures, and are produced in a variety of grades to cover a wide range of mechanical and physical properties for specific applications. Currently, over 57 standard grades of stainless steels are produced as well as proprietary stainless steels with special characteristics. The standard grades are those identified in the American Iron and Steel Institute (AISI) products manual entitled *Stainless and Heat Resisting Steels*.

The AISI classifies the different types of stainless steels according to a three-digit numbering system. The first digit indicates the type of stainless steel that is suggestive of the material's microstructure. The last two digits indicate the specific grade in the group. Letters following the last two digits indicate modifications of a specific grade. The Unified Numbering System (UNS) uses six characters to designate a particular material type and grade. All stainless steels in this system are identified by the letter "S" and followed by five digits.

The five main types of stainless steels include austenitic, ferritic, martensitic, precipitation-hardening, and duplex. Austenitic, ferritic, martensitic, and duplex stainless steels are classified according to the three-digit and six-character number systems. Precipitation-hardening stainless steels are generally classified according to the six-character numbering system.

Maraging Steels

Maraging steels, developed by the International Nickel Company in the 1960s, comprise a special class of high-strength steels that use nickel as the main alloying element. The term "maraging" is derived from "martensite age hardening" and denotes age hardening of a low-carbon, iron-nickel martensitic matrix.

The annealed microstructure of maraging steel is essentially a carbon-free, iron-nickel lath martensite. In the annealed condition, the material is soft and can be readily machined or formed. The material is martensitic at room temperature but reverts to an austenitic, face-centered cubic structure when heated to 1500°F (815°C). During cooling, martensite

starts to form at 310°F (155°C) and is 99% complete at 210°F (100°C). The material is heated to 900°F (480°C) for aging and then cooled to room temperature. During aging, the martensite is strengthened by short-range ordering and subsequent precipitation of nickel-molybdenum and nickel-titanium intermetallic compounds.

Maraging steels are produced by a double-vacuum melting process to maintain high purity and to reduce residual elements. The first process is usually vacuum induction melting which is then followed by a vacuum-arc remelting process. Maraging steels are produced in wrought steel compositions. Common wrought forms are bar, plate, and sheet.

Alloys

Currently only 18% nickel maraging steel alloys are being produced. The 20% and 25% nickel alloys were the two original maraging alloys developed, but they were discontinued because of their brittleness at high-temperature strength levels and the complexity of the annealing and aging treatments.

Nickel rather than carbon is the principal alloying element in maraging steels. Cobalt, molybdenum, and titanium are used to develop the high strength. The use of more common elements like carbon, sulphur, phosphorous, silicon, and manganese is held to a minimum since they serve no significant purpose, and in some cases may promote embrittlement of the alloy. The balance of the analysis is iron. The numerical designations associated with each grade are generally indicative of the ultimate tensile strength of that grade in ksi.

Cast Steels

In wrought steel production, the various alloying elements are melted together in a furnace and then poured into ingots to cool and subsequently be hot and/or cold worked until the desired form and size have been achieved. When steel castings are produced, the various alloying elements are melted together and then poured directly into a mold cavity having the proper design. The cast part is allowed to cool and then removed from the mold.

The compositions of steel castings are similar to those of wrought steels, with the exception of higher silicon and manganese content to ensure thorough deoxidation. Cast steels may contain alloying elements such as nickel, chromium, vanadium, and copper to give desirable combinations of hardness, tensile strength, and toughness not readily available in plain carbon grades. The total alloy content may be as high as 30% or greater. Chemical compositions of the various alloys are usually based on specifications of the ASTM. Cast steels are also available in AISI designations, but the silicon and manganese percentages are higher than in wrought steels. The hardness of cast steels is measured by the Brinell test method because of the coarseness of their microstructure.

Cast Steel Alloys and Applications

Cast steels are available in carbon, low-alloy, corrosion-resistant, and heat-resistant alloys. The following material briefly describes the more commonly used alloys and includes the various areas and industries where these alloys are being used. Also included are tables of the mechanical properties that are most useful for manufacturing engineers.

Carbon and Low-Alloy Cast Steels: Cast carbon steels have carbon as the main alloying element, although other alloying elements are also present. They are usually classified by the amount of carbon contained in the steel; low-carbon steel castings contain up to 0.20% carbon, medium-carbon steel castings contain from 0.20 to 0.50% carbon, and high-carbon steel castings contain more than 0.50% carbon. Cast steels containing more than 1.00% manganese, 0.80% silicon, 0.50% nickel, 0.50% copper, 0.25% chromium, 0.10% molybdenum, 0.05% vanadium, and 0.05% tungsten are normally

considered alloy steel castings. When the percentage of alloying elements, including carbon, is 8% or less, the cast steel is considered low-alloy cast steel. In low-alloy cast steel, carbon content is generally less than 0.45%.

Corrosion-Resistant Cast Steels: Corrosion-resistant, high-alloy steel castings are commonly referred to as cast stainless steels. Alloy composition is based on the alloy designation system adopted by the Alloy Casting Institute (ACI), and the various alloys produced are covered by ASTM A743, A744, A747, and A494 standards.

The principal grades are martensitic, ferritic, precipitation-hardening, austenitic-ferritic, and austenitic. These steels are generally used when manufacturing chemical processing and power generating equipment to resist corrosion in aqueous or liquid-vapor environments at temperatures below 600°F (315°C).

Heat-Resistant Steel Castings: Cast steels discussed in this section are divided into two groups: (1) those that can be used for service up to 1150°F (620°C) and (2) those that can be used for service above 1150°F (620°C). The steels for use below 1150°F (620°C) are made up of carbon and low-alloy cast steels, and the alloys for service above 1150°F (620°C) are made up of high-alloy cast steels.

Carbon and low-alloy steel castings. The two elements common to this group of cast steels and that contribute to creep resistance are molybdenum and chromium. These steels are covered by ASTM A216, A217, A356, and A389 standards.

High-alloy steel castings. To provide effective resistance to oxidation (scaling) or to corrosive gases, these alloys contain chromium content in excess of 12%. Except for their higher carbon content, these cast steels are similar to corrosion-resistant cast steels. The three principal grades in this group are iron-chromium, iron-chromium-nickel, and iron-nickel-chromium. The various alloys are covered by the ASTM A297 standard.

Iron-chromium. The alloys belonging to this grade are designated by *HC* and *HD*. Alloy HD has greater strength because of its high nickel content. Iron-chromium alloys can be used for components in load-bearing applications up to 1200°F (649°C) and in lighter load-bearing applications up to 1900°F (1038°C). Some typical components are rabble arms and blades for ore-roasting furnaces, salt pots, and grate bars.

Iron-chromium-nickel. The alloys in this grade are partially or completely austenitic and have higher strength and ductility than iron-chromium alloys. These alloys are designated by *HE, HF, HH, HI, HK,* and *HL.* Satisfactory results are obtained in either oxidizing or reducing atmospheres.

Typical applications for HE alloys are ore-roasting furnaces and steel mill furnaces. Alloy HF is used for tube supports and beams in oil refinery heaters, in cement kilns, and in ore-roasting and heat-treating furnaces. Alloy HH is used for manufacturing furnace parts that are not subjected to severe temperature cycling. Alloy HI is used in cast retorts for calcium and magnesium production. Alloy HK is used in the production of jet engines, gas turbines, hydrogen reformer tubes, and furnace parts. Alloy HL exhibits the best resistance to high-sulfur environments up to 1800°F (980°C) and is used in gas dissociation equipment.

Iron-nickel-chromium. These alloys—HN, HP, HT, HU, HW, and HX—are high-nickel steels and normally constitute about 40% of the total production of heat-resistant castings. Nickel is either the predominant alloying element or, in some cases, the base metal. The alloys can be used for most applications up to 2100°F (1150°C) and give excellent service life when subject to rapid heating and cooling. Resistance to thermal fatigue is excellent, but they are not recommended in atmospheres with high sulfur content.

Typical applications for alloy HN are brazing fixtures and highly stressed parts. Alloy HP is used for heat-treat fixtures, radiant tubes, and coils for ethylene pyrolysis heaters. Alloy HT is used for parts in heat-treating furnaces, glass rolls, enameling racks, and radiant heater tubes. Alloy HU is used for manufacturing burner tubes, lead and cyanide pots, retorts, and furnace parts. Alloy HW is used for hearths, mufflers, retorts, trays, boxes, burner parts, enameling fixtures, quenching fixtures, and containers for molten lead. Alloy HX finds the same applications as HW,

particularly when improved resistance to hot gas corrosion is required.

Cast Irons

The term "cast iron" is a generic term that designates an entire family of cast ferrous metals. These metals possess a wide variety of properties that distinguish them from the family of steels. In composition, both steels and cast irons are primarily iron that is alloyed with carbon. However, steels always contain less than 2% combined carbon (and usually less than 1%), while cast irons contain more than 2% carbon. The carbon in cast iron is generally in the free state except for a maximum 0.65% combined carbon. Cast irons must also contain appreciable amounts of silicon, usually from 1 to 3%. These differences are not arbitrary, but have a metallurgical basis and effect the differing useful properties of these two families of ferrous alloys.

Because of the high carbon and silicon content, cast irons possess excellent casting characteristics and can be melted more easily than steels. Molten cast iron also flows better than molten steel and is less reactive with the molding material because of a lower pouring temperature. Shrinkage and contraction of cast iron during solidification are nominal and easily compensated for. High-strength parts can be cast close to machine dimensions with minimum material to machine off and discard. Machinability is very good since most of the carbon is in the free state. Since most cast irons are not as ductile as steels, they are not usually rolled or forged.

Types of Cast Iron

In most irons, an appreciable portion of the carbon content precipitates during solidification and appears as a separate constituent in the microstructure of the iron. The form and shape in which the excess carbon occurs determine the type of cast iron and establish the nature of its properties. The structure of the matrix metal around the carbon-rich constituent establishes the class of iron within each category.

The five basic types of cast iron are white iron, malleable iron, gray iron, ductile iron, and compacted graphite iron. In white iron, the majority of carbon occurs as the compound iron-carbide, which is a very hard constituent. Malleable iron is characterized by having most of the contained carbon present in irregularly shaped nodules of temper carbon that forms after annealing. Gray iron has the carbon occurring as graphite flakes. In ductile iron, the graphite occurs in spheres; and in compacted graphite iron, the graphite occurs primarily as stubby flakes with some spheres possible.

A sixth type of iron is composed of the high-alloy irons. High-alloy irons are white, gray, or ductile irons containing appreciable amounts of alloying elements, generally in excess of 3%. Their properties are not just modified, but may be essentially different from those of the base iron. Because of the high alloy content, special facilities are usually required for producing high-alloy iron castings.

It is not practical to designate cast irons by chemical analysis because the ranges of the chemical composition for the different cast irons overlap. The typical range of chemical analysis for different types of unalloyed cast irons is given in Fig. 2-4. Cast irons are usually specified by their mechanical properties and microstructure.

Mechanical Properties

Hardness and tensile strength are the most commonly specified properties for iron castings. While hardness and tensile strength relate directly to

many useful characteristics in metals, there are two aspects of mechanical properties in general that should be discussed.

1. Dynamic properties relate closer to part function than static tensile properties. Low-temperature capability cannot be measured by tensile tests nor can high strain rate applications be indicated by tensile tests.
2. The mechanical properties of metal, especially iron, are not specific to a particular batch or heat as is the chemical analysis of metal. Properties are also influenced by the section thickness in which the metal solidifies and the manner in which the metal cools.

As an example of the first qualification, hardness is a relatively good indication of machinability; however, gray iron and ductile iron with the same hardness can exhibit appreciable differences in tool life. That is, if the microstructure of either contains some free carbides, machinability is reduced much more than indicated by the small increase in hardness.

The second qualification results from the fact that the properties of iron are directly influenced by the rate of solidification and subsequent cooling. Appreciably different properties in various portions of a casting are apt to occur if the sections have sufficiently large differences in thickness or shape to cause a significant variation in cooling rate. With modern technology, however, castings can be more uniform throughout variously sized sections. Thus, both large and small castings from the same ladle of metal will have similar mechanical properties.

Cast iron test bars should have a cooling rate and composition that is relatively similar to the casting

Element	Gray Iron, %	White Iron, %	Malleable Iron (Cast White), %	Ductile Iron and Compacted Iron, %
Carbon	2.5-4.0	1.8-3.6	2.00-2.60	3.0-4.0
Silicon	1.0-3.0	0.5-1.9	1.10-1.60	1.8-2.8
Manganese	0.25-1.0	0.25-0.80	0.20-1.00	0.10-1.00
Sulfur	0.02-0.25	0.06-0.20	0.04-0.18	0.03 max
Phosphorus	0.05-1.0	0.06-0.18	0.18 max	0.10 max

Figure 2-4 Range of compositions for typical unalloyed cast irons

sections they represent. If the casting is of sufficient size, test bars should be cut from the critical areas of the casting and then tested. Test bars that are different in cooling rate than the castings they represent can be used to establish the relative quality of the metal being poured rather than to indicate the actual properties to be obtained in the casting. Often the tensile properties of the metal in a casting can be related to the properties of the test bar by the hardness of each. This is a valid but not a precise relationship when the microstructures are similar.

As a basic concept, hardness is resistance to abrasion or scratching. As it applies to metals, the measurement of hardness is based on the relative resistance to the penetration of an indenter. The most common testing methods for iron—Brinell, Rockwell, Knoop, and Vickers—use this principle. Hardness is the most frequently used test for metal because it is convenient, it is usually nondestructive, and the test results can be related to a number of other properties.

Hardness is not an absolute value, and test results can vary even under ideal conditions. Some impressions of Brinell diameters can vary 0.15 mm in reading when measured by different individuals. In specifying a required hardness, it is important to stipulate where on the casting the hardness is to be determined and a range to allow for variations when reading the impression. Because of the difference in solidification and cooling rate, different portions of the casting may vary in hardness. Edges and thin sections may be of a higher hardness but usually cannot be measured with conventional instruments. Figs. 2-5, 2-6, and 2-7 summarize the mechanical properties of various cast irons.

HIGH-PERFORMANCE ALLOYS

High-performance alloys are a group of alloys used in applications requiring high strength and/or corrosion resistance over a wide range of temperatures. The high-strength, heat-resistant alloys are commonly referred to as superalloys in the aircraft and aerospace industries.

High-performance alloys achieve some of their high-temperature strength characteristics through solid-solution strengthening or a combination of solid-solution strengthening and precipitation hardening.

Specification Standard	Grade or Class	Microstructure	Minimum Tensile Strength, ksi (MPa)	Hardness, Bhn	Minimum Carbon, %
ASTM A-159	G 1800	Ferrite with some pearlite	18 (124)	143-187	
	G 2500	Pearlite with some ferrite	25 (172)	170-229	
	G 3000	Pearlite	30 (207)	187-241	
	G 3500	Pearlite	35 (241)	207-255	
	G 4000	Fine pearlite	40 (276)	217-269	
SAE J431	G 2500a	"A" graphite size 2-4 15% max ferrite	25 (172)	170-229	3.40
	G 3500b	"A" graphite size 3-5 5% max ferrite or carbide	35 (241)	207-255	3.40
	G 3500c	"A" graphite size 3-5 5% max ferrite or carbide	35 (241)	207-255	3.50

Note: The tabulated properties are for comparison purposes only and are not intended for design purposes. For specific values, contact the castings supplier or refer to the latest revision of the specification standard.

Figure 2-5   Tensile strength and hardness of common gray iron castings

Specification Standard	Grade or Class	Microstructure and Condition	Tensile Strength, ksi (MPa)	Yield Strength (0.2% Offset), ksi (MPa)	Total Elongation in 2″ (50 mm), %	Typical Hardness, Bhn
ASTM A536	Common Grades of Ductile Iron					
	60-40-18	All ferrite, annealed	60 (414)	40 (276)	18	149-187
	65-45-12	Ferrite ---	65 (448)	45 (310)	12	170-207
	80-55-06	Ferrite and pearlite ---	80 (552)	55 (379)	6	187-255
	100-70-03	All pearlite, normalized	100 (690)	70 (483)	3	217-269
	120-90-02	Martensite, quenched and tempered	120 (827)	90 (621)	2	240-300+
SAE J434c	Automotive Ductile Iron Castings*					
	D-4018	Ferrite	60 (414)	40 (276)	18	170 max
	D-4512	Ferrite and pearlite	65 (448)	45 (310)	12	156-217
	D-5506	Ferrite and pearlite	80 (552)	55 (379)	6	187-255
	D-7003	Pearlite	100 (690)	70 (483)	3	241-302
	D, Q, & T	Martensite	A wide variety of properties will result from liquid quenching and tempering.			As specified

Note: Mechanical properties listed are for comparison purposes only and are not intended for specifications or design purposes. For specific values, contact the castings supplier or refer to the latest revision of the specification standard.
* Tensile strength, yield strength, and elongation are usually not specified. The graphite structure must be at 80% spheroidal.

Figure 2-6   Tensile properties of most commonly used ductile irons

Grade	Minimum Tensile Strength, ksi (MPa)	Minimum Yield Strength, ksi (MPa)	Elongation (at 0.2% Offset), %	Hardness, Bhn
265**	38 (265)	28 (190)	3	179 max
310	45 (310)	35 (240)	1.5	143-207
345	50 (345)	40 (275)	1	163-229
380	55 (380)	45 (310)	1	170-241
415†	60 (415)	49 (340)	1	207-269

Note: The tabulated values are for comparison purposes only and are not intended for design purposes. For specific values, contact the castings supplier.
  * Matrix is compacted graphite with a maximum of 20% graphite in nodular form.
 ** The 265 grade is a ferritic grade. The castings producer usually determines type of heat treatment performed to obtain required mechanical properties and microstructure.
  † The 415 grade is a pearlitic grade usually produced without heat treatment. Certain alloys are added to promote pearlite as a major part of the matrix.

Figure 2-7   Mechanical properties of compacted graphite cast iron*

However, high-temperature strength as well as ambient temperature strengths are also improved by second-phase particle strengthening. Carbides and gamma-prime-type precipitates function as second-phase strengtheners, with carbides playing a minor role in alloys of the gamma prime precipitate type and a major role in the solid-solution type.

The solid-solution strengthening in high-performance alloys comes from the presence of cobalt, chromium, iron, molybdenum, columbium, and tungsten elements in the face-centered cubic structure of the matrix. Of these elements, tungsten, molybdenum, cobalt, and chromium have the greatest strengthening effect.

The carbides in high-performance alloys are of various types depending on the particular alloy composition and the thermal conditions to which the material has been exposed. The carbides change from one form to another as the thermal conditions vary with time. Titanium carbides tend to be very stable; molybdenum, tungsten, and columbium carbides are moderately stable; and chromium carbides tend to be somewhat unstable. In some alloys used primarily for corrosion-resistant applications, carbon is kept at very low levels because carbides tend to lower corrosion resistance; in particular, intergranular corrosion resistance is lowered when the carbides precipitate at grain boundaries.

Gamma-prime-type precipitates are used in iron, iron-nickel, and nickel-based alloys that contain from 1 to 10% by weight of combinations of aluminum, titanium, and/or columbium. The alloys with the higher amounts of gamma prime formers can be strengthened most.

In high-temperature applications, the oxidation resistance of high-performance alloys is as important as high-temperature strength. Oxidation behavior is complex due to the number of elements involved. In simple terms, the oxidation resistance is primarily due to the adherent surface oxide film that forms as a result of the added elements. Chromium plays a large role in the high-temperature oxidation resistance. Chromium levels of over 15% by weight are normally required to achieve acceptable oxidation resistance. Aluminum and titanium can add to the oxidation resistance at any given chromium level.

However, high-performance alloys with the highest strengths above 1200°F (650°C) must have the highest chromium contents in order to have adequate oxidation resistance at such high temperatures. Excessively high chromium can cause reversals in gamma-prime-type strengthening. Therefore, chromium levels above 20% are not used in these alloys.

For uniform corrosion resistance, molybdenum, chromium, and nickel contents are increased. Molybdenum improves resistance in nonoxidizing acids, chromium improves resistance in oxidizing environments, and nickel improves resistance in alkaline environments. Pitting corrosion can be improved by additional amounts of molybdenum and chromium. Increased amounts of nickel and molybdenum improve resistance to stress-corrosion cracking.

Types of High-Performance Alloys

It is difficult to define the term "high performance" precisely because it has broader or narrower limits depending upon who is using the word. In this chapter, a high-performance alloy is defined as one developed for elevated temperature, above 1000°F (535°C), and/or corrosion plus oxidation resistance service, usually based on Group VIII A elements. The high-strength, heat-resistant alloys encounter relatively severe multidirectional, often cyclical fatigue-type mechanical stressing and require high surface stability as well as internal structure quality.

High-performance alloys are predominantly iron-nickel-based, nickel-based, or cobalt-based, with a few iron-based alloys included in the group. They tend to be of complex composition with relatively large percentages of three or more alloying elements. Some high-performance alloys contain as many as ten or more important elemental constituents, with precisely controlled quantities. Some of the more important elements added include chromium, molybdenum, tungsten, columbium, aluminum, cobalt, titanium, carbon, and nitrogen.

Metallurgically, high-performance alloys are somewhat like austenitic stainless steels. They have the face-centered cubic (fcc) crystal structure, and many of their physical characteristics resemble stainless steels. High-performance alloys sometimes display a reduction in ductility in the intermediate temperature range of 1200 to 1560°F (650 to 850°C). In addition, they are relatively poor conductors of heat. These alloys generally melt at lower temperatures than do steels, typically in the range of 2200 to 2550°F (1200 to 1400°C).

Nickel-Based Alloys

Nickel-based alloys generally have greater resistance to high temperatures than low-alloy steels and stainless steels. These alloys contain 30-75% nickel and up to 35% of both chromium and cobalt. Iron content ranges from relatively small amounts to as much as 35% in certain alloys. Aluminum, titanium, niobium, molybdenum, and tungsten are added to enhance either strength and/or corrosion plus oxidation resistance.

Nickel alloys that are strengthened by solid-solution additions are used in a variety of aerospace applications. Typical parts include jet engine ignitors, combustion can liners, diffuser assemblies, heat shields, exhaust systems, and turbine shroud rings. Precipitation-hardening nickel alloys are frequently used in forged components such as gas-turbine blades, discs, rings, shafts, and various compressor and diffuser components.

Cobalt-Based Alloys

Cobalt-based alloys contain over 38% cobalt, 20% chromium, usually some nickel, and substantial percentages of molybdenum and/or tungsten for strengthening. These alloys are divided into three main groups. The first group consists of those alloys used in high-temperature applications. They maintain their strength at temperatures from 1200 to 2100°F (650 to 1150°C). Some of the common applications of these alloys include nuclear reactor components, surgical implants, and combustors and transition ducts for gas turbines.

The second group consists of those alloys specifically designed to be work hardened. These alloys are generally used for producing fasteners. The third group consists of those alloys used for wear-resistant applications. Common applications are erosion shields in steam turbines and wear pads in gas turbines.

Iron-Based Alloys

Iron-based alloys contain over 12% chromium, at least 9% nickel, and varying amounts of molybdenum, tungsten, cobalt, and titanium. Strengthening of these alloys is usually by precipitation hardening; however, some of these alloys are solid-solution strengthened. Typical applications for precipitation-hardened alloys are blades, discs, and fasteners in gas turbine engines. Iron-based alloys are generally used in the wrought form.

TUNGSTEN, MOLYBDENUM, AND TITANIUM

Tungsten and molybdenum are included among the refractory metals, all of which have exceptionally high melting points. A drawback is that tungsten and molybdenum oxidize readily above 1400°F (600°C). Other common characteristics of tungsten and molybdenum (and other refractory metals) are:

- Excellent strength at high temperatures.
- Low coefficient of expansion.
- High elastic modulus.
- Exceptional resistance to corrosion.
- High resistance to thermal shock.
- Good electrical and heat conducting properties.
- High density and specific gravity (tungsten, not molybdenum).
- High hardness properties at elevated temperatures.

In general terms, "refractory" means resistant to heat or capable of enduring high temperatures. Alloys containing varying amounts of refractory metals are vital to virtually every major industry, including automotive, aerospace, mining, chemical and petroleum processing, electrical and electronics, metal processing, nuclear technology, and ordnance.

Titanium is not classified as a refractory metal; however, it does have a unique set of characteristics and properties, including a high melting point and a high strength-to-weight ratio at elevated temperatures. It also has good stiffness properties, having a much higher modulus than the other light metals, aluminum and magnesium. Titanium alloys generally exhibit good creep strengths, over a wide range of temperatures.

The principal uses of titanium and its alloys are in the aerospace industry, although its exceptional corrosion resistance has led to increasing applications in the chemical industry and in the medical profession, which uses titanium alloy prostheses for implanting in the human body. The major titanium alloy usage is in the form of wrought products, although titanium alloy casting usage, which accounts for about 10% of the total, is growing.

The basic production method for tungsten, molybdenum (and other refractory metals), and titanium is similar. The metals are extracted from ore concentrates, processed into chemicals, and then into sponge or powders. These primary forms are consolidated into finished products or mill shapes and ingots for further processing. Because of their high melting points and ease of oxidation, the metals in the refractory group are typically worked in powder form. Titanium products are usually made from consumable vacuum-melted ingots.

Tungsten

Tungsten (W) has a silver-gray metallic luster. Its melting point, 6150°F (3400°C), is the highest of any metal; and, as illustrated in Fig. 2-8, tungsten is the heaviest engineering material. Other unusual physical properties include the highest modulus of elasticity of all metals (59×10^6 psi; 40.7×10^4 MPa) and extreme hardness. Tungsten is the hardest pure metal; annealed, the hardness can be as high as 425 Bhn.

Tungsten also exhibits superior high-temperature strength characteristics, but is expensive and difficult to fabricate.

Properties

Chemically, tungsten is relatively inert. It is not readily attacked by the common acids, alkalies, or aqua regia (mixture of nitric and hydrochloric acids). It reacts with a mixture of concentrated nitric acid and hydrofluoric acid. Molten oxidizing salts such as sodium nitrite attack tungsten rapidly. Gaseous chlorine, bromine, iodine, carbon dioxide, carbon monoxide, and sulfur react with tungsten only at high temperatures. Carbon, boron, silicon, and nitrogen also form compounds with tungsten at elevated temperatures; hydrogen does not. Fig. 2-8 is a metal density comparison.

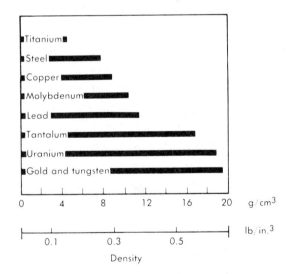

Figure 2-8   Metal density comparison

Applications

When added to iron or steel, tungsten improves high-temperature strength and hardness. More than 75% of the tungsten produced is used in ferrous and aluminum alloys and in tungsten carbide for cutting tools.

A well-known use for tungsten is in the filament material for electric light bulbs. Pure tungsten metal in the form of wire, rod, and sheet is important in the electric lamp and electrical industries. Industrial applications include electrodes for inert gas welding and electrical discharge machining.

Small shapes of tungsten sintered to various densities and porosities are used as filters and in probes for ultrasonic nondestructive testing. Tungsten is also used for high inertia devices and for balancing masses. Because of tungsten's high density, a fly-wheel or balance weight made from tungsten requires only one-third as much space as a steel component.

Some inertial devices use a tungsten-nickel-copper alloy that is more machinable than pure tungsten. Several of the commercially available alloys of tungsten are listed in Fig. 2-9. The rhenium (Re) alloys are more ductile than unalloyed tungsten at room temperature. Thoriated tungsten is stronger than unalloyed tungsten at temperatures up to the recrystallization temperature.

Molybdenum

Molybdenum (Mo) melts at 4730°F (2610°C) and retains useful strength at temperatures of 2000°F (1093°C). The metal is characterized by high thermal conductivity, high modulus, low specific heat, and low coefficient of thermal expansion. Unalloyed molybdenum is produced commercially at the level of purity of 99.95% Mo. In the stress-relieved condition, it has a room temperature hardness of about 240-250

	Nominal Composition, %	Form and Condition	Yield Strength (0.2% Offset), ksi (MPa)	Tensile Strength, ksi (MPa)	Elongation in 2 in., %	Hardness	Density, lb/in.^{3} (g/cm^3)	Melting Point, °F (°C)	Tensile Modulus of Elasticity, 1000 ksi (1000 MPa)
Tungsten-Nickel-Copper Alloy UNS R07030 ASTM B 459 Grade 4	W - 97.5 N + Cu - bal	Sintered powder shapes	80 (552)	100 (690)	3	---	0.67 (18.5)	---	52 (358)
Tungsten-Nickel-Copper Alloy UNS R07100 ASTM B 459 Grade 1	Ni - 7.5 Cu - 2.5 W - balance	Forged from sintered powder	85 (586)	120 (827)	17	285 Bhn	0.61 (16.9)	---	45 (310)
Tungsten-Rhenium Alloy	W - 75 Re - 25	Wire wrought	---	310 (2137)	---	---	0.71 (19.7)	5612 (3100)	57 (393)
		Recrystallized	---	190 (1310)	15	450 Vickers	---	---	---
Tungsten-Rhenium Alloy	W - 50 Re - 50	Sintered powder wrought	210 (1448)	240 (1655)	---	600 Vickers	0.50 (13.8)	4622 (2550)	52 (359)
		Recrystallized	123 (848)	150 (1034)	18	350 Vickers	---	---	---
Tungsten UNS R07004 ASTM B 410 Bars, rods, billets	W - 99.5 min	Sheet hard Cold rolled	360 (2482)	400 (2758)	---	---	0.70 (19.4)	6170 (3410)	50 (345)
		Annealed	---	270 (1862)	---	---	---	---	---

Figure 2-9   Typical properties of tungsten and tungsten alloys

Brinell and a tensile strength of about 100 ksi (689 MPa). Molybdenum has a higher density than steel. Its specific gravity is 10.2 compared with 7.9 for steel.

Molybdenum is similar to tungsten in most of its properties. Its most serious limitation is the ready formation of a volatile oxide at a temperature of approximately 1400°F (760°C). In the worked form, molybdenum is inferior to tungsten in melting point, tensile strength, vapor pressure, and hardness. But, in the recrystallized condition, molybdenum's ultimate strength and elongation are higher.

Alloys

Molybdenum can be alloyed with several other metals to enhance its special properties, but only two alloy groups are produced commercially: (a) TZM, which is molybdenum alloyed with 0.5% titanium and 0.1% zirconium, for high-temperature structural applications and (b) an alloy comprising 70% molybdenum and 30% tungsten, which is resistant to attack by molten zinc.

Unalloyed molybdenum and its two principal alloys cannot be hardened by heat treatment. The hardness and strength of mill products and forgings are developed by working the metal below its recrystallization temperature. To develop an optimum combination of strength and toughness, the technically "cold worked" products are usually stress relieved by heating them to temperatures below the recrystallization temperature. Unalloyed molybdenum and its two commercial alloys are available in the various common wrought, mill product forms: forging billets, tubes, bars, rods, wire, plate, sheet, strip, and foil.

Although molybdenum and its alloys can endure at very high temperatures in vacuum, inert, or hydrogen atmospheres indefinitely, rapid oxidation of molybdenum at temperatures above 1400°F (760°C) precludes application at high temperatures for extended periods of time when exposed to air. The metal reacts with oxygen to form the volatile molybdenum trioxide (MoO_3), which evolves in the form of copious, nontoxic, white fumes. Special silicide coatings can protect unalloyed molybdenum

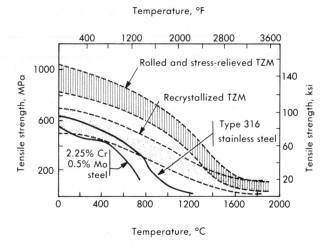

Figure 2-10   Scatter bands of tensile strength versus temperature for rolled TZM molybdenum bar

and TZM from oxidation in air at temperatures as high as 2200°F (1200°C) for up to 50 hours.

Applications

The high-temperature strength of molybdenum is responsible for most of the metal's industrial applications. As shown in Fig. 2-10, TZM molybdenum alloy retains good tensile strength properties at temperatures in excess of 2000°F (1093°C). Steels and nickel-based superalloys are inferior to molybdenum in this respect. As stated previously, molybdenum and its alloys do, however, oxidize rapidly in air at temperatures above 1400°F (760°C); hence, they are suitable for high-temperature usage only in vacuum or inert atmospheres.

Titanium

Titanium (Ti) is a light, strong, silvery gray metal. Pure titanium has a high melting point, 3047°F (1675°C). Its modulus of elasticity (related to stiffness) is 16.5 x 10^6 psi (11.4 x 10^4 MPa), midway between that of steel and aluminum.

Titanium has a lower coefficient of expansion and lower thermal conductivity than either steel or aluminum alloys and is nonmagnetic. Titanium exhibits outstanding corrosion resistance to chlorine and its derivatives in oxidizing or neutral aqueous solutions. It resists organic compounds, oxidizing acids, and nonoxidizing acids in low concentrations.

Titanium is abundant in nature; about 1% of the earth's crust is titanium. Almost all common rocks contain some percentage of titanium dioxide, TiO_2. Deposits of titanium minerals are found in many places throughout the world. Large deposits are located in the United States and Australia.

Alloys

In metallurgical terms, the two crystalline forms of titanium are called alpha and beta. The alpha form, which exists at temperatures below 1620°F (882°C), is a close-packed hexagonal crystal structure. The beta phase, which is formed at temperatures above 1620°F, is body-centered cubic.

Pure titanium is soft, weak, and extremely ductile, and hence is easily fabricated. With appropriate additions of other elements (mostly metals), the titanium base metal is converted into an engineering material that has unique characteristics, including high strength and stiffness, corrosion resistance, and ductility.

The addition of other metals to a titanium base will favor (stabilize) one or the other of the two

Alpha Stabilizers	Beta Stabilizers	Neutral
Aluminum	Vanadium	Zirconium
Oxygen	Tantalum	Tin
Nitrogen	Molybdenum	
Carbon	Chromium	
	Iron	
	Nickel	

Figure 2-11   Common titanium alloy additions

crystalline forms, as listed in Fig. 2-11. The transition temperature (from alpha to beta phase) is raised or lowered, depending on whether a particular alloying element favors the alpha phase or the beta phase. Iron, for example, favors (stabilizes) the beta structure; hence, iron reduces the temperature at which alpha transforms to beta. Aluminum, on the other hand, favors the alpha phase, raising the temperature at which alpha changes to beta.

For convenience in differentiating between the various titanium and titanium alloy compositions, the available commercial grades are classified (depending upon the phases that are present in the metal's microstructure at room temperature) as commercially pure (CP) titanium, all-alpha (single phase) weldable alloys, alpha-beta (two phase) weldable alloys, alpha-beta nonweldable alloys, all-beta alloys, beta-lean alpha alloys, and corrosion-resistant alloys.

ALUMINUM, COPPER, AND MAGNESIUM
Aluminum

Aluminum (Al) is the most abundant metallic element, estimated to form about 8% of the earth's crust. It is a light metal with a bright silvery luster, and the pure metal melts at 1220°F (660°C). With a specific gravity of 2.8, aluminum weighs only about 0.1 lb/in.^{3} (2.77 g/cm^3), as compared with 0.28 lb/in.^{3} (7.75 g/cm^3) for iron and 0.32 lb/in.^{3} (8.86 g/cm^3) for copper. Among the structural metals, only magnesium is lighter. The weight of a given volume of ferrous metals is almost three times that of an equal volume of aluminum.

Although pure aluminum is very ductile, it can be hardened by cold working and alloying. Some aluminum alloys can also be hardened by heat treatment. Pure aluminum is relatively soft and low in strength, but it can be alloyed with other elements to increase its strength and impart other useful properties. The most commonly used alloying elements are copper, magnesium, manganese, and zinc. Iron and silicon are commonly present as impurities.

Aluminum is an excellent conductor of both heat and electricity. Of all the metals, only sodium conducts heat and electricity better on a pound-for-pound basis; and, on a volume basis, only gold, silver, and copper are better conductors. At room temperature, the electrical conductivity of pure aluminum is over 64% of the International Annealed Copper Standard (IACS). Aluminum is also highly reflective of both light and heat.

A unique combination of properties makes aluminum a versatile engineering and construction material. It is light in weight, yet some of its alloys have strengths greater than that of structural steel. It has high resistance to corrosion under the majority of service conditions, and no colored salts are formed to stain adjacent surfaces or discolor products that it comes into contact with, such as fabrics in textile operations and solutions in chemical equipment. It has no toxic reaction. The metal can easily be worked into many forms and readily accepts a wide variety of surface finishes.

Alloy and Temper Designation

The aluminum alloy and temper designation systems are completely set forth in the American National Standard ANSI H35.1 and in various publications issued by The Aluminum Association. Two numbering formats are employed for designating the individual alloys: one for wrought alloys and another for casting alloys.

In format, the two numbering systems differ only slightly. Designations for wrought alloys consist of four-digit numbers, while casting alloys are designated by a three-digit number followed by a decimal point and a fourth digit. In both systems, the basic temper designation (consisting of capital letters and numerals) follows the alloy designation and is separated from it by a hyphen.

These systems provide a standard means for designating aluminum and its alloys in all product forms—wrought, cast, and ingot—and the tempers in which they are produced (see Figs. 2-12 and 2-13).

Group	Alloy Number
Aluminum, 99.00% min and greater	1xxx
Aluminum alloys grouped by major alloying elements:	
Copper	2xxx
Manganese	3xxx
Silicon	4xxx
Magnesium	5xxx
Magnesium and silicon	6xxx
Zinc	7xxx
Other element	8xxx
Unused series	9xxx

Figure 2-12   Designations for wrought aluminum alloy groups

Composition is stated in weight percent maximum unless shown as a range or a minimum.

Standard limits for alloying elements and impurities are expressed to the following places:

Less than 0.001% 0.000x
0.001 to 0.01% 0.00x
0.01 to 0.10%

   Unalloyed aluminum made by a refining process .. 0.0xx

   Alloys and unalloyed aluminum not made by a refining process 0.0x

0.10 through 0.55% 0.xx
(It is customary to express limits of 0.30% through 0.55% as 0.x0 or 0.x5.)

Over 0.55% .... 0.x,x.x, etc.
(except that combined Si + Fe limits for 1xxx designations must be expressed as 0.xx or 1.xx)

Figure 2-13   Standard limits for wrought aluminum alloying elements and impurities

Properties

For aluminum, as for other metals, effective product engineering and manufacturing require an understanding of the material's physical and mechanical properties, its corrosion resistance, and its fabrication, joining, and finishing characteristics.

Typical tensile strengths of aluminum range from as low as 5 ksi (34.5 MPa) for some commercially pure aluminum grades to 90 ksi (620 MPa) or more for high-strength alloys. In the automotive field, commonly used alloys have yield strengths from 18 to 60 ksi (124 to 414 MPa). Young's modulus, an important factor in a material's stiffness and bending strength, is 10×10^6 psi (68.9 GPa) for aluminum.

Aluminum, like steel and the various nonferrous metals, is not a single metal but a family of alloys, each of which has been formulated and developed to provide properties suitable for separate classes or fields of applications.

COPPER

Copper is a comparatively heavy metal, with a specific gravity of 8.96 at 68°F (20°C). The melting point is 1981°F (1083°C). The pure element is salmon pink in color and has a bright metallic luster when polished. Copper is nonmagnetic and has very high thermal conductivity and electrical conductivity. Among metals, only silver has a greater electrical conductivity. On a relative basis, with silver rated 100, copper is 95, aluminum 57, and iron 16. The usefulness of copper is derived from its combination of chemical, physical, electrical, and mechanical properties and its abundant supply.

The copper alloys also have the advantages of corrosion resistance, ease of forming, ease of joining, and are available in colors. On the other hand, copper and its alloys have relatively low strength-to-weight ratios and low strengths at elevated temperatures. Some alloys are susceptible to stress-corrosion cracking unless they are stress relieved. Copper and its alloys tend to work harden, and they can be hot or cold worked to increase strength. Ductility can be restored by annealing or in the heating that accompanies welding or brazing operations.

Alloy Designation System

The Unified Numbering System for Metals and Alloys (UNS) applied to wrought and cast copper and copper alloys evolved from the three-digit system developed by the U.S. copper and brass industry.

The original three-digit designations were expanded to five digits, following a prefix letter C.

UNS System Summary: The UNS numbers are simply expansions of the former numerical system used by the Copper Development Association (CDA). For example, Copper Alloy No. 377 (forging brass) in the original three-digit system became C37700 in the UNS system. The overall UNS is jointly managed by the SAE and the ASTM. For copper, the UNS designation system is administered by the CDA.

Alloy Designation Groups: The UNS designation system is an orderly method of identifying and defining coppers and copper alloys. It is not a metallurgical specification system, and the alloy designation numbers have no direct significance with regard to composition and properties. Numbers from C10000 through C79999 denote wrought alloys. Cast alloys are numbered from C80000 through C99999. Within these two categories, the compositions are grouped into the following families of coppers and copper alloys:

Coppers. Pure copper is metal that has a designated minimum copper content of 99.3% or higher and is essentially unalloyed copper.

High-copper alloys. For the wrought products, these are alloys with a designated copper content less than 99.3% but more than 96% that do not fall into any other copper alloy group. The cast high-copper alloys have a designated copper content in excess of 94%, to which silver may be added to create special properties.

Brasses. These alloys contain zinc as the principal alloying element with or without other designated alloying elements such as iron, aluminum, nickel, and silicon.

Wrought. The wrought alloys comprise three main families of brasses: copper-zinc alloys, copper-zinc-lead alloys (leaded brasses), and copper-zinc-tin alloys (tin brasses).

Cast. The cast alloys contain four main families of brasses: copper-tin-zinc alloys (red, semi-red, and yellow brasses); "manganese bronze" alloys (high-strength yellow brasses); leaded "manganese bronze" alloys (leaded high-strength yellow brasses); and copper-zinc-silicon alloys (silicon brasses and bronzes).

Bronzes. Broadly speaking, bronzes are copper alloys in which the major alloying element is not zinc or nickel. Originally "bronze" described alloys with tin as the only or principal alloying element. Today the term is generally used not by itself but with a modifying adjective.

Wrought. For wrought alloys, there are four main families of bronzes: copper-tin-phosphorus alloys (phosphor bronzes), copper-tin-lead-phosphorus alloys (leaded phosphor bronzes), copper-aluminum alloys (aluminum bronzes), and copper-silicon alloys (silicon bronzes).

Cast. The cast alloys have four main families of bronzes: copper-tin alloys (tin bronzes), copper-tin-lead alloys (leaded and high-leaded tin bronzes), copper-tin-nickel alloys (nickel-tin bronzes), and copper-aluminum alloys (aluminum bronzes). The family of alloys known as "manganese bronzes," in which zinc is the major alloying element, is included in the brasses.

Copper nickels. These are alloys with nickel as the principal alloying element, with or without other designated alloying elements.

Copper-nickel-zinc alloys. Known commonly as "nickel silvers," these are alloys that contain zinc and nickel as the principal and secondary alloying elements, with or without other designated elements.

Leaded coppers. These include a series of cast alloys of copper with 20% or more lead, usually with a small amount of silver present, but without tin or zinc.

Special alloys. Alloys with chemical compositions that do not fall into any of the above categories are combined in the category "special alloys."

Copper and Copper Alloys

More than 300 standard coppers and alloys are produced by the United States copper and brass industry. As a group, these alloys encompass a wide range of wrought and cast materials that are available in virtually all of the commercial mill and product forms. The fabricated forms include strip, plate, sheet, pipe, tube, rod, forgings, wire, bar, foil, extrusions, and castings. Cast products are available in varied shapes and sizes as needed for specific applications.

Commonly Used Alloys: For applications requiring maximum electrical conductivity, the most widely used copper is C11000, "tough pitch," which contains approximately 0.03-0.06% oxygen and a minimum of 99.90% copper (including silver). In addition to high electrical conductivity, oxygen-free grades C10100 and C10200 provide immunity to embrittlement at high temperature. The addition of phosphorus produces grade C12200—the standard water-tube copper.

The high-copper alloys contain small amounts of alloying elements that improve strength with a minimal loss in electrical conductivity. For example, cadmium in amounts up to 1% can increase strength by 50%, with a decline in conductivity to 85%. Small amounts of cadmium raise the softening temperature in alloy C14300, which is used widely for radiator fin stock. Tellurium, lead, or sulfur—present in small amounts in grades C14500, C14700, and C18700—increase machinability.

For machined products, the most used material is copper alloy C36000, which is called free-cutting brass. This alloy has a combination of good physical, mechanical, and fabrication properties, plus an acceptable cost level for a majority of screw machine product applications. A wide variety of alloys is available to provide other properties and characteristics for various applications. For example, alloy C46400, naval brass, provides higher strength and ductility, but has a lower machinability rating than free-cutting brass.

Properties

Copper is among the toughest of pure metals. It is moderately wear resistant and highly malleable and ductile. The principal alloy groups have hardness and tensile strength values that are higher than those for pure copper.

Copper alloys do not have a sharply defined yield point. Yield strength is reported either as 0.5% extension under load or as 0.2% offset. On the most common basis (0.5% extension), yield strength of annealed material is approximately one-third the tensile strength. As the material is cold worked or hardened, yield strength approaches tensile strength.

MAGNESIUM

Magnesium (Mg) is a silvery white metal with a specific gravity of 1.74. In the pure state, magnesium's melting point is 1202°F (650°C), which is approximately the same temperature required to melt aluminum.

Most pure metals, including magnesium, are soft and are not suitable for structural use. However, strength properties comparable to those of many aluminum alloys are obtained by alloying magnesium with other metals, and, in some cases, by heat treating or cold or hot working.

With a unit weight of 0.063 lb/in.^{3} (1.74 g/cm^3), magnesium is the lightest of the commonly used metals. For engineering applications, magnesium is usually alloyed with one or more elements, including aluminum, manganese, rare earth metals, lithium, thorium, zinc, and zirconium. The resultant alloys have very high strength-to-weight ratios.

While its light weight is magnesium's best known characteristic (aluminum weighs 1½ times more than magnesium; iron and steel, 4 times more; copper, 5 times more), there are also other desirable properties. Magnesium's excellent machinability, for example, makes it economical in parts where weight saving may not be of primary importance, but where much costly machining is required. Parts made of magnesium can be machined at higher speeds, with

fewer cuts, and with greater economies than are possible with most other metals.

Alloy Designation System

Primary magnesium, like most metals, lacks sufficient strength in its elemental state to be used as a structural metal. Therefore, it must be alloyed with various other metals, such as aluminum, manganese, thorium, rare earth metals, lithium, tin, zinc, and zirconium. Magnesium alloys are most commonly designated by a system established by the ASTM, which covers both chemical compositions and tempers.

The ASTM designations for alloys are based on chemical composition and consist of two letters representing the two alloying elements specified in the greatest amount, arranged either in decreasing percentages or—if of equal percentage—alphabetically. The letters are followed by the respective percentages rounded off to whole numbers, with a serial letter at the end. The serial letter indicates some variation in composition. Experimental alloys have the letter X between the alloy and serial numbers.

The following letters designate various alloying elements: A—aluminum, B—bismuth, C—copper, D—cadmium, E—rare earths, F—iron, G—magnesium, H—thorium, K—zirconium, L—lithium, M—manganese, N—nickel, P—lead, Q—silver, R—chromium, S—silicon, T—tin, Z—zinc.

Primary magnesium metal and alloys have also been assigned UNS designations according to the Unified Numbering System for Metals and Alloys, SAE HS1086a and ASTM DS-56A. The UNS designation for a metal or alloy consists of a letter followed by five numbers. The UNS system is intended to provide a nationally accepted means of correlating the many alloy designation numbers used by various organizations, and an improved system for indexing, record-keeping, data storage and retrieval, and cross-referencing. The numbers M10001 through M19999 have been reserved for magnesium and magnesium alloys.

ASTM Specification B 296 designates tempers for magnesium alloys. Temper designation is separated from alloy designation by a dash. Fig. 2-14 describes the ASTM tempers commonly used for magnesium cast and wrought products.

Magnesium alloys in their various forms are covered by government and national society specifications.

Description	Temper Designation
As fabricated	-F
Annealed recrystallized (wrought products only)	-O
Strain hardened	-H
Strain hardened only	-H1
Strain hardened and then partially annealed	-H2
Thermally treated to produce stable tempers other than -F, -O, or -H	-T
Annealed (cast products only)	-T2
Solution heat treated and naturally aged to a substantially stable condition	-T4
Artificially aged only	-T5
Solution heat treated and then artificially aged	-T6
Solution heat treated and then stabilized	-T7
Solution heat treated, cold worked, and then artificially aged	-T8

* ANSI/ASTM B296 "Temper Designations of Magnesium Alloys"

Figure 2-14　ASTM temper designations for magnesium*

Properties

Magnesium offers significant advantages in strength-weight and stiffness-weight ratios.

Magnesium alloys do not have the sharp yield point characteristic of carbon steels. Instead, the metal yields gradually when stressed, and the term "yield strength" is used. Yield strength has been defined as the stress at which the stress-strain curve deviates 0.2% from the modulus line. In cast form, the tensile and compressive yield strengths of most magnesium alloys are substantially equal. In most wrought alloys, however, the compressive yield strength is less than

that of the tensile yield. Magnesium alloys have a modulus of elasticity of approximately 6.5×10^6 psi (45 GPa), and Poisson's ratio is 0.35.

Magnesium provides high-speed machinability, good thermal and electrical conductivity, fatigue resistance and damping properties of a high order, high impact and dent resistance, and the ability to be cast and formed by a variety of standard metalworking processes. These factors allow the design of large yet light and rigid tools, and jigs and fixtures of ready portability. Moving machine elements made of magnesium have low inertia forces compared with those of steel or aluminum.

LEAD, TIN, AND ZINC
Lead

Pure lead (Pb) is a bluish gray metal that takes on a silvery gray patina with atmospheric exposure. In industrial atmospheres, it may change to a dark gray to black color. The density of cast lead is 0.409 lb/in.^{3} (11.34 g/cm^3), and the melting point is 621°F (327°C).

Lead is readily and inexpensively fabricated into a great variety of useful forms. The diversity of available forms combined with lead's advantageous properties—high density, low melting point, corrosion resistance, chemical stability, malleability, lubricity, electrical properties, and ability to form useful alloys and chemical compounds—provide a material suitable for a wide range of applications.

Although lead is widely known as a heavy metal, only about 10% of lead applications are based primarily on its high density. In many other applications, lead is selected because it melts at low temperature, is easy to cast and form, is useful for generating electric current in electrochemical reactions, is a good absorber of sound and vibration, or is among the easiest of metals to salvage from scrap. Lead also resists attack by many corrosive chemicals and acids, most types of soil, and marine and industrial environments. It is the most impervious of all common metals to X-rays and gamma radiation.

Nearly three fourths of all U.S. lead consumption is for chemical applications such as paint pigments, gasoline additives, and storage batteries.

Lead Alloy Designation

The basic specification covering pig lead, as produced by most primary and secondary lead smelters in the United States, is the ANSI/ASTM B29-79 Standard Specification for Pig Lead. Used widely in the plumbing trade and for chemical, radiation protection, and sound attenuation applications, this specification is summarized in Fig. 2-15.

Pure lead is available with a purity of 99.999%. By agreement between purchaser and supplier, limits are established for specified elements, and the percentages of unspecified elements may be raised or lowered, depending on the particular application.

The Unified Numbering System (UNS) is a means of describing metal and alloy composition in a logical, numerical manner that is useful to industry and government operations. The system is jointly managed by the ASTM and the SAE. The format Lxxxxx is used in the UNS number series for "Low Melting Metals and Alloys."

Properties

The properties of lead that make it useful in a wide variety of applications are its density, malleability, lubricity, flexibility, and coefficient of thermal expansion, all of which are high; and elastic modulus, elastic limit, strength, hardness, melting point, and electrical conductivity, all of which are low. Lead also has good resistance to corrosion under a wide variety of conditions, is easily alloyed with many other metals, and is easily cast.

	Type			
	Corroding	Common	Chemical	Copper Bearing
	UNS Number			
	L50042	L50045	L51120	L51121
Element	Lead Composition (Weight %)			
Silver, max	0.0015	0.005	0.020	0.020
Silver, min	---	---	0.002	---
Copper, max	0.0015	0.0015	0.080	0.080
Copper, min	---	---	0.040	0.040
Silver and copper together, max	0.0025	---	---	---
Arsenic, antimony, tin together, max	0.002	0.002	0.002	0.002
Zinc, max	0.001	0.001	0.001	0.001
Iron, max	0.002	0.002	0.002	0.002
Bismuth, max	0.050	0.050	0.005	0.025
Lead, min (by difference)	99.94	99.94	99.90	99.90

* ANSI/ASTM B29-79
Standard Specification for Pig Lead

Figure 2-15 Lead chemical requirements*

TIN

Tin (Sn) is a soft, ductile, silvery-white metal. It is highly malleable (similar to silver and gold) and can be hammered into very thin, flat sheets or drawn into thin wire. Tin does not tarnish in air, and it melts at a relatively low temperature, 440.4°F (231.9°C). The specific gravity is 5.77 in alpha form (gray tin), and 7.29 in the normal beta form (white tin). The Brinell hardness at room temperature is 3.9, which is somewhat harder than lead.

The earliest use of tin was in the copper-based alloy, bronze. The use of bronze is known to have been prevalent in Egypt and Mesopotamia before 3000 B.C. Tin was mined in Spain from the beginning of the Bronze Age, while the working of tin mines in France and England began about 500 B.C. Examination of ancient furnaces indicates that tin of 99.9% purity was produced.

The largest use of tin is for tin-coated steel containers used to preserve foods. The next largest uses are in solder alloys, babbitt (bearing metal), bronzes, fusible alloys, type metals, pewter, and dental amalgams. Tin chemical compounds, both inorganic and organic, find extensive use in the electroplating, ceramic, plastics, pesticidal, and antifungal industries.

Tin Alloy Designation

Tin alloys are included in the UNS for Metals and Alloys under the "L" designation for "Low Melting Metals and Alloys." Many of these alloys are solders and often are lead based. Other tin-containing alloys appear in the aluminum alloy section of the UNS, throughout the copper section, and in the reactive and refractory metals section, as well as under miscellaneous alloys.

Grades of Tin

Most applications for tin begin with the metal in ingot form. The purity of the ingot usually conforms to the ASTM B339 Standard Classification "Grade A," with 99.80% minimum tin, as shown in Fig. 2-16. The requirements for Grade A tin have remained virtually unchanged for more than forty years and represent a compromise between the needs of the major tin-consuming industries and the cost to the producers of removing impurities. Since its major use

Element	Composition, %						
	AAA	AA	A	B	C	D	E
Tin, min	99.98	99.95	99.80	99.80	99.65	99.50	99.00
Antimony, max	0.008	0.02	0.04	---	---	---	---
Arsenic, max	0.0005	0.01	0.05	0.05	---	---	---
Bismuth, max	0.001	0.01	0.015	---	---	---	---
Cadmium, max	0.001	0.001	0.001	---	---	---	---
Copper, max	0.002	0.02	0.04	---	---	---	---
Iron, max	0.005	0.01	0.015	---	---	---	---
Lead, max	0.010	0.02	0.05	---	---	---	---
Nickel + cobalt, max	0.005	0.01	0.01	---	---	---	---
Sulfur, max	0.002	0.01	0.01	---	---	---	---
Zinc, max	0.001	0.005	0.005	---	---	---	---

Figure 2-16 Tin grades*

is as a protective coating in the food industry (for example, for cans), there has been strong emphasis on high purity levels.

Properties

Because tin is mechanically weak, there are few uses for the pure metal. Tin easily forms alloys with many metals, however, and is used to increase resistance to corrosion and fatigue and to improve malleability. The metals most commonly alloyed with tin are antimony, copper, lead, zinc, and silver to produce the common tin alloys of bronze, pewter, solder, type metal, and babbitt metal. Some brasses also contain a small amount of tin. The typical physical and mechanical properties of tin are presented in Fig. 2-17. Tin has a highly ordered crystalline structure. When a bar of tin is bent, a distinctive sound called "tin cry" is produced by the reorientation of the crystals.

Property	Value
Melting point	449.4°F (231.9°C)
Boiling point	4118°F (2270°C)
*Shear strength (room temperature)	1817 psi (12.4 MPa)
*Tensile strength 59°F (15°C)	2135 psi (14.7 MPa)
*Elongation on 0.86" (22 mm), 59°F (15°C)	75%
*Hardness 68°F (20°C)	3.9 Bhn

* Beta form

Figure 2-17 Typical physical and mechanical properties for tin

ZINC

Zinc (Zn), in its unalloyed form, is a bluish-white metal with a specific gravity of 7.1, a melting temperature of 787°F (419°C), and a boiling temperature of 1661°F (905°C). It is readily cast and crystalizes in a hexagonal close-packed structure. The tensile strength of as-cast, unalloyed zinc is about 9000 psi (62 MPa), with an elongation of 1%. It can also be readily fabricated into a variety of wrought products such as rolled zinc sheet, which exhibits a tensile strength of 24,000 psi (165 MPa) with 35% elongation. Zinc is highly active in the electromotive series and forms a thin, complex oxide-carbonate-hydroxide film when exposed to air. This property accounts for its wide use in the corrosion protection of steel, in processes such as galvanizing and metallizing, and for zinc-rich paints.

Historically, the first known reference to zinc as a metal was made by Strabos in a passage describing Andriera in Mysia (now the northwestern section of modern day Turkey). The Romans used zinc in brasses as early as 200 B.C., and a zinc alloy idol was found at a prehistoric Dacian settlement in modern day Rumania. The commercial use of zinc in Europe dates roughly from the beginning of the sixteenth century, and the birth of the American zinc industry (in terms of commercial production volume) is generally placed at the time of the U.S. Civil War.

Spelter is an old name for slabs of cast zinc. The first spelter or metallic zinc was produced in the United States in 1838. An early grade of zinc, Sterling Spelter, was 99.5% pure. Today, zinc, its alloys, and its chemical compounds represent the fourth most industrially used metal after iron, aluminum, and copper.

Alloy Designation System

The UNS numbers and ASTM cross-reference specifications for zinc and zinc alloys are given in Fig. 2-18.

UNS No.	Description	Chemical Composition,* %								Specification
		Al	Cd	Fe	Pb	Cu	Mg	Sn	Zn	
Z1300	Zinc anodes, Type II	0.005 max	0.003 max	0.0014 max					Remainder	ASTM B418
Z13001	Zinc metal		0.003 max	0.003 max	0.003 max			0.001 max	99.990 min	ASTM B6, special high grade
Z15001	Zinc metal		0.02 max	0.02 max	0.03 max				99.90 min	ASTM B6, high grade
Z16001	Zinc metal		0.40 max	0.03 max	0.20 max				99.5 min	ASTM B6, intermediate
Z17001	Zinc metal		0.05 max	0.03 max	0.6 max				99.0 min	ASTM B6, brass special
Z19001	Zinc metal		0.20 max	0.05 max	1.4 max				98.0 min	ASTM B6, prime western
Z21210	Rolled zinc		0.005 max	0.010 max	0.05 max	0.001 max			Remainder	ASTM B69
Z21310	Rolled zinc		0.005 max	0.012 max	0.05-0.12	0.001 max			Remainder	ASTM B69
Z21540	Rolled zinc		0.20-0.35	0.020 max	0.30-0.65	0.005 max			Remainder	ASTM B69
Z25630	Zinc casting alloy	8				1			Remainder	ASTM B669 (ZA-8)
Z32120	Zinc anodes, Type I	0.10-0.4	0.03-0.10	0.005 max					Remainder	ASTM B418
Z33520	Zinc alloy AG40A	3.5-4.3	0.004 max	0.100 max	0.005 max	0.25 max	0.02-0.05	0.003 max	Remainder	AMS 4803, ASTM B86 SAE J468 (903), Federal QQ-Z-363
Z33521	Zinc alloy AG40A	3.9-4.3	0.003 max	0.075 max	0.004 max	0.10 max	0.025-0.05	0.002 max	Remainder	ASTM B240, SAE J468 (903)
Z35530	Zinc alloy AC41A	3.9-4.3	0.003 max	0.075 max	0.004 max	0.75-1.25	0.03-0.06	0.002 max	Remainder	ASTM B240, SAE J468 (925)
Z35531	Zinc alloy AC41A	3.5-4.3	0.004 max	0.100 max	0.005 max	0.75-1.25	0.03-0.08	0.003 max	Remainder	ASTM B86, SAE J468 (925), Federal QQ-Z-363
Z35630	Zinc casting alloy	11				1			Remainder	ASTM B669 (ZA-12)
Z35840	Zinc casting alloy	7				2			Remainder	ASTM B669 (ZA-27)
Z44330	Rolled zinc		0.005 max	0.012 max	0.05-0.12	0.65-1.25			Remainder	ASTM B69
Z45330	Rolled zinc		0.005 max	0.015 max	0.05-0.12	0.75-1.25	0.007-0.02		Remainder	ASTM B69

* Chemical compositions are for identification purposes and should not be used in lieu of the specifications.

Figure 2-18 UNS numbers, compositions, and specifications for zinc and zinc alloys

Properties

Aside from zinc coatings, the casting alloys are the most widely used form of zinc. Zinc-based die-casting alloys were introduced in the late 1920s to meet the demand for strong, stable die castings. These alloys, familiarly known as the Zamak or Mazak alloys, show a unique combination of properties that permit rapid, economic casting of strong, durable, accurate parts, and hence have dominated the market since their inception. They have many advantages over other die-casting materials, such as aluminum and magnesium alloys. The zinc alloys are more easily cast, are stronger and more ductile, require less finishing, can be held to closer tolerances, and can be cast in thinner sections. Because of low casting temperatures, die life for zinc die castings exceeds that for other die-cast metals. The production rate (shots per hour) is also higher.

Die casting with zinc-based alloys is one of the most efficient and versatile production methods for the manufacture of accurate, complex metal components. In general, the mechanical properties of zinc alloy die castings used at normal temperatures are superior to those of sand-cast gray iron, brass, and aluminum, particularly fracture toughness and impact strength. Zinc alloy die castings are stronger, tougher, and more dimensionally stable than some injection molded plastics, and can be produced at a higher rate.

POWDERED METALS

Powder metallurgy (PM) is defined broadly as the technology of manufacturing articles from metal powders and of producing those powders, which range in diameter from 4 μin. to 0.04″ (0.1 to 1000 μm). The powders are smaller than shot and larger than dust. The PM technique is one of the oldest kinds of metallurgy, going back 5000 years to the manufacture of Egyptian implements.

Modern powder metallurgy evolved in the last half of the 18th century and became commercially feasible in the 20th century with the development of tungsten wire for incandescent lamp filaments. The idea of producing shapes by powder metallurgy was described in a 1902 German patent; however, serious consideration of this technique has only been recent. A resurgence of research and development in metals, generated by competition from nonmetals and particularly from plastics, has enhanced the interest in potential new methods for fabrication of metals. For instance, rolling powder of special, high-priced compositions to produce strip or sheet is feasible and has become an accepted commercial process.

Powder metallurgy has two broad areas of application: the working of refractory metals (such as tungsten, molybdenum, columbium, and tantalum, which have high melting points and are difficult to process by conventional methods); and the fabrication of parts that are uneconomic, difficult, or impossible to produce by other techniques. The industries most interested in powder metallurgy are aerospace (particularly for the use of refractory metals and alloys); and producers of durable consumer goods and capital goods including automobiles and other transportation equipment, home appliances, business machines, industrial equipment, power tools, and hardware.

Metal Powders

Metal powders are precisely engineered materials, available in numerous types and grades to meet a wide range of performance requirements. Mechanical properties of PM parts compare favorably with metal parts made by other metalworking methods.

Most metal powders are produced by atomization, electrolysis, or chemical or oxide reduction. In powder form, the elemental materials include iron, tin, nickel, copper, aluminum, and refractory and reactive metals. These metals can be mixed and then sintered to produce alloy compositions. Sintering bonds the powder particles together metallurgically.

Molten, prealloyed compositions of low-alloy steels, bronze, brass, nickel-silver, and stainless steel, in which each powder particle is itself an alloy, can also be atomized. In addition, metal and nonmetal powders can be combined to provide composite materials with specialized properties.

The engineering properties of the PM part are significantly determined by the metal powder processing and fabrication techniques. Among the controlling elements are particle size and shape, size distribution or sieve analysis, apparent or bulk density of the powder, rate of powder flow into the die cavity, and powder compressibility in the die.

Ferrous Materials

Iron powder, the most widely used PM material for structural parts, is sometimes used alone but most frequently used with small additions of other powders, singly or in combination, to improve mechanical properties of the pressed and sintered part. Among the powders added are carbon, copper, nickel, or molybdenum. Properties data, code designations, compositions, microstructure, and other information on PM structural parts are available in Metal Powder Industries Federation (MPIF) Standard 35.

Nonferrous Materials

Copper- and aluminum-based powders are the most widely used nonferrous PM materials, although most nonferrous metals and alloys can be converted to powder and fabricated into engineering components. Copper-based materials include the brasses, bronzes, and nickel-silver.

General Engineering Properties

A wide range of powder metallurgy materials that meet the design requirements of particular applications is listed in Fig. 2-19. The following representative physical and mechanical properties data can be augmented when necessary with additional information and data from original sources, standards, and specifications, and from PM powder and parts producers.

Density: Most properties of a PM part are closely related to the final density. This density is the weight per unit volume of the part expressed in grams per cubic centimeter (g/cm³). Normally, density of mechanical and structural parts is reported on a dry unimpregnated basis, while density of bearings is reported on a fully oil-impregnated basis. Density may

Designation	Chemistry	Applications Characteristics
F-0000	Pure Fe (Carbon below 0.03%)	Low strength at high density, a soft magnetic material
F-0005	Fe-0.5% C	Moderate strength, mild steel
F-0008	Fe-0.8% C	Moderate strength, mild steel
FC-0208	Fe-2% Cu-0.8% C	Higher strength structural parts
FN-0205	Fe-2% Ni-0.5% C	High strength when heat treated, good impact resistance
FN-0208	Fe-2% Ni-0.8% C	High strength when heat treated
FX-2008	Fe-20% Cu-0.8% C	Infiltrated steel, high strength, sintered or heat treated
SS-316	316 stainless steel	Good toughness and corrosion resistance
SS-410	410 stainless steel	Hardens during sintering, good abrasion resistance
CZ-0220	Brass: Cu-20% Zn, 2% Pb	Good toughness, elongation, easy machining, good corrosion resistance
CT-0010	Bronze: Cu-10% Sn*	Structural and bearing applications, excellent corrosion resistance
CZN-1818	Nickel silver: Cu-18% Ni-18% Zn	Decorative, tough and ductile, superior corrosion resistance.

Note: For more complete materials standards information, contact the Metal Powder Industries Federation. MPIF Standard 35 provides minimum strength values for design purposes. Designers can select materials based on the physical and mechanical properties of each material. Density need not serve as the basis for material selection.
*Diluted bronze available.

Figure 2-19 MPIF designations for typical PM materials

be calculated by any of several means. A commonly used method is given in Metal Powder Industries Federation (MPIF) Standard 42.

Density is also expressed as percent of theoretical density, which is defined as the ratio of a PM part's density to that of its wrought metal counterpart. In practice, PM parts less than 75% of theoretical density are considered to be low density; those above 90% are high density; and those between these two ranges are considered as medium density. In general, structural and mechanical parts have densities ranging from 80% to above 95%. Many self-lubricating type bearings have densities on the order of 75%, and filter parts usually have densities of 50%.

Porosity: Porosity is the percentage of void volume in a part. It is the converse of density. A part that is 85% of theoretical density will have 15% porosity. Porosity in PM parts can be present as a network of interconnected pores that extend to the surface like a sponge or as a number of closed holes within the part. Interconnected porosity is important to the performance of self-lubricating bearings and is included in the specification for these types of materials.

As a unique structural characteristic of PM parts, porosity is controllable and a function of the raw material and processing techniques. Parts can be produced either with uniform porosity or with variations in porosity (and also density) from one section to another in order to provide different properties. For example, parts such as gears can be made self-lubricating in one area and dense and strong in other areas. The method for calculating pore volume or oil content of self-lubricating PM components in terms of interconnected porosity is given in MPIF Standard 35.

Permeability: The ability to pass fluids or gas, as in filters, is another property that can be designed into PM products. Depending on the forming and sintering techniques, a PM part can provide permeability ranging from highly restricted to highly open flow. The part can be produced with permeabilities that will separate materials selectively, diffuse

the flow of gases or liquids, regulate flow or pressure drop in supply lines, or act as flame arresters by cooling gases below combustion temperatures. Filters can be produced in almost any configuration, including sheets and tubes.

KEY TERMS AND PHRASES _____

AISI
Alloy steel
Alloy steels
Aluminum
ASTM
Austenitic
Capped steel
Carbon steels
Cast irons
Cast steels
Cobalt-based alloys
Compacted graphite iron
Copper
Corrosion resistance
Corrosion-resistant cast steel
Ductile iron
Duplex stainless steel
Ferritic
Formability
Gray iron
Heat-resistant steel castings
High-performance alloys
HSLA
Iron-based alloys
Lead
Low-alloy cast steels
Low-carbon steels
Magnesium
Malleable iron
Maraging steels
Martensitic
Molybdenum
Nickel-based alloys
Plastic strain ratio
Powdered metal

Refractory metals
Rimmed steel
SAE
Stainless steel
Strength
Tin
Titanium
Toughness
Tungsten
UNS
Weldability
White iron
Zinc

QUESTIONS FOR ADDITIONAL STUDY AND REVIEW____

1. Explain the ways that carbon steels may be classified.

2. What are the four types of carbon steels?

3. Explain the grade designation system used to designate standard carbon steels.

4. What is an alloy steel?

5. List four reasons why alloying elements are added to ordinary steels.

6. What are high-strength low-alloy steels?

7. What are stainless steels?

8. List the five main types of stainless steels.

9. Explain the origin of the term *maraging*.

10. How are maraging steels produced?

11. What is the maximum percentage of carbon in low-carbon steel castings?

12. What is cast iron?

13. What are the five basic types of cast iron?

14. What does the term **hardness** mean when applied to cast irons?

15. What are high-performance alloys?

16. What are the three broad categories of high-performance alloys?

17. List five characteristics of refractory metals.

18. Describe the characteristics of tungsten.

19. Describe the characteristics of molybdenum.

20. Describe the characteristics of titanium.

21. What is the heaviest engineering material?

22. Describe the characteristics of aluminum.

23. Describe the characteristics of copper.

24. What is magnesium?

25. Describe the characteristics of the following metals:
   • Lead
   • Tin
   • Zinc

26. What are the two broad areas of application of powdered metals?

CHAPTER 3

Engineering Materials: Nonmetals
(Plastics, Composites, Ceramics, and Elastomers)

MAJOR TOPICS COVERED

- Plastics Overview
- Basic Terminology
- Mechanical Properties
- Engineering Plastics
- Plastics Alloys and Blends
- Advanced Composites
- The Matrix
- Fiber Types and Production
- Fiber Forms and Fabrics
- Composite Construction
- Fabrication of Composites
- Automated Fabrication of Composites
- Ceramics
- Elastomers

Plastics

Plastics are nonmetallic materials that can be formed and shaped by many methods. Plastics can be made from such natural resins as shellac; however, most plastics used in industrial applications are produced from man-made synthetic resins.

Plastics have become one of the most common classes of engineering materials in the past decade. For the last five years, the production of plastics, on a volume basis, exceeded steel output. Engineering plastics, those grades devised to resist severe service conditions or structural loads, are in widespread use and their applications are increasing rapidly.

Industry Structure

Plastics are an outgrowth of the petrochemical industry; hence, the language and terms of plastics are usually expressed in organic chemistry terms. Metals and plastics behave quite differently. To understand plastics materials and their production parts processing, therefore, some of the language of plastics must be learned.

The plastics industry is organized differently from the metals industry. Raw plastics, called resins, are made from oil and gas by large high-technology firms and then sold to custom molders or captive shops for processing into plastics components. Resins are made by three types of firms: Several large oil companies manufacture resins. Corporations with substantial chemical knowledge apply their expertise to produce plastics resins. And a few sophisticated plastics consuming firms have developed resins and produce engineering plastics.

A resin manufacturer usually produces only a few different types of plastics, with numerous variations in some instances. Because the industry is relatively new, patents still play a major role in industrial organization; and, in general, firms manufacture only those types of plastics for which they have a strong patent position.

The industry's organization tends to isolate the end-user from the resin manufacturer. The designers and manufacturing engineers responsible for developing and applying plastics parts usually deal with a custom molder. The molder is the part maker and is frequently considered an expert in plastics. A molder has considerable expertise in designing for ease of processing and selecting the type and grade of plastics that is easiest to process. However, molders generally have limited knowledge of mechanical or corrosion design factors. Molders also usually limit their work to plastics they are familiar with and to the amount of engineering time they can invest in quoting a part. To assure selection of the most suitable plastics material from among hundreds that are available, it is advisable to develop direct sources of information, including contacts with resin manufacturers. Fig. 3-1 lists representative properties for selected thermoplastics and thermosets commonly used in industrial applications.

ASTM Classification System: The American Society of Testing and Materials (ASTM) is a technical organization bringing manufacturers, specifiers, and users together to standardize specifications and test methods. Several individual types of plastics have been covered by specific ASTM standards; D 789 for polyamide (nylon) and D 788 for acrylic are two examples. Standards are useful for two reasons: First, the specifier can be assured of minimum strengths and properties for design calculations. Second, competitive manufacturers' resins can be used. Unfortunately, the rapid growth of the plastics industry also limits the usefulness of single standards. As mentioned previously, there is considerable competition between different types of resins. New and modified grades of resins are being developed more quickly than ASTM standards can be set.

To remedy this situation by establishing an industrywide designation system, in 1982 the ASTM issued the Standard D 4000 "Guide for Identification of Plastic Materials" to "adequately identify plastic materials in order to give industry a system that can be used universally." In D 4000, ASTM is attempting to establish a single designation system for all types and grades of plastics. In essence, D 4000 combines generic designations with a unified system of identifying important modifications to the generic resin and significant engineering property minimums. A regular designation for a glass-filled polyamide (PA) or nylon resin is the ASTM D 4000 specification for 33% glass-filled nylon (polyamide) resin grade, that is, ASTM D 4000 PA120G33A53380GA140 where:

ASTM D 4000 = Plastics material
PA120G33 = Basic—generic resin and modifications
A53380 = Cell—mechanical (physical) properties
GA140 = Suffix—special properties and tests

Basic Terminology

The term "polymer" is commonly used interchangeably with the term "plastics." Neither term is entirely accurate in its delineation. Plastic means pliable, yet most engineering polymers are not plastic at room temperature. Polymer, on the other hand, can include every kind of material made by polymerization with repeating molecules. The ASTM definition (D 883) of a plastic is: "A material that contains as an essential ingredient an organic substance of large molecular weight, is solid in its finished state, and, at some stage in its manufacture or in its processing into finished articles, can be shaped by flow."

In broad terms, plastics are man-made polymers. Polymer is the generic name for all materials composed of long, chainlike molecules. Most living tissue and cells are polymeric. Plastics are created either by modifying natural polymers, such as cellulose fibers, or by causing small synthetic molecules to bond together into a chain. Compared to other classes of materials, the plastics molecular chain is enormous, giving it the term "macromolecule." Millions of macromolecular chains must be put together to make industrially useful quantities.

Mers or Repeating Units: The basic, repeating structural unit of a plastics chain is termed its

Properties of Selected Industrial Plastics

Type of Plastics	Molecular Packing	Specific Gravity	ASTM D-638 Tensile Strength, psi (MPa)	ASTM D-638 Elongation, percent	ASTM D-695 Compressive Strength, psi (MPa)	ASTM D-256 Impact Strength (Izod), ft · lb/in. (J/cm)
			Mechanical Properties (Room Temperature)			
Polystyrene	Amorphous	1.10	7500 (51.7)	2	14,000 (96.5)	0.3 (0.2)
High-impact polystyrene	Amorphous	1.15	5000 (34.5)	10	7500 (51.7)	0.6-10.0 (0.3-5.3)
Acrylics	Amorphous	1.15	10,000 (69.0)	6	15,000 (103.4)	0.4 (0.2)
Polycarbonate	Amorphous	1.20	9000 (62.1)	100	10,000 (69.0)	15.0 (8.0)
ABS	Amorphous	1.05	6000 (41.4)	30	8000 (55.2)	6.0 (3.2)
Acetal (homopolymer)	Crystalline	1.40	10,000 (69.0)	40	18,000 (124.1)	1.8 (1.0)
Nylon 6/6 at 50% RH*	Crystalline	1.15	11,000 (75.8)	400	10,000 (69.0)	2.1 (1.1)
Polypropylene	Crystalline	0.91	4500 (31.0)	500	7000 (48.3)	1.0 (0.5)
Polyethylene (high density)	Crystalline	0.95	4000 (27.6)	600	3000 (20.7)	10.0 (5.3)
Polyethylene (medium density)	Crystalline with amorphous regions	0.93	2400 (16.5)	600	3000 (20.7)	8.0 (4.3)
Polyethylene (low density)	Semi-crystalline	0.91	1500 (10.3)	700	3000 (20.7)	No break
Epoxy	Cross-linked network	1.25	10,000 (69.0)	3	20,000 (137.9)	0.8 (0.4)
Phenolic	Cross-linked network	1.35	7000 (4-8.3)	2	10,000 (69.0)	0.4 (0.2)

*RH = relative humidity

Figure 3-1 Properties of selected industrial plastics

"mer." In essence, the mer is a typical link of the molecular chain. The chemical name of a mer is also the generic name for that type of plastics. Before being reacted to form a chain, the small molecule that becomes the mer is termed a "monomer."

The atoms within a mer are covalently bonded by sharing valence electrons. Polyethylene (PE) is an example of a simple structure. The hydrogen atoms can be replaced either by single atoms with a valence of 1, as in polyvinyl chloride (PVC), or by small organic molecules, as in polypropylene (PP) or polymethyl/methacrylate (PMMA). The small molecules replacing hydrogens are termed "side groups" or "pendant groups." Many mers have carbon atoms as the backbone of the chainlink. However, oxygen can be inserted (as in polyacetal), which then changes a number of properties. New engineering plastics have very complex mers, frequently including small molecules.

Polymerization: Polymerization is the chemical reaction that bonds monomers into plastics chains. Addition polymerization, the most common method, is exemplified in the manufacture of polyethylene (PE). The monomers, molecules of ethylene gas synthesized from petrochemicals, are mixed under precisely controlled temperature and pressure conditions. Initially, the double bond between the carbon atoms of the monomer is broken down to a single, covalently shared electron pair. Using catalysts, the carbons are driven to fill their missing valence positions by covalently bonding with carbons in neighboring monomers, not by rebonding within the same monomer. As polymerization continues, monomers continue to add together, forming a chain. In this form, plastics is termed "resin," indicating it is not a finished product but ready to be used for molding into a plastics part.

During polymerization, chains generally grow to somewhat different lengths and, potentially, different shapes. Chain length is a significant factor in determining molecular weight and ease of processing. Using viscosity or thermal techniques, the average molecular weight and weight distribution are determined for each batch. Molecular weight is directly related to chain length. Since each mer is the same, the molecular weight is the weight of one mer times the number of mers per chain (chain length). Frequently, manufacturers designate specific grades of a plastics as best for molding, indicating that the chain length and distribution of chain lengths have been controlled for maximum flow during molding. Flowability decreases with increased molecular weight. Shapes can be varied by using catalysts to induce monomer additions at chain positions other than the chain ends. Shape modification is generally reserved for special applications. In chemistry, a polymer is described by drawing its physical structure of atoms, as illustrated in Fig. 3-2.

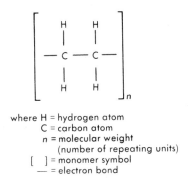

where H = hydrogen atom
C = carbon atom
n = molecular weight
(number of repeating units)
[ ] = monomer symbol
— = electron bond

Figure 3-2 Diagram representing arrangement of atoms in polyethylene

Plastics Chains: Although the mer is the principal chemical unit, the chains determine the unique properties of plastics by class and help differentiate between plastics. The behavior of the molecular chains is a key factor in determining the characteristics of a particular plastics material.

Motion. Plastics chains are in motion, even when the plastics material appears to be a solid. Temperature and applied load determine the rapidity and type of motion. As the temperature increases, chain motion increases until, at the molecular level, the plastics resembles a can of wriggling, intertwining worms. At the "glass transition stage" in amorphous polymers such as polystyrene and polycarbonate, and at the melting point for crystalline polymers such as Celanese Celcon acetal copolymer, chain motion becomes so marked that intertwining has little effect and chains can slide past one another. This condition is evident by a drop in the plastics' viscosity and by the plastics becoming a tarlike liquid. Each type of plastics has a distinctive glass transition temperature range or melting point range.

Strength. The strength of unreinforced plastics is dependent primarily on the forces holding the chains together. These forces arise from the natural intertwining of chains and from structural manipulations made by resin manufacturers. One of the oldest strengthening mechanisms is "crosslinking," or using a small molecule to bond resin chains together as in epoxy. Crosslinked plastics are strong because the chains cannot move. Most crosslinked plastics are thermosets. Plastics that melt are thermoplastics.

Elastic flow. Visco-elastic behavior, a combination of flow and elastic response to applied load, is another characteristic property of plastics. Chain motion is related to the internal structure of a plastics. While visco-elastic behavior is not unique to plastics, plastics are one of the few engineering materials to behave visco-elastically in the room temperature range and under low loads. The design principles governing visco-elastic plastics are different from those for elastic metals. In the next section of this chapter, the fundamentals of visco-elastic properties will be presented as related to plastics materials applications and parts manufacturing processing considerations.

Mechanical Properties

Both metals and plastics are characterized by similar types of mechanical properties. Metals, however, tend to be consistent in the sense that their behavior is adequately characterized by stress-strain relationships. In contrast, while the individual plastics materials also display distinctive stress-strain characteristics, the mechanical properties of plastics are more dependent on the additional factors of temperature and time (under load). In the design application, and to some extent in processing, creep data are of significant importance in the field of plastics materials.

The engineering plastics materials have ultimate tensile and compressive strengths and stiffness properties that are significantly lower than those of metals. This difference is especially true when comparing plastics to tool steels and high-strength steels. However, the differential in ultimate mechanical strength is much less when plastics are compared with metals such as aluminum, magnesium, zinc, and copper.

Engineering Plastics

The thermoplastic engineering resins are usually characterized as those resins having the following combinations of properties:

- Thermal, mechanical, chemical, corrosion resistance, and fabricability.
- Ability to sustain high mechanical loads, in harsh environments, for long periods of time.
- Predictable, reliable performance.

The term "engineering plastics" is neither rigorously defined nor restrictive in the sense that implies there is also a well-defined group of nonengineering plastics. Instead, some industry experts advocate a practical definition of engineering plastics that includes not only the property/performance criteria, but also market/pricing criteria.

The above two sets of criteria, taken together, place certain resins in the engineering category to the exclusion of others. The principal resins of the past decade that meet both sets of criteria are: nylon, acetal, thermoplastic polyester, modified phenylene oxide, and polycarbonate. In the 1980s, new materials, including some grades of acrylonitrile butadiene styrene (ABS), were developed that can be categorized as engineering plastics.

When referring to engineering plastics, some knowledgeable people simply apply a broad definition, based on property/performance criteria. This interpretation includes special grades and compounds of the commodity thermoplastics such as isocyanate-based resins and a variety of polymer alloys and copolymers, as well as polysulfone (PSO) and polyphenylene sulfide (PPS). The new types of rigid polyvinyl chloride (PVC) are also sometimes included. In addition, the growing scope of engineering plastics is commonly recognized to include the specialty plastics that offer high strength along with high-temperature performance. However, common usage of the term generally does not include the thermoset resins that were the forerunners of the engineering thermoplastics.

Other Plastics Used for Engineering Applications:
In some product applications, the five principal groups of engineering plastics compete with other plastics such as ABS, polystyrene, and various thermosetting plastics. Glass- and/or mineral-filled polypropylene and flame-retardant ABS are widely used when their special characteristics are needed, and modified phenylene oxide (Noryl) must compete against flame-retardant ABS in some electronic cabinetry where a relatively low thermal index is acceptable. Ultrahigh molecular weight polyethylene (UHMWPE) offers excellent wear resistance, but limited processability.

Thermosets. Thermosets have long been available as insulators in electric/electronic applications, offering a wide range of capabilities in resistance to heat and other environmental conditions. Thermoset molding compounds may be formulated to satisfy one or more important uses. Typical distinctive properties of thermosets include dimensional stability, low-to-zero creep, low water absorption, maximum physical strength, good electrical properties, high heat deflection temperatures, high heat resistance, minimal values of coefficient of thermal expansion, low heat transfer, and specific gravities in the 1.35 to 2.00 range.

Processing advantages have allowed thermoplastics to replace thermosets in many markets, but competition remains in some of the more demanding uses. Thermoplastics in general offer faster molding, lighter weight, the possibility for thinner walls and more complex design, and greater impact resistance. Thermosets do not commonly exhibit as much creep at elevated temperatures as thermoplastics, including the reinforced grades.

The engineering resins do not compete directly with epoxies, but some of the high-temperature resins are being used for that purpose. The engineering resins rarely compete with polyurethanes or silicones. Among the major engineering thermoplastics, polybutylene terephthalate (PBT) and polyethylene terephthalate (PET) come closest to the thermosets in balance of properties. Polycarbonate comes closest in dimensional stability; but PBT is the first of the major engineering plastics to be considered for some of the most demanding thermoset applications, including industrial machinery and electrical/electronic usage.

Fluoropolymers. Fluoropolymers are often categorized along with the engineering plastics, but the two groups seldom directly compete. As a class, fluoropolymers do not offer the load-bearing capability of the engineering plastics, and load-bearing is generally one of the demands placed on plastics in product engineering specifications. In nonload-bearing uses, however, fluoropolymers have outstanding and unique properties, including resistance to very high and low temperatures, exceptional electrical properties, and a low coefficient of friction.

Plastics Alloys and Blends:
Because of the high cost to develop and introduce a new plastics and provide the necessary marketing and technical support, new materials tailored for specific sets of properties are often made by chemical or physical modifications of existing resins. Desirable characteristics and properties can be obtained by blending or alloying resins, or by adding inorganic or organic fillers and reinforcements. Such modification is being done by primary resin suppliers who use these methods to produce special grades, by custom compounders, and—to an increasing extent—by end-users who tailor-make resins to fulfill their own specific needs.

Description. The distinction between alloys and blends is not clearly defined, but both terms are used for physical mixtures of two or more structurally different polymers. As compared to copolymers, in which the components are linked by strong chemical bonds, the components in alloys adhere primarily through Van der Waals forces, dipole interactions, and/or hydrogen bonding.

The process of alloying to improve certain desired characteristics of a polymer is not limited to adding only one other polymer. There are also terpolymers (three monomers in a chain) and plastics alloys with several polymer additives.

Polymer networks. A new technology that combines incompatible plastics to form interpenetrating polymer networks (IPNs) has been developed by Shell Chemical and other companies. This technique produces a new type of alloy consisting of intimate mixtures of two or more polymer networks held together by permanent entanglements. Unlike conventional alloys, the polymers need not be miscible, and the networks can be devised for optimum properties when they are needed, while using lower cost materials as the predominant ingredient when the property requirements are less severe.

Advanced Composites

A composite material is created by the combination of two or more materials—a reinforcing element and a compatible resin binder (matrix)—to obtain specific characteristics and properties. The components do not dissolve completely into each other or otherwise chemically merge, although they do act synergistically. Normally, the separate components can be physically identified, as well as the interface between components.

A common example of a composite material is fiberglass. Glass fibers are very strong. If notched, however, they fracture readily; or if put in compression, they buckle easily. By encapsulating the glass fibers in a resin matrix, they are protected from damage; at the same time, the resin matrix transfers applied loads to the unified fibers so that their stiffness and strength can be fully utilized in both tension and compression.

The more advanced structural composites use fibers of glass, carbon/graphite, boron, Kevlar (aramid), and other organic materials. These fibers are very stiff and strong, yet lightweight. The strengthening effects of the fiber reinforcements in composites are derived from (a) the percentage of fibers (fiber-resin ratio), (b) the type of fibers, and (c) the fiber orientation with respect to the direction of the loads.

While advanced fiber, resin matrix composites are classified as reinforced thermosets, a special technology has developed involving these materials that sets them somewhat apart from other reinforced thermosets. Called "advanced composites," resin matrix composites can include hybrids, mixtures of fibers in various forms in the resin (usually epoxy) matrix.

Continuous-fiber reinforcements can be directionally oriented; short or chopped fibers can only be randomly oriented. Each fiber form has its advantages and limitations. In general, short fibers cost more than continuous fibers, yet fabrication costs are lower for the short fibers. The properties of composites from chopped fibers are weaker than those obtainable with longer or continuous fibers.

The four basic areas of composites technology are:

- Organic (resin) matrix composites.
- Metal matrix composites.
- Carbon-carbon composites.
- Ceramic matrix composites.

The majority of aerospace, military, and commercial product applications for advanced composites use the carbon or graphite fibers with organic matrices; hence, these are the principal composites discussed in this section of the chapter.

Composite structural materials have evolved as a class of engineering materials that offer some unique properties and combinations of characteristics not exhibited by the more traditional materials systems such as "pure" metals, ceramics, and polymers. Figure 3-3 offers a schematic comparison of

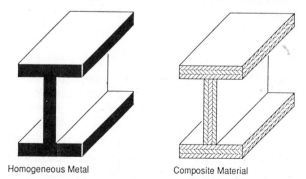

Homogeneous Metal   Composite Material

Figure 3-3   Homogeneous metal compared with a composite material

homogeneous metal and fiber-resin composite material. The industrial appeal of advanced structural composites is based on their inherent ability to replace conventional high-strength metals with lighter weight, higher strength material.

In the manufacture of aircraft, the predominant advanced composite material contains a reinforcing fiber that is almost pure carbon. The term carbon correctly describes the fiber since it contains little or no graphitic structure; however, in common practice, the terms carbon and graphite are often used interchangeably to denote a particular group of fibers used in advanced composites. Generally, the modulus of elasticity of a carbon fiber increases as the degree of graphitization increases.

State of the Art

Generically, a composite can include metal, wood, foam, or other material layers, in addition to the fiber and resin components. The term advanced composites came into use in the late 1960s to designate certain composite materials with properties considerably superior to those of earlier composites. The term is, however, imprecise because it does not identify specific material combinations, nor does it indicate their arrangement or configuration in the composite, the strength level, or other qualities that distinguish an advanced composite from other composites. Currently, the industry defines advanced composites and composites that contain a fiber-to-resin ratio of greater than 50% fiber, with the fibers having a modulus of elasticity greater than 16×10^6 psi (110.3 GPa).

General Description of Advanced Composites: To engineers in the field, an advanced composite has come to denote a resin matrix material that is reinforced with high-strength, high-modulus fibers of carbon, aramid, or boron, and is usually fabricated in layers to form an engineered component. More specifically, the term is applied principally to epoxy-resin matrix materials reinforced with oriented, continuous fibers of carbon and fabricated in a multilayer form to make extremely rigid, strong

structures. Another characteristic that distinguishes composites from reinforced plastics is the fiber-to-resin ratio. This ratio is generally greater than 50% fiber by weight; however, the ratio is sometimes indicated by volume since the weight and volume in composites are similar.

Composites Materials: Organic matrix composites are the most common, least expensive, and most widely used of all advanced composite materials. For purposes of discussion and reference, organic composites may be grouped according to their chronological development and commercialization, as presented in Fig. 3-4.

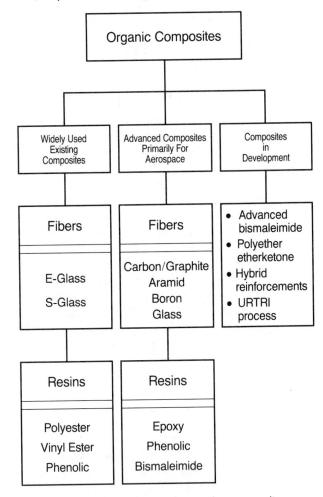

Figure 3-4   Breakdown of organic composites

The Matrix

The matrix serves two important functions in a composite: (1) it holds the fibers in place; and (2) under an applied force, it deforms and distributes the stress to the high-modulus fibrous constituent. The matrix material for a structural fiber composite must have a greater elongation at break than the fibers for maximum efficiency. Also, the matrix must transmit the force to the fibers and change shape as required to accomplish this, placing the majority of the load on the fibers. Furthermore, during processing, the matrix should encapsulate the fibrous phase with minimum shrinkage, which places an internal strain on the fibers. Other properties of the composite, such as chemical, thermal, electrical, and corrosion resistance, are also influenced significantly by the type of matrix used.

The two main classes of polymer resin matrices are thermoset and thermoplastic. The principal thermosets are epoxy, phenolic, bismaleimide, and polyimide. Thermoplastic matrices are many and varied, including nylon (polyamide), polysulfone, polyphenylene sulfide and polyether etherketone. The matrix material must be carefully matched for compatibility with the fiber material and for application requirements. The selection process should cover factors such as thermal stability, impact strength, environmental resistance, processability, and surface treatment of the reinforcing fibers (sizing).

Depending on the application, it is possible to view the role of the matrix in two different ways: either as the binder that contains the major structural elements (the fibers) and transfers load between them, or as the primary phase that is merely reinforced by the secondary fiber phase. The first concept is traditional since most composites have used a relatively soft matrix (such as a thermosetting plastics of the polyester, phenolic, or epoxide type). The strength of such composites is almost entirely that of the fibers; hence, for efficiency, it is desirable to optimize the fiber content. Thus, in most instances, small improvements in the structural properties of the matrix are of little value; its adhesion and processing characteristics, however, are of paramount importance.

Most structural composite components are produced with thermosetting resin matrix materials. In metal matrix composites, the most frequently used matrix material is aluminum, while alloys of titanium, magnesium, and copper are being developed. Boron and graphite fibers are generally used as the reinforcement for metal matrix materials.

Fiber Types and Production

The unique geometry of a fiber provides many of the advantages in an advanced composite. In their fiber form, materials such as carbon/graphite and boron (which are also known as polycrystalline ceramic fibers) show near-perfect crystalline structure. Parallel alignment of these crystals along the filament axis provides the superior strengths and stiffnesses that characterize advanced composites. Various production methods are used for the different fiber types.

Carbon/Graphite: Carbon or graphite fibers (these two terms are often used interchangeably to refer to a specific class of fibers), generally accepted as the most desirable materials for advanced structural composite applications, are produced from either polyacrylonitrile (PAN) or pitch. When superheated to temperatures of 4900°F (2700°C), various carbon grades can be manufactured into a synthetic graphite fiber. It is this graphite fiber, not the graphite mined naturally from the earth, that is woven into tape or fabric and bonded in a matrix of epoxy or other resin to form a composite. The carbon fibers are strong but brittle; hence, they may break rather than bend when forced into tight curves. Within a resin matrix, however, the fibers are positioned and protected. The loads are transmitted and distributed uniformly when grouped and held together by a matrix.

Polyacrylonitrile (PAN). The most widely used carbon fibers are formed by extruding polyacrylonitrile (PAN) through a spinnerette containing approximately 10,000 holes. The resulting fiber goes through ultrahigh heating, oxidation, carbonization, and graphitization processes to produce a filament with extremely high tensile strength and modulus (or stiffness). By varying process temperatures, engineers at Hercules, Inc. have produced both high-strength fibers [e.g., their AS4 graphite fiber at 520 ksi (3585 MPa) and 32,000 ksi (221 x 10³ MPa) modulus] and high-modulus fibers [e.g., their HMS at 50,000 ksi (345 x 10³ MPa) with 320 ksi (2206 MPa) tensile strength].

Pitch. The carbon or graphite fiber may also be manufactured by starting with petroleum pitch. With this method, the pitch must first be stabilized, and then a process is used to spin it into a filament, which is next made into the final carbon/graphite fiber. Pitch-based fibers are only about two-thirds as strong as PAN fibers, but have a greater potential for developing high moduli.

Recent developments at Union Carbide's Carbon Products Division include a petroleum pitch-based carbon fiber with a 100,000 ksi (690 x 10³ MPa) modulus. Under their trade name, Thornel, a typical epoxy matrix composite, grade VS-0054, exhibits a Young's modulus of 60,000 ksi (413 x 10³ MPa) and a tensile strength of 165 ksi (1138 MPa). By comparison, the typical Young's modulus and tensile strength of PAN-based carbon fibers in a similar epoxy matrix are 20,000 ksi (138 x 10³ MPa) and 225 ksi (1551 MPa), respectively. This new pitch-based fiber is expected to be cost-effective in the fabrication of lightweight structures in which stiffness is critical, such as space hardware and driveshafts.

Aramid: As a result of its high tensile strength properties, rated at 525 ksi (3620 MPa), Du Pont's Kevlar aramid has also gained acceptance in the field of advanced composites. Aramid is an organic fiber that is produced from a watery polymer solution extruded through a spinnerette. Du Pont's proprietary spinning process yields a super-rigid molecular chain with a modulus of 12,000 ksi (83 x 10³ MPa) and 18,000 ksi (124 x 10³ MPa), respectively, for Kevlar grades 29 and 49. Aramid fibers exhibit one of the highest tensile strength-to-weight ratios of any commercially used fiber; however, the compressive strength is one of the lowest. These properties must be taken into consideration in the design stage when using the composite. Blending the aramid fibers with other fibers, referred to as hybridization, optimizes the properties obtained.

Boron: Boron begins as a high-priced substrate known as boron trichloride. Through a chemical vapor deposition process, boron is deposited on a heated, moving tungsten filament. The resulting boron filament exhibits an average minimum tensile strength of 400 ksi (2758 MPa), with a tensile modulus of 55 to 60 x 10⁶ psi (379 to 414 GPa). Boron fibers exhibit the highest level of stiffness in resin matrices of all commercial fibers used today.

Fiber Forms and Fabrics

Composites can be classified in a number of different ways. The accepted classification types are fibrous (composed of fibers in a matrix), laminar (made from layers of materials), and particulate (made from particles in a matrix). Within the particulate type are flake and skeletal subcategories.

Continuous Fibers: Continuous fibers in yarns or tows (untwisted yarns) are used in filament windings and in unidirectional tape form. Tapes as wide as 48″ (1220 mm) are formed by collimating continuous fibers, applying a resin-compatible sizing, and impregnating the fibers with resin. The materials are partially cured (B-staged), then separated with a backing material to prevent them from sticking, and are referred to as prepregs. Prepreg tapes are usually processed by laminating them together in a desired configuration, then final curing them with heat and pressure.

Woven-fiber fabrics, or broadgoods, can be easily laid atop complex mold structures. Weaves of carbon/graphite fibers are available in unidirectional orientations that are sometimes bound with nonstructural tie yarns. Hybrid forms may include Kevlar as a locking element. Hybridizing can also be used to combine the impact resistance of Kevlar or cost savings of fiberglass with the superior strength and stiffness of carbon or boron. Multidirectional weaves of single-material fibers and/or multimaterial fibers (hybrids) are available in dry or prepregged forms.

Fabrics: Generally, the fibers are woven into fabrics that come in roll form. Fabrics can be woven for specific part requirements. There are various ways of placing the fibers and fabrics in the matrix; when the fibers are oriented to run in one direction, the resulting material is anisotropic in its strength properties.

Fiber Science:
In the evolving technology of advanced composite materials for high-performance structural components, the term *fiber science* is applied to a materials-tailoring discipline that includes the type of fibers, their percentage of the whole composite, and the oriented placement of fibers in the matrix during parts fabrication and production processing.

Versatility. Fiber science in the field of advanced composites is not limited to off-the-shelf items and concepts. Fiber science may be treated as a separate subscience of the composite structure. The materials are literally devised and produced through techniques that allow the tailoring of materials performance and properties to suit the intended application.

Fiber directionality. Fibers can run longitudinally, called the warp in a fabric; or they can run transversely, called the weft. Traditional bidirectional fabrics are called warp and weft. However, with the new weaving mill technology, fabrics can now run on the bias, as desired. The bias relates to the directionality and distribution of the fibers. Research is currently under way to produce three-dimensional hybrid fiber weaves; the ultimate hybrid fiber weave will be a "3-D" or cartesian weave.

Variable percentage. The first variable in fiber directionality is the percentage of fibers in each direction. The various directional fiber percentages can be specified and controlled to provide the desired strength levels and orientations. The bias fibers can be greater or less than the percentage of longitudinal fibers, which, in turn, may be greater or less than the percentage of weft or transverse fibers.

Fiber type. The other principal variables in the fiber reinforcement package are the type of fiber, and, especially, the growing capability for hybridization of fiber reinforcements for advanced composites.

Hybrid Composites:
Hybrid composites, which combine two or more different fibers in a common matrix, greatly expand the range of properties that can be achieved with advanced composites. They also increase the potential for cost-effective applications since hybrids may cost less than materials reinforced only with graphite, aramid, or boron.

Characteristics. The term *hybrid* generally applies to advanced composites and refers to the use of various combinations of continuous graphite, boron, aramid, and glass filaments in thermoset matrices. Hybrids have unique features that can be used to meet diverse design requirements in a more cost-effective way than either advanced or conventional composites. Some of the advantages of hybrids over conventional composites are balanced strength and stiffness, optimum mechanical properties, thermal-distortion stability, reduced weight and/or cost, improved fatigue resistance, reduced notch sensitivity, improved fracture toughness, improved impact resistance, and, most of all, optimum cost as related to performance.

Fibers. Various types of graphite, boron, glass, and aramid fibers are used in hybrids, as are cloth and fabric woven from the fibers. Fibers are available with the following ranges of mechanical properties: tensile strength from 2500 to 5000 ksi (17.2 to 34.4 GPa) and tensile modulus from 10 to 60×10^6 psi (69 to 414 GPa).

Graphite fibers (five different types are commercially available) offer high stiffness and strength and low density; however, impact resistance is low when compared to glass or aramid fibers. Aramid polyamide fibers combine high tensile strength, low modulus of elasticity, and high impact resistance, but have low compressive strength; with aramid fibers, producing chopped fibers on standard equipment is difficult. Of the two types of glass fibers currently used, S-glass is more rigid and stronger than E-glass. The main limitation of the glass fibers is their high density compared with that of graphite and aramid fibers.

Resins. Both thermoset and thermoplastic resins are used for hybrid composites. The epoxies remain the chief thermoset, but the use of thermoset polyester is growing, especially for automotive applications. The epoxies are available with a wide range of properties, but intermediate-modulus epoxies are used in most hybrids. Epoxies have good-to-moderate elevated temperature properties, but their properties decline when exposed to temperatures near 350°F (177°C) because of moisture absorption. Bismaleimides are used as matrices for composites where extended operation at temperatures near 500°F (260°C) and higher are required.

Forms. The main forms of hybrid composites are interply, intraply, interply-intraply, selective placement, and interply knitting.

Interply. The interply hybrids, illustrated in Fig. 3-5, consist of plies from two or more different fiber types stacked in alternate layers to obtain the desired properties.

Intraply. Figure 3-5 depicts the principle of intraply hybrids, which consist of two or more different fiber strands intermixed in the same ply.

Interply-intraply. The interply-intraply hybrids are made up of plies of interply and intraply hybrids stacked in a specific sequence.

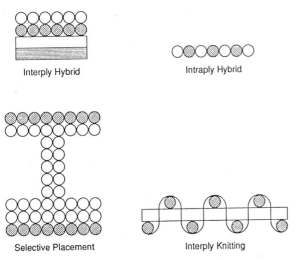

Interply Hybrid

Intraply Hybrid

Selective Placement

Interply Knitting

Figure 3-5   Composite forms

Selective placement. Figure 3-5 illustrates selective placement, which, from the viewpoint of cost-effective tailoring of material properties to design requirements, is regarded as a significant hybridization technique. As an example, the I-beam in the illustration shows the bulk of the fibers made of glass for economy, and places the costlier, higher strength graphite fibers at the extremities of the skins and flanges where the higher modulus (stiffness) qualities are most significant for the type of loading that is applied. Under deflection, the graphite carries the principal loads.

Interply knitting. A recently developed concept in composite fabric assembly called interply knitting or stitching is described in Fig. 3-5. This technique applies a vertical interply stitching with a polyester or aramid strand, thus connecting 2-5 plies together and strengthening the composite against interlaminar shear. Conceptually, the next step involves using a package of the interply-stitched fibers to make a part and selectively applying the stitching or interply knitting at designated places in the structure. Interply knitting enhances resistance to interlaminar shear by placing a vertical stitch through the multiple plies. Interlaminar shear occurs when the resin matrix fractures and the individual layers or plies of fabric peel apart.

Combinations. The potential number of fiber-resin combinations for hybrids is great. With just two resins (epoxy or bismaleimide) and three types of fibers (graphite, aramid, or glass), many different hybrid composites can be produced, depending on the fiber content and orientation of each fiber in the matrix. With two or even three different fibers in a common matrix, it is possible to make the most effective use of each fiber. For example, a hybrid of graphite and aramid is a natural combination, to which each fiber contributes its best properties.

Composite Construction

Composites can be divided into laminates and sandwiches. Laminates are composite materials consisting of two or more layers bonded together. Sandwiches are multiple-layer structural materials that contain a low-density core between thin faces (skins) of composite materials. In some applications, particularly in the field of advanced structural composites, the constituents (the individual layers) may themselves be composites (usually of the fiber-matrix type).

Laminates: In the context of this section, laminates are the general form in which component parts and end products are fabricated from advanced high-strength structural composite materials. Theoretically, there are as many different types of laminates as there are possible combinations of two or more materials. If materials are divided into metals and nonmetals, and if nonmetals divide into organic and inorganic, there are six possible combinations in which laminates can be produced: metal-metal, metal-organic, metal-inorganic, organic-organic, organic-inorganic, and inorganic-inorganic. In laminates containing more than two layers, there are considerably more possibilities, and one or more of the layers may be a composite.

Sandwiches: As was previously stated, sandwiches consist of a relatively thick, low-density core (such as honeycomb or foamed material) between thin faces of a material with higher strength and density. Although this distinction between laminates and sandwiches is more descriptive than technical, some general observations can be made. In sandwich composites, for example, a primary objective is improved structural performance, or, more specifically, high strength-to-weight ratio. The core serves to separate and stabilize the faces against buckling under edgewise compression, torsion, or bending, and provides a rigid and highly efficient structure. Other considerations, such as thermal insulation, heat resistance, corrosion resistance, and vibration damping, dictate the particular choice of materials used. While the choice of materials is an important consideration in sandwich composites, it is the configuration of the structure that controls the essential properties.

Applications Overview: Although advanced composites containing such materials as carbon/graphite or aramid fibers in an organic resin matrix are currently used mainly by the aerospace industries, these stiff, strong, lightweight materials are also used in various other commercial and industrial applications, ranging from aircraft structures to automobiles and trucks, from spacecraft to printed circuit boards, and from prosthetic devices to sports equipment. Products run the gamut from boat hulls and hockey shinguards to an advanced composites hinge for the retractable arm of the space shuttle.

The space shuttle cargo bay doors are the largest graphite-epoxy structures built to date. Filament-wound aramid forms the first, second, and third-stage motor housings of the Trident missile as well as the round pressure bottles aboard the space shuttle. Extensive use is made of composites in military aircraft, with applications also appearing in commercial jetliners and general aviation aircraft.

Fabrication

Current composites fabrication techniques are similar to those used for producing fiberglass, including hand and automated tape lay-up resin injection, compression molding, vacuum bag and autoclave molding, matched die molding, pultrusion, and filament winding. Organic matrix composites are made primarily by molding in autoclaves, while metal (aluminum, titanium, etc.) matrix composites are formed mainly by diffusion bonding.

Lamination, filament winding, pultrusion, and resin transfer (injection) molding are four widely used methods of producing continuous-fiber composites with closely controlled properties. The shape, size, and type of part and the quantity to be manufactured determine construction techniques. The lamination method is used for comparatively flat pieces. Filament winding is a powerful and potentially high-speed process for making tubes and other cylindrical structures. So-called pultrusion and pulmolding can be used for parts with constant cross-sectional shapes. Injection molding can be used for small, nonload-bearing parts. A new epoxy injection process, called URTRI (Ultimately Reinforced Thermoset Reaction Injection), is used for making load-bearing structures, sandwiches, and torsion boxes. See Fig. 3-6.

Automated Fabrication Methods: Composites technology is advancing rapidly, with a great deal of effort applied to improvement and automation in producing, cutting, applying, and handling the composite materials. The main compression molding, pultrusion, filament winding, and advanced RTM processes exhibit high-volume production potential.

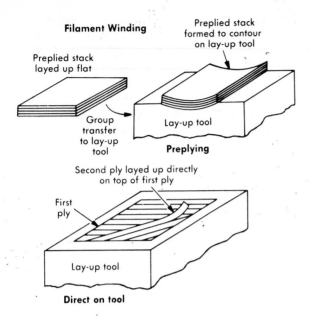

Figure 3-6   Preplying and direct-on-tool lay-up techniques for composites product fabrication

CAD/CAM. In end-product fabrication, research and development programs are making the composite structures increasingly amenable to computer-aided design and numerical control equipment. With CAD/CAM, design changes from metal to composite can be made with minimal risk, since the design can be evaluated as it develops. While the manufacture of advanced composite components is still highly labor intensive and expensive, plans are being implemented by at least one aircraft manufacturer to build an automated factory for producing composite structures of carbon-epoxy construction.

State of the art. Although isolated pieces of automated equipment are now becoming prevalent in composites fabrication, a workcell at the Northrop Corporation shows the extent to which automation can be applied to the composites industry. The cell automates each step of a complexly woven carbon-fiber prepreg lamination process.

In operation, an automated broadgoods spreader lays the prepreg across a cutting table. A computer-controlled reciprocating knife cutter then cuts six to twelve plies of the material. Next, a unique handling system known as the "flying carpet" transports the cutting surface between workstations along 230 ft (70 m) of electrified monorails. The precut prepreg is then carried to a robotic workstation, where a robot with a foam-faced vacuum head lifts the ply and places it in the proper orientation. The robot employs a vision system to search and locate the appropriate ply according to a programmed sequence. Lastly, the plies are laid into a contoured cure mold for delivery to a final cure station.

Elastomers

Elastomers are a special class of linear polymers that have the ability to undergo a great deal of elastic deformation and, when the force is released, return to their original shape and size. They also have the ability to repeat this process numerous times. This concept can be illustrated by stretching and releasing a rubber band.

Natural rubber is the oldest commercially used elastomer; it has been used as an engineering material for over 150 years. Charles Goodyear was the person who discovered that the performance of natural rubber as an engineering material could be improved by adding sulfur and heating the mixture. This process became known as **vulcanization.** It was learned later that vulcanized rubber could be improved further through the addition of such additives as carbon black. Carbon black added to the mixture acts as a stiffener, toughener, and anti-oxidant. Accelerators may be added to increase the rate of vulcanization while simultaneously decreasing the amount of sulfur required in the process.

Natural rubber is an excellent material for electrical insulation and applications in which resistance to organic acids is important. Natural rubber is a poor material in applications where resistance to petroleum products is important. Natural rubbers are not well suited for applications involving high temperatures or prolonged exposure to direct sunlight.

Artificial elastomers were developed in response to shortages of natural rubber. Some of the more widely used artificial elastomers and their typical applications are:

- Polyacrylate (oil hoses and O-rings)
- Ethylene propylene (electric insulation, footware, hoses, and belts)
- Neoprene (wire insulation, belts, hoses, gaskets, seals, linings)
- Polysulfide (seals, gaskets, diaphragms, valve disks)
- Silicone (electric insulation, seals, gaskets, O-rings)
- Urethane (caster wheels, heels, foam padding)

Ceramics

Ceramics have become an important engineering material due primarily to their ability to withstand high temperatures and resist wear. Their usefulness in solid state electronics has also enhanced their importance. Ceramics have the following characteristics:

1. They are hard.
2. They are brittle.
3. They have a high melting point.
4. They have low electrical and thermal conductivity.
5. They are thermally and chemically stable.
6. They have high compressive strength.
7. They are able to resist creep.

Most ceramic materials have crystal structures and are compounds of both metallic and nonmetallic elements such as oxides, carbides, and nitrites. Some ceramics have a noncrystalline structure. These ceramics are known as glasses.

Most people are familiar with clay-based ceramic products. By adding quartz and feldspar to clay, mixing the compound with water, shaping, drying, and heating, the wide variety of ceramic products with which most people are familiar can be produced. These include bricks, tile, drainage pipes, and porcelain.

Ceramics that have been designed especially for use in high-temperature applications are known as refractory materials. Most refractory materials are based on stable oxide compounds. There are three categories of refractory materials: acidic, basic, and neutral. Some that fall in the acidic category are silica, firebrick, and high-alumina firebrick. In the basic category there are magnesite and olivine. In the neutral category there are chromite and chromite-magnesite.

Ceramics have become particularly valuable for use in electronics and magnetic-related applications. They can be used in thermistors, rectifiers, capacitors, and transducers. They are also used for high-voltage insulation.

By mixing ceramics and metals using the same processes used in powder metallurgy, cermets are produced. Products made of cermets are pressed in molds at high pressure and sintered. Cermets are particularly valuable for applications that require strength and toughness at high temperatures.

KEY TERMS AND PHRASES

Advanced composites
Aramid
Blends
Boron
Carbon-carbon composites
Ceramic matrix composites
Continuous fibers
Elastic flow
Engineering plastics
Fabrics
Fiber science
Fluoropolymers
Hybrid composites
Industrial plastics
Interply
Interply-intraply
Interply knitting
Intraply
Laminates
Matrix
Mers
Metal matrix composites
Organic matrix composites

PAN
Plastics
Plastics alloys
Plastics chains
Polymerization
Polymer networks
PPS
PSO
PVC
Resins
Sandwiches
Selective placement
Thermosets

QUESTIONS FOR ADDITIONAL STUDY AND REVIEW

1. What are plastics?

2. Explain the structure of the plastics industry.

3. What is the ASTM standard for acrylic?

4. Define the following terms:

   - Mers
   - Polymerization
   - Plastics chains
   - Crosslinking
   - Elastic flow

5. What are engineering plastics?

6. What are thermosets?

7. What are fluoropolymers?

8. Describe the concept of polymer networks.

9. What are advanced composites?

10. What are the four basic areas of composite technology?

11. What purposes does the matrix serve in a composite?

12. Describe the following fiber types:

    - Carbon/graphite
    - Aramid
    - Boron

13. What are hybrid composites?

14. Contrast interply and intraply composite forms.

15. Distinguish between laminates and sandwiches.

16. What is the URTRI process?

17. Define the term ceramics.

18. What are refractory materials?

19. What are elastomers?

CHAPTER

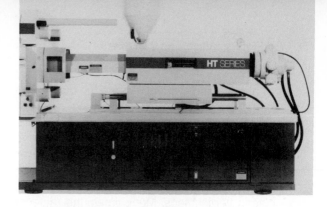

Forming of Materials

MAJOR TOPICS COVERED

- Roll Forming
- Spinning
- Bending and Straightening
- Shearing
- Punching
- Drawing, Extruding, and Upsetting
- Hot Extrusion
- Cold and Warm Extrusion
- Cold and Warm Upsetting
- Swaging
- Hot Forging
- Automatic Cold and Warm Forming
- Plastics Forming
- Injection Molding
- Extrusion Forming
- Reaction Injection Molding
- Reinforced Thermoset Plastics
- Thermoforming Plastic Sheet and Film
- Blow Molding
- Liquid Injection Molding
- Rotational Molding
- Structural Foam Molding
- Processing of Ceramics
- Fabrication of Composites
- Explosive Forming
- Electrohydraulic Forming
- Electromagnetic Forming

- High-Velocity Forging
- Peen Forming
- Ultrasonic-Activated Forming
- Powder Metallurgy
- Safety in Forming

ROLL FORMING

Roll forming is a continuous process for forming metal from sheet, strip, or coiled stock into shapes of essentially uniform cross section. The material is fed between successive pairs of rolls, which progressively shape it until the desired cross section is produced. During the process, only bending takes place; the material thickness is not changed except for a slight thinning at bend radii.

Roll Forming Methods

The two methods used when shaped parts are roll formed are the precut or cut-to-length method and the post-cut method. Method selection is based on the complexity of the cross section and the production length specification.

Precut Method: In precut operations, the material is cut to length prior to entering the roll forming machine. This process usually incorporates a stacking and feeding system to move the blanks into the roll forming machine, a roll forming machine running at a fixed speed of about 50-250 fpm (15-76 m/min), and an exit conveyor and stacking system. The cut-to-length process is used primarily for lower volume parts and whenever notching cannot be easily accomplished in a post-cut line; for example, miter cuts in vertical legs. Many times, the material is run from coil into a shear or blanking press and then mechanically fed into the roll former.

Tooling cost is inexpensive with this method because cutting requires only a flat shear die or end notch die. However, end flare is more pronounced and side roll tooling is required to obtain a good finished shape.

Post-Cut Method: Even though some configurations require the cut-to-length method, the most efficient, most productive, most consistent, and least troublesome is the post-cut method. This method requires an uncoiler, a roll forming machine, a cutoff machine, and runout table. In most segments of the industry, this is the most widely used method. It can be augmented by various auxiliary operations, including prenotching, punching, embossing, marking, trimming, welding, curving, coiling, and die forming. Any or all of these procedures can be combined to eliminate the need for secondary operations, resulting in a complete or net shape product. However, the cost of tooling and the tooling changeover time for this method are greater than the tooling cost and changeover time for the precut method.

Advantages and Limitations

Roll forming is a high-volume process of producing uniform, accurately dimensioned parts. Production speeds of approximately 50-600 fpm (15-185 m/min) are obtained, with 100-180 fpm (30-55 m/min) an average. Parts are produced with a minimum of handling, requiring only the loading of coils at the starting end of the machine and removal of finished parts at the exit end, generally accomplished by a minimum of operators. Roll forming can also be used for low-volume production because setup or change-over time from one cross section to another rarely takes more than a few hours, and length changes generally take only a few minutes on simple shapes. However, considerable time is required for more complex shapes.

The process is readily adaptable for combination with other operations and processes to form automatically a broad variety of metal parts. The initial cost of a roll forming line can be compared quite favorably with the cost of a standard stamping line or progressive die operation.

Maintenance costs are generally low. With proper roll design, the right tooling materials, good forming material, and proper lubricant, the form rolls can produce several million feet (900 000 m) of product before shape and tolerance problems develop. If through-hardened steel rolls are used, they can be recut or retrofitted, at a fraction of replacement cost, to produce for many more years.

The designing of rolls for complicated shapes must be done by experienced roll engineers. Complicated tubular or closed shapes sometimes require mandrels to form the shape properly, and delicate breakable parts require frequent replacement when high-production runs are made.

Materials Roll Formed

Any material known today that can withstand bending to a desired radius can be roll formed. The material can be ferrous or nonferrous, cold rolled, hot rolled, polished, prepainted, or plated. Thicknesses of 0.005 to 3/4" (0.13 to 19 mm) and material widths of ⅛ to 72" (3 to 1830 mm) or more can be used in roll forming. Length of the finished part is limited only by the length that can be conveniently handled after it leaves the roll forming machine.

In some instances, multiple sections can be formed from a single strip or several strips can be fed simultaneously and combined to produce one composite section. The only absolute requirement for a material, whatever the type, coating, thickness, or width, is that it be capable of being formed at room temperature to the specified radii. Some materials, such as certain titanium alloys, have poor forming characteristics at room temperature. Therefore, the material must be heated and then formed on specially designed roll forming machines (see Fig. 4-1).

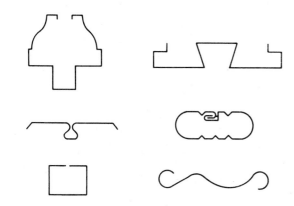

Figure 4-1　Profile attainable with roll forming

Roll Forming Machines

The roll forming machine (roll former) most commonly used has a number of individual units, each of which is actually a dual-spindle roll forming machine, mounted on a suitable baseplate to make a multiple-unit machine. The flexibility of this construction permits the user to purchase enough units for immediate needs only. By purchasing additional length of baseplate on the machine, units can be added at any time for future needs. Some of these machines are provided with machined ends on the baseplates, making it possible to couple several machines together, in tandem, to provide additional units as required.

Adjusting screws, for making vertical adjustment of the top rolls, are designed with dials and scales to provide micrometer adjustment and a means of recording the position of the top shaft for each roll pass and each shape being formed. The shaft diameter of most machines is from 1-4″ (25-90 mm).

Types of Roll Forming Machines

Several different types of roll forming machines or roll formers are used. They can be classified according to spindle support, station configuration, and drive system.

Spindle Support: Roll forming machines can be classified according to the method by which the spindles are supported in the unit. Generally, two types exist: (1) inboard or over-hung spindle machines and (2) outboard machines.

Inboard-type machines have spindle shafts supported on one end which are 1 to 1½″ (25 to 38 mm) in diameter and up to 4″ (100 mm) in length.

Outboard machines have housings supporting both ends of the spindle shafts (see Fig. 4-2).

Station Configuration: As was previously mentioned, a typical roll forming machine consists of several individual roll forming units mounted on a common baseplate. The manner in which they are mounted determines to a great extent the type of shapes that are formed on the machine.

Single-duty machine. This type of machine is built and designed for a one-purpose profile or for one particular set of roll tooling and is not normally designed for convenient roll changing. The cost of this machine is low in comparison to the other styles and is generally used for long production runs.

Conventional or standard machines. This particular type of machine is more versatile than the single-duty machine because the outboard supports are easily removed. This permits the roll tooling to be interchanged with other profiles to make it more suitable for a variety of production requirements.

To change the tooling, the top and bottom spindle lock nuts are removed and the outboard housing is pulled off the spindles. The tooling can then be removed and replaced with the desired profile.

Side-by-side machine. This machine is designed for multiple profiled tooling and provides the flexibility of having more than one set of roll tooling mounted on the spindle shaft at the same time (see Fig. 4-3).

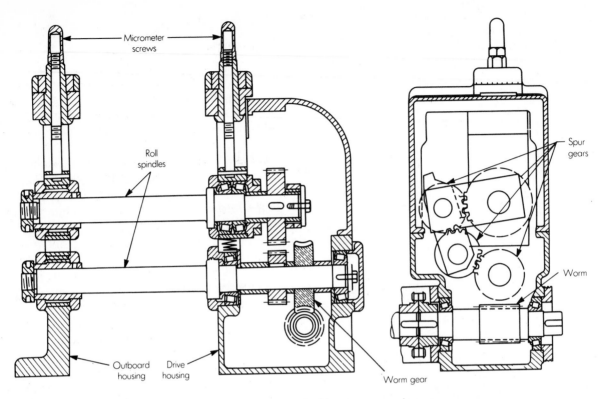

Figure 4-2   Cross section of an outboard roll stand with square gearing

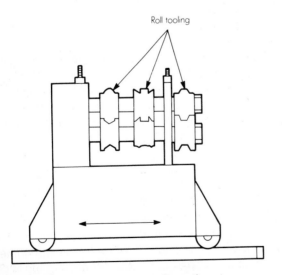

Figure 4-3   Side-by-side configuration

Generally, this type of machine is limited to two sets of rolls at a given time, but there can be up to three or four sets of rolls when small profiles are being run in production.

Double-high machines. The double-high configuration consists of one set of roll tooling mounted on its own roll shafts and housings at one level on the bed frame, and a second complete set of roll tooling and housings mounted at a different level on the same common frame (see Fig. 4-4). This particular type of machine is used in the metal building industry for forming building panels up to 60″ (1520 mm) wide.

Rafted machine. The rafted configuration resembles the single-duty and conventional configurations since each configuration has housings and spindle shafts with one particular set of roll tooling mounted on it. However, the rafted configuration has several roll forming units mounted on rafts or subplates that are removable from the roll former base (see Fig. 4-5).

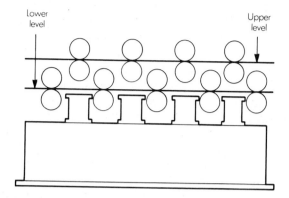

Figure 4-4 Double-high configuration

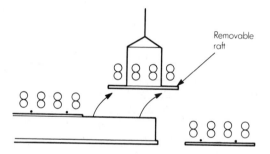

Figure 4-5 Rafted configuration

During tool changeover, the individual rafts are removed from the base and the replacement rafts with the roll forming units and tooling are installed. On a typical 16-stand roll forming machine, there are four sets of rafts containing four forming units each.

Double-head machine. This type of machine is designed and constructed with two separate sets of housings and roll shafts mounted so that they face one another. Each housing is mounted on an adjustable plate mechanism to allow the housing to be shifted for a change in overall width while at the same time maintaining the same profile for the edge formation.

Drive System: The five basic methods used to drive the roll forming unit are chain drive, spur gear drive, worm gear drive, square gearing, and universal drive.

Chain drive. The chain drive consists of a sprocket attached to the individual roll forming unit and connected to the main drive by means of a roller chain. This is accomplished using a continuous roller chain, one long chain driving each unit, or a shorter chain connected to each individual unit. This drive system is inexpensive and allows flexibility in the construction of the machine.

Spur gear drive. The spur gear drive consists of a continuous train of spur gears mounted at the rear end of each spindle shaft. Idler gears are positioned between each unit to transfer the drive equally to all the units (see Fig. 4-6).

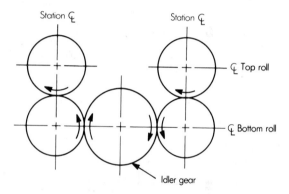

Figure 4-6 Idler gears are positioned between the stations to transfer the drive to each unit

Worm gear drive. The worm gear drive is very similar to the spur gear drive. However, instead of using the idler gear to transfer the drive to each unit, an individual worm gear box is mounted on the bottom spindle of each unit. The worm gear boxes are coupled in-line which permits the machine designer to spread out the horizontal centers of each roll forming station without being concerned about properly meshing the gear train to the idler gear.

Square gearing. Another type of drive system that incorporates both the spur gears and the worm gear is the square gearing system. This type of gearing permits a vertical adjustment of the upper spindle and allows a wide range of roll diameters to be used.

Universal drive. This particular style or design of drive eliminates the need for any spur gearing or roller chain and sprocket drives. It consists of a series of worm driven gear boxes with top and bottom outputs that transfer the power source to the individual shafts through a double-jointed universal coupling. On certain applications, only the bottom spindle is driven.

This drive system is generally used with rafted style machines to permit quick tool changeover (see Fig. 4-7). Simplicity of design and minimal maintenance are two important advantages of this drive system.

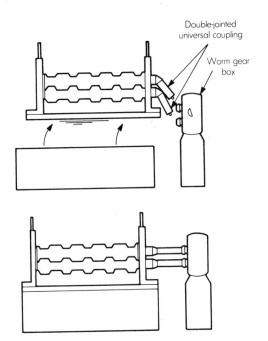

Figure 4-7   Universal-type drives

SPINNING

Spinning is a chipless production method of forming axially symmetrical metal shapes. It is a point deformation process by which a metal disc, cylindrical workpiece, or preform is plastically deformed into contact with a rotating chuck (mandrel) by axial or axial-radial motions of a tool or rollers. Shapes produced include cones, hemispheres, tubes, cylinders, and other radially symmetrical, hollow parts in a wide variety of sizes and contours. Elliptical shapes are also spun; however, forming these shapes is not as easy as producing symmetrical cylindrical parts.

Spinning is an economical, efficient, versatile method of producing parts, especially if the cost of stamping or deep-drawing dies would be substantial. The method is used for requirements ranging from prototypes to high production parts. Parts ranging from ¼" (6.4 mm) to 26 ft (7.9 m) diam have been spun from metals up to 3" (76 mm) or more in thickness.

The spinning process can be classified into four basic types: manual (hand) spinning, power spinning, shear forming, and tube spinning, as illustrated in Fig. 4-8.

Manual Spinning

Manual or hand spinning is a technique for spinning conical, hemispherical, or cylindrical cup shapes requiring several axial-radial tool or roller passes to bend the metal into contact with the chuck or mandrel. The process results in only a slight reduction in the blank thickness or preform thickness.

Manual spinning is one of the oldest known methods of metalforming. It is generally done on lathe-type machines with no mechanical assistance to increase the force. A large mechanical advantage is achieved, however, when using tools of scissor design, discussed later in this section. Normally, a circular disc of metal, called the blank, is clamped between a rotating mandrel (chuck) and a follower on the tailstock of the machine. Manual pressure is applied to a levered tool to progressively bend or flare the metal over the mandrel, practically always with multiple passes of the tool.

Manual spinning is still widely used for development work, prototypes, and both short and long production runs in forming thin metal blanks—up to about ¼" (6.4 mm) thick in aluminum—and the diameter of parts that can be hand spun depends upon the machine available. Some simple shapes can be formed without a mandrel. Tolerances of the spun parts vary with the skill, strength, and fatigue of the operator (see Figs. 4-9, 4-10, and 4-11).

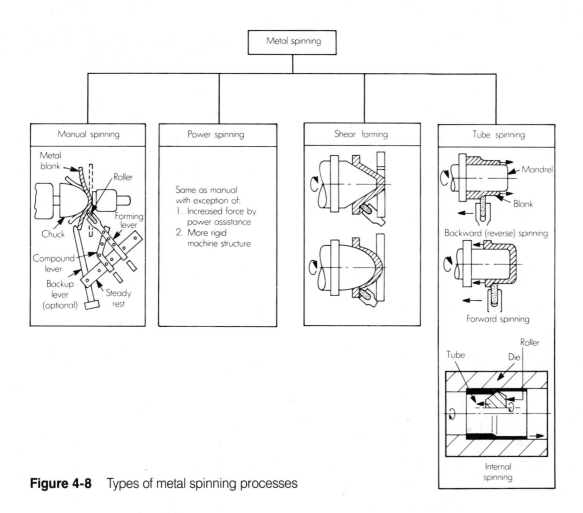

Figure 4-8   Types of metal spinning processes

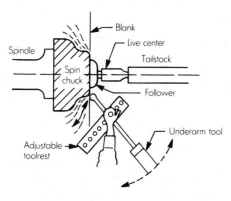

Figure 4-9   Underarm-tool manual spinning

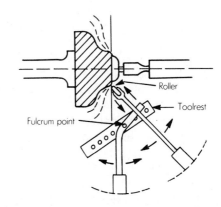

Figure 4-10   Scissor-tool manual spinning

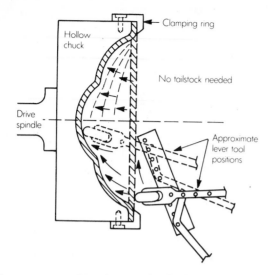

Figure 4-11   Dish (push-in) spinning

Power Spinning

Power, power-assisted, or mechanical spinning employs the same principles as manual spinning, but uses various devices for applying force. The devices employed include (1) toolholding carriages or compounds powered by mechanical, air, hydraulic, or mechanical/hydraulic means and (2) hydraulic or electronic tracing and copying systems using single, multiple, or swivel templates. Machines controlled by CNC (discussed later in this chapter) are also used. The scope of spinning applications has been broadened, and thicker blanks can be spun with power spinning.

Power spinning is commonly used to describe shear forming (discussed next in this section), but the two processes differ greatly. With both manual and power-assisted spinning, the starting blank diameters must be considerably larger than the diameters of the finished workpieces; there is no appreciable or intentional thinning of the material and less working of the metal during spinning than during shear forming. The blank size depends upon the surface area of the spun part. With shear forming, starting blank diameters are approximately the same

as the diameter of the finished parts, and there is a controlled reduction in blank thickness (see Figs. 4-12 and 4-13).

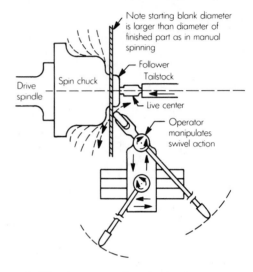

Figure 4-12   Power-assisted spinning

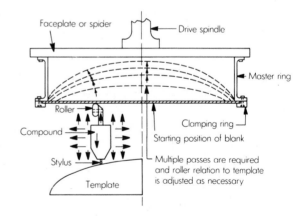

Figure 4-13   Dieless dishing of a tank head

Shear Forming

Shear forming is a rotary-point extrusion process for spinning conical or hemispherical shapes. One axial-radial pass of the roller(s) produces a significant reduction in blank thickness. This produces high compressive shear stresses in the transverse (material thickness) direction, resulting in a thickness reduction that obeys the sine law equation (see Fig. 4-14).

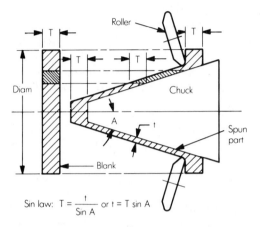

Sin law: $T = \dfrac{t}{Sin\ A}$ or $t = T \sin A$

Figure 4-14   Sine law relationship in shear forming straight-sided conical parts from flat blanks

The process is a variation of power spinning that is sometimes referred to as shear spinning, Hydrospinning, Floturning, flow turning, spin forging, compression spinning, Rotoforming, and rotary extrusion. Required shapes are spirally generated by the metal as it is progressively displaced axially between the rotating mandrels and the power-fed rolls. Metal required for forming is obtained from the blank.

When the required finished thickness, t, and the side angle, A, are known, the blank thickness, T, can be calculated by the sine law.

Example:

To spin a part with a 0.125″ (3.17 mm) thick wall at a 30° side angle, the thickness, T, of the starting blank equals 0.250″ (6.35 mm).

Strict adherence to the sine law, however, only occurs under ideal conditions. Under conditions of true shear forming, the flange of the workpiece is theoretically stress free, the axial thickness of the cone wall remains the same as the original blank, and the bottom and flange on the spun part also

maintain the original thickness. The minimum angle to which a metal may be shear formed from a flat blank is about 15°.

Tube Spinning

Tube spinning is used to reduce the wall thickness and increase the length of tubes or preformed shapes (cast, roll formed and welded, forged, machined, pressed, or spun) without changing their inside diameters. Reductions in wall thicknesses of 90% and increases in length of 800% have been accomplished in this way without annealing between passes. This method follows a purely volumetric rule, and the sine law does not apply because there is no included angle. Limitations depend upon the amount of reduction the specific metal can withstand without the need for annealing; the percentage reduction necessary to make the metal flow, usually about 15-25%; and the force capacity of the machine.

In addition to reducing wall thicknesses and increasing lengths, with resultant improvements in strength due to plastic deformation, this process is often used to form shaped parts from tubing or preforms, such as parts with flanges at various locations. Varying wall thicknesses can also be produced by employing a tracing attachment on the machine or by using a CNC machine (see Figs. 4-15 and 4-16).

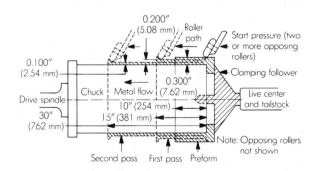

Figure 4-15   Forward method of spinning

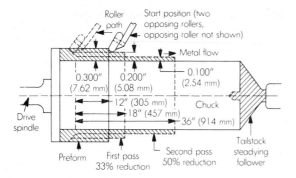

Figure 4-16 Reverse (backward) spinning

BENDING AND STRAIGHTENING

Bending is a method of producing shapes by stressing metal beyond its yield strength, but not past its ultimate tensile strength. The forces applied during bending are in opposite directions, just as in the cutting of sheet metal. Bending forces, however, are spread farther apart, resulting in plastic distortion of metal without failure.

The general term *straightening* is applicable to the straightening of metal stock prior to processing and also to the straightening of workpieces and manufactured parts.

Sheet and Plate Bending

The bending process appears to be simple; yet, in reality, it is a rather complex process involving a number of technical factors. Included are characteristics of the workpiece material, the material flow and reactions during various stages of deformation, the effect of tooling design on force required to form the bend, and the type of equipment used.

In the large, varied field of sheet metal and plate fabricating, several types of bending machines are used. Press brakes predominate in shops that process heavy-gage materials, because they are well suited to such applications and also because they are adaptable to other metalworking operations, such as punching, piercing, blanking, notching, perforating, embossing, shearing, and drawing.

Light-gage metal typically is formed with specialized bending machines, which are also described as leaf, pan, or box brakes; as wing folders; and as swivel benders. Equipment of this type is often manually operated.

The principal kinds of equipment used to bend sheet metal and plate can be grouped into the following categories:

- Mechanical press brakes—elongated presses with numerous tooling options. Work is performed by means of energy released from a motor-driven flywheel. These machines normally have a 3″ or 4″ stroke length.
- Hydraulic press brakes—stretched C-frame presses that are likewise compatible with a wide range and diversity of tooling. High-pressure oil in hydraulic cylinders supplies the force, which is directed downward in most models. The stroking length usually exceeds 6″.
- Hydraulic-mechanical press brakes—presses with drives that combine hydraulic and mechanical principles. In operation, oil forces a piston to move arms that push the ram toward the bed.
- Pneumatic press brakes—low-tonnage bending machines that are available with suitable tooling options.
- Bending brakes—powered or manual brakes commonly used for bending light-gage sheet metal.
- Special equipment—custom-built benders and panel formers designed for specific forming applications.

Terms used to describe various aspects of sheet metal bending are illustrated in Fig. 4-17.

Bend Allowance

Bend allowance is the dimensional amount added to a part through elongation during the bending process. It is used as a key factor in determining the initial blank size.

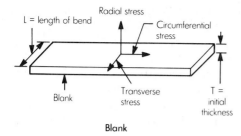

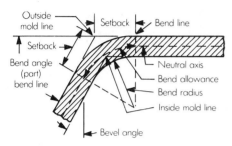

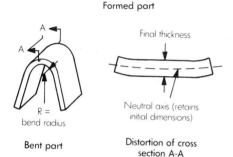

Figure 4-17   Bending terms

The length of the neutral axis, or bend allowance, is the length of the blank. Since the length of the neutral axis depends upon its position within the bend area, and this position is dictated by the material type and thickness and the radius and degree of bend, it is impossible to use one formula for all conditions. However, for simplicity, a reasonable approximation with sufficient accuracy for practical usage when air bending is given by the following equation:

$$L = \frac{A}{360} \times 2 \pi (R + kt)$$

or:

$$L = 0.017453A \ (R + kt)$$

where:

L = bend allowance (arc length of the neutral axis), in. or mm
A = bend angle, deg
R = inside radius of part, in. or mm
t = metal thickness, in. or mm
k = constant, neutral-axis location

Theoretically, the neutral axis follows a parabolic arc in the bend region; therefore, the k factor is an average value that is sufficiently accurate for practical applications. A value of 0.5 for k places the neutral axis exactly in the center of the metal. This figure is often used for some thicknesses. One manufacturer specifies k according to sheet thickness and inside radius of the bend; when R is less than $2t$, $k = 0.33$; when r is $2t$ or more, $k = 0.50$.

Types of Bending

The basic types of bending applicable to sheet metal forming are straight bending, flange bending, and contour bending. Examples of these three types of bending are shown in Fig. 4-18.

Straight Bending: The terminology for a straight bend is shown in Fig. 4-19. During the forming of a straight bend, the inner grains are compressed and the outer grains are elongated in the bend zone. Tensile strain builds up in the outer grains and increases with the decreasing bend radius. Therefore, the minimum bend radius is an important quantity in straight bending since it determines the limit of bending beyond which splitting occurs.

Flange Bending: Flange bend forming consists of forming shrink and stretch flanges as illustrated by views d and e in Fig. 4-18. This type of bending is normally produced on a hydrostatic or rubber-pad press at room temperature for materials such as aluminum and light-gage steel.

Parts requiring very little handwork are produced if the flange height and free-form-radius requirements are not severe. However, forming metals with low modulus of elasticity to yield strength ratios, such as

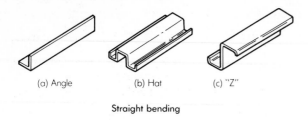

(a) Angle   (b) Hat   (c) "Z"

Straight bending

magnesium and titanium, may result in undesirable buckling and springback as shown in Fig. 4-20, *a* and *b*. Also, splitting may result during stretch-flange forming as a function of material elongation (see Fig. 4-20, *c*). Elevated temperatures utilized during the bending operation enhance part formability and definition by increasing the material ductility and lowering the yield strength, providing less springback and buckling.

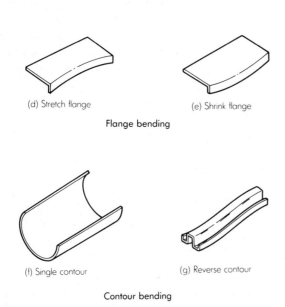

(d) Stretch flange   (e) Shrink flange

Flange bending

(f) Single contour   (g) Reverse contour

Contour bending

Figure 4-18   Types of bend forming

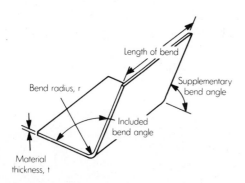

Figure 4-19   Terminology for a straight bend

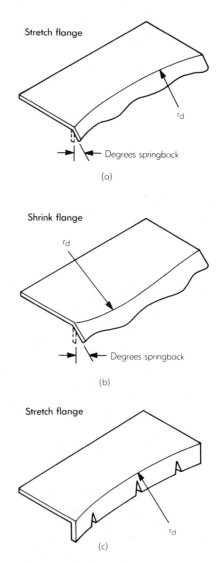

Figure 4-20   Flange forming failure modes

Contour Bending: Contour bending is illustrated by the single-contoured part in Fig. 4-18, *f*, and the reverse-contoured part in Fig. 4-18, *g*. Single-contour bending is performed on a three-roll bender, or by using special feeding devices with a conventional press brake. Higher production rates are attained using a three-roll bending machine, as described later in this chapter. Contour radii are generally quite large; forming limits are not a factor. However, springback is a factor because of the residual-stress buildup in the part; therefore, overforming is necessary to produce a part within tolerance.

Stretch Bending: Stretch bending (see Fig. 4-21) is probably the most sophisticated bending method, and requires expensive tooling and machines. Furthermore, stretch bending requires lengths of material beyond the desired shape to permit gripping and pulling. The material is stretched longitudinally, past its elastic limit, by pulling both ends and then wrapping around the bending form. This method is used primarily for bending irregular shapes; it is generally not used for high production.

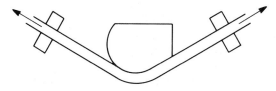

Figure 4-21   Stretch bending

tation, and the presence of this stress can cause part deformation in shape and size. Such stresses are often induced in the cold or hot working of stock material and later cause deformations when the stock is cut or formed into components or shapes.

In rods or tubes, residual stresses usually take the form of bows or snakes (a series of bows) in the part (see Fig. 4-22). In flat rectangular or irregularly shaped parts, deviation from a straight line is generally in the form of camber (see Fig. 4-23). Another out-of-straight condition that can occur in all parts is twist, in which the face of the part is out-of-plane. Stock materials and piece parts can have any or a combination of all of these conditions.

Figure 4-22   Types of stress deformation in rods and tubes

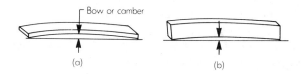

Figure 4-23   Types of stress deformation in rectangular bars

Straightening

Cold or hot metal forming processes can cause residual stresses in rod, bar, sheet, wire, or tubing—and in components made from these materials—as a result of nonuniform plastic flow of the material. Metallurgically, residual stress occurs because of many conditions inherent in the structure and properties of the metal, including molecular disorien-

Principles of Straightening

The general principle of straightening deformations in stock or component parts is to move the material beyond its elastic limit.

At normal room temperatures, straightening can be done by locating a deformation and moving the material in the opposite direction, so that when pressure is removed, the deformation is equalized. Stock or parts can also be heated to high temperatures and placed under continuous pressure for a period of time, allowing the molecular structure to equalize while the material cools. Stretching or drawing of stock materials through dies can equalize molecular surface tensions and overcome deformations. Flexing stock or component parts back and forth, returning them to a straight line, can stress relieve them and bring them to a straight condition.

Advantages

Straightness is important in stock materials, since component parts manufactured from straight stock tend to remain straight. Straightness is obviously necessary for component parts that are used in assembly with other parts, since proper functioning of the assembly depends upon the correct relationship of one part to another. Other advantages of straightness include:

- Parts can be consistently held to close dimensions.
- Relief of residual stresses enhances part stability.
- Straight parts can be machined at greater production rates.
- Less labor and skill are required in subsequent machining operations.
- Part life is increased, since stability of a part provides better resistance to fatigue and improved yield strength.
- Less material is needed when allowances are made for cuts as a means of obtaining straightness.
- Parts which are used alone (that is, hand tools) have a better and more salable appearance.

Limitations

Straightening does not always overcome all stresses; and after machining or heat treatment, a part may need to be restraightened. Straightening does not correct out-of-round conditions such as those caused by mismatch in forgings or ovality.

Stock or Continuous Materials

Stock material can be defined as wire, tubing, sheet metal, or extrusions. It generally is received in coil form. When the stock is used to produce parts, residual curves result from the coiling. On round, cross-section stock, twisting can occur about the axis of the material. This twisting (deformation) may be caused by axial movement during coiling, or it may result from production operations such as welding of tubing, drawing of wire, or feeding and processing of sheet metal.

Stock and continuous materials can be straightened in a separate operation or in line with cutoff or machining operations.

Stretch Straightening: In the stretch straightening method, the ends are clamped and tension is placed on the material. This method is not widely used; it is slow and limited in effectiveness.

Parallel-Roll Straightening: In this method a series of rolls is arranged so that the material moves between them, overbending in diminishing amounts as it moves forward. Sheet, plate, and strip materials are generally straightened only in the flat plane, although some edge guiding can be provided. Wire or tubing, with a round or multisided cross section, can generally be straightened in two planes, one 90° to the other. When necessary, three planes, each 120° from the other, can be used successfully. Rolls in such straighteners can have V-grooves for solid materials or grooves matching the cross section of tubular materials so that they do not distort under the straightening pressure (see Fig. 4-24).

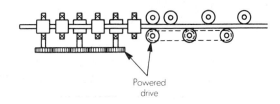

Powered
drive

Figure 4-24   Horizontal and vertical plane-shape straightener

Revolving-Arbor Straightening: Wire, tubing, or small-diameter, coiled rod is pulled through a rotating mechanism that usually contains cast-iron straightening dies. The outer dies on each end are set to keep the wire in the center; the middle sets of dies bend the material as the arbor spins around the material moving through the mechanism. Trial and error determines the setting of the dies. A major advantage of this method is that straightening occurs around the entire circumference of the material as it moves through, covering all planes. A disadvantage is that it cannot generally be performed on material moving any faster than 150-200 fpm (46-61 m/min).

SHEARING

Shearing is a process by which large sheets of material are cut into pieces of smaller length and width. These pieces are often used in subsequent operations such as punching and forming. Shearing is also used to produce blanks or slugs to be used in subsequent forming and machining processes. Because shearing is often the initial step in a series of processes, it is essential that the operating procedures result in an accurate workpiece.

Shearing Principles

The term *shearing* is derived from the method in which the blade edges meet in a progression from one side to the other, the same as an ordinary pair of scissors. The angle at which the blades are aligned to one another is termed blade rake angle, and the distance that the blades are separated is termed blade or knife clearance.

The principle of shearing is simply that as the blades come together and contact the material being sheared, the blades penetrate the material until the tensile strength is overcome and a crack or tear, called the slip plane, develops from both sides.

During the shearing process, as the knife continues down, freeing the sheared piece from the original metal, the wall of the knife rubs against the metal to cause an area of burnish that extends along the length of the metal where the knife makes contact with it. The sheared piece of metal rubs against the wall of the lower knife, causing a second burnish area on the metal.

On most shears, the upper knife is slanted at an angle (see Fig. 4-25). Generally, this angle is set between ½ and 2½°. An angle of 2½° reduces the shear load by as much as 25%, but the squareness of cut and edge quality are affected. This inclination causes the knife to move down and to back away from the lower knife. This action ensures that the

Figure 4-25 Shearing process (Courtesy of the Hill Acme Company)

sheared piece will not become wedged between the two knife blades, and it helps to concentrate the shearing force in the exact area of blade engagement between the two knives. This action also causes the fractures to start on a straight line approximately parallel to the surface of the knife.

Types of Shears

Although shears are made in a wide variety of sizes and styles to satisfy the needs of the metal fabricator, they can be classified according to either (1) the means by which the crosshead is driven or (2) the type of work that the shear was designed to perform. Some shears are capable of performing more than one type of work but can still be classified under these general categories.

Crosshead drive is the means by which the crosshead is powered. It can be (1) manual, (2) mechanical, (3) hydraulic, or (4) pneumatic.

Design of the shear determines to a large extent the type of work that can be performed. Some of the more common designs are (1) gapless shears, (2) gap shears, (3) alligator or pivot shears, (4) ironworkers, (5) cutoff machines, (6) bar-billet shears, (7) computer numerical control (CNC) shears, and (8) rotary shears.

PUNCHING

Punching involves the cutting of holes and results in scrap slugs. It can be performed with punching presses specifically designed to hold the tooling or with stamping presses and utilized tooling. Operations related to punching include nibbling, notching, piercing, perforating, slotting, pointing, and marking.

Both ferrous and nonferrous metals are punched, as well as nonmetallic materials.

Punching on a punch press is fast and economical. A variety of shapes and sizes can be punched with standard tooling. Many presses are capable of nibbling large cutouts and contours in workpieces that would generally be produced with other, more costly metalcutting techniques. Plasma and laser cutting attachments permit small internal angles, scrolls, spirals, etc., to be cut on the punch press.

Punch presses are used to punch holes of different shapes and sizes in various types of materials. Some of the applications for punch presses are in the production of electronic metal work, electrical boxes, appliances, construction equipment, farm machinery, trucks, office furniture, and vending machines.

Other operations that can be performed on the punch press include notching, forming, tapping, nibbling, and louvering.

Types of Punch Presses

The two types of punch presses built are the single-station press and the multiple-station press. Multiple-station punch presses are generally referred to as turret presses. However, some multiple-station presses are built that contain two or three punching stations. The tooling is mounted individually in the toolholder. These presses fall into a classification between single-station presses and turret presses and are generally used when heavy plate, angles, or beams are being punched for structural steel fabrication.

Another type of multiple-station press contains two punching stations, but incorporates removable cartridges to mount the tooling. The cartridges are capable of holding up to 12 different styles of punches and are positioned under the punching head with servo-drive motors. The advantage of this type over the turret press is that the tooling can be mounted in the cartridges for another workpiece while the press is in operation. This type of press is particularly useful when two identical workpieces are being punched simultaneously (see Figs. 4-26 and 4-27).

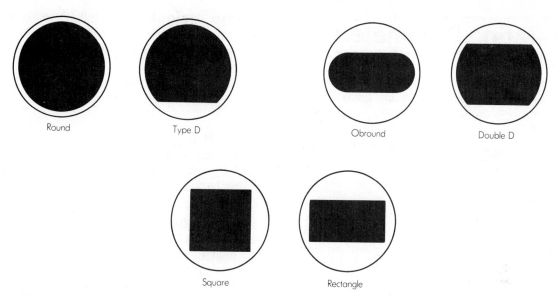

Figure 4-26   Shapes of punches commonly used on punch presses

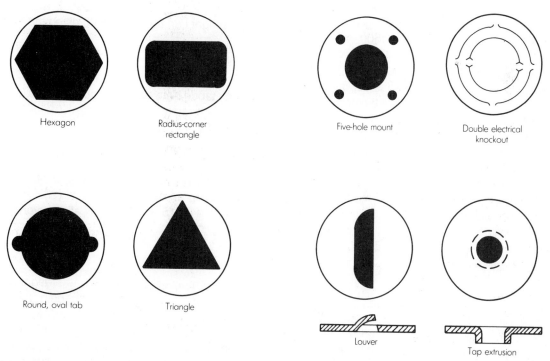

Figure 4-27   Special-shaped punches

Operating Parameters

The type and thickness of material and the hole size determine to a large extent the force required to punch a hole in the workpiece. Punch clearance and type of material determine the amount of force required for stripping the punch from the workpiece.

Speed

The number of strokes per minute (spm) for a press is dependent upon how the ram is driven, the speed at which the workpiece can be positioned under the punch, and the thickness of material being punched. Generally, the maximum spm made by a punch press is fixed, rated at the maximum material thickness that the press is capable of punching, and cannot be varied by the operator. Based on 1" (25.4 mm) centers, the speed of the various presses ranges from 55 to 265 spm. In a continuous punching mode used for nibbling, the press can attain 500 spm. One manufacturer provides the capability to have two different speed settings for nibbling.

The workpiece positioning speed is dependent on the weight of the moving parts and the type of carriage drive motors that are used. The distance that the workpiece must travel during a punching operation is also a factor. Axis positioning speeds up to 3150 ipm (80 010 mm/min) are attained if the workpiece is moved in only one direction and up to 2400 ipm (111 760 mm/min) if the workpiece is moved in both directions at the same time.

Nibbled Path Evaluation

When it is necessary to nibble openings in sheet or plate material with a round punch, a scalloped condition often results on the finished edge. The scallop can create problems for clearance of mating parts and for safety if the opening is used as an access.

Scallop Height: The scallop height for an opening when utilizing a specified punch size and punching center distance can be determined using the formula:

$$S = r - \sqrt{r^2 - (R/2)^2}$$

where:

S = scallop height, in. (mm)
r = punch radius, in. (mm)
R = distance between punch centers, in. (mm)

Example:

Determine the scallop height of a nibbled opening using a 1" (25.4 mm) diam punch and a 0.350" (8.89 mm) center distance.

$$S = r - \sqrt{r^2 - (R/2)^2} = 0.50 - \sqrt{0.50^2 - (0.350/2)^2}$$

$$= 0.031" \ (0.78 \ mm)$$

Punch Center Distance: The required punching center distance for a given punch diameter and scallop height can be determined using the formula:

$$R = 2\sqrt{2rS - S^2}$$

where:

R = distance between punch centers, in. (mm)
r = punch radius, in. (mm)
S = scallop height, in. (mm)

Example:

Determine the required punching center distance when nibbling an opening with a 1" (25.4 mm) diam punch and a 0.015" (0.38 mm) scallop height.

$$R = 2\sqrt{2rS - S^2} = 2\sqrt{2(0.50)(0.015) - 0.015^2}$$

$$= 0.243" \ (6.17 \ mm)$$

These formulas are applicable to straight line and circular operations when utilizing point-to-point or linear interpolation NC programming on contouring machines. The formula accuracy for circular interpolation is only approximate and becomes increasingly accurate when the nibbled arc radius increases.

DRAWING, EXTRUDING, AND UPSETTING
Cold Drawing of Bar, Wire, and Tube

The cold drawing of a metal bar, rod, or wire consists essentially of pulling the part through a die of similar shape but smaller size (see Fig. 4-28). For a tubular part, an internal bar or mandrel can be introduced for simultaneous working of the interior surface (see Fig. 4-29). As the name implies, cold drawing is usually performed with the bar, rod, or wire at room temperature.

Drawing can also be done with the material preheated to temperatures up to the metal's recrystallization temperature. Called warm drawing, this technique can make drawing easier or impart special mechanical properties to the workpiece. For example, brittle materials generally require drawing at an elevated temperature at which the material remains ductile; prior processing of the material by rolling, extruding, or other compression deformation processes to improve the ductility of the material; or a combination of these techniques.

In addition to the production of bar, wire, and tube, many special sections are also cold drawn, thus reducing subsequent processing requirements. Parts produced are generally steel bars having the same cross-sectional shape throughout their length. Individual components are obtained by cutting pieces from the bars. Shapes possible are virtually unlimited and include intricate, nonsymmetrical shapes. Starting stock can be flat, square, round, or hexagonal bars, bars of other shape, or coils. Flat stock, however, is the most common starting material for drawing.

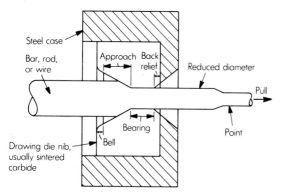

Figure 4-28   Die for drawing bar, rod, or wire

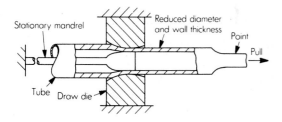

Figure 4-29   Die and internal mandrel for drawing tube

Purposes of Cold Drawing

Cold drawing is performed for one or several of the following purposes:

1. To obtain a smaller size. (There is usually a limitation as to how small a wire can be to be hot rolled or extruded; and with tubes, a parallel situation exists with wall thicknesses.)
2. To produce longer lengths than are available in the hot-worked state.
3. To obtain shapes other than rounds, squares, etc., which often cannot be produced in any other way.
4. To secure better surface finishes than are available from hot-working processes.
5. To obtain closer dimensional tolerances than those generally possible with hot-working processes.
6. To obtain better straightness or alignment along the length of the workpiece than is possible in hot working.
7. To increase certain mechanical properties. Properties increased by cold drawing include tensile strength and hardness.

8. To improve other properties such as machinability. (For example, in certain steels an improvement of as much as 15-25% in machinability can be realized when workpieces are cold drawn.)
9. To make small lots of products of odd sizes or other variables that do not justify a hot mill run.

Drawing Rod and Wire

Methods and equipment used for cold drawing of rod and wire, as well as small-diameter tubing, are generally designed so that the products can be uncoiled and then recoiled after drawing. On multiple-die continuous machines, uncoiling, drawing, and recoiling are repeated at successive stations. Rod coils, when ready for processing, are usually butt welded together for continuous drawing.

In the drawing process, cleaned and coated coils of rod or wire are first placed on a payoff tray, stand, or reel, which permits free unwinding of the stock. The leading end of the rod or wire, after being pointed, is then inserted through the drawing die and seized by a gripper attached to a powered cylindrical block or capstan. On so-called dry machines, the die is mounted in an adapter within a box. This die box contains, if necessary, grease, dry soap, oil, or other lubricants through which the stock must pass before reaching the die.

Drawing Bars

Bars about 1¼″ (32 mm) and smaller in diameter are cold drawn from coil stock by various methods. With one method, cold-drawn coils of rod and wire produced on various machines are straightened and cut into bars in a separate operation on machines designed for that purpose. Some in-line methods and equipment begin by unwinding the starting coil, then pull the stock through a draw die without recoiling, and finally straighten and cut the material into bars in a continuous operation.

Drawing Tubes

Tubes, particularly those having small diameters and requiring working only of their outer surfaces, are produced from cold-drawn coils on machines that straighten the stock and cut it to required lengths. As with bars, however, most tubes are produced from straight lengths rather than coiled stock. With four exceptions, the methods and equipment used for cold drawing tubes in straight lengths are basically identical to those used for bar drawing. The four exceptions are:

1. There are tubes that require more than one drawing pass.
2. Tubes are usually longer than bars. Drawbenches for tubes are usually correspondingly longer, some permitting drawn lengths of over 100 ft (30.5 m).
3. Tube diameters are generally larger than bar diameters, ranging to about 12″ (305 mm). The bigger tube drawbenches have larger components than do bar drawbenches.
4. Tubes require internal mandrels or bars for simultaneous working or support of the interior surface during drawing. Tube drawbenches are usually equipped with one of several available devices, usually powered, for ready assembly of the cleaned, coated, and pointed workpiece onto internal bars or rod-supported mandrels. If rod-supported mandrels are used, they are usually air-operated so that the mandrel can be placed and maintained in the plane of the draw die after pulling starts. Butt or electric-welded tubes are sometimes drawn to smooth the weld seams and tube walls.

Other Drawing Methods

Many other methods of cold drawing are employed, but these methods are not used as extensively as those methods just described.

Vibration-Assisted (Ultrasonic) Drawing: Ultrasonic vibrations imposed on the drawing die, plug, or mandrel are advantageous for some applications. While this process is not being used extensively, it is considered beneficial for drawing hard-to-deform materials and profiled wires, and for some tube drawing operations. Advantages include reduced friction and force requirements, increased reductions per pass, production of improved surface finishes, and reduced die wear. Limitations include the need for high-cost vibrating equipment and low-speed production.

In ultrasonic drawing, the die is expanded and contracted radially or the plug or mandrel is vibrated axially. This is accomplished by magnetostrictive transducers that convert electrical energy to mechanical vibrations. Electrical power is supplied to the transducers by a generator and frequency converter. Force-insensitive tool mountings are provided to isolate the vibrations from the machine structure.

Dieless Drawing: This process, which involves heating the workpiece material during drawing, has limited application. It has been reported that one aircraft engine manufacturer is using the process to make titanium tubes, and that large area reductions are possible with low draw loads. A limitation is the difficulty of achieving uniform input of heat to the workpiece.

In dieless drawing, one end of a rod or tube is gripped in a fixed head and the other end is held in a movable drawhead. The workpiece is heated locally, near the drawhead, by a movable induction-heating coil encircling the workpiece. When the desired reduction in cross-sectional area occurs at the heated zone, the drawhead continues to move away from the fixed head and the heating coil moves toward the fixed head. Speed of the drawhead and heat from the coil are adjusted to provide uniform reduction.

Hot Extrusion

Extrusion is a plastic deformation process in which material is forced under pressure to flow through one or more die orifices to produce products of the desired configuration. In hot extrusion, heated billets are reduced in size and forced to flow through dies to form products of uniform cross section along their continuous lengths. With special tooling, stepped and tapered extrusions are produced.

The extrusion process provides a practical forming method for producing a limitless variety of parallel-surfaced shapes to meet almost any design requirement. Other advantages include improving the microstructure and physical properties of the material, maintaining close tolerances, material conservation, economical production, and increased design flexibility.

Methods of Extruding

The extrusion process can be classified into two main groups: direct and indirect extrusion, with direct extrusion being more common. Another method of extrusion is the hydrostatic process, which is used with both heated and unheated billets.

Direct Extrusion: In direct, or forward, extrusion, a billet of metal is placed in a heavy-walled container and the extruded product exits through a die secured in a holder. The force for extruding is applied by a pressing stem or ram with an intermediate, reusable dummy block. Metal flow from the die is in the same direction as the forward movement of the stem (see Fig. 4-30).

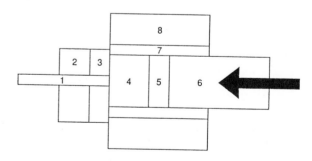

1. Extruded product
2. Die backer
3. Die
4. Billet
5. Dummy block
6. Pressing stem
7. Container liner
8. Container liner

Figure 4-30 Forward extrusion

The direct method is by far the most common method of extrusion, but it does have some disadvantages. The surface of the entire length of the billet must slide along the container wall. The ease with which this is done depends upon the material being extruded and whether a lubricating film is present. In all cases, part of the extrusion load (the amount depending upon the length of the billet) is expended in overcoming the friction between the billet and the container, or in shearing inner billet material from the slower moving, peripheral layer of billet material adjacent to the container wall.

Indirect Extrusion: In indirect, or backward, extrusion, the billet remains stationary relative to the container wall while the die is pushed into the billet by a hollow stem (ram); or the container and billet are pushed over the stationary stem and stem-mounted die. The die is loosely attached to the end of the stem, and the extrusion exits through the hollow stem. Lengths of the billets used in indirect extrusion are limited only by the column strengths of the stems. Since there is no relative motion between the outer surface of the billet and the bore of the container, friction between these two surfaces is eliminated and the force necessary is decreased (see Fig. 4-31).

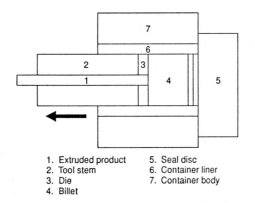

1. Extruded product
2. Tool stem
3. Die
4. Billet
5. Seal disc
6. Container liner
7. Container body

Figure 4-31   Backward extrusion

Hydrostatic Extrusion: In hydrostatic extrusion, the billet is surrounded by a pressurized liquid acting on all surfaces of the billet except that at which the billet contacts the die opening. As with indirect extrusion, virtually no friction exists between the billet and the container wall. Hydrostatic extrusion is not exclusively a hot process; it is frequently performed with the billets at room temperature or with the billets only warmed. In fact, the billet temperature is limited by the stability of the fluid medium used.

Cold and Warm Extrusion

Cold and warm extrusion differ from hot extrusion in that the starting workpieces (often called slugs) are cold (at room temperature) or warm (heated to below the critical temperature of the metal). Metal is forced to flow by plastic deformation under compression around punches and into or through shape-forming dies to produce parts of the desired configuration. Since the temperatures of the slugs are always below the recrystallization temperatures of the metals to be formed, the process is essentially one of cold working. Most steels, nonferrous metals, and superalloys can be extruded cold or at low deformation temperatures, with stresses in the tooling being the primary limiting factor.

Cold extrusion is now being used for producing more economically a wide variety of parts that were previously cast, forged, or machined by metal-removal processes. Some large, hollow extrusions, such as wheel spindles and axles, are replacing parts formerly shaped from tubing by hot swaging. Industries using cold-extruded products include automotive, aircraft and aerospace, appliance, ordnance, hardware, farm and construction equipment, electrical equipment, and air conditioning. Typical parts produced by cold extrusion include bearing races, a variety of fasteners, piston pins, spark plug shells, socket wrenches, track link bushings, transmission and axle shafts, pinions and gear blanks, ball joint sockets, switch housings, and steering and suspension components.

The use of cold extrusion should be considered when the parts to be produced require one or more of the following:

- Strength, toughness, and grain structure superior to those machined from hot-rolled carbon steel.
- Close tolerances and smooth surface finishes.
- A hollow cross section with one end closed or partially closed and having bosses, projections, or recesses.
- Walls of zero draft and/or variable thickness.
- Longitudinal projections or depressions on either the inside or outside walls.
- A base thickness greater than the side walls.
- Multiple diameter surfaces.
- Liquid or gas pressure tightness.
- Flanges on either the open or closed ends.

Warm extruding is being increasingly applied, especially on high-alloy and some stainless steels. Heating the slugs reduces the flow stress (resistance to deformation), increases the ductility, and reduces the strain hardening of the workpiece material. Warm extruding, however, increases the production costs because of the need for heating and often requires the use of tooling materials and lubricants that are more heat resistant and higher in cost.

Methods of Extruding

Cold and warm extrusion are performed in several ways. Methods employed include backward, forward, radial, combination, impact, and continuous extrusion.

Backward Extrusion: In backward (indirect or reverse) extrusion, metal is forced to flow in the opposite direction to the travel of the punch (see Fig. 4-32). Backward extrusion is most commonly employed for the production of hollow parts, but metal can also be forced to flow into recesses in the punch to form splines and other shapes. The outside diameters of the parts formed take on the shapes of the dies and/or recesses in the punches, and the inside diameters of hollow parts are controlled by the punches.

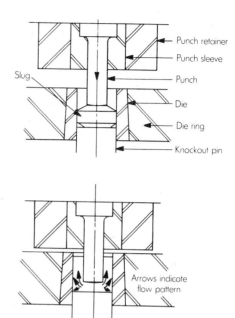

Figure 4-32   Backward extrusion

Forward Extrusion: In forward (direct) extrusion, metal is forced to flow ahead of the punch through an orifice in the die (see Fig. 4-33). Forward extrusion is most commonly employed to produce shaft-type components, but is also used to form other shapes. The punch closely fits the die cavity to prevent backward flow of the metal. With forward extrusion, very high reductions in cross-sectional area can be produced in one operation. The length of the extrusion depends upon the material, the lubricant spread, and the space in the press beyond the die orifice.

Radial Extrusion: Radial extrusion, sometimes called cross, lateral, or transverse extrusion, is an adaptation of forward extrusion in which the die orifices allow the metal to flow radially, usually at an angle of 90° to the direction of punch travel.

Combination Extrusion: Backward, forward, and radial extrusion are sometimes performed simultaneously with a single press stroke, permitting

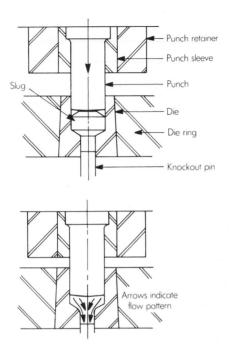

Figure 4-33 Forward extrusion

the forming of more-complex-shaped parts. Upsetting (heading), discussed later in this chapter, is also often combined with extrusion to enlarge the diameters of parts at desired sections.

Impact Extrusion: Impact extrusion, often called simply impacting, is similar to backward, forward, and combination extrusion except that faster speeds, shorter strokes, and shallower dies are employed. Impact of the punch causes the metal to move upward, downward, or both upward and downward without being confined by the punch or die walls. Large reductions are possible because of the impulsive force applied. Production rates to 18,000 parts per hour have been achieved with automatic feeding equipment.

Cold impacting is used extensively for the easy extrusion of nonferrous metals having low melting points and good ductility, such as lead, tin, zinc, aluminum, copper, and alloys of these metals. Applications include the production of collapsible tubular

containers (such as used for toothpaste), battery cases, cartridge cases, and beverage cans. Impacting is sometimes done hot, especially for extruding steels, as in the production of valves and tubes.

The Hooker process of impact extrusion is similar to forward impacting except that preformed cups are used instead of slugs. The punch is provided with a shoulder or chamfer (see Fig. 4-34) that first upsets the cup and then causes the metal to flow through an annulus formed between a projection on the punch and the die, thus elongating and thinning the walls of the cup. Harder metals can be formed in this way.

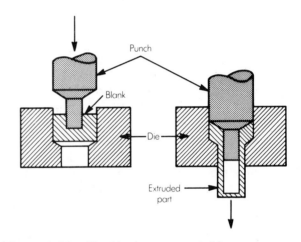

Figure 4-34 The Hooker process of forward impacting

Continuous Extrusion: Several methods have been developed for semicontinuous and continuous extrusion. In Conform machines, the extrusion chamber is comprised of a three-sided groove in the periphery of a rotating wheel with a stationary shoe making up the fourth side of the chamber. One type of machine has the wheel in the vertical plane (horizontal shaft) to accept powder metal as the feedstock, although it can also use solid feedstock. The other type, with the wheel in the horizontal plane, is designed for use with either solid or bunched scrap feedstocks and incorporates a Turk's head to preform the feedstock before it reaches the groove.

As shown in Fig. 4-35, three sides of the groove in the rotating wheel grip and advance the feedstock, while sliding friction against the stationary shoe acts to retard this advancement. Advancement occurs, however, because the groove walls have more surface area than the shoe. A die, supported in the groove, blocks passage of the stock, causing the stock to upset. As the wheel rotates, pressure at the die face increases, causing the upset length to increase. The process continues until pressure is sufficient for extrusion to take place, at which point the upset length stabilizes and the process runs continuously.

Linex system. For the Linex linear-type continuous extrusion machine, feedstock is preformed to a roughly rectangular cross section. Preforming round feedstock to a rectangular cross section is accomplished by pulling the stock through a Turk's head. Lubrication is provided to the opposing ungripped surfaces of the feedstock before it upsets against the constraining walls of the extrusion chamber (see Fig. 4-36). Two sides of the extrusion chamber, composed of the legs of a fork-shaped die, are fixed. Top and bottom gripping surfaces, making up the other two sides of the chamber, are hardened steel blocks assembled on two chains which are pulled by drive sprockets past the die.

The gripper blocks compress the feedstock, deform it plastically to a point beyond its yield strength, and carry it into the die fork. Lubricant on the ungripped sides of the feedstock reduces the coefficient of sliding friction between the upset feedstock and the legs of the die fork. The stock is made narrower than the opening between the die fork legs and fills the extrusion chamber as it is upset. As in the Conform process, the upset length stabilizes when sufficient pressure for extrusion has been developed.

Extrolling. This process combines the extrusion process with rolling. Feedstock is fed to the extrusion die, which can be multiholed, by friction between grooved rolls (see Fig. 4-37). The stock is reduced in cross-sectional area between the rolls, pressure

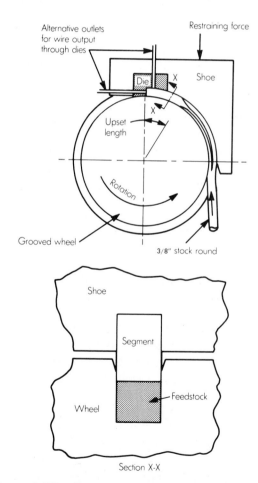

Figure 4-35 Feedstock is advanced by a grooved wheel, while friction against a stationary shoe acts to retard the advance

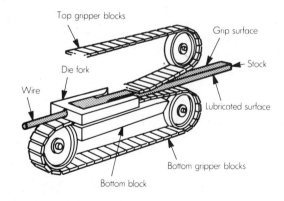

Figure 4-36 Friction-actuated, linear-type continuous extruder

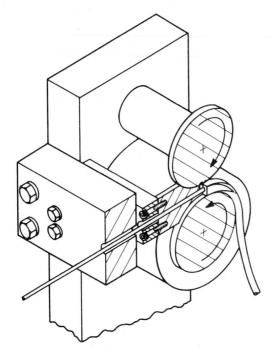

Figure 4-37   Extrolling combines the extrusion process with rolling

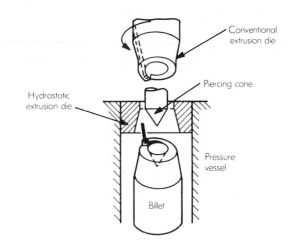

Figure 4-38   Helical extrusion

builds up in front of the obstructing die, and the material is extruded.

Helical extrusion. This process combines hydrostatic and conventional extrusion with "machining." A billet is hydrostatically extruded over a piercing cone (see Fig. 4-38). The upper end of the tube formed is cut by the edge of a helical ramp on a rotating, conventional extrusion die, and the metal is extruded through the aperture in this die.

Cold and Warm Upsetting (Heading)

Upsetting is a forming operation for reshaping metal by plastic flow. Force applied to the end of a blank, contained between a punch and a die, causes metal flow, increasing the diameter and decreasing the length of the blank. Upsetting is commonly called heading because the process was first used to form heads on nails. The method is now employed extensively to form the heads on bolts, screws, rivets, and other fasteners. The name *heading*, however, is misleading in that metal can be gathered anywhere along the length of the blank or all of the stock can be increased in diameter.

Upsetting is accomplished by inserting a blank of a specific length into a stationary die. A punch, moving parallel to the axis of the blank, contacts the end of the blank protruding from the die and compresses the metal. Impressions in the punch or die, or both, determine the upset shape produced. Some parts are upset in the punch, some in the die, some in both, and some in an open space between the punch and the die (see Fig. 4-39). Fig. 4-40 illustrates limits for upsetting.

Methods of Upsetting

Most upsetting is done on horizontal mechanically powered machines, often called headers or formers. The process is also performed on conventional vertical presses and special machines, powered either mechanically or hydraulically, with the starting metal unheated (cold upsetting) or heated (warm upsetting).

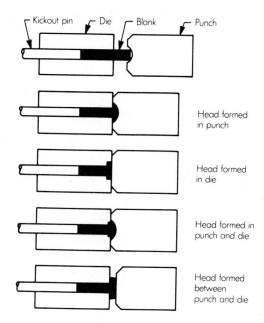

Figure 4-39   Various types of upsetting

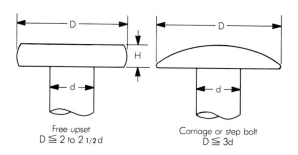

Figure 4-40   Generally accepted limits for maximum upset diameters

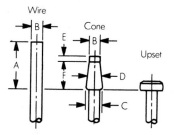

Volume finished upset ÷ area B = length A
Length A ÷ diameter B = number of diameters of stock
Diameter B × 1.25 = diameter C
(Area B + area C) ÷ 2 = mean area D
Volume section AB - volume section EB = volume section BCF
Volume section BCF ÷ mean area D = length F

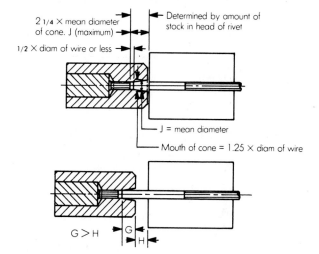

Figure 4-41   Two-blow upsetting sequence

Mechanical presses are generally preferred for forming because of their higher production capability, but they cost more than hydraulic presses of comparable force capacity. Hydraulic presses generally provide longer tool life when cold forming; for warm forming, the longer contact time between the tools and the workpieces tends to shorten punch life. Fig. 4-41 illustrates a two-blow upsetting sequence.

SWAGING

Swaging is a metalforming process in which a rapid series of impact blows is delivered radially to either solid or tubular work. This causes a reduction in cross-sectional area and/or a change in geometric shape. The method is basically a forging process, especially similar to radial forging. Applications of swaging include tapering, pointing, reducing, external and internal forming, compacting, sizing, and assembling. In swaging, impact blows are transferred to the work in rapid succession by dies in the machine. The contour built into the dies controls the cross section formed.

The various methods of swaging include solid, tube, mandrel, cold (room temperature), hot, and internal methods. Swagers can be through-fed to reduce an entire bar or tube, or the workpiece can simply be fed in and out to reduce only the end. Multiple passes may be necessary to make long tapers. In central reductions, the part is advanced into the swager for a given distance, the diameter is reduced for a specified length, and the entire part is removed from the machine. It is possible to produce regular or irregular internal shapes. Stationary-spindle machines can swage external shapes.

HOT FORGING

Forging is one of the oldest metalworking processes known to man. As early as 2000 B.C., forging was used to produce weapons, implements, and jewelry. The process was performed by hand using simple hammers.

Hot forging is defined as the controlled, plastic deformation or working of metals into predetermined shapes by means of pressure or impact blows, or a combination of both. In hot forging, this plastic deformation is performed above the recrystallization temperature to prevent strain hardening of the metal.

During the deformation process, the crystalline structure of the base metal is refined and any non-metallic or alloy segregation is properly oriented. In bar stock, the grain flow is only in one direction. When the contour of the part is changed, the grain flow lines are cut, rendering the metal more susceptible to fatigue and stress corrosion. Hot forging develops the grain flow so that it follows the outline of the part being formed. The directional alignment of the grains or fibers helps increase strength, ductility, and resistance to impact and fatigue in the metal.

Deformation is affected by the stress inherent in the metal, the microstructural characteristics of the starting material, the temperature at which the deformation occurs, the rate at which the deformation occurs, and the frictional restraint between the material being forged and the die surface.

Forging Processes

Metal flow during the forging process normally falls into two categories: upsetting and extrusion. Upsetting occurs when the metal is compressed parallel to the longitudinal axis of the workpiece. This action enables the metal to flow freely in one direction as in open-die forging, or it can be restrained as in impression-die forging. Extrusion occurs when the metal is compressed parallel to the longitudinal axis of the workpiece and allowed to flow through an orifice in the die cavity.

Open-Die Forging

Open-die forging, also referred to as smith forging, blacksmith forging, hand forging, and flat-die forging, is generally performed without special tooling. The forms obtained and the dimensions maintained are usually dependent upon the skill of the operator and the type of equipment used. However, with the addition of computer control to the equipment, more complex forgings can be produced and better dimensional control is maintained. This equipment may range from the simple anvil and hammer of the blacksmith to giant, computer-controlled, hydraulic presses capable of delivering up to 75,000 tons (667 MN) of force and producing single forgings weighing several thousand pounds. Most open-die forgings are simple geometric shapes such as discs, rings, or shafts. Open-die forging is also used in the steelmaking industry to cog ingots or to draw down billets from one size to a smaller one.

The open-die forging process is employed when only a few parts are needed and when the part is too large to be produced in closed dies. Quantities of less than 100 parts are generally good candidates to be produced in open dies because designing and manufacturing closed dies for such a small quantity is often too costly. However, large quantities are produced with open dies. The open-die process is also used to obtain the mechanical properties in a workpiece that are not obtainable by machining. Generally, most forgings begin with the open-die process before the final forging operation.

Impression-Die Forging

In impression-die forging, the workpiece is placed between two dies containing the impression of the forging shape to be produced. The dies are brought together and the workpiece is plastically deformed until the sides come in contact with the walls of the die. As the deformation continues, a small amount of material begins to flow outside the die impression, forming flash. The thin flash cools rapidly, creating a pressure increase inside the workpiece. The increased pressure assists the flow of material into the unfilled portion of the impression. The majority of the forgings produced are done using impression-die forging.

Closed-die forging or flashless forging, which is a special form of impression-die forging, does not depend on the flash to achieve complete die filling. Generally, the material is deformed in a cavity that does not allow excess material to flow outside the impression. Therefore, die design and workpiece volume are more critical than in impression-die forging so that complete die filling is achieved without generating excess pressures due to overfilling.

Currently, closed-die forging is moving more and more toward near-net-shaped and net-shaped forging. Near-net-shaped parts are those parts that require minor metal removal before assembly. Net-shaped parts have finished functional surfaces that do not require additional metal removal. Gears, airfoils, and high-temperature jet engine disc forgings are being produced using this process.

Some of the more widely used forging processes are ring rolling, orbital forging, isothermal forging, gatorizing, incremental forging, roll forging, wedge rolling, and electric upsetting (see Figs. 4-42 through 4-45).

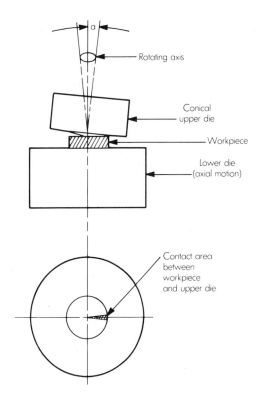

Figure 4-42   Orbital forging.

Automatic Cold and Warm Forming

Automatic cold and warm forming is done on completely automated, multistation machines equipped with a high-speed device for automatically transferring parts through a series of punch and die setups. Operations commonly performed on these machines include extruding and upsetting (discussed previously in this chapter), shearing (cutoff), coining, piercing, trimming, threading, and knurling.

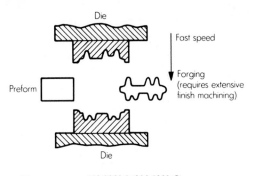

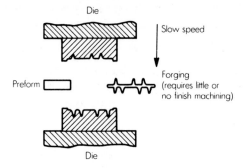

Die temperature: 570-930° F (300-500° C)
Preform temperature: 1400-1800° F (760-980° C)
Forging speed: 0.16 fps (50 mm/sec)

Conventional Forging

Die temperature: 1400-1800° F (760-980° C)
Preform temperature: 1400-1800° F (760-980° C)
Forging speed: 0.00013 fps (0.04 mm/sec) (near die closure)

Isothermal Forging

Figure 4-43   The isothermal process compared to conventional forging

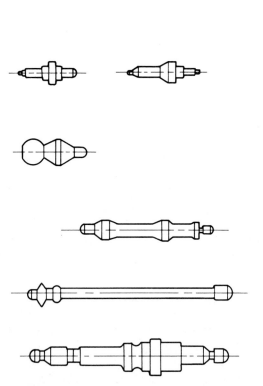

Figure 4-44   Wedge rolling

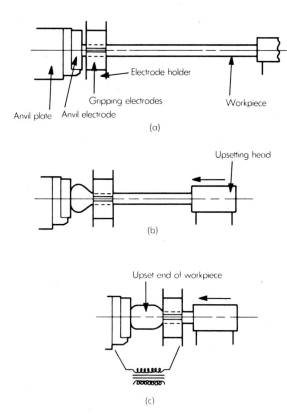

Figure 4-45   Electric upsetting

Part Shapes and Sizes Formed

Symmetrical parts having solid, hollow, or cup-shaped cross sections are the most economical to form and the most widely produced. However, parts with other geometries, including noncircular and complex-shaped components, are also formed, but at higher cost.

Cylindrical parts are the most common shapes produced by automatic forming, but components having square, rectangular, hexagonal, oval, tapered, splined, or toothed surfaces, as well as multiple diameters, are also formed. Projections or depressions can be formed on or in one or both faces and can be flat, conical, hemispherical, or other shape.

While many small components are formed automatically, there is an increasing number of large parts now being produced in this way.

Applications of Automatic Forming

Parts produced on automatic forming machines are used by many different industries for a wide variety of applications. They have replaced many components which were previously cast, forged, machined, or produced by other processes. The versatility of automatic forming machines has led to their being referred to as parts makers. Considerable savings can be realized by forming different parts of similar size and shape. This minimizes tooling costs and changeover time, and makes the production of smaller lot sizes more economical.

Figs. 4-46 through 4-50 illustrate the process of automatic cold and warm forming. Fig. 4-46 shows a multidiameter shaft produced on a four-die cold former at the rate of 35 parts per minute. Fig. 4-47

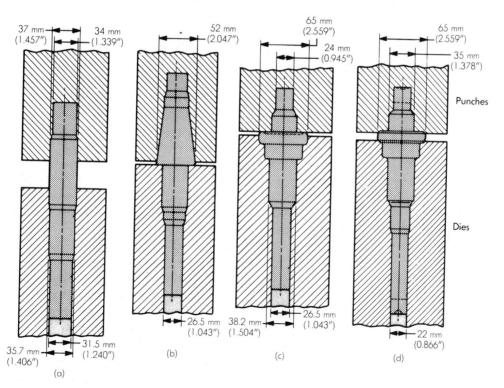

Figure 4-46   Multidiameter shaft

shows a multidiameter shaft produced on a five-die cold former at the rate of 45 parts per minute. Fig. 4-48 shows a ball joint produced on a five-die cold former at the rate of 40 parts per minute. Fig. 4-49 illustrates the forming sequence for producing gear and stem blanks on a five-die cold former at the rate of 40 parts per minute. Fig. 4-50 shows special nuts that are cold formed from 1030 steel coil stock at the rate of 50 per minute.

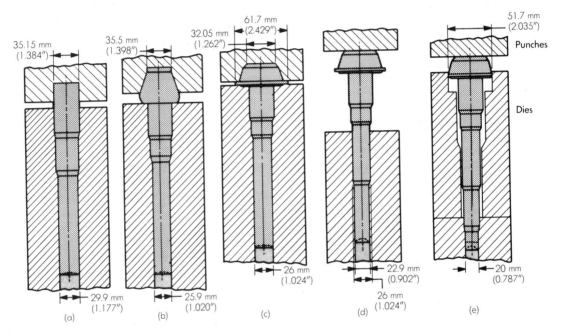

Figure 4-47 Five-die cold former

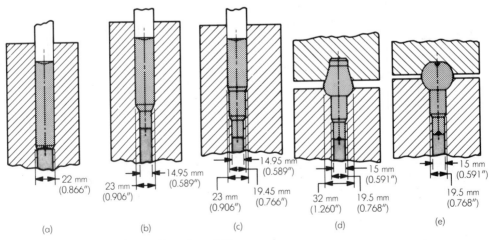

Figure 4-48 Ball joint produced on a five-die cold former

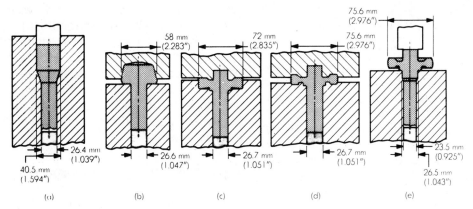

Figure 4-49   Forming sequence for producing gear and stem blanks

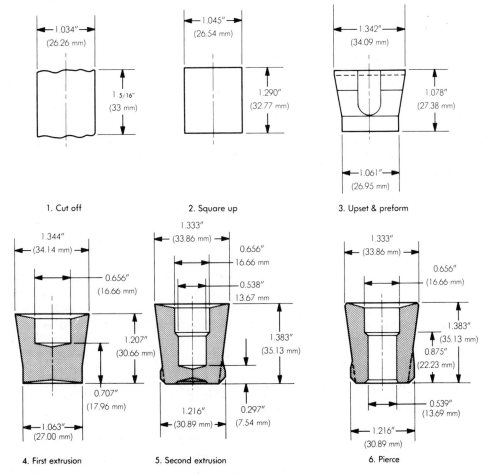

Figure 4-50   Special nuts are cold formed from 1030 steel coil stock

PLASTICS FORMING

The commercially important plastics resins are all derived from natural resources that are in plentiful supply. Many of the plastics are by-products from gasoline refining operations. Principal raw material sources for plastics are coal, air, water, petroleum, natural gas, limestone, salt, sulfur, and agricultural by-products. Products called intermediates are made from these basic materials and are subsequently combined to make plastics resins. In the plastics industry, the sectors involved with the production of plastics products include resin producers, compounders, processors, mold and die makers, manufacturing companies, consultants, and chemical additive suppliers.

Thermoplastics is the family of plastics that can be recycled. Thermosets, the other key family of plastics, is so named because once it is set it cannot be reset in any other shape or cannot be recycled, although by-product uses are found for thermoset scrap material. Processors usually receive the thermoset plastics resins in a partially polymerized state to facilitate molding by the traditional techniques.

Plastics as a word is not the precise name of all the available materials, hence the need to adopt the term *polymer*. This term denotes a material that has gone through a polymerization cycle, which is essentially a chemical process for which the original base material can be oil, gas, or coal.

Thermoset Plastics Molding

Types of thermoset materials that are capable of being molded include phenolic, urea, melamine, melamine-phenolic, diallyl phthalate, alkyd, polyester, epoxy, and the silicones. Thermosetting molding compounds processed from the individual heat-reactive resin systems are available in a wide range of formulations to satisfy specific end-use requirements. Depending upon the type of material, products may be supplied in granular, nodular, flaked, diced, or pelletized form. Polyester materials are supplied in granular, bulk, log, rope, or sheet form, and polyurethanes are made in many forms, ranging from flexible and rigid foams to rigid solids and abrasion-resistant coatings.

Principles of Plastics Molding

As the term implies, thermoset molding compounds when placed within the confines of a mold (generally hardened steel) are subjected to heat to plasticize and cure the material, and to pressure to form the desired shape. The mold is held closed, under pressure, sufficiently long to polymerize or cure the material into a hard, infusible mass.

Molding Methods: All of the thermoset compounds, except epoxies and silicones, may be molded by the following methods: compression, transfer, thermoset injection, and the new runnerless injection/compression process. Fig. 4-51 lists factors to be considered in the selection of a molding method.

Compression Molding

In compression molding, the plastics compound is placed in a heated mold. The compound softens and becomes plastic as the upper part of the die moves (down or up, depending on the movable platen location), compressing the material to the required shape and density. Continued heat and pressure produce the chemical reaction that hardens the thermosetting material.

Transfer Molding

Transfer molding, as the name implies, is a method of molding specific parts when it is desirable that the two halves of the mold, containing the shape of the part, are closed before any material is introduced.

Factors to Consider: Advantages—Limitations	Compression	Transfer
Close tolerances, projected area	●	
Close tolerances, over flash line, minimum flash		●
Lowest mold shrinkage	●	
Uniform shrinkage, all directions	●	
Maximum uniform density	●	
Reduced cure, thick sections		●
No weld lines, less molded-in strains	●	
Small holes, longer length, through holes		●
Extremely thin mold sections, telescoping		●
No venting problems	●	
Impact strength	●	
Molds with movable sections or cores		●
Molded-in inserts		●
Large projected area parts	●	
Lowest mold-flash scrap	●	
Generally less mold maintenance		●
Gate or sprue removal necessary		●
Maximum number cavities per clamp force	●	
Mold erosion, sprues, runners, gates		●
Generally higher mold cost		●

Figure 4-51 Selection of molding method

The material is loaded into a pot or transfer sleeve, and transfer pressure is applied to cause material to flow into the closed section of the mold. In a single-cavity mold, the material flows generally through a sprue bushing and is gated directly into the part. In the case of a multicavity mold, it flows from a sprue bushing or transfer sleeve into a runner system and is gated into each cavity and part.

There are two distinct transfer methods of molding. One is known as pot-type transfer, and the other (more widely used) is the plunger transfer method.

Molding Process Comparison

A thorough evaluation should be made of the advantages and disadvantages of molding by the compression method as compared to the transfer method. It is desirable for the design engineer, process engineer, and material representative to meet and discuss all options before deciding upon the best method of molding a particular part.

Compression Molding: Although it is the oldest method of molding, compression molding probably will continue to be a major technique for processing most thermoset molding compounds. The following applications are representative of the market areas for which many parts are molded by compression:

- Wiring devices—wall plates, outlet boxes and receptacles, switches.
- Closures—bottle and tube caps for drugs and cosmetics.
- Electrical switch gear—home and low-voltage circuit breakers.
- Automotive parts—brake and transmission parts, grilles and body parts, ignition parts.
- Dishware—melamine dishware.
- Small appliances—knobs, handles, bases for motor mounts and cookers.
- Housings—sanitary tubs, stall shower units or bases, electrical outlet boxes.

Transfer Molding: Because of the part design, dimensional tolerances, mold design options, etc., many parts are well suited for molding by the transfer method. The following applications are representative of the market areas for which many parts are molded by transfer:

- Electronic devices—capacitors, transistors, integrated circuits, wire-wound power resistors, diodes, semiconductors, rectifiers, connectors, data processing devices.

- Electrical switch gear and motor starters—heavy switch gear circuit breaker and related parts.
- Automotive parts—transmission parts, solenoid covers, ignition parts.
- Cookware—handles, stick handles, housing.
- Appliances—housing for motors, pumps, and timers.

Injection Molding

Injection molding is a versatile process for forming thermoplastic and thermoset materials into molded products of intricate shapes, at high production rates and with good dimensional accuracy. Injection molding makes use of the heat-softening characteristics of thermoplastic materials. These materials soften when heated and reharden when cooled. No chemical changes take place when the material is heated or cooled, the change being entirely physical. For this reason the softening and rehardening cycle can be repeated several times. While this is true for thermoplastics, with certain thermosets and rubbers that can be injection molded, a chemical reaction does occur.

Molding Process

The basic injection molding process involves the injection, under high pressure, of a metered quantity of heated and plasticized material into a relatively cool mold in which the plastics material solidifies. The granular molding material is loaded into a hopper which gravity feeds to a rotating screw. The screw melts the plastic and conveys it to a reservoir at the end of the screw. Melting is accomplished by both frictional heat generation and conduction from a heated barrel. When sufficient material has accumulated in the reservoir, the screw is moved forward, injecting the plastics into the mold. A special ring at the end of the screw prevents the plastics from flowing back into the screw. In the mold, the material is solidified, then the mold is opened, and the part is ejected.

Since speed is one of the main advantages in injection molding, complex molds with inserts should be avoided whenever possible. Injection molds need not be single-cavity, but the high rate of production reduces the need for a large number of cavities. The savings resulting from higher production rates are partially offset by higher capital expenditure for machines and molds, and higher operating costs.

Injection molding is generally limited to forming thermoplastic materials, but equipment is available for converting the machines to enable molding thermosetting plastics and compounds of rubber.

The size of the article that can be molded is determined by the pressure and heating-cylinder capacities of the machine.

Equipment

Injection molding machines are comprised of two basic sections: the clamp unit and the injection unit. The clamping unit supports, opens, and closes the mold and maintains it in the closed position under suitable clamping pressure. The injection unit converts the plastics from solid particles into a continuous, semifluid mass and injects it into the closed mold.

Injection machines are commonly self-contained, hydraulically actuated machines that are operated from a central hydraulic system. Suitable valves control the sequence of operations.

Injection machines are usually classified by the capacity or quantity of molding material that the heating cylinder can deliver in one stroke of the injection ram. The capacity is expressed in ounces (grams). The rated capacity is the amount of plastics deliverable in one shot, including the weight of the part, runners, and sprue. Flat parts impose another additional limiting factor: the pressure requirements for their projected area cannot surpass the capacity of the clamping pressure on the mold. Fig. 4-52 shows the gates used in injection molding. Figs. 4-53 and 4-54 are examples of injection molds.

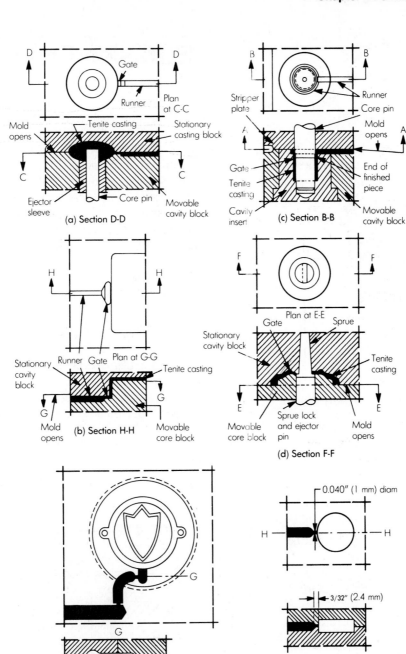

Figure 4-52   Types of gates used in injection molding

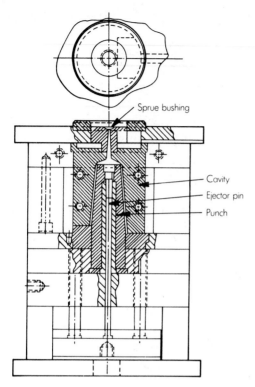

Figure 4-53 Injection mold with sprue leading to the cavity

Extrusion Forming

The extrusion process is a continuous operation in which hot plasticized material is forced through a die opening that produces an extrudate of the desired shape. The most commonly extruded materials are rigid and flexible vinyl, ABS, polystyrene, polypropylene, and polyethylene. Nylon, polycarbonate, polysulfone, acetal, and polyphenylene are included among other plastics that can be extruded.

The extrusion process is used to produce film (thinner than 0.030", 0.76 mm), sheets (thicker than 0.030", 0.76 mm), filaments, tubes, and a variety of profiles. The process of plastics extrusion also is used to coat cables, wires, and metal strips.

Extrusion Process

In the profile extrusion process, the material in pellet, granular, or powder form is placed into a feed hopper which feeds the cylinder of the extruding machine as required (see Fig. 4-55). The cylinder is heated by electricity, oil, or steam, and closely

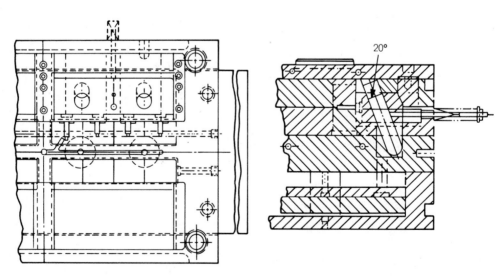

Figure 4-54 An interchangeable, multiple-cavity injection mold

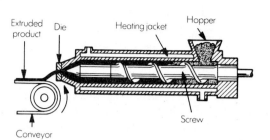

Figure 4-55 Plastic extrusion machine

controlled temperature zones are set up along its length. A rotating screw carries the material through the cylinder, mixing and working the material where necessary, and forcing it through a die orifice of the proper shape.

The extruded shape coming from the die is carried through a cooling medium; and when it has been cooled sufficiently to retain shape, it is cut to length or coiled. In some instances the material must be held to shape during cooling. Cooling is done by exposure to air at room temperature, by passing through a liquid bath held at a controlled temperature, or by jets of compressed air. Too-rapid cooling must be prevented because it causes warpage and sets up internal strains in the finished pieces.

The raw material must have a uniform particle size and a controlled moisture content to maintain close dimensional tolerances and a smooth surface on the finished extrusion. The temperature of each heat zone of the cylinder must be held constant to ensure a good extrusion.

The speed of extrusion (pounds or kilograms per hour handled by the machine) varies considerably depending upon the size of the die opening, the delivery of the screw, and the nature of the material being processed. Variable-speed machines are generally considered best for all-round flexibility, particularly in job shops. A wide variation of temperatures, speeds, methods of handling, and design of equipment is necessitated by the wide variation in characteristics of different thermoplastics.

Plastic extrusions are produced as tubes, rods, sheets, flat strips, profiles, filaments, and coatings for wire, cable, pipe, and rope.

Extrusion Equipment

Common extrudes consist of three basic units: the drive (power source); the process unit (screw and barrel); the forming unit (head and die). Fig. 4-56 is an example of a die assembly for extruding plastic materials.

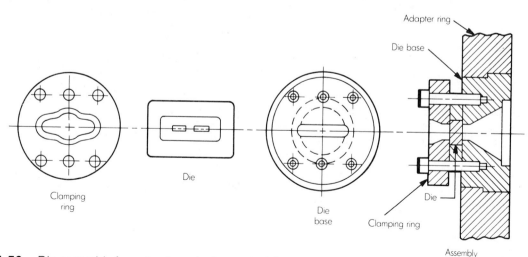

Figure 4-56 Die assembly for extruding plastics materials

The screw is the heart of the extruder and consists basically of feed, transition, and metering sections. The feed section is deep flighted and intended to convey solid or sometimes half-molten or molten plastics (for example, the second extruder in a multistage extrusion line) out of the feed throat area to the transition zone which begins compressing the preheated material. This section forces the plastics against the heated barrel and continues or begins the melting process, which should be completed at the end of the transition or the beginning of the metering zone.

In the transition zone the depth of the flights becomes continuously shallower until the final depth of the transition zone phases into the metering zone. As homogenously as possible, the metering zone conveys the molten plastics to the head and die at uniform rates and high pressure. The compression ratio (c.r.) is dependent on the material, the different metal densities, and the bulk densities.

The extrusion machine has a pilot for the attachment of adapter rings or plates on the outboard end of the cylinder. A die base is placed within the adapter ring to direct the flow of the material toward the die orifice.

Reaction Injection Molding

Reaction injection molding (RIM) is a form of injection molding that brings temperature and ratio-controlled, liquid-reactant streams together under high-pressure impingement mixing to form a polymer directly in the mold. Two liquid reactants (monomers) are mixed together as they enter the mold. A chemical reaction produces the plastics as it forms the part.

When compared to other molding systems, RIM offers more design flexibility, lower energy requirements, lower pressures, lower tooling costs, and lower capital investment. Significant advantages in design and production are gained from the RIM fabricating capability for incorporating a load-bearing, structural skin and a lightweight, rigid, cellular core into a part in one processing operation.

While initial RIM applications were primarily automotive, nonautomotive uses are increasing in industrial, business, and consumer-product applications. Recent production applications include business machine cabinets and vacuum cleaner housings. Thermosetting polyurethanes are the most commonly used RIM materials. Recently, however, the successful completion of development and testing programs on other plastics, such as nylons and epoxies, has led to RIM production usage of these materials.

Reinforced Thermoset Plastics

The reinforced plastics described in this chapter primarily encompass polyester and fiberglass systems. The most commonly used processes can be divided into two categories: high and low volume. Several less-common intermediate volume processes also are described in this chapter.

The low-volume processes fall in the 2,000-25,000 parts per year range. They are characterized by essentially low-pressure to pressureless hand or spray lay-up in low-cost molds with a high labor cost. High-volume processes are those in which more than 30,000 parts per year are produced (100,000 parts per tool for automotive components). They involve an initial high cost for tooling and equipment, but the labor intensity is low. These processes are not competitive with the metal stamping process unless they eliminate the need for multipiece assembly operations.

High-Volume Processes

The high-volume processes for reinforced thermoset plastics are sheet molding compound (SMC), thick molding compound (TMC), bulk molding compound (BMC), pultrusion, and pulforming.

Sheet Molding Compound: Sheet molding compound is a mixture of chopped fiberglass and thermosetting polyester resins that is formed into a sheet up to ¼" (6.4 mm) thick. This sheet can be easily handled and can be cut into strips or squares and used as a compression molding compound.

The resin system initially has a low viscosity to ensure complete mixing of the additives and wettability of the glass reinforcement. The viscosity is increased after the sheet compound has been formed. This creates a tack-free sheet for handling purposes.

Thick Molding Compound (TMC): This manufacturing process uses a mixture of chopped fiberglass and thermosetting polyester resins that is formed into a sheet up to 2" (51 mm) thick or into a billet shape for compression and injection molding.

The thick molding compound system has a 50% advantage in production rates over SMC systems. Greater filler contents can also be tolerated. The production of thick sheets reduces handling costs and consumption of carrier sheets.

The use of the TMC process for some large automotive parts (grille opening panels) has been successful in providing good strength and improved surfaces (in comparison to the use of the SMC process). The injection-molding method is used. A typical process is shown schematically in Fig. 4-57.

Bulk Molding Compound: The bulk molding compound (BMC) manufacturing process predates the SMC and TMC systems and has been used to produce a large number of automotive and electrical parts. The automotive companies use large amounts

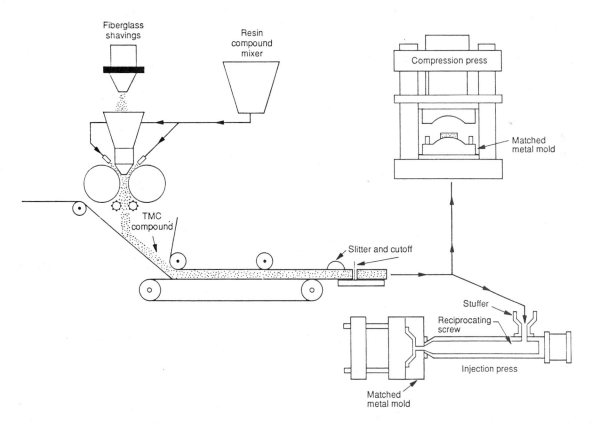

Figure 4-57   TMC manufacturing process

of BMC for heater and air conditioning housings. Some compounders have used sisal as the primary reinforcing fiber. A typical BMC process is shown in Fig. 4-58.

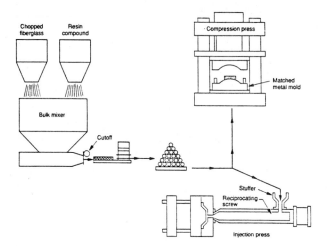

Figure 4-58   BMC manufacturing process

Pultrusion Manufacturing Process: Pultrusion is a continuous method of manufacturing various reinforced plastic shapes of uniform cross sections (rods, tubes, and I beams). This method

consists of pulling various reinforcing materials through a resin bath and subsequently forming and curing them. The cured section of material is then cut to any predetermined length. Fig. 4-59 is a schematic drawing of this process.

Pulforming Manufacturing Process: Pulforming (see Fig. 4-60) is a continuous process similar to pultrusion, except the finished product is not a uniform, straight section cut to length. This process is used to produce a curved part that has a constant volume, yet also has a changing geometry. An example is an automotive monoleaf spring which has a square cross section in the center and a flat, rectangular shape at each end. This is a recent development to meet high strength requirements. Fig. 4-60 illustrates the pulforming process.

Low-Volume Processes

Commonly used low-volume processes include (1) hand or spray lay-up, (2) vacuum bag, (3) pressure bag, (4) autoclave, (5) wet preform, (6) resin injection, and (7) filament winding. The second and third processes make use of the hand or spray lay-up, but embody a low-pressure system to improve glass content. The wet preform, resin injection, and filament winding processes also are suitable for intermediate-volume operations.

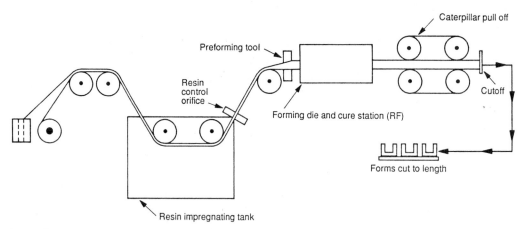

Figure 4-59   Pultrusion manufacturing process

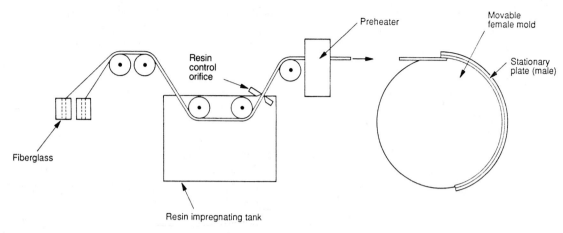

Figure 4-60   Pulforming manufacturing process

Hand or Spray Lay-Up: The hand or spray lay-up (see Fig. 4-61) is an open-mold system. The mold may be a simple wood or plaster unit (male or female) or a cast or sheet metal construction for which permanence is required. The size can vary from a 12″ (305 mm) box to a large yacht.

The mold surface must be heavily waxed and then sprayed with a polyvinyl alcohol solution to prevent the laminate from sticking to the surface. To make a smooth surface, a gel coat is applied. Thickness of the gel coat, which is either brushed or sprayed on, is approximately 0.020″ (0.51 mm). The gel is a catalyzed polyester resin that is highly filled (may be pigmented for color) and stabilized for weather

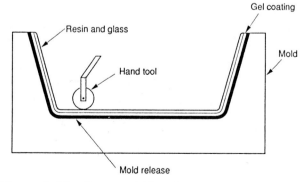

Figure 4-61   Open mold hand or spray lay-up process

resistance. It must be allowed to partially cure before the subsequent resin and glass system is applied. A smooth surface is produced if the mold has a smooth surface. The laminate is built up by spraying catalyzed polyester resin onto the gel coat, then laying a glass mat on it and working the resin up through the mat with a hand (squeegee) tool. Subsequent resin and glass layers are applied to attain the required thickness.

Vacuum Bag, Pressure Bag, and Auto-clave: The vacuum bag (see Fig. 4-62), pressure bag (see Fig. 4-63), and autoclave molding processes are modifications of the open-mold process. Pressure is applied to the laminate to control thickness and glass content. The pressure bag is generally used in conjunction with a heated metal mold. This is an expensive mold that is justified by a long-life part that should undergo only minor changes. The vacuum bag and pressure bag systems are used extensively in the aerospace industry and in the manufacturing of boats and fishing rods.

Vacuum bag. The vacuum bag method uses a film of styrene-resistant plastics (mylar or cellophane). The film is sealed around the mold, and a vacuum is created under the bag. This flattens the fibers, draws air from the resin, and produces a glazed surface on the back of the part.

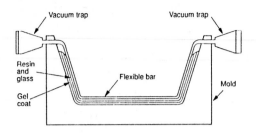

Figure 4-62   Vacuum bag process

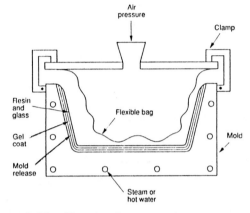

Figure 4-63   Pressure bag process

Pressure bag. The pressure bag process differs from the vacuum bag process in that positive pressure is applied to the top surface of the film. Steam heat sometimes is introduced into the mold cavity.

Autoclave. The autoclave method is widely used in the aerospace industry to produce parts from impregnated epoxy. A woven fabric is impregnated with epoxy resin. It then is dried and heated to a stage at which it is partially polymerized and is susceptible to heat.

The impregnated fabric is cut and placed in a mold, which may have a phenolic or aramid honeycomb core. The mold then is covered with a vacuum bag and placed in an autoclave. Vacuum is held at 28 in. Hg (95 kPa), while the autoclave is pressurized to 50 psi (345 kPa). The mold is heated to 250-350°F (121-177°C) for about 2½ hours.

Wet Preform: The wet preform process (see Fig. 4-64) has been used for heavy truck front ends in

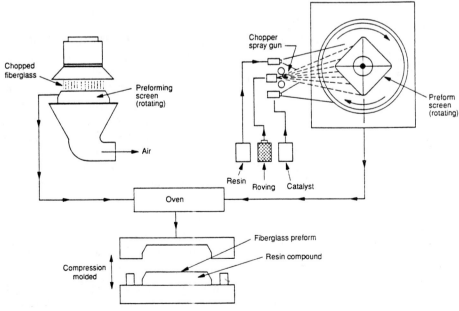

Figure 4-64   Wet preform process

the past, but is giving way to the SMC process. It is still a viable process for intermediate-volume applications that do not specify Class A surface requirements. The process consists of making a fiberglass form that roughly represents the part shape (preform). The form is made by two methods. One is through the use of a plenum chamber that deposits chopped rovings on a revolving screen with air and a polyester resin binder sprayed on the preform. The form is baked on the screen to retain its shape. The form is placed in a matched metal mold, catalyzed resin (predetermined amount) is poured on, and pressure and heat are applied. The plenum chamber is used for small parts that are not complicated in design so that a uniform layer of glass fibers can be deposited on the screen.

The other form-making method is used for large parts (truck front ends). The fiber and binder are applied with a chopper spray gun by an operator. A significant amount of operator skill is required to obtain a uniform fiber buildup over the entire geometry of these large, multicontoured parts. The binder is oven-cured. The more sophisticated units have an attached oven, and the preform is rotated into the oven while another form is being sprayed up.

Resin Injection: Resin injection molding (see Fig. 4-65) as an intermediate-volume process uses tooling and equipment that is lower in cost than that used in conventional compression or injection-molding techniques. Molding cycles are much slower than those for compression and injection methods, but production rates far exceed those for the open-mold techniques.

The closed mold made from plastics or spray metal or cast aluminum produces parts with smooth surfaces on both sides. A gel coat may be used to obtain a desired color, improve weatherability, increase corrosion resistance, and permit post-finishing operations. The mold has cooling coils for exotherm control, a perimeter gasket to prevent resin and pressure leakage, and air vents to bleed off air and to determine part fill. The resin compound, including catalyst and filler, is pumped into the mold through an injection port. The curing cycle is about

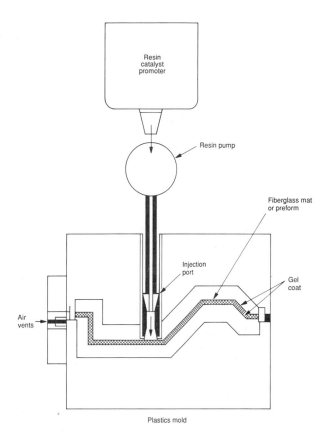

Figure 4-65   Resin injection molding

10-20 minutes because the resin is injected rapidly and thus allows for the faster gelling and curing permitted in lay-up systems. This closed-mold technique also allows for foam encapsulation and the use of ribs and inserts.

Filament Winding: Filament winding (see Fig. 4-66) uses continuous fiberglass rovings fed through a catalyzed resin bath (polyester or epoxy) onto a revolving mandrel by a traveling head on the winder. The fiber is wound to a predetermined pattern under an applied tension that provides an even share of load bearing by the fiberglass reinforcement. In some instances, inflatable or soluble mandrels are used to facilitate their removal from the completed part. The filament winding process produces storage tanks

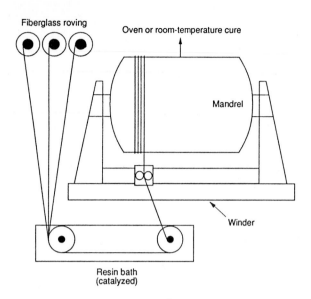

Figure 4-66   Filament winding process

and various aerospace items, as well as high-strength, lightweight pipes and tubes.

This process is also used to make high-strength molding sheet. A simple round mandrel is used to produce a laminate that is formed by a wide-angle winding operation. When the desired thickness is reached, the laminate is slit lengthwise to make a flat sheet. This sheet is cut into suitable strips and compression molded with SMC into parts that have high-strength areas provided by the filament-wound material.

Thermoforming Plastic Sheet and Film

Thermoforming consists of heating a thermoplastic sheet to its processing temperature and forcing the hot, flexible material against the contours of a mold. This pliable material is rapidly moved either mechanically with tools, plugs, matched molds, etc., or pneumatically with differentials in pressure created by a vacuum or by compressed air.

When held to the contours of the mold and allowed to cool, the plastics material retains the detail and shape of the mold. To obtain better optics, some parts, such as skylights and aircraft windshields, can be thermoformed without molds, using only vacuum or compressed air and holding fixtures.

Thermoforming has several advantages including (1) low costs for machinery and tooling because of low processing pressures; (2) low internal stresses and good physical properties in finished parts; (3) capability of being predecorated, laminated, or coextruded to obtain different finishes, properties, etc.; (4) capability of forming light, thin, and strong parts for packaging and other uses; and (5) capability of making large, one-piece parts with relatively inexpensive machinery and tooling. The main disadvantages are: (1) higher cost of using sheet or film instead of plastics pellets and (2) necessity of trimming the finished part.

Thermoforming Techniques

A variety of techniques is used for the thermoforming of plastics sheets. They include vacuum forming, free forming, drape forming, plug and ring forming, vacuum snap-back forming, airslip forming, plug-assist forming, matched-die forming, and twin-sheet forming. Most of the processes are based on the principle of forcing a heated, pliable thermoplastic sheet to conform to the contours of a mold, then allowing the formed material to cool. The most commonly used thermoforming techniques can be classified as vacuum, pressure, mechanical, pre-stretching, twin-sheet, and rigidizing methods.

Other Processing Methods

A variety of special techniques is used in processing plastics, in addition to the basic procedures described previously in this chapter. Combinations of several processes often may be used advantageously for producing specialty plastics products.

Blow Molding

Blow molding is a process for shaping thermoplastic materials into one-piece, hollow articles by means of heat and air pressure. The method consists basically of stretching a hot thermoplastic tube with air pressure, then hardening it against a relatively cool mold. A wide variety of blow molding techniques and equipment is used to suit specific applications.

The principal difference between blow molding glass and blow molding plastics is attributed to the different material properties. Molten glass is much less sensitive than plastics—not only in the melt viscosity, but also in its chemical stability. For this reason, modified glass blowing machines cannot be used for plastics. Another difference is that glass blowers start with a drop of molten glass, while the plastics blowers use a preformed plastics part, which usually is a tube of molten plastics called a parison (see Fig. 4-67).

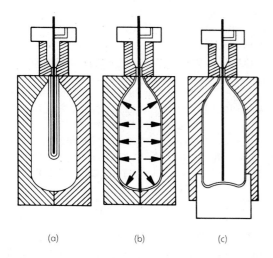

(a)   (b)   (c)

Figure 4-67   Two-stage injection, stretch-blow operations

Liquid Injection Molding

In comparison to other processes, the new liquid injection molding (LIM) method has the potential necessary to replace compression and transfer molding of thermoset plastics in some applications.

The LIM Process: Instead of being charged into the cavity of a compression mold or a transfer pot as powder, pellets, or other molding compound, two LIM material components are pumped directly from the shipping containers through a mixing device and injected into a heated mold, where they cure.

Liquid injection molding differs considerably from reaction injection molding (RIM), with which it sometimes is confused. The pumping systems used in LIM are generally lower pressure systems than those used for RIM, and mixing in LIM is accomplished more often mechanically than by impingement. Also, while RIM parts usually are large, LIM parts typically are quite small.

LIM Applications: Most of the early LIM development activity and production applications involve the use of silicone elastomers. Although LIM experimental work is underway with epoxies, polyesters, and urethanes, most applications relate to the use of liquid silicones as replacements for gum-silicone rubbers and organic rubbers.

Liquid injection molding applications are found in the automotive, aerospace, furniture, and pharmaceutical industries. Products include such diverse items as ignition system parts, weather seals, diaphragms, connectors, valves, grommets, O-rings, and other types of seals.

Rotational Molding

Rotational molding is a process for forming hollow plastics parts. The process utilizes the principle that finely divided plastics material becomes molten in contact with a hot metal surface, and then takes the shape of that surface. When the polymer is cooled while in contact with the metal, a reproduction of the mold's interior surface is produced.

The Process: Rotational molding employs the simultaneous rotation of thin-walled molds about two axes, primary and secondary, which are perpendicular to each other. After being charged with plastics material, the molds are heated externally while rotating. This causes the particles to melt on the inner surface of the mold as they tumble. Successive layers are deposited until all of the material is uniformly distributed and fused. The molds are cooled by air or external water spray while still rotating. They are then opened for removal of the finished article and recharged.

The process is employed for the production of hollow objects from thermoplastic materials. The main benefit of the rotational molding process is its versatility and applicability to the production of parts ranging from small, intricate products, to larger items such as automobile fuel tanks, to very large (5000 gal; 19 000 L) liquid storage tanks.

Rotational molding differs from other molding processes in that, while the others require both heat and pressure to plasticize the resin, rotational molding requires only that the mold is heated. Because of its long time/temperature cycle, this process cannot be used with all polymers. A material with good oxidative stability and high melt flow characteristics is required.

Structural Foam Molding

A structural foam is a plastics product with a rigid cellular core and an integral skin. The solid skin is typically 0.030-0.080″ (0.76-2.03 mm) thick. Density reductions compared with solid plastics are in the range of 20-40%, depending upon part configuration, thickness, and molding conditions. Structural foams can be molded and extruded. Since the bending stiffness of parts increases proportionately to the cube of the part's thickness, structural foam parts can be made quite rigid, with good strength-to-weight ratios.

All thermoplastics can be foam-molded. Typical materials are polystyrene, polyethylene, polypropylene, polycarbonate, acrylonitrile butadiene styrene (ABS), and vinyl. The plastics used in this process range from preblended resins and foaming agents, to materials that are dry blended with the foaming agent in a machine-mounted hopper blender. The foaming agents usually are combined with inorganic solids which, when decomposed by the heat in the plasticizing cylinder, generate carbon monoxide or nitrogen gases.

In the foam-molding process, the solid skin is formed when the injected foaming mass is chilled by cool mold surfaces. This skin creates an insulating barrier that still permits the central mass to complete its expansion to form the foamed core. Because of the heat insulating properties of the foam-molded products, the molding cycle times are slower than the cycle times normally attained in injection molding operations.

The basic processes fall into two categories: high pressure and low pressure. Both processes are performed with reciprocating screw, injection molding machines. In a typical operation, an inert gas (nitrogen) is introduced into the resin melt under pressure. The resin-gas mixture is subsequently expanded into a mold at low pressure. The gas then expands, causing the mixture to foam and fill the mold. When contact is made with the cool mold surface, the gas bubbles collapse and form the solid skin.

Casting

Casting processes are applicable to some thermoplastics and thermosets. These materials can be cast at atmospheric pressure in inexpensive molds to form large parts with section thicknesses that would be impracticable for other manufacturing processes. Casting resins are molded on a production basis in lead, plaster, rubber, and glass molds.

In a typical operation, the liquid resin is poured into the mold and the product is cured in an oven by applying heat, or it is cured exothermically with a catalyst. Shrinkage during curing facilitates removal of the product from the mold. Finishing operations include the removal of flash and, in cold molds, removal of the gate. In some instances, the parts are buffed or tumble polished to improve the appearance.

Plastics products made by the casting process include sheets, rods, tubes, and profile shapes. Embedments and encapsulations are also accomplished by casting.

Forging

The forging process sometimes is used in manufacturing thermoplastic parts that would be difficult to produce by other processes. The forging technique is capable of producing thick parts with abrupt changes in sections. An example of the application of forging is its use to produce thick, large-diameter gears from polypropylene.

Although identified by the term *forging*, this process is misnamed since it is not truly a forging process, but rather a reforming operation. In this process, a preheated blank or billet of the required shape and volume is placed between a pair of forging dies, which are then closed to deform the work blank and fill the die cavity. The dies remain closed for 16-60 seconds to minimize elastic recovery of the part when it is released from the dies.

Typical forging equipment is a hydraulic press or a mechanical toggle press. Forming pressures range from 1-10 ksi (6.9-69 MPa). Dies are generally made of a machinable prehardened steel, similar to the steel used for injection molds. The most commonly used plastics in the forging process are those that are difficult to process by the usual injection methods. The blank used for forging is made by cutting it from an extruded bar, or by compression molding.

Film and Sheet Forming

The basic methods for producing film or thin sheets are calendering, extrusion, blowing, and casting. The method chosen for a particular application is determined mainly by the type of thermoplastic that is to be processed.

Calendering: Calendering, illustrated in Fig. 4-68, is the formation of a thin sheet by squeezing a thermoplastic material between rolls. In principle, it is a continuous "extrusion" process in which a pair of mating rolls establishes the thickness and surface characteristics of the sheet that is formed.

The material, composed of resin, plasticizer, filler, and color pigments, is compounded and heated before being fed into the calender. The thickness of the sheet produced depends upon the roll spacing and the speed of the finishing rollers that stretch the plastics material. Before the sheet (film) is wound, it passes through water-cooled rolls. Vinyl, polyethylene, cellulose acetate films and sheeting, and vinyl floor tile are products of calendering.

Extrusion: In making sheets of polypropylene, polyethylene, polystyrene, or ABS, an extrusion process is used. This process is illustrated schematically in Fig. 4-69. After the material has been compounded, it is placed in the feed hopper. The material is heated to 320-425°F (160-240°C) and forced into the die area at pressures of 2-4 ksi (14-28

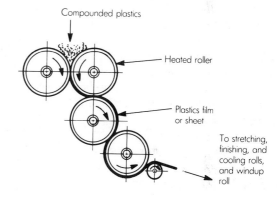

Figure 4-68 Film forming by the calendaring process

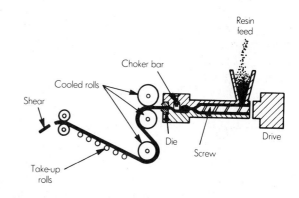

Figure 4-69 Process for extruding thin plastic sheets and film

MPa) by the screw conveyor. The thickness of the sheet is controlled by a combination of the choker bar and the die opening. After extrusion, the sheet passes through oil- or water-cooled, chromium-plated rolls before being cut to size. Plastics sheet and film materials produced by extrusion can range in thickness from 0.001 to 0.126″ (0.03-3.2 mm). [Material with a thickness less than 0.01″ (0.3 mm) is called film.]

Blown Tubular Extrusion: The blown tubular extrusion process produces film by first extruding a tube vertically through a ring die and then blowing it with air into a large-diameter cylinder. The blown cylinder is air cooled as it rises, and then it is flattened by driven rolls before reaching the winder. This technique is used to produce thin film such as that used in trash bags and packaging materials.

Film and Cell Casting: In film casting, the plastics resins are dissolved in a solvent and spread on a polished continuous belt or large drum and conveyed through an oven in which they are cured and the solvent is removed. In cell casting, a cell is made up of two sheets of polished glass, separated according to the film thickness that is desired. Gaskets retain the liquid catalyzed monomer. The cell is heated to the desired temperature in an oven in which it is held until curing is completed. Cell casting is used for the production of acrylic transparent sheets.

Processing of Ceramics

Based on their material properties, ceramics can be divided into two broad categories: glasses and crystalline ceramics. Different processes are used for forming ceramics in these categories into useable products. In general terms, glasses are formed using the following steps:

1. The glass material is converted into a viscous liquid
2. The material is shaped as desired

3. The material is cooled so that it solidifies and forms the desired shape

Crystalline ceramics are too brittle to be processed in the same manner as glass. In general terms, crystalline ceramics are formed using the following steps:

1. Begin with powdered material
2. The powdered material is moistened and pressed into the desired shape
3. The new shape is dried
4. Bonding is produced through a chemical reaction, vitrification, or sintering.

The key step in each process is forming the material into the desired shape. With glass, forming is accomplished by rolling, molding, pressing between dies, blow molding, or drawing through dies. With crystalline ceramics, the forming is accomplished by dry axial pressing, isostatic processing, slip casting, injection molding, or extrusion.

Fabrication of Composites

There are a number of different types of composite materials. The most widely used can be divided into three broad categories: particulate, laminar, and fiber-reinforced composites. The fabrication methods used vary for each of these categories.

Particulate composites are fabricated in the same manner as powdered metals, covered earlier in this text. As the name implies, laminar composites consist of built-up layers of material. The key in fabricating laminar composites lies in forming a strong bond between layers. Roll bonding and explosive bonding are the most commonly used processes for producing the necessary bond between layers.

Roll bonding involves passing sheets of material simultaneously through a rolling mill to create a solid-state bond between layers. Explosive bonding involves detonating a sheet of explosive material above successive layers to be joined. A wave of pressure engulfs the interface, causing surface films to liquify. This forces metal surfaces together under high pressure, producing a solid-state bond.

There are number of different methods that can be used for fabricating fiber-reinforced composites. The method used depends on such factors as fiber orientation, length of continuous filaments, and the desired characteristics of the finished product. All of the various processes used involve embedding the fiber in a selected matrix in such a way as to produce the desired characteristics in the finished product.

Two processes commonly associated with the fabrication of composites are pultrusion and filament winding. Pultrusion is a process that is similar to metal extrusion. It involves immersing bundles of continuous reinforcing fibers in a resin bath and then drawing them through a succession of heated dies to produce the desired cross section. After the bundles are cooled, they are cut to the desired length.

Filament winding involves winding high-strength plastic-coated filaments around a form and curing the resin. This binds adjacent fibers together to form the desired shape. After cooling, the form and the product are separated. By varying the winding pattern and/or by varying the density of fibers at selected points on the form, a product can be produced that is strong where strength is needed and lighter where strength is not critical.

SPECIAL FORMING METHODS

A group of techniques, commonly referred to as the high-energy-rate forming (HERF) processes, predominates the general category of special forming methods. Some argument exists (and not without justification) that HERF might more accurately be termed high-velocity forming (HVF). No matter which nomenclature is preferred, however, of importance is the fact that these processes share a common feature: each technique imparts, through the application of high rates of energy transfer, a high rate of strain to the material being formed. While the exact means used to achieve this high rate of energy transfer varies from process to process, the effect for most processes is the same; the velocity component of the forming operation becomes very large and, in sheet metal forming, improved formability and closer tolerances can result.

It has been suggested that a HERF process can be defined as any process in which forming speeds of more than 50 fps (15 m/s) are utilized. Historically, the usual list of HERF processes has included the explosive, electrohydraulic, electromagnetic, and compressed-gas forming methods. In subsequent sections of this chapter, each of these techniques is described in detail and a comprehensive discussion of the theory, equipment, application, and limitations of each method is provided as well.

Because of their increased utilization and importance as forming methods, ultrasonic forming and stress peen forming, though not conceded to be HERF processes, have been added to the list of special forming methods discussed in this chapter. Finally, it is acknowledged that the acronym HERF has, on occasion, been used elsewhere as an abbreviation for high-energy-rate forging. This topic is included in the section on high velocity forging.

Explosive Forming

Explosive forming is a high-velocity process in which the punch or diaphragm is replaced by an explosive charge. The explosives used are generally highly explosive chemicals, gaseous mixtures, or propellants (see Figs. 4-70 and 4-71).

Electrohydraulic Forming

Electrohydraulic forming (EHF) is a process that converts electrical energy into mechanical energy for the forming of metallic parts. The amount of electrical energy discharged is controlled by varying the charging voltage from zero to its maximum. The discharged electrical energy causes explosions inside the hollow workpiece, which is filled with water or another suitable medium. These explosions

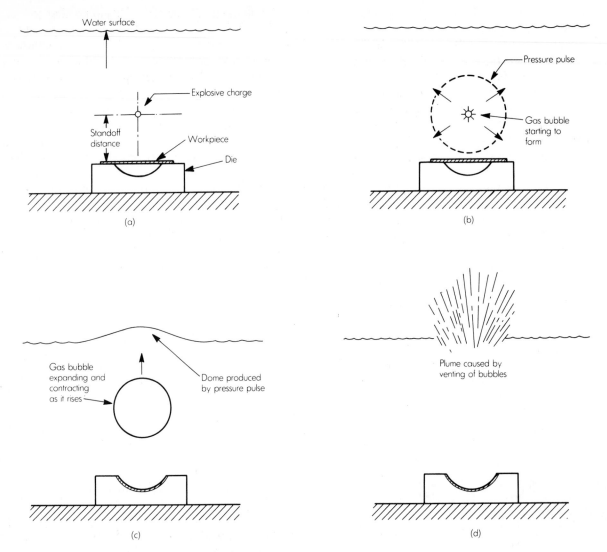

Sequence of underwater explosive-forming operations: (a) explosive charge is set in position, (b) detonation occurs producing pressure pulse and gas bubble, (c) workpiece deformed, and (d) gas bubble vents at surface of the water.

Figure 4-70   Sequence of underwater explosive-forming operations

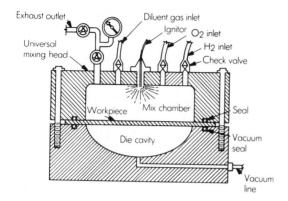

Figure 4-71 Combustible gas forming operation

Electromagnetic Forming

Electromagnetic forming, also referred to as magnetic pulse forming, was developed in the 1960s as a means for shaping, forming, and assembling metallic parts. It is currently the most widely used HERF process in industry. In this process, electrical energy is converted into mechanical energy by means of a magnetic field that exerts a force on a current-carrying conductor, the workpiece (see Figs. 4-73, 4-74, and 4-75).

produce shock waves that emanate in all directions until some obstruction is encountered. If the energy is of sufficient magnitude, the workpiece is deformed. The deformation is controlled by applying external restraints in one or more of three ways: in the form of dies, by varying the magnitude of the energy released, and by using shapers within the transfer medium (see Fig. 4-72).

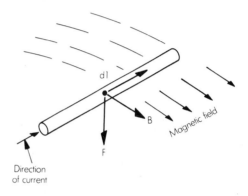

Figure 4-73 Force on a current-carrying conductor in a magnetic field

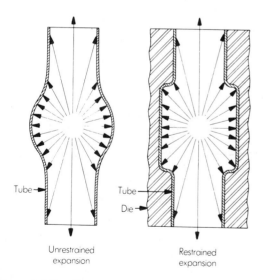

Figure 4-72 Energy patterns in unrestrained and restrained electrohydraulic forming

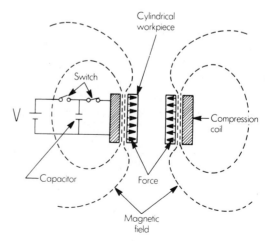

Figure 4-74 Magnetic field in electromagnetic forming

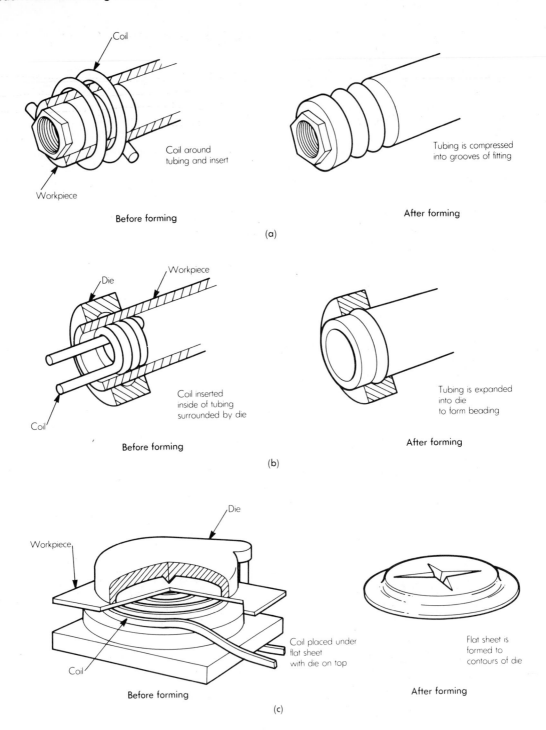

Coil

Coil around
tubing and insert

Workpiece

Before forming

Tubing is compressed
into grooves of fitting

After forming

(a)

Die

Workpiece

Coil inserted
inside of tubing
surrounded by die

Coil

Before forming

Tubing is expanded
into die
to form beading

After forming

(b)

Die

Workpiece

Coil placed under
flat sheet
with die on top

Coil

Before forming

Flat sheet is
formed to
contours of die

After forming

(c)

Figure 4-75   (a) Compression coil; (b) Expansion coil; and (c) Flat coil

High-Velocity Forging

In high-velocity forging, the energy stored in a high-pressure gas or the energy from a burning fuel-oxidizer mixture is used to accelerate a ram to high velocity for accomplishing the forging. The ram velocities attained in this process are about three to four times those of conventional drop hammers. The concept of using compressed gases as an energy source to drive machines was applied in the late 1940s in the testing of materials, and a shock loading device was developed in 1955. The concept of using a burning fuel-oxidizer to develop the high-pressure gas is basically derived from the principles of an internal combustion engine (see Figs. 4-76, 4-77, and 4-78).

Peen Forming

Peen forming is a dieless forming process performed at room temperature. During the process, the surface of the workpiece is impacted by pressure from small, round steel shot. Every piece of shot impacting the surface acts as a tiny hammer, producing elastic stretching of the upper surface. The impact pressure of the peening shot causes local plastic deformation that manifests itself as a residual compressive stress. The surface force of the residual compressive stress combined with the stretching causes the material to develop a compound, convex curvature on the peened side. When curvatures are being formed within the elastic range of the metal, the core of the metal remains elastic with a small,

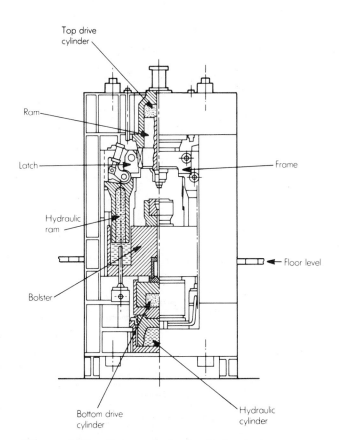

Figure 4-76 Pneumatic-hydraulic hammer

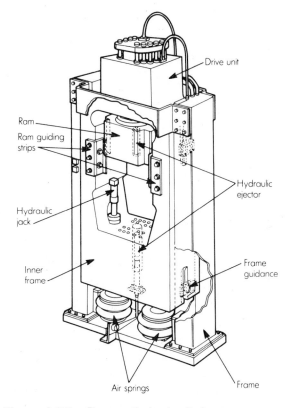

Figure 4-77 Pneumatic-hydraulic hammer

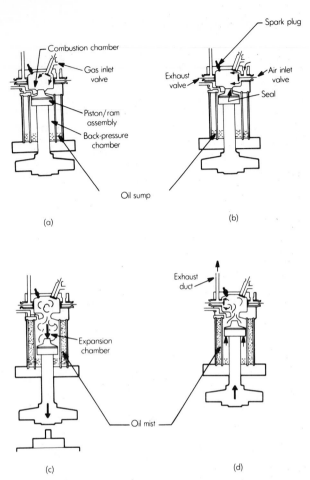

Figure 4-78 (a) Injection; (b) Charging and ignition; (c) Working stroke; and (d) Return stroke

balancing, residual tensile stress. Other mechanical forming processes that require overforming with subsequent springback induce high tensile stress. Although high tensile stress can be minimized by stretch forming techniques, stretch forming is usually not performed on tapered or sculptured sections.

The size, velocity, and angle of impingement of the shot as well as the distance of the wheels or nozzles (the wheels or nozzles propel the shot) from the workpiece are automatically controlled in specially designed machines. Peen forming can be performed with or without an external load applied on the workpiece.

Ultrasonic-Activated Forming

Ultrasonic-activated forming is a metalforming process that applies high-frequency vibrations to the workpiece through the tooling. The vibrations are usually greater than 15,000 cycles per second (cps) and are generally no more than a few thousandths of an inch (0.08 mm) in amplitude.

Metalforming with the aid of ultrasonic energy dates back to the mid-1950s. Tests showed that when a wire was stressed in tension with ultrasonic activation, the yield strength of the material appeared to be reduced and the elongation seemed to increase. It was also determined that this effect increased linearly with an increase in vibratory power and was independent of the frequency. This phenomenon was attributed to ultrasonically facilitated formation and movement of dislocations within the crystal lattice structure that assisted inter-crystalline slip (see Fig. 4-79).

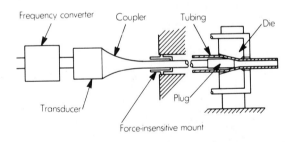

Figure 4-79 Ultrasonic plug-activated system

POWDER METALLURGY

Powder metallurgy is a metalworking process used to consolidate particulate matter, both metals and/or nonmetals, into discrete shapes. Although the scope of this section is confined to metallic materials, the principles of the process apply to ceramics and other types of nonmetallic materials. Complex composite materials that combine metallic and nonmetallic powders are also fabricated by this technique, especially to provide the properties required in certain aerospace, electronic, and nuclear applications.

Modern powder metallurgy began in the early 1900s when incandescent lamp filaments were fabricated from tungsten powder—the same way they are made today. Other important products followed, such as cemented carbide cutting tools, friction materials, and self-lubricating bearings. Today, structural PM parts and products are used widely in automobiles, trucks, farm machinery, diesel engines, home appliances, power tools, aircraft engines, lawn and garden equipment, business machines, and wherever small mass-produced metal components can be utilized.

It is instructive to ask: Why would it be desirable to produce a metal product with a given shape starting with metal powders rather than molten metal? One important reason has an economic basis. The cost of producing a product of a particular shape and the required dimensional tolerances by powder metallurgy may be lower than the cost of casting or making it as a wrought product, because of scrap reduction and the fewer processing steps that are needed. The production equipment and processes for these PM structural parts are the principal subjects of this section. Such parts must, of course, have adequate physical and mechanical properties and completely fulfill functional performance specifications. But, in many instances, the cost advantage, rather than significantly different or unusual properties, is the main reason for fabricating the part from powder.

Producing structural parts is, however, not the only application of powder metallurgy. Other diverse applications are based on the unusual properties that can be obtained by this technique. These applications range from metals with very high melting points, to materials for which high wear resistance is needed, to porous material (filters, oil-impregnated bearings, etc.), to products with special frictional, magnetic, or electrical properties, to many other applications. In general, PM products of these kinds are outside the scope of this section; hence, they are not covered in depth.

Process Fundamentals

As diagrammed in Fig. 4-80, there are three basic steps in the most widely used conventional powder metallurgy process. These steps are mixing or blending, compacting, and sintering.

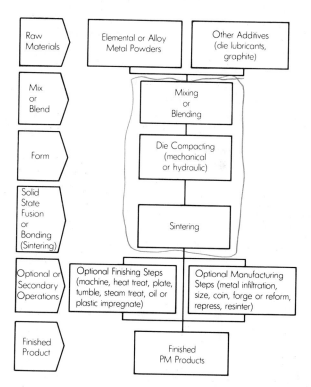

Figure 4-80   Powder metallurgy process

Mixing: In this first step of the conventional PM process, elemental metal powders or alloy powders are mixed together with lubricants or other alloy additions to produce a homogeneous mix of ingredients.

Compacting: Compacting is the second step of the conventional PM process. In it, a controlled amount of mixed powder is automatically fed into a precision die and compacted or pressed, usually at room temperature, at pressures as low as 10 tons/in.² (138 MPa) or as high as 60 tons/in.² (827 MPa) or more.

Compacting consolidates and densifies the loose powder into a shape called a "green compact." With conventional pressing techniques, the compact has the size and shape of the finished product when ejected from the die. It has sufficient strength for in-process handling and transport to the sintering furnace.

Dies and tools, made of either hardened steel and/or carbides, consist of at least a die body or mold, an upper punch, a lower punch, and in some cases one or more core rods to provide for holes parallel to the pressing direction. A typical set of tools for producing a straight cylindrical part such as a sleeve bearing is shown in Fig. 4-81. The pressing cycle for this simple part, illustrated in Fig. 4-82, is as follows: (1) The empty die cavity is filled with mixed powder. (2) Both top and bottom punches simultaneously press the metal powder in the die. (3) The top punch is withdrawn, and the green compact is ejected from the die by the bottom punch. (4) The green compact is pushed out of the pressing area to make ready for another operating cycle.

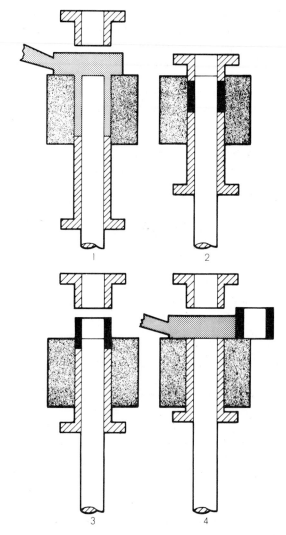

Figure 4-82   Powder metallurgy pressing cycle

In general, this compacting cycle is essentially the same for all parts. However, when more than one pressing level is needed, as for example in producing flanged shapes, multiple punches are used and separate pressing action may be required.

Sintering: The third step of the conventional PM process is sintering. During sintering, the green compact is heated in a protective-atmosphere furnace to a relatively high temperature, but below the melting

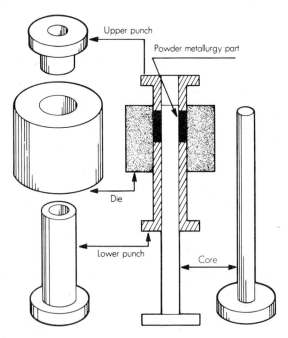

Figure 4-81   Typical set of PM tools

point of the metal. Representative temperatures: ferrous PM, 2050°F (1120°C); bronze PM, 1500°F (815°C); stainless steel PM, 2200°F (1200°C). Sintering, which is mainly a solid-state process, develops metallurgical bonds among the powder particles and thus produces the PM part's mechanical and physical properties. It also serves to prevent oxidation, removes the lubricant from the powder, reduces oxides, and controls carbon content on the surface of the part and inside of it. Typical sintering atmospheres are endothermic gas, exothermic gas, dissociated ammonia, or nitrogen.

Secondary Operations

For many applications, PM parts are ready for use after sintering. However, any one of several secondary operations can be applied to provide specific or special properties. Parts can be repressed, infiltrated with oil, or impregnated with plastic. They can be modified by coining, sizing, machining, tumbling, plating, and heat treating.

The controlled porosity of PM parts makes it possible to infiltrate them with another metal or impregnate them with oil or a resin to either improve mechanical properties or provide additional performance characteristics such as self-lubrication.

The oil-impregnated PM bearing, which has been used in automobiles since the late 1920s, is one of the best known examples of the use of impregnation. Conventional PM bearings can hold from 10-30% by volume of oil. Generally, additive-free oils (nonautomotive engine oils) are used. Impregnation is accomplished by soaking the parts in heated oil or by vacuum techniques. During use, when the parts heat up from friction, the oil expands and flows to the bearing surface. Upon cooling, the oil returns into the metal mass by capillary action.

Metal Powders

The most common metals available in powder form are iron, tin, nickel, copper, aluminum, titanium, and refractory metals such as tungsten, molybdenum, tantalum, and columbium. Also, prealloyed powders such as low-alloy steels, bronze, brass, and stainless steel are produced in which each particle is itself an alloy.

Powder particles are specific sizes and shapes. They are not merely ground-up chips or scraps of metal. The major methods for making metal powders are atomization, reduction of oxides, electrolysis, and chemical reduction. Shape and other particle characteristics—whether spherical, irregular, porous, or dense—are dependent upon the manufacturing process.

Advantages of PM

The following is a list of some of the advantages that the powder metallurgy process offers:

1. Machining is eliminated or reduced.
2. Material loss (scrap) is eliminated or reduced.
3. Close dimensional tolerances can be maintained.
4. Almost any alloy system under equilibrium or non-equilibrium conditions can be achieved.
5. Good surface finishes are obtained.
6. Controlled permeability for filtration is available.
7. Complex or unique shapes, impractical with other metal forming processes, can be designed.
8. Powder metallurgy is suited to high-volume production and quality control techniques.

Limitations

The limitations of powder metallurgy are concerned primarily with the fact that a typical PM part must be of such a configuration that it can be ejected from a die. This means that reentrant angles, featheredges, or deep and narrow splines must be handled as secondary operations at additional cost.

In pressing a PM part, the powder does not flow laterally; thus, in a multilevel part, each column of powder for each part level must be controlled independently or unequal density will result. Equipment is available to ensure uniformity of density, thus opening a new field in high-quality, multilevel parts.

Size is another limitation. Typical PM parts are in the range of 1-2 lb (0.5-1 kg) or less; most are under 10 lb (4.5 kg), although parts as heavy as 70-100 lb (32-45 kg) are produced by special PM processes. Using conventional compacting systems, the costs of the equipment and the power necessary to compress the part increase greatly as the size and surface area of the part increase to the point at which a 3000 ton (26 668 kN) press represents the state-of-the-art maximum.

The main limitations of PM include the following:

1. Initial tool costs are relatively high. Production volume of less than 10,000 identical parts is normally not practical. However, part applications must be evaluated on an individual basis rather than on a strict quantity basis, because some case histories have shown lesser quantities to be economical.
2. Shapes requiring weak, thin sections should be avoided.
3. Featheredges and narrow and deep splines should be avoided.
4. Internal angles must be provided with lands.
5. Length of part in pressing direction is normally limited to 3-6 times cross-sectional dimension.
6. Corrosion protection requires special attention and precaution, depending upon the material used.

SAFETY IN FORMING

What conditions should exist for an effective safety program? First, a management commitment must be evident. Secondly, responsibility for the safety function must be assigned to a qualified person who serves as a focal point and coordinator for the program. Thirdly, a safety program cannot succeed without acceptance and support by employees. Sustained effort and constant attention are needed. Solutions to safety problems require application of sound management principles and practices similar to those used to solve production quality and cost problems. It is important that management "close the loop" by providing a systematic means of verifying that the intended safety program is being carried out.

Small business operations may have special problems in dealing with workplace safety and health hazards. While large companies usually can justify the full-time services of safety engineers and industrial hygienists, small firms often cannot. Yet the workplace hazards that cause injury and illness are as prevalent in small businesses as in large firms. A principal purpose of this section is to provide basic information that can help manufacturing companies of all sizes to establish their own safety programs.

General Considerations

At the outset, it is fundamentally important to distinguish between the meaning of "accident" and the term "act of God," as used in the insurance business. The distinction can be made clearly: floods and tornadoes cannot be prevented by the manager of a manufacturing plant, but workplace accidents can be prevented or reduced in number and severity. The key requirements are recognition of the problem and application of recognized accident prevention principles and techniques.

An accident may be defined simply as an unplanned event. In a carefully planned manufacturing operation, when an unplanned event or incident occurs, corrective action should be taken to avoid repetition. The unplanned event (accident) may have caused interruption of the planned production sequence, damage to parts or equipment, damage to property, or injury to employees.

It is also important to distinguish between physical provisions for safety and the training of people to act safely. No matter how well working conditions are designed and constructed, few situations can be safeguarded to the extent that the human element is completely absent. For example, an adjustable barrier guard is a standard safeguard on a power press, but unless employees are trained to have it in place, it does not prevent injuries. Thus, maximum safety is attained by the combination of safe facilities and people who are properly trained in safe procedures.

Operators and maintenance and setup personnel should be trained to make sure safeguards and safeguarding devices are in place and functioning properly before a machine is put into operation. Thus maximum safety is attained by the combination of safe facilities and people trained in safe procedures.

An accident prevention program should be concerned with only the types of accidents that can occur in a particular area or workplace. Because each workplace is different, the safety programs vary and each program should be adapted to the circumstances in a particular plant. However, while the details of safety programs may vary considerably, effective programs share the common elements listed in Fig. 4-83.

- Management leadership

- Assignment of responsibility

- Identification and control of hazards

- Employee and supervisor training

- Safety and health recordkeeping

- First-aid and medical assistance

- Employee awareness, acceptance and participation

- Management follow-up

Figure 4-83   Key factors in workplace safety

Management Leadership:
The top local executive should assume a leadership role. The attitude of management personnel toward job safety and health is reflected by other employees. If management is not interested in preventing accidents, workers are unlikely to be safety conscious.

At all times, the manager should demonstrate interest in safety and health and give these matters the attention they require. There should be no doubts about genuine personal concern for employee safety and health and the priority placed on them in the workplace. The safety policy must be clearly set. Procedures and actions, taken with management support, demonstrate its importance. Some action items for consideration include:

- Posting the OSHA workplace poster, "Job Safety and Health Protection," where employees can see it. (This is an OSHA requirement.)
- Meeting with employees to discuss job safety and health matters. Discussion should cover mutual responsibilities under the Act. (The text of the OSHA workplace poster can aid in this task.)
- Showing all employees a copy of the Act and a copy of OSHA standards that apply to their business. They should be told where these documents are kept and where they may have access to them.
- Writing a "policy statement" and posting it near the OSHA workplace poster so that everyone is reminded of the concern for safety.
- Establishing a "Code of Safe Practices and Operating Procedures" to provide specific instruction for employees.
- Including job safety and health topics in meetings or in conversations with employees.
- Personally reviewing inspection and accident reports to ensure follow-up when needed.
- Commenting on good or bad safety records and providing accident prevention guidance on a routine basis.
- Setting a good example. If, for instance, eye protection is required to be worn in specific areas, then the manager must wear eye protection when visiting that area, too.

Assignment of Responsibility:
Responsibility for safety and health activities must be clearly assigned. In terms of management responsibility, the direct supervisors of employees are usually the key personnel.

After top management has set the basic safety policy, detailed responsibility for carrying out the program can be delegated to the same persons who oversee the operating and production details. Supervisors, group leaders, "straw bosses," or other key persons can be assigned specific responsibilities for safety and health and should be held accountable for getting the job done.

A good rule of thumb is to assign safety and health responsibilities along with production responsibilities. It then becomes "part of the job" to operate safely.

When considering responsibility, all employees should be included. Each employee has the responsibility to follow safety and health procedures and instructions, and each has the responsibility for recognizing hazards in his or her immediate work area and for taking action to control them. A general understanding of this key point should be fostered. Supervisors should be evaluated and rated on the degree to which they assume responsibility for safety, as well as on the usual criteria such as production quantity and quality, etc. Safety must be treated as an integral part of the ongoing operations.

Identification and Control of Hazards:
Possible accident causes should be properly identified and either eliminated or controlled. To maintain a safe and healthful workplace, it is necessary to do two things:

1. Identify workplace hazards that exist now or could develop.
2. Install procedures to control these hazards or to eliminate them if possible.

When beginning the planning process, it is helpful to keep in mind that the safety program should be tailored for the particular operations to which it is applied. It should deal with the specific materials, processes, equipment, employees, and production operations in a particular plant or manufacturing area. Safety program planning and implementation may be viewed as a two-stage process:

1. Getting started and working up to a satisfactory level.
2. Maintaining the safety activity at a satisfactory level over a period of time.

Employee and Supervisor Training:
Appropriate safety-related training should be instituted. An effective accident prevention program requires proper job performance from everyone in the workplace.

The manager must ensure that all employees know about the materials and equipment they work with, what known hazards are in the operation, and how the hazards are controlled or eliminated.

All employees need to know the following (especially if these items have been included in a policy and in a code of safe practices):

- No employee is expected to undertake a job until he or she has received job instructions on how to do it properly and has been authorized to perform that job.
- No employee should undertake a job that appears to be unsafe.
- Mechanical and electronic safeguards must be kept in place.
- Each employee should report unsafe conditions encountered during work.
- Any injury or illness, even a slight one, suffered by an employee must be reported at once. Accidents should be investigated and corrective action taken when necessary.

In addition, any safety rules that are a condition of employment, such as the use of protective footwear or eye protection, should be explained clearly and enforced.

The direct supervisors must know how to train employees in the proper approach to doing their jobs. Appropriate training for the supervisors should be provided. (Many community colleges offer management training courses for little or no cost.)

There are some specific training requirements in the OSHA standards which must be met. Included are those pertaining to first aid, powered industrial trucks (including forklifts), power presses, and welding. In general, they deal with situations in which the use of untrained or improperly trained operators on machinery requiring skill could cause hazardous situations to develop not only for the operator but also for nearby workers.

Safety and Health Record Keeping:
Records of financial, engineering, and manufacturing data are essential to all successful businesses. They enable the owner or manager to learn from experience and to make corrections for future operations. Records of accidents, related injuries, illnesses, and property losses can serve the same purpose if they are used effectively.

The record keeping provisions in OSHA regulations require employers to collect and store factual information about accidents that occur. When the facts have been determined, causes of accidents can often be identified and control procedures can be instituted to prevent a similar occurrence from happening.

Injury/illness records. The injury/illness record keeping requirements under OSHA necessitate some paperwork. These records provide information for evaluating the success of safety and health activities. Success would generally mean a lack of, or a reduced number of, employee injuries or illnesses during a calendar year. Five important steps are required by the OSHA record keeping system:

1. Obtain a report on every injury requiring medical treatment (other than first aid).
2. Record each injury on OSHA Form No. 200 according to the instructions provided.
3. Prepare a supplementary record of occupational injuries and illnesses for recordable cases either on OSHA Form No. 101 or on workers' compensation reports giving the same information.
4. Every year, prepare the annual summary (OSHA Form No. 200); post it no later than February 1 and keep it posted until March 1.
5. Retain these records for at least five years.

During the year, the records should be reviewed to see where injuries are occurring. Recurring patterns or repeat situations should be noted. These records can help to identify high risk areas that require immediate attention.

The basic OSHA records include only injuries and illnesses. However, in some plants the system is extended to include all incidents, including those in which no injury or illness results. This is done to aid in pinpointing unsafe conditions and/or procedures. Safety councils, insurance companies, and other service organizations can assist in instituting such a system.

Injury/illness record keeping can be useful and is advisable if done on a reasonable basis. However, companies that employ ten or fewer employees are not required to keep records under the OSHA injury/illness record keeping system.

Regardless of the number of employees, a plant or shop may be chosen by the federal Bureau of Labor Statistics (BLS) or a related state agency for inclusion in an annual sample survey. Instructions are provided in letters sent by the agency directly to plants and shops selected for the BLS survey.

Exposure records. The injury/illness records may not be the only records to be maintained. Certain OSHA standards which deal with toxic substances and hazardous exposures require records on the exposure of employees, physical examination reports, employment records, etc.

As the work is done to identify possible exposure hazards, determination can be made, on a case-by-case basis, concerning possible applicability of the additional record keeping provisions. It is necessary to be aware of this category of record keeping so that, if required, such records can be embodied into the safety program control procedures and the self-inspection activities.

Documentation of activities. Essential records, including those legally required for workers' compensation, insurance audits, and government inspections must be maintained as long as the actual need exists. The employer must ensure the ready availability of medical personnel for advice and consultation on matters of employee health. This does not mean that on-site health care must be provided; but if health problems develop in the workplace, the employer is expected to get medical help to treat them and their causes.

To fulfill the above requirements, the following actions should be considered:

- Develop an emergency medical procedure for handling injuries, transporting ill or injured workers, and notifying medical facilities with a minimum of confusion. Posting emergency telephone numbers is a good idea.
- Survey the nearby medical facilities and make arrangements for them to handle routine and emergency cases. Cooperative agreements possibly could be made with larger plants having medical personnel.
- Install a procedure for reporting injuries and illnesses that is understood by all employees.

- If the business location is remote from medical facilities, ensure that at least one trained first-aid person is available at all times. Arrangements for training this person can be made through the local Red Cross Chapter, an insurance company, the local safety council, and other service organizations.
- Check battery-charging stations, maintenance operations, laboratories, heating and ventilating operations, and any corrosive-material areas to make sure they have the required eye wash facilities and showers.
- Consider retaining a local doctor or an industrial nurse on a part-time or as-needed basis to advise in medical and first-aid planning.

It is worthwhile to maintain records of safety activities, such as policy statements, training sessions for management and employees, safety and health meetings, information distributed to employees, and medical arrangements. Maintaining essential records: (1) demonstrates sound business management as supporting proof for credit applications, for showing "good faith" in reducing any proposed penalties from OSHA inspections, for insurance audits, etc., and (2) affords an efficient means to review safety and health activities for better control of operations and to plan improvements.

First Aid and Medical Assistance: A medical and first-aid system should be ready for use when needed. Large manufacturing companies usually have the necessary systems and services. However, most small businesses do not have an organized medical and first-aid system, nor are they expected to have one. But all businesses are required to have the following:

- In the absence of a nearby infirmary, clinic, or hospital that can be used for the emergency treatment of injured employees, the employer must ensure that a person or persons be trained and available to render first aid. Adequate first-aid supplies must be readily available for emergency use.
- When the eyes or body of any employee may be exposed to injurious corrosive materials, suitable equipment for quick drenching or flushing of the eyes and body must be provided in the work area for immediate emergency use. Employees should be trained in using the equipment.

Employee Involvement: A properly conducted safety program is an ongoing activity designed to foster an on-the-job awareness and acceptance of safety and health responsibility by every employee. Employee awareness, acceptance, and participation are vitally important in determining the effectiveness of a safety program.

Large companies have the advantages of size, including in-house expertise and a number of resources. They can, however, tend to become impersonal unless special attention is paid to retaining "the human touch." Small companies have inherent advantages in the area of safety and health, such as close contact with the employees, a specific acquaintance with the problems of the whole business, and usually a low labor turnover. Small business owners and managers often have developed a personal relationship of loyalty and cooperation which can be built upon when establishing a safety program.

Some tips for persuading employees to accept their responsibilities for safety and health are as follows:

- The manager must be convinced of the need to have a safe and healthful workplace. If management acts without conviction, the employees sense it quickly.
- Each employee needs to know that management is sincerely interested in preventing accidents. Realistically, it is known that accidents may occur, but it is also recognized that almost all accidents can be prevented.
- Genuine effort should be made to "sell" the idea to employees, and to impress upon them that job safety and health is a condition of their employment. It is, of course, essential to be reasonable and rational in communicating the safety requirements and benefits.
- A job safety analysis (JSA) should be prepared for all jobs and work stations, and a commitment

should be undertaken to implement the JSA program's principal findings.

- A start should be evident; some specific safety activities should be initiated. While it may not be possible to anticipate all of the job-related hazards, the necessity for developing sound safety practices should begin to be recognized. Employees should become aware that management shares their concerns and is interested in doing something about safety problems.
- Safety pamphlets should be displayed on a workplace safety bulletin board; safety and health-related posters and information devices maintain awareness of the concern for on-the-job safety.
- All employees should become involved in inspecting, detecting, and correcting. Employees should participate in planning, and they should be asked for suggestions and assistance.
- It is important to let employees know when they are doing a good job, and also when their lack of response to a safety program is unacceptable and is a cause for mutual concern.

Consideration should be given to forming a joint labor-management safety committee. This committee can assist in starting a program and can help maintain interest in the program once it is operating. Committees can be an excellent way of communicating safety and health information. If there are few employees, consideration should be given to rotating them so that all can have an active part in the safety and health programming.

KEY TERMS AND PHRASES _____

Autoclave
Automatic cold and warm forging
Backward extrusion
Bend allowance
Bending
Blow molding
Bulk molding compound (BMC)
Calendaring

Ceramics
Cold extrusion
Cold upsetting
Combination extrusion
Compression molding
Continuous extrusion
Contour bending
Dieless drawing
Direct extrusion
Drawing
Electrohydraulic forming
Electromagnetic forming
Explosive forming
Extruding
Extrusion molding
Flange bending
Heading
High-velocity forging
Hot extrusion
Hot forging
Hydrostatic extrusion
Impact extrusion
Impression die forging
Indirect extrusion
Injection molding
Liquid injection molding
Open-die forging
Parallel-roll straightening
Peen forming
Plastics forming
Plate bending
Powder metallurgy
Power spinning
Pressure bag
Pulforming
Pultrusion
Punching
Radial extrusion
Reaction injection mold (RIM)
Reinforced thermoset plastics
Resin injection
Revolving-arbor straightening
Roll forming
Rotational molding
Scallop height

Shear forming
Shearing
Sheet bending
Spinning
Spray lay-up
Straight bending
Straightening
Stretch bending
Stretch straightening
Structural foam molding
Swaging
Thermoforming
Thermoset plastics
Thick molding compound (TMC)
Transfer molding
Tube spinning
Ultrasonic-activated forming
Ultrasonic drawing
Upsetting
Vacuum bag
Warm extrusion
Warm upsetting
Wet preform

QUESTIONS FOR ADDITIONAL STUDY AND REVIEW

1. Describe the roll forming process.

2. How are roll forming machines classified?

3. Describe the spinning process.

4. What is shear forming?

5. What is tube spinning?

6. Describe the bending process.

7. Describe the straightening process.

8. Describe how to calculate a bend allowance.

9. List three different types of bending.

10. Describe the straightening process.

11. List three different types of straightening.

12. Describe the shearing process.

13. How are shears classified?

14. Describe the punching process.

15. What are the two basic types of punch presses?

16. What does the term *scallop height* mean in punching?

17. Describe the following processes:
   • Drawing
   • Extruding
   • Upsetting

18. What is dieless drawing?

19. Describe the hot extrusion process.

20. List three hot extrusion processes.

21. Distinguish between cold, warm, and hot extrusion.

22. Distinguish between backward and forward extrusion.

23. List four types of cold/warm extrusion.

24. What is upsetting?

25. Describe the swaging process.

26. Describe the following forging processes:
   • Open-die forging
   • Impression-die forging

27. What are the primary applications of automatic cold and warm forging?

28. What are thermoset plastics?

29. Describe thermoset plastics molding.

30. Distinguish between compression and transfer molding.

31. Describe the injection molding process.

32. Describe the extrusion forming process.

33. What is reaction injection molding (RIM)?

34. What are reinforced thermoset plastics?

35. Describe the pultrusion process.

36. Describe the pulforming process.

37. List five low-volume processes used in forming reinforced thermoset plastics.

38. What is resin injection?

39. What is thermoforming?

40. What is blow molding?

41. Describe the following processes:
    - Liquid injection molding
    - Rotational molding
    - Structural foam molding

42. Describe how ceramics are processed.

43. Described how composites are fabricated.

44. What is explosive forming?

45. What is electrohydraulic forming?

46. What is high-velocity forging?

47. What is peen forming?

48. Define the term *powder metallurgy.*

49. List seven key factors in a safety program.

CHAPTER  5

Traditional Casting Processes

MAJOR TOPICS COVERED

- Casting Overview
- Sand-Mold Casting
- Green-Sand Molding
- Dry-Sand Molding
- Shell Molding
- The Full-Mold Process
- Cement Molding
- Vacuum Molding
- Coremaking Processes
- Melting and Pouring
- Cleaning and Finishing
- Heat Treatment
- Inspection
- Finishing

CASTING OVERVIEW

Casting is a manufacturing process in which molten metal is poured or injected and allowed to solidify in a suitably shaped mold cavity. During or after cooling, the cast part is removed from the mold and then processed for delivery.

Casting processes and cast-material technologies vary from simple to highly complex. Material and process selection depends on the part's complexity and function, the product's quality specifications, and the projected cost level.

Castings are parts that are made close to their final dimensions by a casting process. With a history dating back 6000 years, the various casting processes are in a state of continuous refinement and evolution as technological advances are being made.

Casting Mold Elements

In Fig. 5-1, a typical green-sand mold section is depicted to illustrate the various basic elements that are common to most casting processes. In most casting processes, the terms used to describe the molds are the same. Molds are usually, but not always,

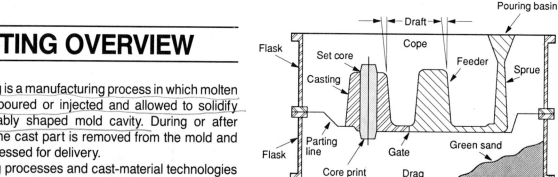

Figure 5-1   Cross section of typical cored casting

made in two halves. Exceptions are the investment casting and coreless casting processes, in which one-piece molds are used, and die casting and permanent or semipermanent-mold casting, which may use molds or dies made up of more than two parts for casting complex shapes.

In most processes, the upper half of the mold is called the cope and the lower half is referred to as the drag. Cores made of sand or metal are placed in the mold cavity to form inner surfaces of the casting. The mold requires a gating system to distribute metal in the mold and risers (liquid reservoirs) to feed the casting as it solidifies. The sprue is the channel, usually vertical, through which the metal enters. A runner, usually horizontal, leads the metal into the mold. The metal leaves the runner through a gate to enter the mold cavity or a riser above or adjacent to the cavity. A riser is a reservoir connected to the cavity to provide liquid metal to the casting to offset shrinkage as the casting solidifies.

General Characteristics

In many applications, castings offer cost and performance advantages because their shape, composition, structure, and properties can be tailored for a specific end product. The precision casting processes also offer near-net-shape economic benefits in materials, labor, and energy usage.

Except for certain high-volume production items, such as automotive parts, cast materials usually are produced in batches or melt-lot quantities that are smaller than those obtained from typical wrought-material production runs; hence, castings may more easily be made to accommodate specific application requirements.

Casting Properties: Castings generally exhibit nondirectional properties. Wrought metals, on the other hand, usually are anisotropic—stronger and tougher in one direction than in another. Some casting processes do, however, provide directional strength properties that can be utilized by part designers and manufacturing engineers to increase performance of the finished part.

In some instances, the properties and performance attainable in cast components cannot be obtained readily by other manufacturing methods. For example:

- Cast iron has desirable wear and damping properties for air-conditioner crankshaft and diesel engine cylinder liner applications.
- Compacted graphite (a recent cast iron alloy development) offers the heat and wear-resisting characteristics of gray iron and the strength approaching nodular iron.
- Cast bearing alloys have a controlled dispersion of lubricating materials.
- High rupture strength superalloy airfoils are made possible by the use of nonmachinable cast alloys with creep resistance superior to that of wrought materials.
- Castings allow the manufacture of parts from alloys that are difficult or impossible to machine or forge, and are especially advantageous for cored internal passages.
- Fine equiaxed, directionally solidified, single-crystal, eutectic structures provide a variety of useful properties made possible by modern casting processes and material technology.

For simple shapes, near-net-shape castings often cannot compete economically with forgings. However, the casting processes offer a design flexibility and a capability for size and configuration complexity that are beyond the usual limits for feasible or economic use of the forging techniques. Castings are best used for complex part geometries—components that would require considerable machining and multipiece assembly if made by other processes.

Mold Considerations: Molds are generally made by surrounding a pattern with a mixture of granular refractory and binder. This mixture may be dry or wet, and the composition varies with the mold and casting materials that are used. The choice of mold material depends on casting quality and quantity requirements, as well as on metal temperature and chemical reactivity.

The mold cavity is designed to be oversize to compensate for volume changes due to liquid-to-solid-phase transformations and thermal contraction. The pattern provides the shape and size of the cavity into which the molten metal is poured. Gates and risers may be attached to the pattern or molded in separately. The casting manufacturer generally uses tapered sections, chills, risers, insulation, and hot tops to provide adequate soundness through directional solidification.

Internal surfaces are formed by casting against cores. Cores are generally made from a similar mold material, but sometimes are made from a material that offers a greater resistance to the physically harsh and chemically reactive environment in the mold cavity before and during solidification. Hollow parts may also be made by one of the coreless casting techniques, such as centrifugal casting and slush casting.

After the binder hardens sufficiently, the pattern is removed. Sometimes special mold coatings are applied to improve the casting surface finish or reduce cleaning costs. A variation of this practice is found in evaporative-pattern (full-mold) casting, in which a shape made from low-density, expanded polystyrene is left in the sand to evaporate when hot metal is poured into the mold. Another variation is the use of permanent molds that may be reused several thousand times.

The mold is such an important aspect of most casting processes that the name of the molding process and the type of mold media are commonly used to identify the processes used to make castings. Examples include no-bake sand-molded steel castings, green sand molded brass castings, and investment-molded nickel-based superalloy castings.

Sand-Mold Casting

Of all the forming processes, sand-mold casting is the most versatile and provides the greatest freedom of design in terms of size, shape, and product quantity. Sand-mold castings can be produced singly or by the millions and in sizes weighing from a fraction of an ounce to hundreds of tons (several grams to hundreds of megagrams).

One of the main advantages of sand-mold casting is the flexibility it permits in shaping the part so that the imposed load is distributed evenly throughout the part for minimum stress concentration. When well-designed castings are used, stress concentrations can be reduced as much as 50%, and in many cases significant increases in service life and strength can be achieved.

Design Considerations

To ensure maximum dispersal of stress, minimum stress concentration, and the most effective configuration for the function of a given design, the following guidelines are applicable to sand-mold castings:

1. External corners should be rounded with radii that are 10-20% of the section thickness (see Fig. 5-2). Rounded corners increase resistance of ductile metals to fatigue rupture, increase static strength of gray iron in bending by 4-7%, and increase gray iron's deflection by 10-20%. Rounding of corners is also the most efficient method of decreasing, or eliminating, chilled edges in gray-iron castings. If a notation to round all external corners is included in the part drawing, the patternmaker must provide for rounded corners at partings and at core prints.
2. Radii equal to the thickness of the smaller section are used when sections of dissimilar size are joined or when L or T junctions are used. This proportioning provides significant increases in resistance to fatigue stresses in all metals and in resistance to static stresses in gray iron (see Figs. 5-3 and 5-4). A radius equal to the section

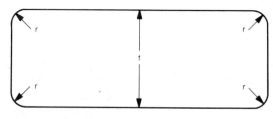

Figure 5-2 Sand-casting external corner radii guideline: r = 0.10 to 0.20t

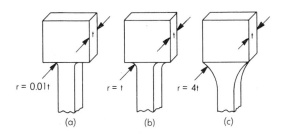

Figure 5-3   Sand-casting fillet radii comparison for stress endurance and fatigue strength

C or U section does not have properties about the X axis (70-90% of the I section) that are as good as those of the tubular section, yet shows even better properties about the Y axis than does the tubular section.

5. The largest possible radii should be used with L junctions or when joining sections with slightly varying sectional moduli. Radii of ten or more times the thickness of the section can be used.

thickness, as shown in Fig. 5-3, *b*, has a 40-50% higher endurance limit than a sharp corner, as shown in view *a*. A further increase in fillet radius to 4t, as shown in view *c*, increases the endurance limit to 120% more than that of view *a*. Figure 5-4 shows the average fatigue life of ⅝″ (16 mm) thick sections with fillets stressed in tension to a maximum fiber stress of approximately 50,000 psi (345 MPa).

3. Tapered sections and irregular sections should conform to stress patterns, particularly in bending, as illustrated in Fig. 5-5. The section modulus at the plane of maximum stress *AA* is five times greater with the tapered connecting member (view *b*) than with the straight connecting member (view *a*). This increase in section modulus decreases maximum fiber stress in bending by 60%. The lower stress concentration at *AA* in design *b* decreases maximum stress even more and is particularly important in fatigue loading.

4. For complex loads, tubular and reinforced C sections should be used rather than standard I, H, and channel sections to obtain improved load-bearing capabilities (see Fig. 5-6). For a given weight and overall size, the tubular section has moments of inertia and section moduli about the X axis that are 9-17% greater than those of the standard I section. The tubular section also has design properties about the Y axis that are 140-170% greater than those of the I section. This significant increase in properties makes the tubular section ideal for complex loading. The reinforced

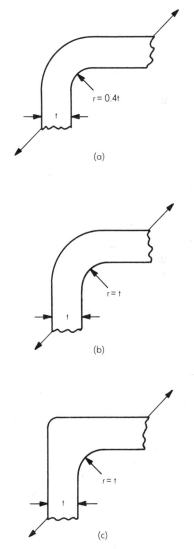

Figure 5-4   Average fatigue life of cast fillets

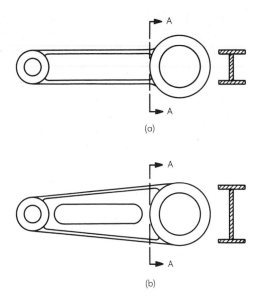

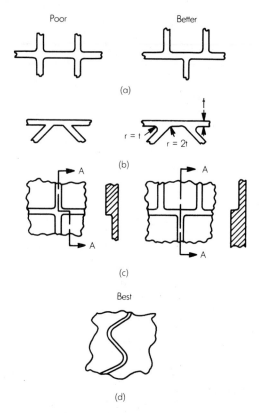

Figure 5-7   Casting stiffness can be improved by streamlining the cross sections

Figure 5-5   Tapered sections increase the section modulus and fatigue strength of castings

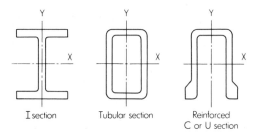

Figure 5-6   Tubular and reinforced sections are used in castings designed to sustain complex loads

6. Complex sections such as X, V, Y, K, and X-T junctions should be simplified to staggered T junctions and, if possible, to corrugated sections, as illustrated in Fig. 5-7. As shown in view *a*, X junctions should be simplified to staggered T junctions; and as shown in view *b*, V, Y, and K junctions should be streamlined. The X-T junctions should be staggered to T-T junctions as shown in view *c*, and if possible, stiffness should be obtained with corrugated sections such as shown in view *d* rather than with rib-stiffened plates as in *c*.

7. Ribs should be eliminated entirely, if at all possible, particularly those stressed in tension. Corrugated or U sections should be used instead (see Fig. 5-8).

Strength of castings can be ensured by specifying minimum hardness, generally Brinell hardness. Many reports of low casting strength properties can be attributed to improper sampling, in which only the very centers of the cast sections were tested, with as much as 50-80% of the cast sections removed by machining.

If machine finishing requirements specify that less than 50% of the original cast section can be removed by machining from both sides of the section, then the physical properties of ferrous castings will approach the properties of classical test specimens.

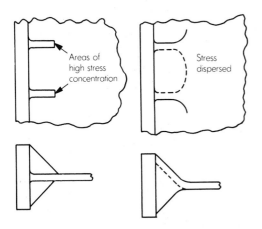

Figure 5-8   Stress concentrations are avoided by using U-shaped or corrugated sections

Maximum physical and mechanical properties in nonferrous castings are usually obtained with special chilling techniques.

Practically all metals are available as castings, and some metals, such as gray iron and some of the superalloys that are not forgeable, can be formed only by casting. There are, on the other hand, some immiscible alloys that cannot be cast, and these can be formed only by powder metallurgy techniques.

Green-Sand Molding

More than 20 million product tons of castings are produced annually in the United States, and more than 90% of this foundry product is cast in sand molds, primarily green-sand molds (80%). In green-sand molding, a mold is formed around a pattern with sand-clay-water mixtures which may contain other additives. The molding medium is readily compacted; and when the pattern is removed, the compacted mass retains a reverse of the pattern's shape.

The molding mixture is formulated to withstand the heat and pressures generated as the mold is filled with molten metal. Almost all commercial castings weighing up to 500 lb (227 kg) are cast in green sand because of the preferred quality, production capability, and relatively low cost of this process. Comparatively few castings of this size and weight are produced by other casting methods.

Among the products made by green-sand molding are automotive castings such as cast-iron cylinder blocks, connecting rods, crankshafts, and differential housings. Fluid-transmission castings and plumbing castings and fittings are almost entirely produced by green-sand molding.

The railroad industry is a large consumer of steel castings produced by this method, and much of the machinery and transportation industries' equipment and components are made from cast steel, gray iron, ductile iron, and malleable iron; and from aluminum, brass, bronze, or other nonferrous castings produced in green sand.

There are a variety of ways in which castings, even the simplest types, can be made in green sand. The selection of pattern equipment, which to a large extent determines the moldmaking technique to be used, is predicated principally on production quantities. The cost of a pattern for very limited bench-scale production is relatively low, but the production costs are high. The man-hours required to produce a ton of castings ready for shipment can vary from as many as 250 man-hours to as few as 10 man-hours with green-sand castings. Production can be accomplished almost entirely by hand labor or by practically full automation. Moldmaking equipment now in use is capable of producing more than 300 molds per hour. The type of automated equipment to be used depends largely on the type and size of the casting to be produced. Although most of the automated systems use flasks, flaskless molding has found wide acceptance in industry.

Dry-Sand Molding

The term *dry-sand molding* refers to the method of molding in a sand mold that has been dried after the pattern has been removed. This method is used mainly for large castings weighing up to 100 tons (91 metric tons). The drying process increases the strength of the molding sand many times. This additional strength is needed to withstand the higher static pressures of the liquid metal when casting heights are measured in feet (meters). Occasionally, the more rigid walls of dry-sand molds are used in conjunction with precision patterns to obtain more accurate casting dimensions. Generally, the dimensional tolerances and finish stock of clay-bonded, dried-mold castings are smaller than the average tolerances and finish stock for green-sand mold castings.

Molds can be dried in an oven at approximately 450°F (232°C), or they can be dried by portable heaters. A widely used variation of this method is skin drying, in which the mold surface is dried only to a depth of from ⅛ to 1″ (3 to 25 mm) or slightly more. This variation is used largely to dry a mold surface that has been washed or blackened with a powder refractory suspended in liquid to improve the mold's surface finish. Some dry-sand molds are an assembly of cores that are bonded with clay, cement, sodium silicate, or any of the resin and oil bonds used for cores. The cores are baked or hardened before assembly.

Shell Molding

The shell molding process is used when extreme dimensional accuracy and precise duplication of intricate shapes are the principal requirements. Basically the method consists of the following steps:

1. A metal pattern (or several patterns) is placed on a metal plate.
2. The pattern is coated with a mixture of fine sand and phenolic resin, 4-6 lb (1.8-2.7 kg) of resin to each 100 lb (45 kg) of sand.
3. The pattern is heated and the resin is allowed to melt to the specified thickness.
4. The resin is cured.
5. The excess sand is dumped.
6. The hardened mold is stripped from the pattern.

The resultant "shell" duplicates the pattern in reverse, with the shape of the pattern forming either a cavity or a projection in the shell. If the shape to be cast is such that one half duplicates the other, then one pattern may be used for both shells. The two shells can then be joined with a phenolic-resin paste or mechanical joiners to form a mold cavity that holds the molten metal and reproduces the shape of the casting desired. When the shape of the casting is unsymmetrical, two patterns must be prepared and, subsequently, two shells must be produced and joined to form the proper mold cavity. If the casting requires internal cavities, sand cores can be placed within the shell mold.

Patterns for shell molds are generally made of iron or steel, although aluminum can be used for limited-quantity production. The metal that is used is largely determined by the degree of casting accuracy specified and the number of castings to be produced. Iron and steel patterns provide greater dimensional accuracy than aluminum patterns, but aluminum patterns are generally more economical.

In casting larger and heavier parts, it is necessary to back up a shell mold, usually by placing it upright in a metal box and filling the space behind it with steel shot. This reinforces the shell and prevents it from breaking up under lateral pressure of the cast metal. After the casting has been poured and has hardened, the shell is broken away and the casting is ready for cleaning and machining, if needed.

Shell molding can be used to form almost any shape—small pipes, camshafts, bushings, spacers, valve bodies, brackets, manifolds, bearing caps, gears, and shafts. The size and weight of the casting and of the shell mold are usually the limiting factors of shell molding applications. Casting sizes of more than 20-24″ (500-600 mm) are considered large for shell molding. However, this process lends itself to the incorporation of more than one pattern on a single plate, and plates with as many as 12 patterns are commonplace.

Shell molding offers dimensional accuracy up to 0.003-0.004″ (0.08-0.10 mm). This degree of accuracy is often superior to that attainable with either green or dry-sand molding, although it cannot match the accuracy of the permanent-mold process or the precision of investment casting methods.

The Full-Mold Process

The full-mold or cavityless process (also known as the evaporative-pattern process) is a method of making metal castings by the use of expanded polystyrene foam patterns that eliminate the need for traditional mold cavities. Basically, the process consists of embedding the foam patterns in sand and then pouring the casting metal directly into the foam. This vaporizes the polystyrene and leaves a casting that duplicates the original pattern (see Fig. 5-9). Since the patterns are the exact size and shape of the casting, there is no need for the patternmaker or molder to think in mirror images as with the conventional moldmaking methods.

More significantly, the process eliminates the need for draft allowances, cores, coreboxes, parting lines, and many conventional foundry operations. The reduced costs that result can make full-mold castings competitive with weldments. It is often more economical to pour metal into foam patterns made from cut-out and glued sheets of expanded polystyrene than to cut out and weld steel plates. In addition, many part shapes that would normally be made of steel (to meet welding requirements) can be made satisfactorily of iron at reduced costs.

Since its introduction (about 1960), the full-mold process has produced millions of tons of castings; and some foundries produce over a thousand tons of these castings each month. Although a pattern is required for each casting, expanded polystyrene patterns are more economical than wood patterns and consequently are widely used for large, single-unit castings. In these cases, the foam patterns are fabricated by hand. If multiple castings are needed, they can be assembled by production-line techniques.

Cement Molding

Sand molds using a cement binder are probably the most durable of all the sand-process molds. Cement molding, also called the Randupson process, is used to form large molds for ship stools and other ship parts, and for ingots.

Cement molds are made of washed and graded silica sand to which is added 10% Portland cement mixed with 4-5% (and sometimes more) water. This mixture can be mulled like a green-sand mixture and soon sets to produce an air-dried mold of great strength which may be stored for long periods without deterioration.

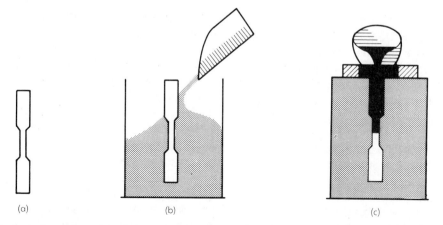

(a)   (b)   (c)

Figure 5-9   Steps in the full-mold casting process: The polystyrene pattern (a) is buried in sand (b) and vaporized by molten metal (c)

Two disadvantages of cement molding are that (1) once the sand-cement mixture is mulled, it must be quickly formed around the pattern before the cement sets and (2) cement is much more expensive than green sand or dry sand for molding. The chief advantage of cement molding, maximum mold-wall rigidity, can also be a disadvantage with some shapes and metals that are subject to hot tearing.

Vacuum Molding

The vacuum molding method (V-Process) is a molding process in which the sand is held in place in the mold by vacuum. The mold halves are covered with a thin sheet of plastics to retain the vacuum. This is a licensed process with the North American rights being owned by the Herman-Sinto V-Process Corporation. Tilghman Wheelabrator possesses the rights in the United Kingdom. The license is purchased outright, and a royalty fee is paid for each ton of product shipped for sale.

The licensor designs, engineers, and manufactures equipment for making vacuum molds, but it is not imperative that the foundry buy the equipment. Some plants design and build their own equipment or buy from a third source. The licensor maintains a technical and service staff to aid and assist the foundries in producing castings by this method. Following are some of the salient points of the method.

Process Description: Patterns are made in the usual manner; however, because they are not subject to the jolting and abrasive actions of sand, they do not have to be constructed as strongly as for conventional sand molding. The patterns can be distorted by the negative pressures, so they must be accurately supported in a pattern carrier to withstand the stresses. The pattern carrier is airtight and is evacuated by a connecting line at certain stages in the process.

There is also a connection to a positive air supply. Patterns and mounting boards are vented by various methods—usually by core box screens. The placement of gates and risers is similar to conventional methods. Experience indicates that it is not always

necessary to use bottom entry tile gates. Simple parting-line gates also produce a clean, sound casting. However, there is one additional feature that must be included in the pattern rigging—communicators.

The communicators are vents of "flow-offs" that have a greater diameter than the sprue and should be located at the uppermost places in the mold cavity. The communicators maintain the pressure differential necessary for mold integrity. Gases are created and exhausted through the communicator. As the hot metal rises in the mold cavity, a portion of film above the metal line is vaporized, causing a vacuum leak. At this point, air enters the mold cavity through the communicators to maintain atmospheric pressure. The difference in pressure between the mold sand and the cavity and exterior surfaces keeps the mold and pattern together.

Coremaking Processes

Cores are needed to create the recesses, undercuts, and interior cavities that are often a part of castings. The sands, binders, methods, and equipment used to make these cores are described in this section, with the exception of those for shell cores, which are discussed in the previous section on shell molding. The processes described here may also be used in the production of molds as well as cores.

Oil-Oxygen Process: The oil-oxygen process is based on the oxidation and polymerization of a combination of oils containing chemical additives which, when activated by an oxygen-bearing material, gel or set in a predetermined time. More precisely, the drying oils absorb oxygen by auto-oxidation, isomerize to the conjugated form, and then polymerize to the solid state. When mixed with sand and an activator, the oil provides cores that have excellent dimensional stability, uniformity in hardness, and nondeforming properties. The oxygen-oil either eliminates or reduces the need for ramming, rodding for support, and long oven curing. The oxidation process is accelerated by metallic driers, by light and heat, and by the oxidation decomposition products that are formed concurrently.

The resulting core has better physical properties than it would have if it were made by conventional methods, and is ready for casting many hours sooner. When the finished casting is cooled and removed from the flask, the core simply collapses and pours out, eliminating the need to remove sand forcibly from recessed areas.

There are two main limitations to the oil-oxygen process. First, the sand mixture has a short bench life. Once the mix sets, it is no longer usable. Secondly, the process is limited to core production that normally does not exceed six to eight cores per box in an eight-hour period, thus lending itself to job work rather than production runs.

Carbon Dioxide Process:

In the carbon dioxide (CO_2) process, clean, dry sand is mixed with a solution of sodium silicate and is rammed or blown into the corebox. When this mixture is gassed for several seconds with CO_2 gas, it forms a silica gel which binds the sand grains into a strong, solid form. Additional hardening of the resulting core may be carried out by baking at about 400°F (204°C), but baking is usually not necessary. The core is normally ready for use as soon as a suitable refractory coating has been applied.

Cores that are CO_2 gassed may be used to form all the usual alloys in a wide range of applications and sizes. A major application is the production of cores for steel, iron, aluminum, and copper-based alloy castings. Tolerances of CO_2 cores are equivalent to tolerances of cores developed by other processes.

Carbon dioxide consumption is an important economic factor in the CO_2 process. Not only is overuse of the gas costly in high-volume production, but extensive overgassing of cores may cause them to be broken easily and may reduce their shelf life. Any method of passing the CO_2 through the corebox may be used as long as a thorough combination of the gas with the binder in all corners and crevices of the core is ensured.

The CO_2 process corebox may be filled either by hand ramming or by blowing. Because the core does not need to be removed from the box before it has set, core driers and ovens are not needed and tolerances may be improved. Currently, there is no method of recovering the used sodium silicate sand mixture. Thus, the CO_2 process is impractical for the production of large molds.

Coreboxes for CO_2 process cores are usually made of metal or plastics. Most wood varnishes used on wooden coreboxes are attacked by the sodium silicate. If wood boxes must be used, they should be protected by an application of a varnish or silicone lacquer that is resistant to the effects of the binder.

Furan No-Bake System:

The development of the furan no-bake system is an outgrowth of research on the oil-oxygen process aimed at reducing or eliminating the need for oven baking. Among its advantages are a simplified sand mix (resin, activator, and sand), excellent flowability, and reduced rodding (high tensile strength restricts needed rodding to lifting hooks only). In addition, only semiskilled coremakers are needed, less core and mold finishing is required, hardness throughout the core is uniform, exact dimensions are attainable, cores are better fitting, and better shakeout is possible. The need for rough cleaning is reduced, machining and layout costs are lower, the need for oven baking is reduced or eliminated, and thermal cracks in the cores are absent.

No-bake binders are materials that convert from liquid to solid at room temperatures. It would be misleading to say that these materials never require oven drying or curing, since many cores cannot be cast successfully without some drying, usually because of the configuration of the casting and the type and temperature of the metal poured.

Furan is a generic term denoting the basic structure of a class of chemical compounds. The resins used in the no-bake system are composed of furfural alcohol, urea, and formaldehyde. When catalyzed with acids, these synthetic liquid resins form a tough, resinous film. The reaction is exothermic and forms a thermosetting resin. The temperature and type of sand, the speed and type of muller or mixer, the binder formulation, and the type and amount of activator used influence the speed of reaction.

Oil No-Bake Process:

A significant advancement in binder development for medium to large castings, the oil no-bake process implements a synthetic-oil binder which, when mixed with basic sands and activated chemically, produces cores that can be cured at room temperature. This binder can be used either as a fast-baking oil-oxygen binder or as a substitute for the furan no-bake resin.

When compared with the oil-oxygen or the furan no-bake processes, the oil no-bake process offers optimum flowability, better depth of set, faster baking at reduced temperatures, easier draw, and lower production costs. The oil no-bake process can be used with all types of mullers and mixers; good castings are assured as long as the sand is clean and dry and well mixed with the oil no-bake ingredients.

Cores made with the oil no-bake process generally can be drawn with greater assurance of a complete set than those made with the oil-oxygen or furan no-bake processes, because the polymerization reaction results in a complete and uniform setting of the sand mass.

Phenolic Core Binders:
The trend in the foundry industry is toward increased use of room temperature curing binders to make cores and molds by cold pressing techniques. Recent developments in phenolic no-bake technology make this binder system an economical choice for a variety of casting applications.

Acid-catalyzed binders. When mixed with sand, the phenolic-based (phenol formaldehyde) acid-catalyzed binders undergo an exothermic condensation reaction to form a cured polymer. Produced by reacting phenol with formaldehyde, phenolic-based resins are subject to autopolymerization reaction at ambient or slightly higher temperatures. It is recommended that this type of binder be stored at temperatures of 80°F (27°C) or lower. Phenolic resins cannot be used with phosphoric acid, but they work well with the stronger sulfonated products such as exlene sulfonic (XSA), tulene sulfonic (TSA), and benzene sulfonic (BSA).

The curing characteristics of acid-catalyzed resins, as well as other no-bake systems, are typically monitored through the use of compressive strength cure curves, with the work and strip time defined as the time required for the sand mix to develop 1 psi (7 kPa) and 20 psi (140 kPa) compressive strength, respectively.

Sand mixes having compressive strengths approaching 1 psi lack the flowability needed to produce dense cores or molds. Likewise, 20 psi represents the point at which the sand mix has reached sufficient strength to be drawn from the pattern or corebox without sag or distortion. Ideally, a no-bake resin would have a work/strip time approaching one.

Urethane binders. The urethane binders fall into two categories: alkyd and phenolic. The alkyd types are actually three-part systems consisting of alkyd resin, metal driers, and/or amine catalysts and isocyanate. These binders are characterized by deep-setting curing properties because the urethane reaction does not produce detrimental by-products that may retard the curing process.

Two characteristics distinguish phenolic urethane binders from other no-bake binders: (1) the work/strip time ratio is typically on the order of 0.80 to 1, and (2) the reaction produces no by-products that affect cure rate. The phenolic binders consist of three components: phenolic resin, isocyanate, and amine-based catalysts. A typical silica sand mix is made with equal parts of phenolic and isocyanate ingredients and 2% catalyst.

The sand surface, chemistry, temperature, and moisture content have an effect on the cure of phenolic urethane resins. However, unlike acid-catalyzed binder systems, small fluctuations in sand temperature do not cause significant changes in curing properties. Moisture content should be maintained below 0.2% of sand weight.

Phenolic urethane no-bake binders are generally recognized as state of the art in chemically bonded sands. As stated previously, curing is achieved by the reaction of a phenolic polyol with a polymeric isocyanate in the presence of a base catalyst. This resin system exhibits excellent working properties and uniform deep setting. Most cores or molds develop strength rapidly and can be poured within an hour after stripping.

Microwave Curing:
The growing use of fast-reacting sand binders and the improvements in output of core and moldmaking equipment have led to a need for new technology in other foundry operations. Most cores and molds must be coated and post-

baked and often must be assembled by being glued together. The capability for rapid production of cores and molds must be matched with increased production rates in subsequent operations so that final casting can be accomplished in the least time.

Microwave principle. Microwave technology is being applied to foundry core heating and curing. When an electromagnetic wave is propagated in a heatable dielectric material, its energy is converted to heat. In the foundry field, water is a major dielectric material that can be heated by microwave energy.

The water molecules consist of hydrogen and oxygen atoms arranged so that the molecule is electrically neutral. The electrical charges within the molecule have a dipole moment and are said to be polar. An electrical field exerts a twisting force that attempts to align the molecules with the field.

When the direction of the electrical field is reversed, the molecules attempt to reverse their orientation. However, in doing so, frictional forces created by the molecules' rubbing together must be overcome and energy is dissipated as heat. Friction generates heat, and the dielectric material becomes hot.

Dielectric materials. In addition to water, other good, heatable dielectric materials used in foundries include phenolic resins of all types, furan hotbox resins, urethane no-bakes, and all the inorganic binder systems. Green sand is very heatable due to its water content and carbon impurities. Reactivity of the binders increases as the temperature rises. Microwave heating can raise the temperature of the binder to the point at which its exothermic property carries the curing reaction through completion.

Advantages. While initial microwave equipment costs are high, the following advantages merit consideration in some applications for processing cores and molds.

- Speed of processing yields increased throughput.
- Cores and molds are processed at reduced temperatures, facilitating handling.
- Low core temperature eliminates sand binder thermoplasticity problems.
- Complete removal of water from cores and molds reduces casting defects.
- It is compatible with low-cost, hot melt adhesives.

- Elimination of separate core glue curing cycle is possible.
- New microwave sand binders can be used that can be water-based and nonpolluting and that require lower cost coreblowers and coreboxes.
- Processing is effectively controlled due to uniform heating and accurate instrumentation.
- Energy savings can be made.

Melting and Pouring

Changes in melting and pouring practices have resulted from state and federal pollution-abatement regulations, but have no effect on the finished casting. The most significant change has resulted from the air-emission regulation, which has made it necessary to replace cupola melting with electric melting of gray iron. The quality of the iron is the same for both, but the costs of controlling air emissions from a cupola are often many times higher than the costs of controlling those from an electric furnace.

Melting Methods: As far as the user is concerned, the differences are negligible between the various electric melting methods—direct arc, indirect arc, and high- and low-frequency induction. Each method is suited to a particular application, depending upon the type of metal to be melted, refractory life, and fume-control requirements. When properly operated, all these methods can provide satisfactory results.

The direct-arc electric process is almost universally used to melt carbon and low-alloy steel for castings. The open-hearth, converter, and crucible processes are practically extinct. However, the argon-oxygen decarburization (AOD) process is gaining acceptance for melting of both low- and high-alloy steels due to the ability to control sulfur and gas levels and to minimize oxidation losses of chromium. The basic oxygen melting process has not been adapted to cast steels. High-frequency induction melting is used for high-alloy steels and especially for very low-carbon steels with less than 0.10% carbon; however, it is at an economic disadvantage with the direct-arc method for carbon and low-alloy steels. Low-frequency induction melting of steel is impractical because of refractory problems.

The electric melting method is advantageous for melting ductile iron because of its ability to produce low-sulfur iron (iron with less than 0.05% sulfur). However, the basic cupola produces even less sulfur than the acid electric process. Acid cupola iron can be desulfurized to give comparable low-sulfur iron. Again, airborne pollution is usually the controlling factor determining the melting process; equally acceptable metal can be produced by any of the processes.

The same pollution and economic factors are the chief determinants in the melting processes for malleable iron. Many nonferrous metals are melted by some form of the crucible process as well as by electricity. In most cases metal quality depends on skilled operators, not equipment variations.

Pouring Methods: Only one significant exception (centrifugal force) exists to the stationary, nonpressurized pouring of sand-mold castings because any appreciable increase in pressure over that imposed by the atmosphere and gravity only forces the metal into the interstices between the grains of sand. No increase in density can be obtained in a static sand mold above that obtained by directional solidificaton.

Centrifugal force, however, assists in producing a large volume of iron pipe by spinning a sand or metal mold about its horizontal axis. It is not generally recognized that in using this process, tubular shapes with wall thicknesses from a fraction of an inch to several inches and diameters measured in feet are economically produced in practically any metal. The designer has more freedom with centrifugal tubular castings than would be possible if these shapes were to be formed by a wrought process.

Cleaning and Finishing

The cleaning of castings is a critical cost factor to both the producer and the user. With costs necessarily calculated to four-decimal accuracy, it is important that the producer and user specifically define what a cleaned or finished casting should entail before signing any purchase agreement. Some of the items to be specified are: (1) finish; (2) size; (3) locators; (4) allowable ranges in hardness, chemistry, and gate and riser tolerances; (5) weight; (6) amount of machining; (7) surface condition, including oil, paint, and degree of oxidation; (8) impregnation; (9) type of cleaning medium; (10) types of repairs; (11) procedure for repairing; and (12) acceptable repaired locations.

These and many other items that apply to special alloys must be considered. Various trade associations have established standards for each alloy system. What may be a workable system for one producer may be beyond the capabilities and equipment of a competitor, and unit costs between producers could differ appreciably.

The producer should be able to provide a schematic process line layout that indicates whether the casting is accurately located for finishing. In some instances, it may be advantageous to do some preliminary machining, locating, etc., at considerable savings to the purchaser.

The line process selected for cleaning depends on whether the alloy is tough, ductile, or brittle. Proper gating design and mechanical flagging allow easy removal of gates to within ⅛″ (3 mm) or less on small, brittle, mechanical-mixture alloys such as gray iron. The same problem in ductile brass, aluminum, steel, and other alloys means that gates must be sawed, flame cut, or press trimmed before the casting goes to the next step in the process. In either jobbing or production foundries, cleaning can usually be divided into two categories—rough cleaning in the foundry and finishing in a special foundry area (the cleaning or finishing room). It is recommended that as much metal as possible be removed in the foundry to prevent double and triple handling.

Castings are hauled from the foundry to the cleaning area by a variety of means. In production foundries, they are usually conveyed; in job shops, batch handling is normally used to prevent mixing. The hard, brittle alloys, with their gates and risers occasionally removed, go directly to some type of surface-cleaning device. The cleaning methods control the final finish to a great degree. The general methods used are (1) wire brushing, (2) shotblasting, (3) tumbling, and (4) chemical treating.

The following are a few considerations for each process.

1. Wire brushing:
   - Type of brush—manual or power-driven.
   - Brush material.
   - Size of wire in the brush.
   - Size and shape of the casting.
   - Casting production rate.
2. Shotblasting:
   - Whether wet or dry.
   - Whether air-blown or centrifugal.
   - Size, hardness, and shape of casting.
   - Size and type of blasting material—metallic, nonmetallic, organic.
   - Finish desired.
   - Effect on physical and mechanical properties.
   - Whether continuous, by batch, or programmed.
3. Tumbling:
   - Whether wet or dry.
   - Barrel-loading design.
   - Abrasive composition and geometry.
   - Finish desired.
   - Size and shape of the casting.
4. Chemical treating:
   - Type of chemical—acid, basic, or salt.
   - Size of the casting.
   - Contamination of the casting surface.

With the emphasis on pollution abatement, many foundries clean castings prior to grinding and trimming. This reduces excessive gassing or pinholing in some melting processes and results in less slag and effluent. The next step involves cleaning the gate and riser areas to meet specified tolerances. This varies with the type of alloy and the degree of cleaning the casting has already received up to this point.

Heat Treatment

Depending on specifications, the heat treatment of castings may or may not precede final inspection. The following is a breakdown of the two generally applied heat-treatment methods for castings.

1. Softening treatments:
   - Full annealing.
   - Process annealing.
   - Spheroidizing.
   - Solution annealing.
   - Isothermal annealing.
   - Malleabilizing annealing.
   - Tempering.
   - Normalizing.
2. Hardening treatments:
   - Quenching—brine, water, or oil.
   - Precipitation hardening.
   - Flame hardening.
   - Induction hardening.
   - Austempering.
   - Marquenching.
   - Martempering.

Inspection

Final inspection depends upon the agreement between the producer and the user. Inspection can be very simple or extremely complicated, depending upon the end use of the casting. Aerospace requirements usually call for high-integrity castings; therefore, they involve extensive destructive, environmental, and nondestructive testing methods.

Finishing

Castings can be finished in a number of ways by a variety of painting, plating, and coating processes. However, the specific alloy used and the particular applications are the main determinants in selecting the finish for the final finished part.

KEY TERMS AND PHRASES _____

Batch handling
Carbon dioxide process
Casting

Cement molding
Centrifugal force
Cope
Coremaking processes
Curing
Dielectric materials
Draft
Drag
Dry-sand molding
Evaporative-pattern process
Feeder
Flask
Flow-offs
Foundry
Full-mold process
Furan no-bake system
Green sand
Green-sand molding
Microwave curing
Oil no-bake process
Oil-oxygen process
Parting line
Pattern
Phenolic core binders
Pouring basin
Resin
Sand-mold casting
Shell molding
V-Process
Vacuum molding

QUESTIONS FOR ADDITIONAL STUDY AND REVIEW _____

1. Define the term *casting*.

2. Define the following casting terms:
   - Draft
   - Drag
   - Cope
   - Flask
   - Feeder
   - Pour basic

3. Describe the sand-mold casting process.

4. Describe green-sand molding.

5. Describe dry-sand molding.

6. Describe shell molding.

7. Describe the full-mold process.

8. What is cement molding?

9. What is vacuum molding?

10. Describe the coremaking process.

11. What is the oil-oxygen process?

12. What is the carbon dioxide process?

13. Describe the furan no-bake system.

14. Describe the oil no-bake process.

15. What are phenolic core binders?

16. What are urethane binders?

17. Explain the principle behind microwave curing.

18. Describe the melting methods used with traditional casting processes.

19. Describe the pouring methods used with traditional casting processes.

20. What items should be specified for cleaning of castings?

21. Explain the two generally applied heat-treatment methods for casting.

22. List four approaches used in cleaning castings.

CHAPTER 6

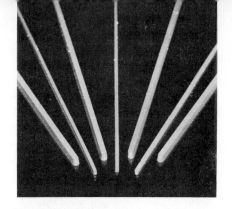

Contemporary Casting and Molding

MAJOR TOPICS COVERED

- Metal-Mold Casting
- High-Pressure Die Casting
- Permanent-Mold Casting
- Centrifugal Casting
- Plaster Molding
- Investment Casting
- Solid-Ceramic Molding
- Ceramic Cores

Advances in casting and molding technology have led to the development of a variety of new processes that do not depend on sand. The more widely used of these are explained in this chapter.

Metal-Mold Casting

In metal-mold casting, molten metal is poured or forced into a mold made entirely of metal or into a mold in which the outer form is made of metal. The principal methods of producing castings in metal molds are high-pressure die casting, permanent and semipermanent-mold casting, low-pressure casting, and centrifugal-mold casting.

A metal-mold casting generally exhibits superior surface finish, close dimensional tolerances, and improved mechanical properties as compared to those of a sand casting. The process can be justified economically when the quantity of castings and the savings in per-piece machining justify the cost of the metal mold and associated equipment. Refinements in mechanical metal-mold cycling that increase output, reduce machine downtime, and decrease the direct labor content have greatly increased the economic return from these casting methods.

Successful metal-mold casting requires a knowledge of (1) melting, cooling, and handling of alloys; (2) metal flow in metal molds and dies; (3) solidification and shrinkage of alloys; (4) correct gating and venting for sound casting structure; (5) tolerances as they affect mold costs and casting dimensions; and (6) required production rates. In addition, knowledge of sound mechanical concepts of mold design and automation is critical.

High-Pressure Die Casting

Die casting has long been recognized as one of the most economical and effective methods of producing moderate to high-volume quantities of near-net-shape components. The primary requirements for producing commercially acceptable high-pressure die castings (referred to hereafter as die castings) are an efficiently operating casting machine; a well-designed and well-constructed die; and a suitable casting alloy. In addition, the product must be designed for production by die casting.

In die casting, molten metal is forced under pressure into metal molds or dies. Necessary equipment consists essentially of the molds and a die-casting machine that holds, opens, and closes the molds or dies. The process is economical for producing castings with complex contours; holes and contours can be cast which would be costly to produce by machining operations. Holes are cast to tolerances that often compare with those of drilled, reamed, or counterbored holes, and surfaces and dimensions of die castings usually require little or no machining or finishing.

Casting Machines: A die-casting machine has four main elements: (1) the die mounting and clamping system, (2) the die, (3) the injection mechanism, and (4) a source of molten metal. The machine frame incorporates a stationary platen (cover) and a movable platen (ejector) to which the die halves are attached. The basic function of the casting machine is to open and close the die and to lock it against the pressure of the molten metal developed by the injection mechanism.

The opening and closing mechanism, which actuates the movable platen, can be pneumatic, mechanical, hydraulic, or a combination of these. The most common method uses compound toggles, with the force supplied by a hydraulic cylinder. Other closing methods are (1) direct hydraulic, (2) wedge-lock hydraulic, (3) cam-lock hydraulic, and (4) mechanical with hydraulic lock.

Die casting machine clamping systems generally are four-bar presses. Solid, one-piece frame machines are used to a lesser degree. Machines are normally rated by the magnitude of the clamping force, generally expressed in tons or kilonewtons. Another method specifies the shot-weight capacity of the injection system.

Two general types of metal injection mechanisms for high-pressure die-casting machines are the hot-chamber type and the cold-chamber type.

Hot-chamber machines. The oldest type of die-casting machine, and the simplest to operate, is the hot-chamber machine. Depending on size, such machines can operate at about 100 shots per hour for castings up to 50 lb (23 kg), or several thousand shots per hour for single-impression castings weighing fractions of an ounce. In the United States, hot-chamber die casting is usually limited to the zinc alloys and, in a minor way, to the lead and tin alloys. In recent years, hot-chamber magnesium has been introduced and is gaining acceptance for certain product applications.

Hot-chamber die-casting machines are limited to use with alloys that do not chemically attack or erode the submerged metal injection system. Aluminum and copper alloys are not suitable for use in the hot-chamber machines (see Fig. 6-1).

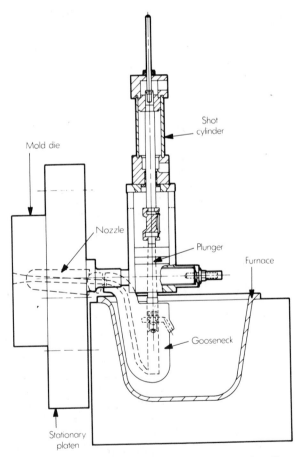

Figure 6-1 Hot-chamber injection system for die-casting machine (Courtesy of Prince Corporation)

Recent developments in hot-chamber machine design provide quicker injection speeds to minimize cavity fill times. At the same time, new injection systems minimize final plunger impact. These features and better process control and gating technique allow for production of castings having reduced cross-sectional thickness.

Thin-wall zinc casting and new, highly integrated automatic machines have given the zinc casting industry the capability to be competitive with alternative metals and plastics.

Cold-chamber machines. In the horizontal configuration commonly used for cold-chamber machines, the pressure chamber is separate from the melting pot and is not heated. Hence, the pressure chamber is not exposed directly to the erosive and thermal characteristics of molten metal. The material, in a liquid form, is injected by a plunger to fill the die cavity. Molten metal from a separate holding furnace is ladled into the cold-chamber sleeve after the die is closed and all cores are locked into position. The hydraulic cylinder ram forces the metal into the die and after solidification, the die is opened and the cores are withdrawn. The ejector mechanism then removes the casting from the movable, or ejector, half of the die (see Fig. 6-2).

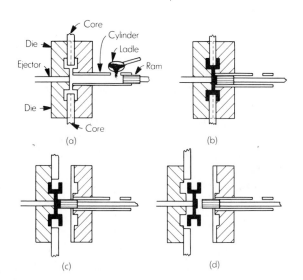

Figure 6-2   Cold-chamber die-casting machine sequence of operations

Another type of cold-chamber machine is the verticast machine wherein molten metal is drawn into a vertical shot chamber by vacuum and is then rammed into the die by a plunger operating from below. This type of machine is used to cast certain aluminum specialty alloys, in addition to the traditional aluminum alloys, and to manufacture radially symmetrical castings and castings requiring minimum porosity and maximum pressure tightness (see Fig. 6-3).

Permanent-Mold Casting

Permanent-mold castings are produced by forcing molten metal, under pressure of a gravity head or a low-pressure feed system, into a static mold consisting of a clamped metal assembly. In permanent-mold casting, the mold cores are also made of metal. Various metals can be cast in permanent molds, but the process is most common for the lighter nonferrous metals. Fig. 6-4 is a permanent-mold casting machine. Fig. 6-5 is a low-pressure permanent-mold casting machine.

Permanent-Mold Casting Production:
The basic steps in the production of a permanent-mold casting are as follows:

1. A general analysis of the casting drawing is made to establish parting lines, draft requirements, gating methods, core requirements, and ejection-pin placement.
2. The mold drawing is prepared to show the cavity and gating dimensions, insert locations, and ejection-pin mechanisms.
3. A master pattern is crafted if the mold is to be cast to size. From this pattern a plaster cast is made. The plaster cast is then cast in the mold material by either a sand-mold or ceramic-mold process.
   If the mold is to be machined to size, a wood pattern of the mold halves is made and finish allowance is given in the areas in which machining is required. A casting is then produced from the wood pattern and is processed to drawing

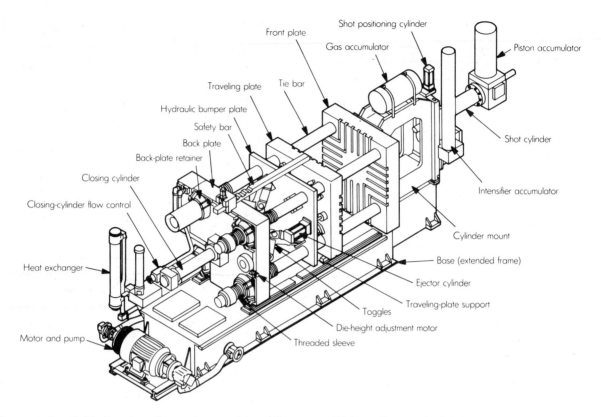

Figure 6-3   Cold-chamber die-casting machine (Courtesy of Prince Corporation)

requirements. Iron or steel blanks can be used as stock items and processed to mold dimensions if the mold is not too complex.

4. After the mold is formed, it is stress-relieved at its approximate operating temperature and any distortion or warpage that appears is corrected.

5. The mold is then heated and coated as described earlier.

6. Metal is poured into the cavity; and after solidification, the casting is ejected. Pouring temperature of the molten metal is critical and, after it is determined for a specific job, should be maintained. The casting cycle, which is determined experimentally, should be held constant since castings tend to sag, warp, or break if they are removed from the mold prematurely. The casting cycle and the casting-metal temperature vary the mold temperature, which determines the quality of the casting.

Melting the casting metal should follow the best practice. No matter how well a mold is constructed and how well a casting operation is carried out, a strong casting cannot be made unless its metal meets the prescribed composition and has been protected from oxidation, contamination, gassing, and overheating.

7. The casting is stacked to cool. Ejected castings are very hot, relatively soft, and easily bent, so racks are normally provided to prevent warpage in the cooling process.

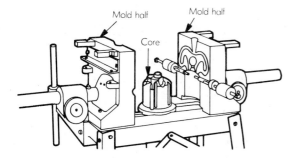

Figure 6-4 Permanent-mold casting machine

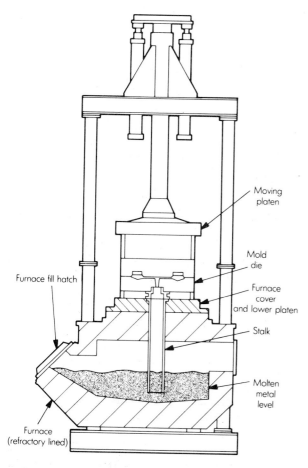

Figure 6-5 Typical low-pressure, permanent-mold casting machine (Courtesy of Prince Corporation)

Centrifugal Casting

Centrifugal castings are made by pouring molten metal into a mold that is being rotated or that starts to rotate at a certain point during pouring. The centrifugal force generated by rotation forces the metal under constant pressure against the interior mold wall until it solidifies. Cylindrical parts are usually the most preferred shapes for the centrifugal-casting processes. Tubular castings produced in permanent molds by the true centrifugal-casting method have higher structural strengths and more distinct cast impressions than castings produced by the static permanent-mold or sand-mold processes.

Metals that can be cast by ordinary static casting methods, including carbon and alloy steels, high-alloy corrosion and abrasion-resistant steels, gray iron, brass, and bronze containing up to 30% lead, aluminum, and magnesium, can be cast centrifugally. In addition many other materials, including glass, plastics, and ceramics, may be centrifugally cast.

Either permanent molds or sand molds may be used for centrifugal casting. The selection of the type of mold is determined by the shape of the casting, the quality desired, and the number of castings to be produced.

Centrifugal-Casting Methods: The three methods of centrifugal casting are true centrifugal casting, semicentrifugal casting, and centrifuge casting.

True centrifugal casting. True centrifugal castings are produced by spinning a mold about its own axis, either vertically or horizontally, to produce a casting that has a straight, uniform inner diameter. The casting may have a more or less symmetrical configuration on its outer contour, and it does not require any center core. Castings produced in this manner have one direction of cooling—from the outside toward the axis of rotation. Thus, the true centrifugal-casting method provides conditions that set up directional solidification to produce castings free from shrinkage—the predominant cause of defective castings. True centrifugal methods are used to produce bearings for electric motors and industrial machinery, cast-iron pipe, alloy-steel pipe and tubing, liners for internal-combustion engines, and other symmetrical parts.

Semicentrifugal casting. Semicentrifugal castings are produced in molds that surround the castings on all sides and are spun about their own axis. Vertical centrifugal-casting machines are normally used in this method. A core is required to form the center of the castings, and directional solidification must be obtained by proper gating of the castings themselves. Typical castings of this type are gear blanks, sheaves, and wheels (see Fig. 6-6).

Centrifuge casting. Centrifuge castings have the widest field of application, since in this type of casting the casting cavities are arranged about the center of rotation like the spokes of a wheel. This permits the production of odd-shaped castings and also allows the accumulation of many castings in one mold. If multiple layers are produced in one mold, the method is called *stack molding*. This method of casting is used in the production of valve bodies, valve bonnets, plugs, yokes, pillow blocks, and a wide variety of other industrial castings (see Figs. 6-7 and 6-8).

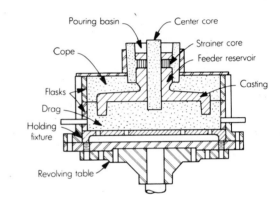

Figure 6-8   Vertical centrifugal-casting machine

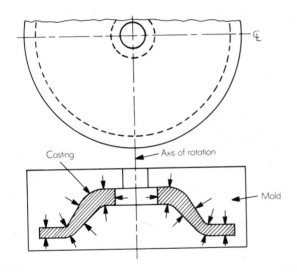

Figure 6-6   Typical semicentrifugal mold and casting

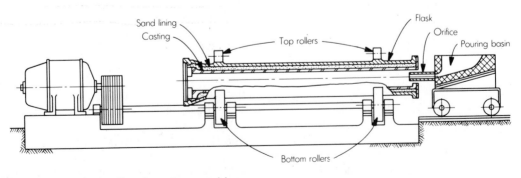

Figure 6-7   Horizontal centrifugal-casting machine

Advantages of Centrifugal Casting: The primary reasons for using centrifugal-casting processes are (1) to obtain better quality castings, (2) to produce castings more economically, and (3) to cast parts that cannot be satisfactorily cast by static methods. These reasons do not necessarily have equal importance in all instances. For example, certain parts are centrifugally cast to increase the yield or to decrease cleaning-room expense without the intent of affecting quality. Thus, improved quality accrues as a bonus.

High yield. Statically poured castings that normally have a yield of 40-55% have been centrifugally cast to attain a yield from 65% to nearly 100%. Centrifugal casting seldom requires feed heads or risers, and even if they are necessary in rare instances, much smaller heads can be used. Cleaning-room costs are therefore considerably reduced.

Density. Centrifugal casting also produces denser castings with physical properties comparable to those of forgings. In static casting, the castings cool from the inside and outside surfaces simultaneously toward the midsection, where impurities are trapped and dendrites forming from both surfaces meet at the center. This sometimes results in the concentration of shrinkage porosity and inclusions at the center of each casting section (centerline of shrinkage).

This leaves a weak, amorphous structure identified as *coring*. The centrifugal-casting action forces all denser impurities in the molten metal to the inside diameter of the casting, where they are easily machined away. A dirty, unsound midsection is therefore avoided, and trapped flaws are not hidden within the casting only to be found after machining has uncovered them. The uniformly dense, fine grain structure which results from centrifugal casting has caused the process to sometimes be called liquid forging.

Strength. In some metals, centrifugal casting improves tensile strength because of the resultant increased density and homogeneity. Dimensions are more uniform, and the castings have equal strength in all directions. They also tend to have finer grain size on their outer diameters, making the centrifugal-casting method preferred for gears, sprockets, and pinions having bearing surfaces that wear. Centrifugal molecular compression on peripheral surfaces, together with the purifying action of the centrifugal force, produces, in effect, a tougher case. Rather than having flow lines parallel to the lines of force, as is characteristic of conventional gear castings, centrifugal castings have no flow lines and the grain structure runs perpendicular to the gear-tooth line of force, an advantage otherwise provided only by precision machining.

Plaster and Ceramic-Mold Casting

The general term *precision casting* is commonly used to categorize the plaster and ceramic-mold casting processes. These processes are characterized by their use of nonmetallic ceramic and plaster mold materials. The materials may be sand or sand-like materials such as aluminosilicates, materials such as gypsum plaster, or highly refractory, proprietary ceramic powders. The binders used in molding these materials range from sodium silicate to complex, proprietary organic silicate formulations. In the case of plaster, a binder is not necessary since the material is self-supporting.

The material is usually used as a fine powder suspended in the binder as a slurry. Because of the fine particle size of ceramics, molds made from ceramic materials are typified by their extreme accuracy, tolerance, and capability of reproducing extremely fine detail in as-cast parts.

The major precision-casting methods are plaster molding, investment or lost-wax casting, ceramic molding, and ceramic-core molding. Although ceramic-core molding is not really a casting method or process, the production of ceramic cores utilizes similar materials and techniques.

Plaster Molding

Plaster-mold casting employs molds formed with a gypsum-plaster base. This process is basically similar to that of sand casting in that the mold, usually made in two halves corresponding to the cope and drag of sand molding, is assembled for pouring of the metal.

In plaster-mold casting, a permanent pattern is surrounded by a gypsum-based slurry that sets to a solid, self-supporting mold rigid enough to be handled. The mold parts are then stripped from the pattern and baked, or "burned out," to remove moisture. Undercut areas or internal surfaces are formed by separate pieces and cores as in sand casting. The viscosity of the plaster allows it to flow around the pattern to form a uniform mold with excellent detail and finish, using a minimum of skilled labor. The mold material does not have to be heated, rammed, vibrated, or pressed while it is being poured. This increases accuracy over a period of time and allows lightweight pattern construction; in fact, flexible patterns can be used in this process.

Setting time, usually about 20 minutes, is a disadvantage of plaster-mold casting when high production rates are required, but this disadvantage can be offset by using duplicate pattern equipment. Only alloys with casting temperatures below the dissociation temperature of gypsum can be cast by this process. These alloys include the sand-castable aluminum alloys (with the understanding that an increased magnesium content increases casting difficulty); low-melting point, lead/zinc alloys; and brasses and bronzes if they are not heavily leaded. Magnesium has been successfully cast in plaster molds, but special precautions must be taken and the process has not found commercial application.

Molding Methods:

Plaster is a mixture of basic gypsum stucco, similar to that used in building materials, with refractory material and accelerators or retarders added to control setting rate. The gypsum itself is not a refractory and is somewhat weak after burnout. Thus, a fibrous material such as asbestos or fiberglass may be added as reinforcement, together with some form of refractory, such as finely ground silica or magnesia. Plaster may be purchased already formulated, or it may be mixed by the foundry. When mixed with water, the gypsum, calcium-sulfate hemihydrate ($CaSO_4 \cdot \frac{1}{2}H_2O$) recrystallizes as the dihydrate $CaSO_4 \cdot 2H_2O$, which causes the plaster to set by the interlocking of crystals.

A considerable excess of water is used to ensure slurry fluidity. When the excess moisture bakes out, fine channels are left in the solid plaster, giving rise to a limited permeability. When used in this way, the material is known as low-permeability plaster or regular metal-casting plaster. It is usually mixed to a consistency of from 130-160, in which consistency is defined as the number of parts of water added to 100 parts of plaster. Permeability can be improved in two ways—either by using foam plaster or by a recrystallization cycle known as the Antioch process.

Foam plaster. Foam plaster is made by the addition of a foaming agent to either the plaster or the mixing water. The plaster stucco usually consists of alpha gypsum, which is produced by calcining the natural gypsum rock under steam instead of calcining it in open kettles as regular metal-casting plaster. Alpha gypsum requires less water to form a fluid slurry and normally sets to a harder, denser condition than regular plaster. A consistency of about 80 is normally used.

The plaster may be bought with the foaming agent incorporated, or a suitable foaming agent (usually a sulfonated hydrocarbon) can be added to the mixing water. Mixing takes place in two stages. At first the mixer impeller, which is frequently a rubber disk, is allowed to break the surface of the slurry, causing air to be beaten into the mixture. The entrapped air bubbles are then broken down, by the impeller held under the surface, to about 0.01" (0.3 mm) diam, forming a uniform, porous structure. When the resulting slurry is poured onto the pattern, surface tension causes the surface of the mold to become a solid layer of plaster backed by a fine, cellular structure. During setting, the cell walls rupture, forming interconnecting cells that make the material highly permeable.

A slight variation of this process involves mixing a separately generated foam with a plaster slurry. The main advantage of this method is that it lends itself to continuous mechanical mixing instead of the batch mixing necessary with other foam plaster techniques.

The use of foam plaster reduces burnout time (and thus the costs associated with burnout) and material cost by decreasing the mass of a given mold. On the other hand, it is difficult to keep the surface of the mold free from bubbles, and this increases the finishing costs. Foam-plaster molds are much more difficult to strip from the pattern because of their weak subsurface, and particular attention must be paid to draft and parting agents unless flexible patterns are used. Generally, foam plaster is used in large castings, if the surface finish is not extremely critical, because of its low cost. For small castings, the cost differential is not as great and permeability is less necessary. For an intricate core, low-permeability plaster is preferred because of its increased strength. Many plaster-mold foundries use both types of molds according to the application, just as they use various pattern materials for best results.

Antioch process. In the Antioch process, no foaming agent is used. After stripping, the molds are heated in an autoclave. Calcium-sulfate hemihydrate is in the stable form under these conditions; when the plaster is removed from the autoclave and allowed to stand, recrystallization to the dihydrate form and grain growth results in the development of a fluffy, permeable structure inside the mold with no effect on the surface.

This process is patented and can be used only under license. The autoclaving is an additional operation and must necessarily be carried out on a batch basis, which adds to the cost. However, a high permeability is achieved with a more consistent finish than is usual with foam plaster.

Investment Casting

Investment casting involves the formation of an expendable pattern in a die or mold and the use of the pattern to form a mold in an investment material. When the mold of investment material (refractory particles and a liquid) has set, the pattern is melted, burned, or dissolved out and the part is cast.

This process, sometimes called the lost-wax process because of the loss of the pattern during mold formation, is an ancient one and has been used traditionally to produce fine metal sculpture. In modern industry, the advent of the jet engine provided the impetus to use the investment process to fabri-

cate difficult-to-work alloys into highly complex shapes such as hollow, air-cooled turbine blades. Parts for valves, sewing machines, locks, rifles, golf clubs, aerospace and military equipment components, and burner nozzles are a few of the applications that have demonstrated the versatility and economy of this process.

Parts made by the investment-casting process require a minimum of finishing and can be held to close metallurgical specifications.

The Investment-Casting Process: All casting processes consist of five basic steps:

1. Preparing a pattern of the part to be cast.
2. Preparing a mold around the pattern.
3. Removing the pattern from the mold, leaving a cavity having the configuration of the desired component.
4. Pouring molten metal into the mold cavity.
5. Removing the cooled casting and performing the required finishing operations.

Investment casting differs from traditional casting in the first three steps of these procedures, and it is in these steps that the advantages of investment casting are derived.

Pattern. In investment casting the pattern is made of either wax or plastics. These pattern materials have several inherent advantages: they provide a very smooth surface, they allow the inclusion of exceptionally fine details, and they can be readily removed from a monolithic mold.

Molding and pattern removal. In sand casting, sand or another material is placed around the pattern in two sections, a top (the cope) and a bottom (the drag). The material is hardened, the mold sections are separated (along the parting line), and the pattern is removed. There is always a loss of dimensional control across the parting line. In investment casting, the pattern is dipped into a solution that hardens into a ceramic material. When the mold hardens, the disposable pattern is melted out. The mold cavity is in one piece, allowing close tolerances to be achieved, and the cavity surface is exceptionally smooth.

Advantages of Investment Casting: In comparison with other processes, investment casting has the following advantages:

- Complex-shaped parts can be produced close to final configuration.
- Tighter dimensional tolerances can be achieved.
- Less machining and fewer other finishing operations are usually required.
- Castings are generally sounder, with less porosity, etc.

Solid-Ceramic Molding

Solid-ceramic molding is a unique foundry process aimed at economically providing a high degree of precision and outstanding metal soundness in the production of cast parts and tooling. The process can be described as filling the gap between conventional sand foundry systems and the plaster-casting or investment-casting methods; it yields the types of tolerances normally associated with the investment process at costs often approaching those of ordinary sand molding. This method of molding has no size limitations, and castings weighing up to several tons are not uncommon. The process is commonly known as the Unicast Process or the Shaw Method and is available under a licensing arrangement.

Because the solid-ceramic process provides a high degree of accuracy and a fine surface finish (generally 65-90 μ in. [1.7-2.3 μ m] or better), castings made in ceramic molds are frequently used without further machining. This suits the process to production of tools, dies, and similar mold forms, particularly those of varied geometry that would otherwise be too time-consuming and costly to machine.

The refractory properties of ceramic molds make them capable of withstanding the high pouring temperatures of almost all castable ferrous and nonferrous alloys.

Process Variations: There are basically two process variations that meet the criteria established for solid-ceramic molding. They are the Shaw Pro-

cess and the Unicast Process. Both employ similar technology, but they differ in mold chemistry and processing technique. Both systems are marketed on a licensing basis.

Shaw Process. The patented Shaw Process employs a free-flowing ceramic slurry composed of a special blend of ceramic refractory powders that may be exposed to metal-pouring temperatures as high as 3000°F (1649°C); a volatile binding agent that agglomerates the ceramic powders; and a gelling agent that causes the slurry to set in a predetermined period of time, usually 2-4 minutes.

The steps in the production of a Shaw mold are illustrated Fig. 6-9. The refractory is composed of a variety of specially blended groups of refractory powders. The liquid binder medium is usually based on ethyl silicate and is produced specifically to proprietary formulations. During the mixing stage, a small amount of gelling agent is added to the binder and mixed with the refractory powder to produce a creamy slurry. The slurry is poured over a permanent stable pattern made of such conventional materials as wood, metal (usually aluminum), and plastics (usually epoxy). Pouring is always a gravity operation. After the mold gels, it is stripped from the pattern when it reaches a consistency similar to that of vulcanized rubber. This consistency is critical because it enables the ceramic mold to be easily removed from patterns with minimum draft (and sometimes with no draft), with straight sides, and with extremely fine detail—all without expansion or contraction.

The hard, rubberlike mold is then ignited, and it burns until virtually all the volatile substance it contains is consumed. During this burnoff, a microscopic network of cracks, called *microcrazing* is created throughout the mold, induced by the rapid evaporation of the volatiles. This microcrazing, a key factor in the Shaw Process, is largely responsible for the dimensional accuracy and surface finish of the process.

Microcrazing results in separation of each jagged ceramic particle from its neighbors by minute fissures or air gaps. The gaps are small enough to prevent molten metal from penetrating the mold, yet large enough to permit the venting of air and other gases and to accommodate the expansion of the ceramic

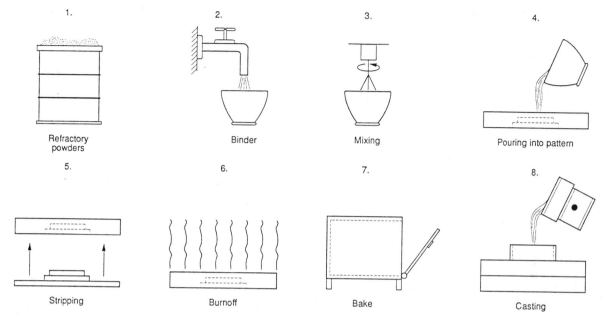

1. Refractory powders
2. Binder
3. Mixing
4. Pouring into pattern
5. Stripping
6. Burnoff
7. Bake
8. Casting

Figure 6-9 Shaw process

particles when they come into contact with molten metal. The Shaw mold dimensions are "frozen." The mold is immune to thermal shock; high-temperature mold curing at 1800°F (982°C) is possible; and the dimensional stability of the mold is constant whether the mold is hot or cold, or empty or full of metal.

Baking is the final stage in processing a Shaw ceramic mold. Baking removes all remaining volatile substances and strengthens the mold even further to resist erosion by the molten-metal stream. Thus, molds may be poured cold with molten metal only slightly above liquidus so that a fine-grained, tough, sound casting is produced without gas inclusions, porosity, or internal voids or cracks.

Cope and drag mold pieces are assembled along with any necessary cores, and metal is poured either directly from the melting furnace or from a ladle. Pouring should proceed rapidly to avoid cold shock and gas voids in the casting. After the casting solidifies, it is shaken out of the mold.

Unicast Process. Unicast molds are prepared by pouring chemically activated liquid ceramic slurry over a standard foundry pattern. The activated slurry sets in three or four minutes to form a tough, rubbery mass that becomes the "green" ceramic mold. The slurry is made just prior to use by combining a liquid chemical binder with a critical blend of ceramic refractories. The liquid binder is usually a modified alkyl silicate, an alcohol-based silicon ester. Several ceramic blends can be used, depending on final mold requirements. Some vary according to strength, crushability, and thermal properties, and others according to metal compatibility, surface finish, and permeability. Each blend is specially formulated to maintain a constant balance between particle-size distribution and specific gravity, resulting in a uniform slurry dispersion when mixed with the binder. The binder alone is the slurry component that sets. When setting occurs, the refractory particles that were previously in full liquid suspension are locked in position within the set binder and can no longer float or move.

The binder at this stage has become a hard, rubbery gel consisting of a liquid phase and a solid phase. The liquid phase is largely free alcohol, and the solid phase is a form of polysilicic acid. Polysilicic acid by itself is unstable and rapidly forms new chemical chains that are of larger mass than the original molecule. If the mold were allowed to remain for any length of time in its green state, the molecular growth would apply sufficient pressure to the suspended ceramic particles to cause them to move or separate. At the very least, the mold would develop a "crazing" consisting of microscopic cracks and fissures, but the condition would worsen as the molecular growth was continued. The cracks would become larger, and the entire mold structure would expand, warp, and disintegrate. Therefore, growth of the chemical chains must be halted at a point before it destroys the mold.

A common method of arresting molecular growth is to ignite the green mold shortly after it sets, thus allowing free burning of volatile alcohol from the liquid-gel phase. This is the method employed in the Shaw Process. The heat developed by the burning is sufficient to dehydrate the polysilicic acid solid phase partially, rendering it more stable.

The Unicast Process achieves mold stabilization by chemical means using a patented method that involves catalytic interaction with the liquid phase of the set mold, resulting in a more stable form of polysilicic acid. Stabilization is accomplished by spraying or immersing the green mold with a chemical stabilizing solution. Molds treated in this manner can be torched or oven-dried to yield a stable structure.

Production steps. Basic steps in production of a Unicast Process casting include the following:

1. The pattern is mounted on the baseplate and enclosed within the flask.
2. A thin coating of ceramic fine-facing slurry is applied to the exposed surfaces. The coating becomes tacky almost immediately and is ready to receive the backing material.
3. A ceramic backing slurry is charged onto the facing coating until the molding box is filled.
4. The flask is removed, the vacuum clamping plate is located in position, and the entire assembly is inverted on the stripping machine.
5. The pattern is stripped from the mold, and the clamping vacuum is released.
6. The stripped mold is transferred to the location at which hardening fluid is applied by spray or immersion.
7. The hardened mold is heat-cured by direct flame, or it is heat-cured in a furnace.
8. An upper (cope) half is similarly prepared and assembled to the mold, and then the metal is poured to form the casting.

Advantages. The Unicast Process provides accurate dimensional control, and warpage or distortion is almost entirely eliminated. As a result of the stabilized molecular growth, the mold develops a cellular or spongelike structure caused by interstitial separation of particles. This structure provides for gas venting and particle expansion during casting. Benefits of this structure are metal soundness; ease of casting long, thin sections; and reductions in traditional mold venting. Molds can be poured hot or at room temperature without any change in thermal characteristics. Directional solidification of the cast alloy is fully controlled, resulting in high physical properties and outstanding metal soundness.

The major advantages of solid-ceramic-mold casting include:

1. Only a short lead time is necessary due to simple tools and a fast mold build cycle.
2. A modest installation cost can be maintained using simple equipment.
3. The manufacturing cost is considerably lower than that of machining or other alternate methods.
4. Patterns are usually inexpensive and quickly prepared.
5. The die life of cast tooling is longer in comparison to that of dies made from wrought materials.
6. Cast tooling can frequently be used as cast without further machining.
7. The process is suitable for "impossible-to-machine" grain and texture details for large injection mold bodies.

8. The process is feasible for casting sizes ranging from small to very large.

Composite mold. While the Unicast Process commonly employs a solid-ceramic mold for smaller and short-run castings, it generally employs a composite-ceramic mold for large parts and for those produced in high volume. In this case, the Unicast ceramic is used as a ¼ to ½″ (6-13 mm) facing backed by a specially blended, coarse-sand aggregate for support. Use of this technique sharply reduces mold cost by conserving the ceramic material and also permits mechanized production of molds.

Ceramic Cores

Ceramic cores are widely used in the production of precision castings, particularly when the core cannot be formed integrally with the mold. The two types of ceramic cores are molded cores and extruded (injected) cores.

While ceramic cores are intended primarily for use in precision casting processes, they are also becoming more widely used in sand casting and other processes in which the internal sections of the castings formed by the core require greater accuracy and surface finish than would otherwise be obtained.

Molded Ceramic Cores: Molded ceramic cores are most commonly formed by pouring a ceramic molding slurry into a suitable corebox. They can be produced in any suitably equipped foundry. The techniques employed conform generally to the Unicast Process or the Shaw method.

Cores made by this system provide adequate strength for handling and are designed to break down readily under contracting metal pressure. Removal of the core from the finished casting is done by manual or mechanical means. The uniform breakdown properties of the core permit good accuracy with minimal resistance during casting solidification. Since most cores are made by gravity pouring, it is normally possible to use standard coreboxes throughout. Some consideration has to be given to core designs that can entrap air due to the need for filling from a small aperture, and typical in this category are cores for impeller production.

The Unicast Process produces cores of this type by filling the slurry into a centrifugally rotating corebox and combining with either vacuum or pressure to obtain a dense form.

The special ceramic slurries employed often include a percentage of ceramic fiber materials to permit easier core breakdown after casting, and to further improve core permeability. These cores can often be used in sand or similar molds in which the external surfaces of the casting are less critical than the internally cored areas. Castings for the pump and impeller field fall typically into this category.

Extruded or Injected Ceramic Cores:
Preformed cores are primarily intended for use in the investment-casting industry, particularly for sections that cannot be formed in the normal ceramic shell dipping process. The cores can be assembled with separately made patterns, or they can be inserted into the pattern injection die prior to injection. The cores are strong, and they normally withstand the high pressures of pattern material injection without fracture. Because of their strength and density, core removal after casting is almost invariably by a leaching technique in molten caustic salts. Special leaching techniques have also been developed using pressurized autoclaves and water solutions of caustic materials at temperatures up to 550°F (290°C).

Preformed ceramic cores are normally manufactured by extruding and injecting a specially prepared, dense ceramic paste into a suitable corebox. Because of the pressures of injection, coreboxes are normally machined metal molds. Subsequent processing of the cores requires carefully controlled firing and specialized handling. It is not customary for foundries to be able to produce cores of this type themselves; the cores must usually be purchased from an outside source.

Preformed cores have also successfully been used in sand molding operations, although their relatively high cost restricts them to specialized applications such as impellers. Because of their relatively high density, cores must often be preheated prior to insertion in a sand mold, particularly when steel alloys are being cast.

KEY TERMS AND PHRASES _____

Centrifugal casting
Ceramic core
Cold-chamber machine
Die
Die mounting and clamping
Draft
Ejection-pin
Extruded ceramic core
Foam plaster
Gating
High-pressure die casting
Hot-chamber machine
Injection mechanism
Investment casting
Metal flow
Metal-mold casting
Molded ceramic core
Pattern
Permanent-mold casting
Plaster molding
Platen (moveable)
Platen (stationary)
Precision casting
Semicentrifugal casting
Shaw Process
Shrinkage
Solid-ceramic molding
Solidification
Unicast Process
Venting

QUESTIONS FOR ADDITIONAL STUDY AND REVIEW _____

1. Describe metal-mold casting as a process.

2. Describe high-pressure die casting.

3. What are the four main elements of a die-casting machine?

4. Contrast hot-chamber and cold-chamber casting machines.

5. Describe permanent-mold casting.

6. Describe centrifugal casting.

7. Describe the following centrifugal-casting methods:
   - True centrifugal
   - Semicentrifugal
   - Centrifuge

8. Explain three advantages of centrifugal casting.

9. What is precision casting?

10. Describe the plaster molding process.

11. What is foam plaster?

12. What is the Antioch process?

13. Describe the investment casting process.
    List 5 Basic Steps   P143

14. List four advantages of investment casting.

15. Describe solid-ceramic molding.

16. What is the Shaw Process?

17. What is a ceramic core?

CHAPTER 7

Heat Treatment

MAJOR TOPICS COVERED

- Heat Treatment of Steel
- Heat Treatment Principles
- Hardenability of Steels
- Solution Treating and Aging
- Tempering
- Annealing
- Normalizing
- Cold Treatment
- Surface (Case) Hardening
- Carburizing
- Nitriding
- Carbonitriding
- Chromizing
- Boronizing
- Heat Treating Furnaces
- Safety Considerations
- Selective Surface Hardening
- Heat Treatment of Other Metals

HEAT TREATMENT OF STEEL

Heat treatment is an operation or combination of operations involving the controlled heating and cooling of solid metals and alloys to obtain a required microstructure with resultant desired properties. The properties desired vary widely, depending upon the applications for the metals. With current know-how and equipment, heat treatment is very versatile and can provide many different and predictable properties or combinations of properties.

Most heat treating operations can be classified into the two following types of processes:

1. Processes such as through hardening and surface (case) hardening that increase the strength, hardness, and toughness of metals.
2. Processes such as annealing and normalizing that decrease the hardness of metals in order to improve their homogeneity, machinability, and formability, or to relieve stresses.

Proper heat treatment of any metal requires the combined input of design engineers, metallurgists, and manufacturing engineers. Essential information required for optimum heat treatment includes the following:

1. The composition and condition of the metal to be heat treated, and the intended applications.
2. The critical time-temperature transformation relationship for the specific metal to be heat treated.
3. The response of the metal to quenching and the method of cooling or quenching to be used.
4. The desired hardness and/or strength.

Heat Treatment Principles

The three major operations performed in the hardening of steel by heat treatment are: austenitizing, equalizing, and cooling.

Austenitizing

As steel is heated and cooled, its structure changes in certain predictable steps that must be recognized for each alloy. Initially, steel that has not been previously heat treated is usually composed of a mixture of ferrite and carbides, often present in a lamellar microstructure known as pearlite.

When steel with this ferrite-pearlite structure is heated, it reaches a temperature at which the carbides in the lamellar pearlite begin to dissolve into the iron. As the temperature is raised, more of the carbides are dissolved until the steel reaches a point at which all the carbides are dissolved and the steel consists completely of a solid solution of carbon in iron called austenite. The temperature at which pearlite begins to transform into austenite is identified as the lower critical temperature. Ac_1, the temperature at which the steel becomes composed completely of austenite, is called the upper critical temperature. Ac_3, and the temperature range between, is the critical range or transformation range for the particular alloy.

The lower critical temperature is shown by the line A_1 in the iron-carbon equilibrium diagram (see Fig. 7-1). In actual practice, this temperature varies slightly depending upon whether the pearlite is beginning to be transformed to austenite or the austenite has completed transformation to pearlite—in other words, whether the steel is being heated or cooled. This difference is designated by the letters Ac_1 upon heating and Ar_1 upon cooling. These temperatures vary with the chemical composition of the steel.

The upper critical temperature varies in the same way. Shown as A_3 in the equilibrium diagram, it is known as Ac_3 upon heating and Ar_3 upon cooling. It is also designated as A_{cm} when the carbon content of the steel is above 0.80%. The temperature at which the steel is completely converted to austenite or at which pearlite just begins to form is partially dependent upon the alloying element content of the steel but primarily upon the carbon content.

As shown in Fig. 7-1, a plain carbon steel of 0.80% carbon will have the lowest full transformation temperature because, at this composition, the upper critical temperature A_3 is the same as the lower critical temperature A_1. This 0.80% carbon composition is called eutectoid steel; it is 100% pearlite below the transformation temperature and is characterized by the complete change from pearlite to austenite (and back to pearlite) at a single temperature. All other compositions of various percentages transform over a range of temperatures.

Equalizing

The rate of heating is usually not significant unless the steel is highly stressed initially, and then it should be heated slowly. Preheating in another furnace is often necessary during production when a furnace temperature cannot be altered because other parts are being processed at the same time or because productivity would decline. For equalizing or soaking (the operation that holds the steel at Ac_3, the upper critical temperature, until all sections are uniformly at heat), an adequate soak time is generally about ½-1 hour for each inch (25 mm) of the thickest cross section.

Quenching

Quenching, or the rate of cooling, is important in heat treating operations because it dictates the structure and properties of the steel.

Hardenability of Steels

Hardenability is the relative ability of ferrous metals to harden. It is the property that determines the depth and distribution of hardness induced by quenching

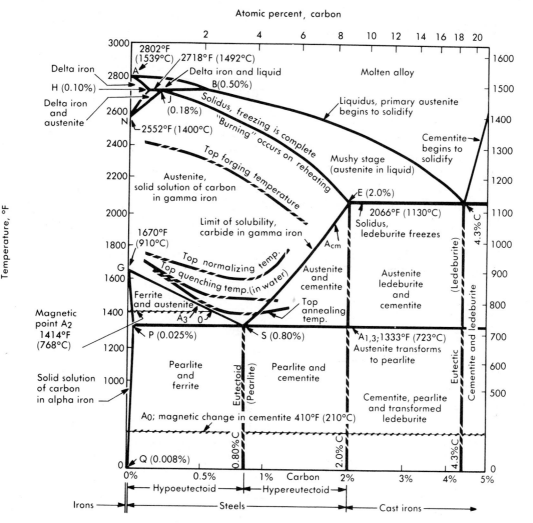

Figure 7-1   Iron-carbon phase diagram

or the size of a workpiece that can be hardened under given cooling conditions. It does not refer to the maximum hardness that can be attained in a given steel.

Hardenability is commonly measured as the distance below a quenched surface where the metal has a specific hardness or a specific percentage of martensite in the microstructure, as discussed later in this section. Metals having low hardenability—called shallow hardening—require faster cooling rates and can only be hardened to relatively shallow depths. Those with high hardenability can be

hardened more deeply or completely through the material with slower cooling rates.

Effect of Carbon and Alloy Content

Unalloyed iron is soft and ductile and cannot be hardened by heat treatment. The maximum as-quenched surface hardness attainable in any steel is dependent primarily upon the carbon content of the steel and the cooling rate. The more carbon present in the steel, the higher hardness possible.

Hardenability, however, is largely governed by the nature and percentage of alloying elements, as well as the carbon content, grain size of the austenite, time and temperature during austenitizing, and prior structure.

All alloying elements except cobalt and vanadium increase the hardenability of steels. Alloy steels transform more slowly from austenite than unalloyed steels, thus permitting an increased hardening effect with slower quenching rates.

Hardenability requirements depend upon many factors, including the specific material to be heat treated and the size, design, and application of the workpiece. For highly stressed parts, through hardening, followed by tempering, is generally preferred. For parts stressed primarily at or near their surfaces, or for applications requiring wear resistance or resistance to shock, shallow or surface hardening is often satisfactory.

H Steels and Hardenability Bands

For the identification of steels specified to hardenability limits, the suffix letter H is added to the conventional series number. In the unified numbering system (UNS), the H appears as a prefix. To permit steel producers to meet the standards for hardenability limits, the chemical compositions of some steels have been modified somewhat from the same grades of steels that do not have a specified hardenability band.

Hardenability bands for carbon and alloy H steels are specified in SAE Standard J1268. The band graphs and tabular values show maximum and minimum hardenability limits, in Rockwell C-scale values, for various steels, based on standard end-quench tests. Steels are available with narrower (about one third) bands than standard hardenability bands. Such steels are sometimes used to help control distortion when heat treating certain parts, such as gears.

Problems in Hardening

Many problems can occur in hardening, most of which are the result of improper heat treatment specifications or poor heat treating practices. Some of the more common problems are due to decarburization, scaling, quench cracking, residual stresses, retained austenite, and dimensional changes.

Decarburization: Steel parts are often decarburized to some extent during heating for hot forming operations, such as rolling, extruding, and forging. The loss of surface carbon may prevent attaining full hardness in the finished parts. This situation may necessitate the removal of the softer surfaces of the parts by grinding or other means, preferably before heat treatment.

Decarburization during heating can be eliminated by using protective atmospheres in the furnaces. Decarburization can also be corrected by carbon restoration (carburizing), but it is better prevented than corrected.

Scaling: The formation of surface layers of oxidation products, called scaling, is another undesirable result of hardening. Such a condition often requires machining, grinding, cleaning, or other methods of descaling. Scaling can be minimized by using protective atmospheres in the heating furnaces.

Quench Cracking: The formation of cracks when quenching heated steels is a major problem. As the carbon content of steel increases, the tendency to crack increases. Higher austenitizing temperatures also increase the tendency toward quench cracking. Steels with coarser grain size are more susceptible to cracks than fine-grained steels because the latter have more grain boundary area to block the movement of cracks, and grain boundaries help to absorb and redistribute residual stresses, as discussed next in this section. Nicks, scratches, too small a radius between section changes, and impurities on the surfaces of workpieces to be hardened are also possible sources of cracks. Careful machining, grinding, and cleaning prior to heat treatment is generally advisable.

Residual Stresses: Residual stresses (stresses that exist in a part that is free of external forces or thermal gradients) can cause distortion, warpage, cracking, or breakage, especially after quenching and before tempering. Major reasons for the formation of residual stresses are the nonuniform contraction of heated parts during cooling, expansion during transformation, or a combination of the two, as well as variations in heating and cooling rates.

Fast quenching produces higher stresses, and therefore the slowest cooling rate for producing the desired microstructure and hardness should be used. Subsequent tempering reduces the hardness and tensile strength, but minimizes stresses and improves ductility and toughness.

Distortion or warping is generally greater for more completely shaped workpieces or when there is a large thickness change in the workpieces. Preheating, special cooling methods, or the use of workholding fixtures is sometimes necessary. Straightening of bars and other parts after thermal treatment can introduce stresses, which can cause distortion in subsequent machining or processing operations. Stress relieving prior to heat treatment is often required to minimize distortion, but some distortion and dimensional change are inevitable as the result of heat treatment.

Retained Austenite: Austenite that is not transformed during the heat treating cycle is soft and weak, and lowers the overall hardness of the steel if excessive in amount. It may also cause dimensional instability because of the possible transformation of the austenite at room temperature over a long period of time. In addition, retained austenite will often transform to martensite with the application of stresses.

The amount of retained austenite is affected by the alloy content of the steel, the austenitizing temperature, the cooling rate, and, in some cases, the amount and distribution of the stresses in the quenched parts. The effect of alloy content is so strong that some steels are entirely austenitic at room temperature. High austenitizing temperatures can result in increased amounts of retained austenite. Slow cooling rates also increase the tendency to retain austenite.

One method of eliminating retained austenite is cold treating—cooling the quenched parts to temperatures below freezing where transformation of austenite to martensite proceeds to completion. Another method, applicable to certain steels in which the austenite has not stabilized for too long a period prior to treatment, consists of heating the quenched parts to a temperature of about 300°F (150°C) or more to permit transformation to ferrite plus carbide.

Solution Treating and Aging

Solution treating and aging are processes employed to harden and strengthen many nonferrous alloys and some steels. The procedure generally requires the following two consecutive operations:

1. Solution heat treatment to produce a homogeneous solid solution that is retained by rapid quenching to room temperature.
2. Aging to produce fine precipitates in the solid solution.

Solution Heat Treatment

In solution heat treatment, an alloy is heated to a suitable temperature, held at this temperature for sufficient time to allow a desired constituent to enter into solid solution, and then rapidly cooled to hold the constituent in solution. Most of these solid solutions are comparatively soft and ductile. They are also structurally unstable and have a tendency to return to the form of an aggregate with aging.

Metals with solid solutions that age harden at room temperature can be prevented from doing so by cooling below the freezing temperature after quenching and holding at a subzero temperature for as long as required. Such a delay in precipitation facilitates forming or other operations prior to aging. For example, rivets made from heat-treatable aluminum alloys are often refrigerated after solution treating, removed from low-temperature storage for assembly, and then allowed to age at room temperature.

Aging

Aging, also called age hardening or precipitation hardening, is a time-temperature dependent change in the properties of certain metals (higher strength and hardness) occurring at room or elevated temperatures. Aging at room temperature is called natural aging; aging above room temperature, which requires less time, is termed artificial aging. Quench aging is aging by rapid cooling after solution heat treatment.

Interrupted aging is aging at two or more different temperatures, with cooling to room temperature after each heating; step aging is also aging at two or more different temperatures, but without cooling to room temperature after each step. Double aging refers to a solution annealing followed by reheating, a second quenching, and a second reheating. Some alloys will precipitation harden after a double-aging cycle with no prior solution annealing.

Tempering

In its hardened, as-quenched, fully martensitic form, steel is hard and brittle, thus restricting its usefulness. Hardened steel must be subsequently tempered to relieve quenching stresses and to provide a limited but necessary degree of toughness and ductility, protecting the part from cracking in storage, installation, and use. Impact resistance and improved elongation and area reduction qualities are afforded by tempering, but are brought about by a sacrifice in hardness, tensile strength, and wear resistance. Tempering consists of reheating previously hardened metal to a relatively low temperature (below the transformation range),

generally followed by slow cooling. During this treatment, the martensite phase transforms to the more stable, two-phase mixture of ferrite and carbide. Certain steel parts, tempered in the temperature range of 400 to 700°F (205 to 370°C) may be water quenched to increase their impact strength.

Machinability is a function of hardness and toughness and is seldom changed appreciably by hardening and tempering at low temperatures. With tempering at low temperatures, grinding is often the only machining possible on some tempered steels. After tempering operations at 900 to 1200°F (480 to 650°C), turning or milling of medium-carbon steels is possible.

The higher the tempering temperature, or the longer the time at that temperature, the softer and more ductile the steel. Alloy steels containing carbide-forming elements show greater resistance to softening during tempering than do plain carbon steels. Therefore, higher temperatures and longer times should be used in tempering the higher alloy steels, as shown in Fig. 7-2. Tempering may be performed to give almost any desired combination of properties by correct selection of the time-temperature cycle, because the strength of steel is

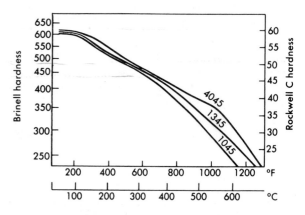

Figure 7-2   Tempered hardness as affected by alloy content

proportional to its hardness, as shown in Fig. 7-3. The composition of the steel, its condition before quenching, and the effectiveness of the quench all affect the tempering temperature required to produce a specified hardness.

uniform physical properties and replaces the slower, less consistent annealing of coil stock in batch furnaces (see Fig. 7-4).

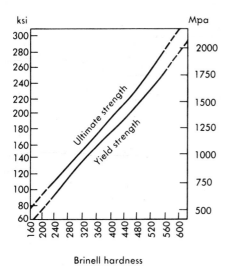

Figure 7-3   Increase in strength of steel with increased hardness

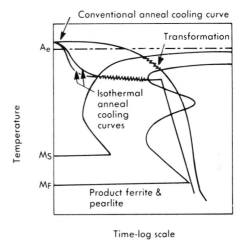

Time-log scale

Figure 7-4   Time-temperature transformation curves for conventional annealing and isothermal annealing

Annealing

Annealing is a heat treatment process that consists of heating metal to a suitable temperature, followed by slow cooling. The purposes of annealing include one or more of the following:

1. To reduce hardness or brittleness.
2. To relieve stresses.
3. To improve machinability or facilitate cold working.
4. To produce desired microstructure or properties.
5. To remove gases.
6. To alter the electrical or magnetic properties.

There are many different types of annealing. Continuous annealing of sheet steel is now being done by some steel producers. This method ensures more

Normalizing

Normalizing involves the heating of steel to above the critical temperature Ac_3, followed by still-air cooling to room temperature to obtain a uniform, fine-grained pearlitic structure. Normalizing differs from stress relieving, annealing, and quenching in that it is carried out from temperatures of about 1600 to 1700°F (870 to 925°C)—approximately 100-200°F (55-110°C) higher than the regular hardening temperature and as much as 200-250°F (110-140°C) over the regular annealing temperature (fully air-hardened steels are exceptions, however)—and in that the cooling is neither restricted nor accelerated.

Normalizing was originally applied to forgings of medium-carbon steels to refine their coarse grain structure. Normalizing results in finer grained, harder, more homogeneous structures than annealed structures because of the more rapid air cooling involved in the process. This finer microstructure (usually pearlitic) often coincides with higher mechanical properties for the normalized steels. In fact, normalized materials sometimes provide the specified properties without further heat treatment. Ferrous castings are frequently normalized to remove the strains of solidification and improve toughness or impact strength.

Higher alloy, medium-carbon steels may be given good strength and ductility by normalizing them and then tempering at 1200 to 1250°F (650 to 675°C). High alloyed, air-hardening steels, however, are never treated by other than a stress-relieving process at approximately 1200°F. A true normalizing would cause these steels to reaustenitize and then harden fully, thus defeating the primary purpose of the operation.

Cold Treatment

Cold (cryogenic) treatment consists of exposing metal parts or tools to subzero temperatures for the purposes of obtaining desired conditions or properties. Such treatment can provide improved strength, dimensional or microstructural stability, greater resistance to wear, stress relieving, and retarded aging.

For steels, proper cold treatment ensures a more uniform and completely transformed microstructure. Primarily, soft, retained austenite is transformed into hard, more stable martensite, which can be subsequently tempered.

The Cold Treatment Process

Cold treatment immediately after heat treatment is generally the best procedure. However, care must be taken to prevent cracking. Workpieces especially susceptible to cracking may require tempering prior to cold treatment. Some firms specializing in cold treatment recommend controlled soaking for longer

times at lower temperatures. Most parts are tempered after cold treatment.

SURFACE (CASE) HARDENING

Surface hardening (also called case hardening) processes are thermochemical treatments in which the chemical composition of steel surfaces is altered. The processes involve adding carbon, nitrogen, or both to the steel surfaces in order to provide a hardened layer or "case" having a definite depth. Common processes used to create hardened cases include carburizing, nitriding, and carbonitriding.

Surface-hardening thermochemical processes are used extensively for low-to-medium carbon steel parts requiring high hardness or fatigue strength primarily at their surfaces, as in wear-resistant applications. The processes also provide sufficient core strength and toughness to withstand tensile or impact stresses and fatigue.

Carburizing

Carburizing is a heat treating process for increasing the carbon content of exposed surfaces on steel parts, usually low-carbon grades with carbon contents below 0.30%. This procedure is accomplished by heating the steel above its upper critical temperature under controlled conditions and in contact with a suitable carbonaceous medium. Carburizing is normally done in the temperature range of 1600 to 1800°F (870 to 980°C). With proper conditions, an enriched carbon case is produced to the desired depth.

The basis for any carburizing operation is the equilibrium of the system. Given the proper conditions, the carbon content of the steel and the carbon potential of the surrounding gases—in the case of gas carburizing—will try to equalize. If the atmosphere has a higher potential than the steel, the steel will absorb the carbon. With atmospheres having extremely high carbon potential, iron carbides may form on the surface of the steel. If the carbon potential of the atmosphere is too low, the steel may yield carbon to the atmosphere and become decarburized.

Being a diffusion process, carburizing is affected by the amount of alloying elements in the steel. The case depth produced is temperature and time dependent, as shown in Fig. 7-5. For any given set of carburizing conditions, the case depth can be determined by using the following formula:

$$CD = k \sqrt{t}$$

where:

CD = case depth
 k = a constant based on the temperature and the chemical composition of the steel
 t = time

It is important to distinguish between total case depth and effective case depth. The effective case depth is typically about two-thirds to three-fourths of the total case depth. It is critical that the required effective depth be specified so that the heat treater can process the parts for the correct time at the proper temperature. Most carburizing is done in a one- or two-cycle process. For total case depths less than 0.030″ (0.76 mm), one carburizing cycle is used. For deeper cases, two cycles (carburize and diffuse) are generally used.

Typically, carburizing and quenching produce a case hardness of R_C 60-63, with a core hardness of R_C 10-40, depending upon carbon content. If low-carbon steels, such as SAE 1020, are carburized, it may be difficult to attain this hardness, owing to the low hardenability of the metals, and a more severe quenching medium is generally specified. Case and core hardnesses are dependent upon the composition of the steel, the section size of the workpiece, and the heat treating procedure.

Most steels that are carburized are killed steels (deoxidized by the addition of aluminum), which maintain fine grain sizes to temperatures of about 1900°F (1040°C). Steels made to coarse grain practices (semikilled, rimmed, or capped) should not be carburized. For coarse-grained steels, carbonitriding (discussed later in this section) is more appropriate because of the lower temperatures and shorter cycle times.

Parts carburized to a carbon content over 1% can have a brittle structure if slowly cooled from the carburizing temperature, due to the formation of proeutectoid carbides on the grain boundaries. For this reason, surface carbon is generally limited to about 0.9%.

The three major methods of carburizing are liquid, pack, and gas. Gas carburizing is the predominant method, with liquid and pack carburizing being used less frequently.

Nitriding

Nitriding is a surface hardening process in which nitrogen is diffused into the surfaces of ferrous alloys at subcritical temperatures to produce a shallow case

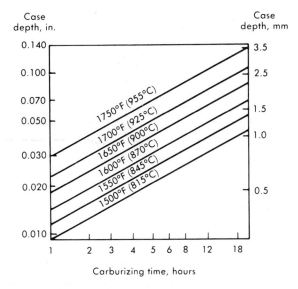

Figure 7-5   Relationship of case depth to carburizing time

of nitride without requiring quenching. The purposes of nitriding include the following:

1. To increase the surface hardness.
2. To improve wear resistance.
3. To increase fatigue life.
4. To possibly increase corrosion resistance slightly, except in the case of stainless steels.

The low temperatures employed and the lack of quenching in nitriding minimize distortion, but the process may require considerable time, especially for producing deep cases with gas nitriding. Also, allowance must be made for a small amount of dimensional growth, generally less than 0.001-0.002″ (0.03-0.05 mm), resulting from the formation of the nitrides. Distortion and growth are much less when using ion (plasma) nitriding. The amount of growth with all methods of nitriding is dependent upon the depth of the nitride layer. See Fig. 7-6.

Steels Nitrided	Typical Maximum Surface Hardness	Usual Surface Hardness, R_C
Nitralloy 135M	R_C 70	63-65
AISI Series:* 4100, 4300, 5100, 6100, 8600, 8700, 9300, 9800	R_C 60	52-60
AISI Tool Steels: H11, H12, H13, M2, M42	R_C 70	64-68
Stainless steels**	1200 Knoop	64-70

* These should be medium-carbon steels.
** Generally, stainless steels cannot be nitrided in a conventional system. Stainless steels also lose some of their corrosion resistance when nitrided.

Figure 7-6 Steels nitrided and typical surface hardness attained

Carbonitriding

Carbonitriding is similar to cyaniding, except that the simultaneous absorption of carbon and nitrogen into the steel surfaces is accomplished by heating in a gaseous atmosphere. The process is sometimes referred to as dry cyaniding or gas cyaniding. The composition of the case produced depends upon the atmosphere, temperature, time, and steel composition. While carbonitriding is done above the phase-transformation temperatures, the process called nitrocarburizing is performed at temperatures below phase transformation. However, both processes are performed at temperatures higher than required for nitriding.

Temperatures of 1450 to 1650°F (790 to 900°C) are commonly used for carbonitriding steel parts to be quenched, generally in oil. Lower temperature processing, such as nitrocarburizing, is sometimes used where a liquid quench is not required. Endothermic atmospheres, however, are explosive at temperatures below 1400°F (760°C). Most heat treating furnaces have safety devices that prevent the introduction of endothermic gases into the furnace unless the chamber is at a temperature of at least 1400°F.

Atmosphere cooling is valuable whenever there is danger of distortion and core properties are of no concern. The case resulting from atmosphere cooling, however, is brittle and not generally satisfactory when parts are subjected to impact or bending in service. Case depths may range from 0.001 to 0.030″ (0.03-0.76 mm) or more, but generally vary from 0.003 to 0.015″ (0.08-0.38 mm).

Chromizing

Chromizing is a high-temperature process in which chromium is transported to and diffused into the surface of metals to provide a chromium-enriched alloy layer with high corrosion, heat, and wear-resistance properties. Current commercial techniques that provide for the simultaneous transportation and diffusion of chromium are:

1. Powder-pack cementation process. In this process, parts to be chromized are placed in a retort in direct contact with a powder mixture of a chromium source, chromium halide salts, and inert refractory oxides. The retort may be sealed, or it may be designed so that a reducing or inert atmosphere can be maintained in it. It may also be placed under a vacuum.

2. Fused salt-bath process. In this process, parts are placed in a salt bath containing chromium halide salts and elemental chromium, and the bath is protected by an inert atmosphere such as argon. The process may be carried out with or without the use of an external current that, if used, deposits chromium on the base part, which serves as the cathode. Faster deposition is possible with the fused salt-bath technique, but its major disadvantages include the need for increased facilities for production and the need for special handling fixtures.

3. Granular-pack process. The granular-pack process uses only porous granules of chromium containing halides within the pores; no inert refractories are used. Workpieces may be either in direct contact with the granules or out of contact if a smoother finish is required. Parts and granules are packed in a retort; and upon heating, the chromium halides vaporize and pass to the parts, where chromium is deposited and diffused into the surfaces. The gaseous reaction products are then transported back to the chromium-source granules to generate more chromium halides. Upon completion of the diffusion, the retort is cooled, and the halides are reabsorbed into the granules, thereby providing primed granules for the next chromizing heat.

4. Gas convection process. In this method, also called chemical vapor deposition (CVD), the parts are placed apart from the chromium sources. Gaseous halogens or halogen acids are then made to react with the chromium to form a gas that is conveyed by forced circulation to the parts. The gaseous reaction products are then exhausted or returned to the source, where a reverse reaction generates additional chromium halides.

Differences among these processes are chromizing potential, heating and cooling rates, surface finish, transporting power, and economy. For example, the simultaneous chromizing and heat treatment of air-hardening tool steels and austenitic stainless steels require a subsequent rapid cooling cycle to develop their respective martensitic and austenitic structures, free of chromium carbides in the grain boundaries. This freedom from carbides can be achieved by the granular-pack process, which employs solid, porous chromium granules with good heat conductivity, but not with the powder-pack cementation process, which uses refractory oxides having poor heat conductivity. The gas convection process provides smooth chromized surfaces not attainable by any of the other processes. The chromium potential, which is dependent upon the activity of the chromium, dictates the chromium gradient and the surface chromium content in the alloy layer of metals containing little or no carbon. See Figs. 7-7 and 7-8.

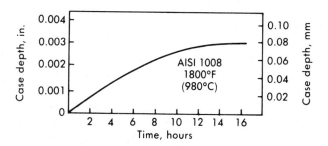

Figure 7-7 Chromized case depth versus chromizing time

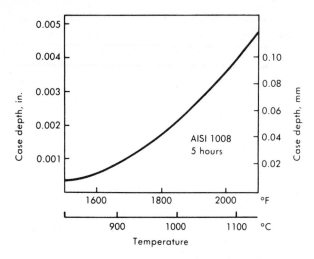

Figure 7-8　Chromized case depth versus chromizing temperature

Boronizing

Boronizing is another diffusion process for the surface hardening of steels. Compatible materials for this process include mild steels, tool steels, cast irons, nickel-based alloys, and cobalt-based alloys. When a boride layer is applied to the appropriate substrate, the layer will provide additional wear and abrasion resistance, often comparable to that of sintered carbide.

Boronizing can be carried out in a variety of media: gases, molten-salt mixtures or powders, and by plasma processes. The temperature at which the boron is diffused depends upon the material and case depth required. Usually the temperature is between 1550 and 1850°F (845 and 1010°C).

The case depth that can be achieved with boronizing depends primarily upon the material being processed. For example, case depths of 0.005″ (0.13 mm) can be produced on low-alloy and carbon steels. Usually, case depths greater than 0.002″ (0.05 mm) are not economical for high-alloyed materials, such as stainless steels and tool steels. The most common case depths are 0.001-0.002″ (0.03-0.05 mm) for low-alloy and carbon steels, and 0.0005″ (0.013 mm) for high-alloyed materials.

The Vickers (diamond pyramid) hardness of boride cases ranges from 1300 to 2300. This range exceeds hard chrome electroplate or hardened tool steels, but approximates the hardness of tungsten carbide. In general, the hardness will increase with an increasing amount of alloy in the substrate.

Size changes result from the processing parameters of boronizing. Typically, a growth can be expected in the range of 15 to 30% of the boride case thickness per surface. This growth may vary with the composition of the substrate but is reproducible for a given combination of material and thermal cycle.

Boronizing provides good wear-resistant properties and reduces the coefficient of friction. The final properties are comparable to carbide. The thermal stability of the boride compounds is good at subcritical temperature, and the dependent factor for performance is the hot strength of the substrate material. Boride case hardness is unaffected by exposure to subcritical temperatures in service.

It is important to provide a core material with sufficient strength to support loads applied to the case. This is not of particular concern in sliding wear situations, but it is crucial when high unit loads are applied. The core material can yield under such high loads and cause the case to spall. Boronized cases are brittle and should not be used for impact loading applications.

Another advantage of boronizing is additional corrosion resistance. While each corrosive situation is unique, low-alloy and carbon steels usually increase in corrosion resistance, while the stainless steels are unchanged or decreased in corrosion resistance, depending upon the environment.

TYPES OF FURNACES

Heat treating furnaces are heat-holding enclosures that can be classified as either batch or continuous types. There are many variations in design and construction within each type. Selection of a specific furnace depends primarily upon the size, weight, and shape of the parts to be heat treated; the type of heat treatment to be performed; production rates required; and the initial and operating costs. The productivity of furnaces can be rated in pounds-per-hour production per dollar of capital expenditure (including installation), per dollar of energy cost, and per dollar of labor costs (including maintenance).

Direct-fired, batch-type furnaces are the simplest kind. Continuous furnaces, with automatic control for high-production requirements, are much more sophisticated. Many furnaces are equipped for controlling the atmospheres in their work chambers. While standard furnaces are available in a wide variety of sizes, many are of special design to suit a specific application See Figs. 7-9 and 7-10.

Salt-Bath Furnaces

Salt-bath furnaces are basically ceramic or metal containers with molten salt in which workpieces are immersed for either heating or cooling within a temperature range of 300 to 2400°F (150 to 1315°C). The molten media generally consist of one or more salts, such as nitrates, chlorides, carbonates, cyanides, or hydroxides. The furnaces are heated by gas, oil, or electricity.

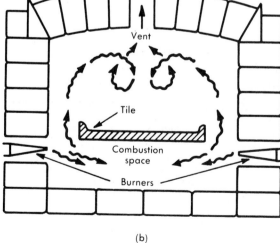

(a)

(b)

Figure 7-9 Direct-fired heat treating furnaces

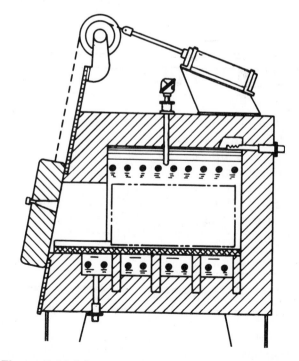

Figure 7-10 (a) Typical batch-type box furnace

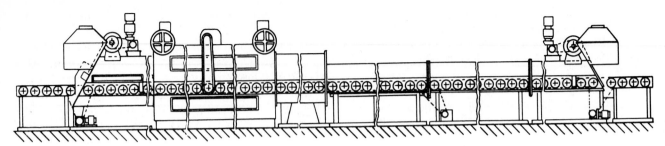

Figure 7-10 (b)   Typical continuous-type furnace

Furnace Types

The two major kinds of salt-bath furnaces are ceramic lined and metal pot types. Ceramic-lined furnaces, used primarily for neutral chloride applications, are generally heated electrically. They are available with submerged electrodes or immersed electrodes that conduct electrical current to heat the bath internally for maximum temperature uniformity. Pot furnaces are externally heated and have less temperature uniformity, typically ± 10°F (6°C).

Vacuum Furnaces

Vacuum furnaces basically consist of a container that is evacuated to create a vacuum in which workpieces are thermally treated by electric radiant heat. Substantial advances have been made during recent years in the design, operation, control, and versatility of vacuum furnaces. As a result, they are being used extensively as an alternative to atmosphere-controlled and salt-bath furnaces.

Fluidized-Bed Furnaces

Fluidized-bed heat processing is performed in a retort containing mobile, inert particles of uniform size that are suspended in a flowing stream of gas. When properly fluidized, the bed attains liquid-like properties, and products are heated by direct immersion. A variety of materials may be used for the bed media, such as aluminum oxide, silicon carbide, or zirconia sand. The primary requirements of the medium are that it be uniform in size and remain inert at operating temperature.

Operating Principles

The general nature of fluidized-bed heat transfer is illustrated in Fig. 7-11 with a graph of the heat transfer coefficient versus fluidizing-gas velocity. Heat transfer characteristics of a fluidized bed fall into three distinct areas. In Section I, the bed is in a static state, with the gas velocity insufficient for fluidization. The

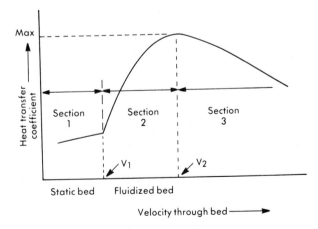

Figure 7-11   Heat transfer coefficient versus gas velocity in fluidized-bed furnace

heat transfer coefficient rises only slightly with relation to gas velocity and is at a low value.

The minimum velocity for the start of fluidization is indicated by V_1 (Fig. 7-11). Across Section 2, the heat transfer coefficient rises rapidly until the optimal velocity V is reached. Beyond this velocity, the bed becomes separated and attains gas-like properties. Thus, in Section 2, the heat transfer coefficient decreases with increasing velocity. See Figs. 7-12, 7-13, and 7-14.

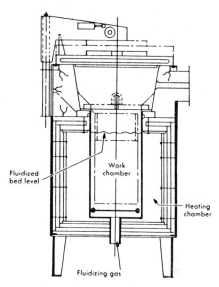

Figure 7-14 Indirectly heated fluidized-bed furnace

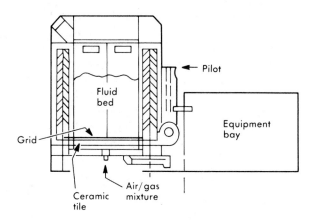

Figure 7-12 Internally fired fluidized-bed furnace

Safety Considerations

Since heat treating presents many potential hazards, a number of precautions are necessary to ensure safety of personnel, equipment, and buildings. Proper design of equipment and control systems, as well as periodic inspection and preventive maintenance are essential. The National Fire Protection Association (NFPA) Standard 86C contains many requirements with respect to furnace design, operation, and safety. Adequate training programs for personnel in proper procedures for operating furnaces are critically important. Furnaces that are out of service for extended periods should be properly maintained and serviced.

Safety Programs

Safety in heat treating requires management commitment and qualified personnel to execute an effective program. The program must also be accepted and supported by well-trained employees.

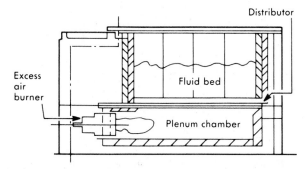

Figure 7-13 Externally fired fluidized-bed furnace

All safety programs should be designed to minimize the exposure of personnel to hazardous conditions.

Safeguards provided to protect workers against hazards include barriers, shields, guards, and other safety devices, as well as warning signs. Thorough training in material handling safety is essential. Adequate ventilation is essential to prevent heat stress, and first aid and medical assistance should be immediately available.

SELECTIVE SURFACE HARDENING

Processes discussed in this section involve surface hardening by thermal treatments—heating and quenching with no chemical change occurring on the surfaces of the work. They thus differ from thermochemical surface-hardening processes in which the chemical composition of steel parts is altered prior to quenching and tempering.

Methods used for surface hardening without any chemical change of the metals are induction, high-frequency resistance, flame, electron beam, and laser hardening. For most applications, these methods are used to harden selected surface layers of parts, but they are also used to harden all surfaces, as well as for through heating of workpieces.

Induction Hardening

Induction heating is based on the concept of electromagnetic inducement of electrical energy into an electrically conductive part. The electrical considerations involve the phenomena of hysteresis and eddy currents, with the major factor being eddy currents. However, the only requirement of a material in order to respond to induction heating is electrical conductivity. An induction heating circuit is fundamentally a transformer wherein the inductor, also called the induction heating coil, carrying the alternating current is the primary of a transformer, and the part to be heated is made the secondary by merely placing it within the confines of or in close proximity to the inductor loop or coil.

There is no contact or connection between coil and workpiece. The current, usually flowing circumferentially through the inductor, sets up magnetic lines of flux in a circular pattern, which link or thread through the material being heated and induce a circumferential flow of electrical current to flow in the workpiece. It is important to note that the current flow pattern in the workpiece is essentially a mirror image of inductor current flow (see Figs. 7-15 through 7-19).

Inductor coil and workpiece configurations are not limited to an encircling arrangement, with the workpiece surrounded by a single-turn or multi-turn (solenoid) coil. Many other configurations are possible: internal, pancake, and other shaped coils.

Encircling-type coils are usually most efficient electrically. Other types, however, can be very effective in heating applications and are used to suit specific application requirements or part handling considerations. Current patterns must be closed loop.

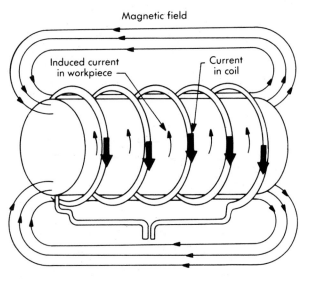

Figure 7-15   Current flow in workpiece is opposite to current flow in coil

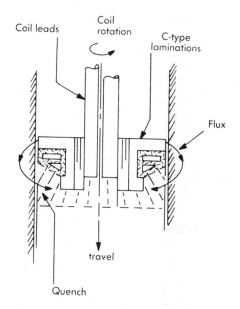

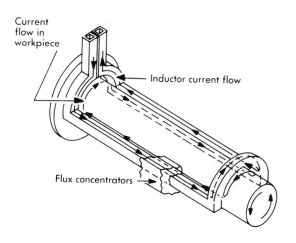

Figure 7-18   Nonencircling single-shot inductor for heating a long shaft

Figure 7-16   Progressive inductor with integral quench for hardening bores

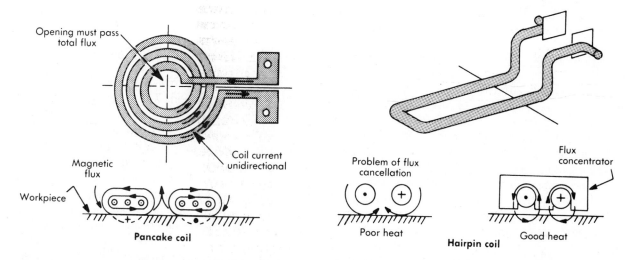

Figure 7-17   Two variations of inductors for surface heating

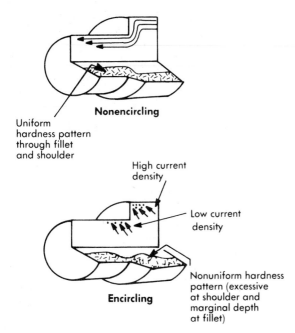

Uniform
hardness pattern
through fillet
and shoulder

Nonencircling

High current
density

Low current
density

Nonuniform hardness
pattern (excessive
at shoulder and
marginal depth
at fillet)

Encircling

Figure 7-19   Comparison of effect of hardening
pattern

High-Frequency Resistance Hardening

High-frequency (400 kHz) resistance heating is used to selectively harden specified areas on the surface of workpieces, rather than entire surfaces. In this way, only those areas most subject to wear are hardened, thus considerably reducing energy requirements and distortion of the workpieces. The fast heating cycles make this process especially suitable for high-production applications.

An advantage of resistance heating with high-frequency current is that a closed loop of current is not required, as is the case with high-frequency induction heating, discussed previously in this chapter. A line or stripe of almost any reasonable shape can be heated between two points. The basic principle is that a block of hardenable steel is arranged

with a pair of contacts on its outer edges. A water-cooled proximity conductor is placed close to the surface to be heated and connected to the contacts. The source of 400 kHz power for heating is typically 50-300 kW, depending upon the area to be hardened.

When 400 kHz current is applied, a shallow line of heat is rapidly generated on the surface of the workpiece, immediately underneath the proximity conductor. In hardening steel, the metal is heated to about 1600°F (870°C), and the power is then turned off. The high power densities generated by this process heat very rapidly (typically in ½ second or less), thus resulting in hardening through self-quenching by the cold steel surrounding the hot stripe.

The depth of the hardness varies from 0.025 to 0.035″ (0.64 to 0.89 mm) in steel, depending upon the time of heating and the power level. Also, two, three, or even four stripes can be hardened simultaneously from a single power source.

The contacts used for high-frequency resistance heating are normally very small, about 3/8″ (9.5 mm) square, and are water cooled. Contact pressure is light, and there is no pitting or marking of the work surfaces under the contacts, although the surfaces must be smooth to begin with.

Flame Hardening

Flame hardening of steels and cast irons is a practical method of developing general or local surface hardness to increase resistance to wear under abrasive conditions and to increase resistance to surface breakdown under concentrated unit loading. Basically, the hardening of structural carbon and alloy steels, tool steels, and cast irons is accomplished by rapid heating of surface areas followed by suitable quenching. Flame-heating equipment may be a single torch with a specially designed head or an elaborate apparatus that automatically indexes, heats, and quenches parts.

Flame hardening has become a standard method of surface hardening as a result of the development of equipment and techniques that have refined the process. Large parts such as gears and machine-tool ways, with sizes or shapes that would make furnace heat treatment impractical, are easily flame hardened. With improvements in gas-mixing equipment, infrared temperature measurement and control, and burner design, flame hardening has been accepted as a reliable heat treating process that is adaptable to many varied applications.

Electron-Beam Hardening

Recent technological advancements have accelerated the use of electron-beam (EB) heat treating (transformation hardening), a relatively new process for localized surface hardening of components made from carbon and alloy steels.

The EB heat treating process uses a concentrated beam of high-velocity electrons as an energy source to selectively heat desired surface areas of ferrous parts. Electrons are accelerated and formed into a directed beam by an electron-beam gun. After exiting the gun, the beam passes through a focus coil, which precisely controls beam density levels (spot size) at the workpiece surface, and then passes through a deflection coil.

The deflection coil allows the beam spot to be moved about on the workpiece surface at speeds to 400,000 ips (10 160 m/s), forming geometric patterns appropriate for the configuration of the zone to be hardened.

Heating patterns are applicable to both the static and traveling methods of EB heat treating. Static methods employ no relative motion between the workpiece and the heating pattern. Traveling patterns generally use workpiece motion to accomplish surface hardening of large areas. Both methods permit an infinite variety of geometric shapes.

The surface of the component being bombarded by the electron beam heats rapidly to a high temperature, confined to the target area of the beam; the rest of the component remains relatively cold.

This rapid and precise buildup of heat, which austenitizes the surface and metal immediately under the surface, normally occurs in 0.5 to 3.0 seconds.

When the beam is turned off, heat flows from the high temperature zone to the region that is still cold. The result of this flow is called self-quenching and is more rapid and just as effective as immersion into a liquid.

Self-quenching is controlled by the mass of the workpiece relative to the volume of metal austenitized, hardenability of the metal, initial temperature of the workpiece, and the rate of heating. Self-quenching produces a martensitic structure with beneficial surface compressive stresses. Surface hardness values are typically one or two Rockwell C points higher than achieved with conventional heat treating processes.

The EB heat treating process therefore consists essentially of the following two primary functions:

1. Distribute the energy delivered by the electron beam over the precise geometrical area to be hardened, thus achieving a uniform surface temperature.
2. Control the beam power as a function of temperature magnitude and time to produce the maximum possible surface hardness to the depth desired.

Laser Hardening

Surface-transformation hardening with lasers (*laser* is an acronym for "light amplification by stimulated emission of radiation") is a relatively new process made possible by the development of high-power industrial lasers. As in other surface-transformation hardening processes, a relatively thin surface layer is generated in which the material has undergone transformation to martensite. The process is limited to materials, such as hardenable cast irons and steels, that are capable of undergoing such a transformation. A carbon content of at least 0.30% is generally necessary to attain any significant hardness in steels.

In surface hardening, only the surfaces of the workpieces need to be heated to the austenitizing temperature, and it is desirable that the surface heating be as rapid as possible. This requirement makes the laser an ideal heat source because it can easily produce the energy fluxes (power densities) needed. In fact, lasers are capable of heating surfaces so rapidly that the required, subsequent quenching occurs by fast heat conduction to the still-cold interiors of the workpieces. This so-called self-quenching is a major advantage of laser surface hardening.

The Hardening Process

For surface-transformation hardening with lasers, the required power density is much lower than for laser welding and cutting, but the exposure time is longer. The power densities for laser hardening generally range from 15.5 to 1550 W/in.² (2.4 to 240 W/cm²). Laser output power is spread uniformly over a relatively large area (spot), typically 0.4" (1 cm) square, depending upon the area to be hardened.

Hardening is performed by moving the spot over the workpiece surface at a controlled speed. With the proper power density and speed, the desired hardened strip is produced. Output power of the laser can be shaped or raster scanned into other forms to cover broad-area spots, but the principle is the same. When more than one path is required to cover an area, consideration must be given to overlap of the paths. Insufficient overlap produces a thinning of the case. Overlap may also cause a tempered zone in the previous path. See Figs. 7-20, 7-21, and 7-22.

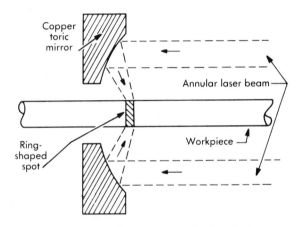

Figure 7-21 Use of toric mirror for hardening OD of cylindrical part

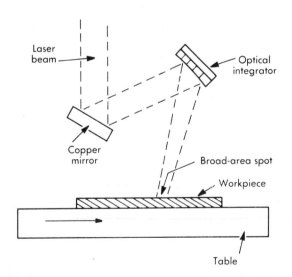

Figure 7-20 Surface hardening a flat plate with an optical integrator

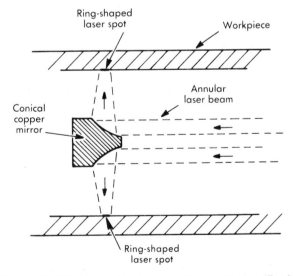

Figure 7-22 Use of toric mirror for hardening ID of hollow cylinder

HEAT TREATMENT OF OTHER METALS

Many other metals besides steels are heat treated. This section provides information on the heat treatment of some of the other, more common metals: titanium alloys; heat-resisting, high-strength alloys; and aluminum, magnesium, and copper alloys.

Titanium and Its Alloys

Titanium and titanium alloys are readily heat treated. The response to heat treatment, however, depends upon the composition of the metal. In general, the more highly alloyed the alloy, the more heat treatable it will be. Not all types of heat treatment are applicable to all titanium alloys. Alpha stabilizers, such as aluminum, in the alloys raise the alpha-to-beta transformation temperature; beta stabilizers, such as vanadium, lower the transformation temperature.

The grain size of titanium and its alloys cannot be refined by heat treatment alone. Either hot or cold working of the metal is necessary for grain refinement. The degree of cold working performed on single-phase alloys also affects the recrystallization temperature and time of heating required. Mixed-phase alloys are recrystallized during hot working and are generally not cold rollable to a degree sufficient to cause grain refinement during recrystallization. The final properties of the heat-treated materials thus reflect the variables introduced during prior cold or hot working.

Types of Heat Treatment

Many types of heat treatment are performed on titanium and titanium alloys to suit specific requirements. The more common treatments include stress relieving, annealing, stabilizing, betatizing, solution treating, and age hardening. Solution treating and age hardening are usually combined in a two-stage thermal treatment to provide high strength. Another heat treatment, recrystallizing, is done at intermediate-to-high temperatures to produce a uniform, dislocation-free microstructure. Recrystallizing may or may not induce grain refinement or a new texture, depending upon prior working of the metal.

Aluminum Alloys

In high-purity form, aluminum is soft and ductile. Most commercial uses, however, require greater strength than pure aluminum affords. Strengthening of aluminum is achieved first by the addition of other elements to produce various alloys, which singly or in combination impart strength to the metal. Further strengthening is possible by means that classify the alloys roughly into two categories, nonheat-treatable and heat-treatable.

Nonheat-Treatable Alloys

The initial strength of alloys in this group depends upon the hardening effect of elements such as manganese, silicon, iron, and magnesium, singly or in various combinations. The nonheat-treatable alloys are usually designated in the 1000, 3000, 4000, or 5000 series. Since these alloys are work-hardenable, further strengthening is made possible by various degrees of cold working, denoted by the H series of tempers. Alloys containing appreciable amounts of magnesium, when supplied in strain-hardened tempers, are usually given a final elevated temperature treatment called *stabilizing* to ensure stability of properties.

Heat-Treatable Alloys

The initial strength of heat-treatable aluminum alloys is enhanced by the addition of alloying elements such as copper, magnesium, zinc, and silicon. Since these elements singly or in various combinations show increasing solid solubility in aluminum with increasing temperature, it is possible to subject them to thermal treatments that will impart pronounced strengthening.

The first step, called solution heat treatment, is an elevated temperature process designed to put the soluble element or elements in solid solution. Solution heat treatment is followed by rapid quenching, usually in water, which momentarily freezes the structure and for a short time renders the alloy very workable. It is at this stage that some fabricators retain this more workable structure by storing the alloys at below freezing temperatures until they are ready to form them.

At room or elevated temperatures the alloys are not stable after quenching, however, and precipitation of the constituents from the supersaturated solution begins. After a period of several days at room temperature, termed aging or room temperature precipitation, the alloy is considerably stronger. Many alloys approach a stable condition at room temperature; but some alloys, particularly those containing magnesium and silicon or magnesium and zinc, continue to age harden for long periods of time at room temperature.

By heating for a controlled time at slightly elevated temperatures, even further strengthening is possible, and properties are stabilized. This process is called artificial aging or precipitation hardening. By the proper combination of solution heat treatment, quenching, cold working, and artificial aging, the highest strengths are obtained. Aging for extended periods of time or at high temperatures can result in a reduction of mechanical properties. Restoration of the properties requires repeating the cycle of solution treatment, quenching, and aging.

Magnesium Alloys

Like many other metals, magnesium alloys are heat treated to improve their mechanical properties or to facilitate fabrication. The type of heat treatment used depends upon the specific alloy, the form of the product (wrought or cast), and the service require-

ments. Die castings are not usually heat treated; but sand, investment, and permanent-mold castings are generally heat treated to improve their properties. See Fig. 7-23.

Magnesium Alloy	Starting Temper	Annealing Temperature, °F (°C)
AZ Commercial	F	650 (345)
AZ31B	F, H24, H26	650 (345)
AZ31C	F	650 (345)
AZ61A	F	650 (345)
AZ80A	F, T5, T6	725 (385)
HK31A	F, H24	750 (400)
HM21A	F, T5, T8, T81	850 (455)
HM31A	F, T5	850 (455)
ZK60A	F, T5, T6	550 (290)

* Time at temperature is one hour minimum, no maximum.

Figure 7-23   Annealing temperatures for various wrought magnesium alloys

Annealing

Annealing of magnesium alloys is generally restricted to wrought products. This treatment is performed to achieve maximum ductility, but also results in lowered mechanical properties. The temperatures employed for annealing range from 550 to 850°F (290 to 455°C), depending upon the alloy.

Recommended temperatures for annealing some of the more common magnesium alloys are presented in Fig. 7-23. The time the workpieces are held at these temperatures is generally one hour or more, with no maximum time limit.

Solution Treating and Aging

Solution heat treatment of the thermally responsive magnesium alloys provides maximum toughness and shock resistance. Artificial age hardening (precipitation heat treatment) after solution heat treatment

Magnesium Alloy	Temper	Solution Heat Treatment		Artificial Age Hardening		Ultimate Tensile Strength, ksi (MPa)	
		Temperature, °F (°C)	Soak Time, hr	Temperature, °F (°C)	Soak Time, hr	Typical	Minimum
Sand, investment, and permanent-mold casting alloys:							
AM100A	T61	775 (415)	18[b]	400 (205)	24	40 (276)	34 (234)
AZ63A	T6	725 (385)	12	425 (220)	5	40 (276)	34 (234)
AZ81A	T4	775 (415)	18[b]	---	---	40 (276)	34 (234)
AZ91C	T6	775 (415)	18[b]	335 (170)	16	40 (276)	34 (234)
AZ92A	T6	765 (405)	18[c]	425 (220)	5	40 (276)	34 (234)
EZ33A	T5	---	---	650 (345)	2	---	---
				then 420 (215)	5	23 (159)	20 (138)
HK31A	T6	1050 (565)	2[d]	400 (205)	16	32 (221)	27 (186)
HZ32A	T5	---	---	600 (315)	16	30 (207)	27 (186)
QE22A	T6	975 (525)	8	400 (205)	8	40 (276)	28 (193)
ZE41A	T5	---	---	625 (330)	2	---	---
				then 350 (175)	16	30 (207)	28 (193)
ZH62A	T5	---	---	625 (330)	2	---	---
				then 350 (175)	16	40 (276)	35 (241)
ZK51A	T5	---	---	350 (175)	12	40 (276)	34 (234)
ZK61A	T6	930 (500)	2	265 (130)	48	40 (276)	30 (207)
Extruded solid shapes:[e]							
AZ80A	T5	---	---	350 (175)	16	55 (379)	48 (331)
HM31A	T5	---	---	425 (220)	16	44 (303)	37 (255)
ZK60A	T5	---	---	300 (150)	24	52 (359)	45 (310)
Extruded tube:[e]							
ZK60A	T5	---	---	300 (150)	24	50 (345)	46 (317)
Sheet and plate:							
AZ31B	H24	---	---	275 (135)[f]	2	37-42[e] (255-290)	29-39[e] (200-269)
AZ31B	H26	---	---	250 (120)[f]	2	38-40[e] (262-276)	35-39[e] (241-269)
AZ31B	0	---	---	650 (345)	2	36-37[e] (248-255)	32[g] (221)
HK31A	H24	---	---	620 (325)[h]	1	37-39[e] (255-269)	33-34[e] (228-234)
HM21A	T8	---	---	715 (380)	1	33-37[e] (228-255)	30-33[e] (207-228)

[a] Heated magnesium alloy parts are generally cooled in air, with a fan or fans, after removal from the furnace. However, some alloys, such as QE22A, are sometimes quenched in water or other suitable media from the solution heat treating temperature.

[b] As an alternative, if necessary to prevent grain germination, soak for 6 hours at 775° F (415° C), 2 hours at 665° F (350° C), and then 10 hours at 775° F.

[c] As an alternative, if necessary to prevent grain germination, soak for 6 hours at 765° F (405° C), 2 hours at 665° F (350° C), and then 10 hours at 765° F.

[d] Furnaces should be heated to temperature before loading castings.

[e] Tensile strengths vary with metal thickness.

[f] Partial annealing after strain hardening; not age hardening.

[g] Maximum tensile strength of 40 ksi (276 MPa) for complete annealing.

[h] Temperature applies only to sheets. For plates, soak at 400° F (205° C).

Note: Magnesium-aluminum-zinc casting alloys, such as AZ63A, AZ81A, AZ91C, and AZ92A alloys, should be slowly heated (for about 2 hours) from 500 to 700° F (260 to 370° C).

Figure 7-24   Solution heat treatment and age hardening of some magnesium alloys

usually results in maximum strength and hardness, with some reduction in toughness and ductility.

Recommended temperature/time cycles for solution treating and aging some of the more common magnesium alloys and product forms are presented in Fig. 7-24. The temperatures and times given are typical for various workpiece sizes and different production methods. As a result, they may not be optimum for a specific workpiece.

For cast magnesium alloys containing thorium, such as HK31A and HZ32A alloys, it is advisable to bring the furnace load to temperature as fast as possible to avoid grain coarsening. For other alloys, the furnace load can be raised to temperature more slowly, thus guarding against melting of eutectic compounds and minimizing condensation on workpiece surfaces, with resultant staining.

Stress Relieving

A stress-relieving heat treatment is sometimes required for wrought magnesium alloy parts. Such a treatment will reduce the residual stresses present due to welding or cold working operations, such as forming or bending. Stress relieving is also required for some castings to reduce residual stresses caused by welding, contraction resulting from mold restraint, preferential cooling after heat treatment, or machining.

The temperatures and time cycles recommended for stress relieving in this section are intended to reduce stresses and provide practical dimensional stability, while not affecting mechanical properties. See Fig. 7-25.

Wrought Magnesium Alloy	Temper/Product Form	Stress-Relieving Temperature, °F (°C)	Soak Time, min
AZ Commercial	All tempers and forms	500 (260)	15
AZ31B	Extrusions, forgings, and annealed sheets	500 (260)	15
AZ31B	H temper sheets	300 (150)	60
AZ61A	Extrusions, forgings, and annealed sheets	500 (260)	15
AZ61A	H temper sheets	400 (205)	60
AZ80A	F temper	500 (260)	15
AZ80A	T5 and T6 tempers	400 (205)	60
HK31A	F and O tempers	650 (345)	60
HK31A	H24 temper	550 (290)	30
HM21A	F, T5, and T8 tempers	700 (370)	30
HM21A	T81 temper	750 (400)	30
HM31A	F and T5 tempers	800 (425)	60
ZK60A	F temper	500 (260)	15
ZK60A	T5 and T6 tempers	300 (150)	60

Figure 7-25   Stress-relieving temperatures and times for various wrought magnesium alloys

Coppers and Copper Alloys

The wrought coppers and many copper alloys are single-phase metals. As a result, heat treatment is limited to the annealing of cold worked metal for recrystallization or stress relieving. Castings are also sometimes annealed to soften them and increase their ductility and/or toughness. Annealing may be carried out in roller-hearth, batch-type, and strip or strand-annealing furnaces. Since some lubricants on the metals can cause staining, such lubricants should be removed before annealing. Furnace atmospheres should be controlled to suit the composition of the metal being annealed in order to minimize oxidation.

Castings and billets of copper alloys are sometimes given a homogenizing heat treatment to reduce chemical segregation and to attain the required hardness, ductility, or toughness. Homogenizing consists of heating to temperatures above the upper annealing range and soaking at temperature for up to ten hours. Temperatures and times vary with the alloy, the size of the cast grains, and the desired results.

KEY TERMS AND PHRASES

Aging
Annealing
Austenitizing
Batch-type furnace
Boronizing
Carbonitriding
Carburizing
Chromizing
Cold Treatment
Continuous flow furnace
Electron-beam hardening
Equalizing

Flame hardening
Fluidized-bed furnaces
H steels
Hardenability
Hardenability bands
Heat treatment
High-frequency resistance hardening
Induction hardening
Laser hardening
Nitriding
Normalizing
Quench cracking
Quenching
Residual stresses
Salt-bath furnaces
Scaling
Solution treating
Stress relieving
Surface (case) hardening
Tempering
Vacuum furnaces

QUESTIONS FOR ADDITIONAL STUDY AND REVIEW

1. Explain how most heat treating operations can be classified.

2. Describe the following heat treatment operations:

   • Austenitizing
   • Equalizing
   • Cooling

3. Explain four problems commonly associated with hardening steels.   P 152

4. Describe the process of solution treating.

5. Describe the process of aging.

6. Explain the following heat treatment processes:

- Tempering
- Annealing
- Normalizing
- Cold treatment

7. What is surface hardening?

8. Describe the following case hardening processes:

- Carburizing
- Nitriding
- Carbonitriding
- Chromizing
- Boronizing

9. Describe three different types of heat treating furnaces.

10. What are the key elements of an effective safety program in heat treating?

11. Describe the following selective surface hardening processes:

- Induction hardening
- High-frequency resistance hardening
- Flame hardening
- Electron-beam hardening
- Laser hardening

12. Explain how titanium is heat treated.

13. What are nonheat-treatable aluminum alloys?

14. Explain the process of annealing magnesium alloys.

15. What is the difference between continuous type and batch heat treating furnaces?

CHAPTER 8

Broaching and Sawing

MAJOR TOPICS COVERED

Broaching

Broaching is a process for internal or external machining of flat, round, or contoured surfaces. Machines of different types are used to push or pull a multitooth cutting tool or the workpiece in relation to each other to remove material. Each tooth on the cutting tool (broach) is generally higher than the preceding tooth (see Fig. 8-1). As a result, the depth of the cut increases as the operation progresses.

Generally, broaching machines differ from other machine tools in that they provide only cutting speed and force—the feed is built into the broach. Infeed, however, is provided by the workholding fixture for some applications. Another exception is helical broaching in which the machine provides rotary motion.

Broaching also differs from other machining processes in that roughing, semifinishing, and finishing teeth are often positioned along the axis of a single tool. This permits completing an operation in a single pass. Several types of broaches are

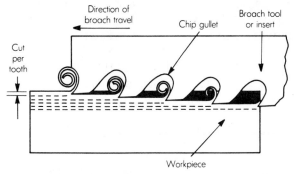

Figure 8-1   Broach tool

175

sometimes used in combination to cut different surfaces on the workpiece simultaneously.

Broaching applications are of two major types: external (surface) broaching and internal broaching. Both types are used for machining configurations ranging from flat surfaces to complex contours on or in workpieces varying from small precision components to very large parts made from any different materials. For some applications both external and internal broaching are combined in one operation. While broaching is generally not considered to be a heavy stock removal operation, there are applications of surface broaching in which ½" (12.7 mm) or more of stock is removed in a single pass.

Workpieces with internal surfaces to be broached require a starting hole for insertion of the tool. Surfaces to be broached must be parallel to the direction of tool or work travel, but uniformly rotating sections such as helical gear teeth can be broached by rotating the tool or work as each moves in relation to the other. No obstructions such as protuberances on or in the workpieces can block the passage of the broach, but blind holes may be broached by limiting the travel of a series of short push-type broaches. A recess, however, larger in diameter than the hole to be broached must be provided at the bottom of the blind hole for chip space.

Surface broaching applications are practically unlimited. Any external form can be produced as long as the surfaces are in a straight line and unobstructed. Such forms include slots and keyways, flat and contoured surfaces, rack and gear teeth, and serrations.

An infinite number of forms can also be produced by internal broaching. In addition to machining round, square, rectangular, and other shaped holes, the process is used to cut contoured surfaces, keyways, splines, serrations, and gear teeth. This method is also used to rifle the bores of gun barrels. Starting holes for internal broaching are generally produced by casting, forging, punching, drilling, or boring.

Advantages of Broaching

Important advantages of broaching include high productivity, the capability of maintaining close tolerances and producing good finishes, economical operation, and versatility.

Productivity: When the process is properly applied, with the right machines and tools, broaching can remove metal faster than any other machining method. Broaching is competitive with many other machining processes, particularly milling and occasionally grinding, and high production rates are common. The ability to rough and finish machine in one pass increases productivity. Smaller parts are often stacked and broached in multiple in a single pass; larger parts are often produced two at a time. The availability of semiautomatic and automatic loading/unloading and material handling equipment, as well as improved machine controls, further increases productivity.

Accuracy and Finishes Produced: Broaching is capable of consistently maintaining close tolerances because of its inherent accuracy. Several surfaces on a workpiece can also be held in accurate relationship because the relationship is built into the tooling.

Surface finishes produced are smooth compared to many other machining processes, and noncutting burnishing elements can be provided on the finishing end of the broach to further improve the finish obtained. In many applications the need for subsequent grinding has been eliminated.

Economical Operation: While initial tool costs can be high unless standard tooling is employed, cost per workpiece produced is generally low because of long tool life. This is the result of the comparatively low cutting speeds used in broaching and the small portion of total stock removed by each tooth. Long tool life provides the additional benefit of reducing downtime for tool replacement.

Today there is increased availability of standardized, general-purpose tooling that permits more economical broaching for many applications. The use of automation equipment and automatic machine controls permits employing unskilled or semiskilled operators, which can further reduce operational costs.

Versatility of Broaching: Broaching can be used for a wide range of workpiece sizes—from small screw machine parts, components formed by cold heading or other methods, and stampings to large castings, forgings, and weldments. The process is also suitable for machining many different materials.

External surfaces on several parts can often be broached simultaneously on wide-ram machines. Universal machines are available to perform a variety of operations, including push and pull broaching and external and internal cutting.

An old misconception that still persists is that broaching is limited to high production requirements necessitating special and costly machines and tools. Instead, broaching is being used for shallow cuts and finishing operations, as well as heavy stock removal in some applications, and even short runs are now often economical. The availability of standard and universal machines plus general-purpose tooling makes small-lot production of families of parts both feasible and economical.

Limitations of the Process

As previously mentioned, workpieces must be suitable for broaching. The surfaces to be broached must be of uniform rotation or parallel to the direction of tool or work travel, and there cannot be any obstructions in the path of the tool. Complex contoured surfaces with curves in two or more planes cannot be formed in a single broaching operation, with the exception of helical surface broaching. In surface broaching, it is not possible to broach to a shoulder if the shoulder is not parallel to the broach axis. Internal broaching requires starting holes in the workpieces. Tapered holes generally cannot be broached, but with some materials, such as aluminum, a tapered swedge can be mounted at the end of a broach. Parts to be broached must also be strong enough to withstand high thrust forces or must be adequately supported.

The high forces produced in broaching require rigid machines and workholding devices which add to capital equipment costs. When special machines and

tools are required, production requirements must be sufficient to economically justify the higher costs.

While light burrs are sometimes produced in broaching, they can generally be removed easily by conventional methods such as brushing or tumbling.

Types of Broaches and Broach Design

Broaches, the cutting tools used for broaching, in their simplest form consist essentially of a slightly tapered round or flat bar with rows of cutting teeth located on one or more surfaces. Because the teeth are stepped, additional stock is removed as each successive tooth contacts the workpiece. Broaches can be classified according to their purpose or use (internal, external, or combination); method of use (pull, push, helical, or rotary); construction (solid or sectional); and required surface finish (form relieved or generating).

The standard nomenclature used to describe essential parts of most broaches is presented in Fig. 8-2 which illustrates a typical round internal pull-type

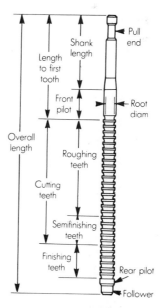

Figure 8-2   Typical internal broach nomenclature

broach. Fig. 8-3 contains additional terms pertaining to broaches. In using an internal pull-type broach, the pull end and front pilot are passed through a starting hole in the workpiece and the pull end is locked to the pull head of the broaching machine. The front pilot on internal pull-type broaches ensures correct axial tool alignment with the starting hole and also serves as a check on the starting-hole size. The rear pilot on the broach, which has a diameter slightly less than that of the finishing teeth, maintains tool alignment as the final finishing teeth pass through the workpiece hole. A notched retriever end is often added to the broach to engage a handling mechanism that supports the rear of the tool.

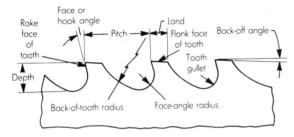

Figure 8-3   Terminology used to describe the geometry of broach teeth

Cutting Action and Wear: The cutting action of broaches is essentially the same as that for all other tools which remove metal by shear deformation. As each tooth moves across the workpiece surface, the material in front of the tooth is sheared to form a chip which travels up the rake face of the tooth. When brittle materials such as cast iron are broached, the chips usually break into small segments. When ductile materials such as mild steel are broached, the chips are less likely to break and will tend to coil in the tooth gullets. When certain ductile materials are broached, the material adheres to the tip of the tooth and form a built-up edge (BUE). The BUE generally grows in size until it becomes unstable. When this happens, part of the BUE will adhere to the chip moving up the rake face; the remainder will pass under the clearance face of the tool, producing a rough deposit on the machine workpiece surface.

Metalcutting tools generally fail as the result of wear taking place simultaneously on the rake and flank faces of the tools. In most broaching operations, however, very little wear takes place on the rake faces because of the low cutting speeds and protection provided the rake faces by the BUEs. The bulk of the wear on a broaching tool occurs on the tooth flank (clearance face) in the tooth gullet. Flank wear is generally used to determine tool life. While the BUE helps protect the rake face, breakdown of the BUE causes small bits of tool material to be torn from the tool flank. As abrasive and adhesive flank wear progresses, surface finish suffers and dimensional accuracy is reduced. Broaching of high-temperature alloys, in particular, is characterized by short tool life resulting from rapid flank wear.

Tooth Geometry: The cutting edges or teeth on a broach increase in size (usually height) or change in shape from the starting end to the finishing end of the broach. Each tooth takes a bite of fixed thickness; this bite, called chip load, corresponds to the feed rate in most other machining operations and cannot be altered by the machine operator.

The teeth on each round or slotting-type broach are usually divided into three separate sections and function as roughing, semifinishing, and finishing teeth. The first roughing tooth is proportionately the smallest tooth on the broach. Subsequent teeth progressively increase in size up to and including the first finishing tooth. On many broaches, all finishing teeth are the same size, but on others, a slight step is provided, primarily to compensate for any elastic springback of the workpiece. Teeth on spline broaches are divided into sections indicative of the workpiece surfaces broached; i.e., round, spline generating, major diameter finishing, minor diameter finishing, and in the case of full-form finish broaching, involute profile finishing.

Broach Materials: Most broaches are made of high-speed steels (HSSs). A list of the more commonly used HSSs and the materials normally broached with them is presented in Fig. 8-4. HSSs made by powder metallurgy processes are becoming

Broach Material	Materials Broached and Special Applications
High-Speed Steel, AISI Type:	
M2	General purpose broaching of low and medium-carbon steels with a hardness of R_C34 or less, alloy steels with a hardness of R_C32 or less, aluminum, brass, magnesium, low-alloy bronze, nylon, plastic, lead, and copper.
M3-1	Medium-carbon steels with a hardness of R_C35-42, alloy steels with a hardness of R_C33-38, work-hardening bronze, and alloyed cast irons.
M3-2	Cast iron, aluminum diecastings, stainless steels, graphite, and malleable iron.
M4	High-silicon steels, silicon bronze, aluminum diecastings, and armature-grade iron.
M42	Medium-carbon steels with a hardness of R_C35-42, steel forgings, stainless steels, cast steels, work-hardening bronze, malleable iron, and tool steels. Used as a substitute for M2 HSS at broaching speeds above 50 fpm (15.24 m/min).
T15	High-temperature alloys, stainless steels, titanium, Stellite, work-hardening bronze, silicon iron, and silicon bronze.
Powdered Metal High-Speed Steel	For high-speed applications. Can be used in place of M2, M3, T15, and other high-speed steels to obtain longer tool life.
Tungsten Carbide	For broaching gray cast irons and for high-speed broaching applications.

Figure 8-4 Materials commonly used for broaches to cut various materials

increasingly popular for large broaches, those having a diameter greater than 6″ (152 mm), and broaches used at higher cutting speeds. Some tool manufacturers are also using these materials for smaller broaches with good results.

Cutting Fluids for Broaching: As is the case with other machining operations, successful broaching often depends on the proper selection and application of a cutting fluid. Accuracies maintained, surface finishes produced, and tool life are all sensitive to temperature changes during broaching and can be improved with the proper cutting fluid.

Primary functions of a cutting fluid used for broaching are:

1. Lubricating the chip/tooth interface, thus reducing friction and heat, decreasing wear, and minimizing the development of built-up edges when broaching certain materials.
2. Keeping the tool and workpiece cool by carrying away the heat generated, thus permitting more accurate broaching and the production of smoother surface finishes.
3. Washing chips away from the tooth gullets, thus preventing possible damage and lengthening broach life.

Selection of a cutting fluid depends on the specific broaching application including the material to be broached, design of the broach and machine, operating parameters, and production requirements. The use of a proper cutting fluid can sometimes improve chip formation, resulting in desirable curled chips. Some materials are broached dry. Some applications require a fluid with higher cooling capabilities; while for others, the fluid's lubricating properties are more important.

Broach Sharpening: Allowing broaches to become too dull can result in damaged teeth, excessive power requirements, the production of inaccurate parts with poor surface finishes, and the need to remove more material from the broaches than desirable, thus shortening tool life. It is advisable to constantly monitor tool wear and keep careful performance records after each production run. Doing this will help in determining when the broaches should be resharpened.

The purpose of resharpening is to restore keen cutting edges and the original tooth geometry. Broaches are often returned to the manufacturer for resharpening, but resharpening can be done by the user with proper care. The following recommendations apply only to sharpening HSS broaches. Carbide broaches are generally of the indexable insert-type and are seldom reground.

Internal broaches. Internal broaches are sharpened by grinding only the faces of the teeth. Removing metal from the tops of teeth would change the dimensions of the broached surfaces.

Grinding of the tooth faces requires that the wheel be inclined at an angle greater than the face angle of the teeth to avoid interference. An approximate formula for determining the wheel angle is:

$$W = \frac{FD}{R}$$

where:

W = wheelhead angle, degrees
F = face angle of broach tooth, degrees
D = grinding wheel diameter, in. or mm
R = root diameter of tooth, in. or mm

Surface broaches. Flat surface broaches are also generally resharpened on the faces of the teeth, but they may be reground on the tops of the teeth if excessive wear lands exist. When this is done, the original dimensions of the broach can be reestablished by adjusting the holder or placing shims under the broach. The gullets must be reground to their original depths so that adequate chip space is maintained.

Because of the rapid stock removal possible with broaching at conventional speeds, the limiting factor for many applications is material handling rather than cutting speed. Doubling the cutting speed will not double production; it merely shortens part of the cycle since cutting time is generally only a small percentage of total cycle time. Even with complete automation, the loading, clamping, unloading, and ejecting of workpieces usually takes longer than the cutting. As a result, improved automation can often offer more potential for higher production than increased speeds. Slight reductions in broaching times, however, can result in substantial yearly cost reductions, depending on the number of parts produced.

Problems that have been encountered in the design of high-speed broaching machines include controlling the high forces resulting from rapid acceleration and deceleration of heavy masses (machine ram and tooling). Another limitation is the present state of the art with respect to high-pressure hydraulic technology. Heat transfer from the hydraulic cylinders to the machine slides, guideways, and frame must also be minimized. Other problems involve optimizing the design of the machine and broach tooling and selecting the best cutting fluid. Chip formation, which is different when broaching at higher speeds, can cause packing in the tooth gullets when cutting some materials.

Broaching Machines

Broaching is done on a variety of types of equipment, including portable units, hand-held pulling units, and machines ranging from small manually operated or powered arbor presses to large horizontal surface broaching machines. Conventional presses, however, are multifunction machines and are seldom used for production broaching. Major requirements for any broaching machine include accurate relative motion between the tool and workpiece and rigid construction to withstand the high forces encountered. Most machines are of simple design and are very reliable.

Classification of Machines: Broaching machines can be classified by operational characteristics and/or the type of operation performed when the machines are properly tooled. With respect to the direction of cutting stroke, broaching machines are classified as vertical, with the axis of the cutting stroke perpendicular to the floor; horizontal, with the cutting stroke parallel to the floor; and special, which encompasses all other variations or combinations. They can be further classified as surface, internal, and universal or combination broaching machines.

Types of power used to drive the broaching machines are also used to describe them. Machines are powered hydraulically or mechanically, with hydraulic drives in greatest use for vertical and smaller horizontal machines. Some machines, however, such as continuous (chain) types and large, horizontal surface broaching types, are almost exclusively powered electromechanically. With the energy savings possible with electromechanical drives, this type of power is now being used on other broaching machines.

Further classification of broaching machines is based on operational characteristics such as single or dual-ram, pulldown or pullup, pushdown or pushup, rotary, continuous, pot-type, and blind spline.

Vertical Surface Broaching Machines:
Single-ram broaching machines. Standard vertical surface broaching machines with a single ram and downward cutting stroke are available in sizes from 1 ton (8.9 kN), 18″ (457 mm) stroke to 50 ton (449 kN), 120″ (3048 mm) stroke, and larger size machines are available on special order. Most are equipped with an in-and-out motion shuttle table or a tilting-type table that allows the operator to unload and reload during the return (upward) stroke of the machine ram. Vertical surface broaching machines are usually adaptable to automatic workpiece handling and most have power take-off or an auxiliary power supply for clamping and fixture motion. Machines equipped with wide rams can sometimes hold two or more sets of broaching tools to machine several workpieces simultaneously.

Cutting speeds on these single-ram vertical surface broaching machines are generally adjustable or variable. On hydraulically powered machines rated at 10 tons (89 kN) or more, the speed range is usually 25-60 fpm (7.6-18.3 m/min) with 100 fpm (30.5 m/min) being common in Europe. Some small hydraulic machines are available with maximum speeds approaching 300 fpm (91.4 m/min). Some larger machines, powered electromechanically, have speeds to 200 fpm (61 m/min).

Vertical machines having strokes longer than 24″ (610 mm) require either an elevated platform for the operator or a pit in the floor for the machine. Available ceiling clearance heights must be considered when ordering such machines, and a means for chip removal should be provided when floor pits are provided for machine installation.

. Cutting tools for vertical surface broaching machines are generally mounted in broach holders to form an assembly. An adapter plate is attached to the machine ram and the subholder assembly is bolted and cross-keyed to the main holder. For high-volume production requirements, it is common practice to have three holders, one on the machine, a second preassembled for standby use, and a third in the cutter grinding department.

Dual-ram broaching machines. Dual-ram machines operate like two single-ram vertical surface broaching machines mounted side by side in a common frame, with the two rams moving alternately upward and downward. These machines are preferable to single-ram machines for high production requirements because they permit one operator to load and unload in front of one ram on its return stroke while broaches on the other ram are in the cutting mode.

Production rates on dual-ram machines are not double that of two single-ram machines, however, because the speed of the return stroke must be the same as the cutting speed of the alternate ram. Usually a 60-70% increase in productivity can be achieved by tooling both rams to perform the same operation as previously done on a single-ram machine. Workpieces requiring multiple broaching passes can often be transferred from one ram to the other with reduced part handling. In such cases, however, the longest cutting stroke required will determine the stroke of each ram.

Dual-ram machines are usually not practical for operations requiring less than 42″ (1067 mm) of stroke because the short ram-return time is generally not sufficient to permit loading/unloading. Cutting speeds do not normally exceed 60 fpm (18.3 m/min) for hydraulic machines of this type or 200 fpm (61 m/min) for electromechanically powered machines. All other considerations are the same as for single-ram machines.

Vertical Internal Broaching Machines:
Standard vertical internal broaching machines are available in sizes from 2 ton (17.8 kN), 12″ (305 mm) stroke to 75 ton (667 kN), 120″ (3048 mm) stroke and are made in various styles for different

applications and production requirements. The length of the broach tool to be used in relation to its cross section may determine whether it must be pulled or pushed through the workpiece because the tool is stronger in tension than compression.

Pushdown broaching. Vertical internal broaching machines of the pushdown type are basically presses, most of which are of C-frame construction and hydraulically powered. In some cases, the broach is attached to the machine ram and is pushed downward and pulled upward through the work-piece—a process called strip broaching. For most applications, however, the broach drops into a catcher tray after being pushed through the workpiece or a lower powered slide is provided to lift the broach for retrieval.

Pushdown vertical internal broaching is normally used only for low-volume production or for applica-tions requiring manual alignment of the broach with respect to the workpieces. Some high-volume appli-cations exist, however, primarily for burnishing-type jobs. In all cases, stock removal is usually minimal.

Pullup broaching. The pullup method was the original one used on vertical machines for internal broaching. Workpieces are manually or automatically placed in alignment with the broach pull-shank, and the broach is raised through both the workpiece and a thrust plate called a platen until the upper end of the broach engages an automatic broach puller. The upward pulling motion of the broach lifts the workpiece until it contacts a bushing fixture mounted on the platen. Cutting force holds the workpiece against the bushing face until the broach is pulled through, after which the workpiece drops onto a sloping surface for gravity ejection from the machine.

Standard pullup vertical machines for internal broaching are available in sizes from 6 ton (53.4 kN), 24″ (610 mm) stroke to 50 ton (445 kN), 72″ (1829 mm) stroke. Practically all of these machines are hydraulically powered and generally tooled to pull from one to six broaches simultaneously. Problems with chip disposal, cutting fluid application, and the handling of large and heavy workpieces, however, make them undesirable for some applications, and they are now specified less frequently.

Pulldown broaching. The pulldown method of broaching is by far the most commonly used on vertical internal broaching machines. Pulldown broaching is often preferred to the pullup method because large workpieces can be handled more easily and because gravity helps the cutting fluid reach the cutting teeth and facilitates chip removal. Progressive work, in which several broaches are used in succession, is easier to perform, and the machines lend themselves well to automatic loading and unloading.

The construction of vertical internal broaching machines of the pulldown type varies to suit different applications. Small table-top machines often rely on the operator for manual handling of the workpieces and broaches and have one or two stations. High-speed machines usually range in size from 5 ton (44.5 kN), 24″ (610 mm) stroke to 20 ton (178 kN), 48″ (1219 mm) stroke and are available with one to four stations and cutting speeds of about 120 fpm (36.6 m/min).

Machines with a way-type main slide and a movable, upper broach-handling slide are the most common. The broach-handling slide travels in unison with the main slide throughout the cutting stroke for maximum broach support and alignment. Pulldown slide-type vertical internal broaching machines generally range in size from 4 ton (35.6 kN), 24″ (610 mm) stroke to 75 ton (667 kN), 120″ (3048 mm) stroke, with one to six stations and cutting speeds to 100 fpm (30.5 m/min). Most are hydraulically powered, and a few have electromechanical drives.

Pulldown slide-type and high-speed vertical internal broaching machines are usually equipped with shuttle tables that move in and out or with automatic loading/unloading fixtures. Floor pits or operator platforms are required for machines having strokes longer than 24″ (610 mm).

Vertical Combination Broaching Machines:
Vertical combination (universal) broaching machines feature a swing-away or detachable tool-handling slide for internal broaching and a machined slide face for surface broach tooling. On three-way

machines the broach can be pushed down for broaching external surfaces or pushed or pulled down for cutting internal surfaces.

These machines are of the slide type, and most are hydraulically powered. They are generally available in sizes from 4 ton (35.6 kN), 18″ (457 mm) stroke to 15 ton (133.4 kN), 36″ (914 mm) stroke, with cutting speeds to 50 fpm (15.2 m/min). The combination machines are usually employed for job shop or multiple operation requirements.

Horizontal Internal Broaching Machines:
At one time, horizontal machines were the predominant type used for internal broaching. Today, however, with the high cost of floor space and a generally lower productivity rate compared to vertical machines, they represent less than 10% of the broaching machines purchased. They are still used where ceiling heights prohibit vertical machines, for large and heavy broaching tools that require in-line pulling, for small tools that require manual handling, for some special low-profile equipment that is adaptable to automated transfer lines, and for short-run job shop applications.

Horizontal internal broaching machines have a box-type framework with a platen on one end. The platen is equipped with a clearance hole to allow the broaches to be pulled through the stationary workpieces in a horizontal direction. A pulling head rides on ways within the machine frame and is aligned with the hole in the platen. Most modern machines have optional outboard and inboard broach supports. They can be supplied with automatic equipment for broach handling and workpiece loading and unloading.

Sizes of horizontal machines for internal broaching generally range from 1 ton (8.9 kN), 18″ (457 mm) stroke to 100 ton (89 kN), 120″ (3048 mm) stroke. The first machines of this type were screw driven; however, this type drive is now obsolete. Most machines are now hydraulically powered. The hydraulic cylinder is mounted on the machine frame, at the opposite end from the platen, and aligned with the pulling hole and head to provide in-line

pulling force. Some machines are electromechanically driven.

Horizontal Surface Broaching Machines:
In a class by themselves, large horizontal machines for broaching external surfaces are used extensively by the automotive industry for heavy stock removal. Surfaces are machined on large parts such as cast engine blocks, cylinder heads, manifolds, and bearing clusters, with stock removals of ¼″ (6.4 mm) or more using carbide broach inserts. Close tolerances are maintained and smooth surface finishes produced, and the machines have proven to be reliable and efficient with little downtime for toolchanging and maintenance.

One-way and two-way broaching machines. These horizontal surface broaching machines are made in single-station, one-way models that cut in one direction only and in two-way models that are capable of cutting in both directions. Workpieces are cradled in swing-up fixtures. On two-way machines for V-type and in-line engine blocks, the pan-rail, half-bore, and bearing-lock surfaces are broached as the machine ram moves in one direction. Then an automatic transfer mechanism moves the block to a rollover fixture that rotates the casting 180°. The head joint face or both bank faces on the block are broached on the return stroke of the ram.

Horizontal surface broaching machines were originally powered hydraulically and available in sizes to 30 ton (267 kN), 120″ (3048 mm) stroke, with cutting speeds from 30-100 fpm (9-30.5 m/min). Most machines today are driven electromechanically and are available in sizes over 100 tons (890 kN), with strokes to 30 ft (9 m) and speeds to 200 fpm (61 m/min) for cast iron or 300 fpm (91 m/min) for aluminum.

With the introduction of thin-wall iron and aluminum castings to reduce weight and increase the fuel efficiency of car and truck engines, problems were encountered because of the possibility of breaking weaker sections of the castings due to the high cutting loads. Deflection of the thinner casting ribs also created problems in maintaining required surface flatness. These problems, however, have been solved by changing the design of the tooling and using lighter chip loads.

Continuous broaching machines. Continuous chain-type surface broaching machines consist of a horizontal framework having a drive sprocket mounted at one end and an idler sprocket at the opposite end. These sprockets support and power a pair of parallel, continuous chains which move workholding fixture carriers suspended between them. The carriers are guided by a set of ways within the machine frame, and the broaching tools are mounted in a tunnel on top of the machine (see Fig. 8-5).

Workpieces to be broached are manually or automatically placed in the moving fixtures at one end of the machine. Clamping of the workpieces in the fixtures is generally done automatically, and safety devices can be provided to automatically stop the machine if misaligned workpieces or workpieces with excessive stock are detected before they enter the broaching tunnel.

Properly aligned workpieces with the correct amount of stock are pulled through the stationary broachholder assembly (tunnel) to complete the broaching operation. The workpieces are auto-matically unclamped and ejected from the fixtures by gravity at the other end of the machine.

Production rates from continuous broaching machines are high, usually from four to ten times that of vertical surface broaching machines. This is because of the continuous cutting action and elimination of the noncutting portion of other broaching machine cycles. Productivity from these machines can also be varied by changing the speed of the chain or increasing or decreasing the number of fixtures used; the maximum number of fixtures is limited by the length and tonnage capacity of the machine.

High production requirements are necessary, however, to justify the high cost of these machines. Their use is also usually restricted to workpieces small enough to pass through the tunnel and sturdy enough to permit gravity ejection without damage. Automatic loading and unloading equipment is available for most workpieces.

While stationary tooling is most common on these continuous machines, one variation, used for heavy stock removal, is to mount the broaches on the chain-driven carriers to cut a stationary workpiece. This adaptation has been used with the chains operating

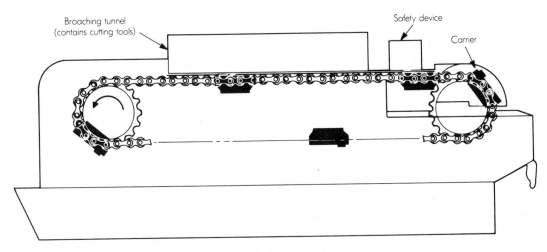

Figure 8-5 Schematic of a continuous surface broaching machine

horizontally (over, under, or alongside the stationary workpiece) and vertically, with the chains making one complete revolution each cycle. Chain lengths up to 480″ (12 192 mm) are possible. Continuous broaching machines designed for this modified method are generally restricted to special applications because of the high cost of the equipment.

Conventional continuous machines are generally available with ratings from 2.5-60 tons (22.2-533.8 kN) and broach tunnels from 18-250″ (457-6350 mm) long. Cutting speeds are usually adjustable through change gears from 12-60 sfm (3.7-18.3 m/min); some continuous machines have d-c motor drives that provide infinitely adjustable speeds within a given range. One manufacturer offers machines with hydrostatic hydraulic drive that permits variable speeds and constant torque.

Special Machines: Pot broaching machines.

Pot broaching derives its name from the hollow surface-type broaching tool assembly, called the pot, which is used to surround a workpiece for broaching external contours, such as gear teeth, splines, slots, and cam surfaces, in a single pass. Pot broaches are assembled from ring or stick-type cutting tools, or a combination of both.

One of the older methods of pot broaching consists of mounting the workpiece on a post-type fixture and pushing the pot broach assembly, which is mounted on the ram of a vertical surface broaching machine, downward to cut the part. With this method, work unloading is automatic but loading is done manually and can slow the operation.

Modern machines designed specifically for pot broaching have a stationary pot assembly. Three types of machines are available: pushdown, pushup, and pullup. Pushup pot broaching, in which workpieces are pushed up through the stationary pot, offers the advantages of chips falling, by gravity, away from the tool and workpiece; simple work feeding; easy loading and unloading; and simplified toolchanging.

Pullup pot broaching, in which workpieces are pulled up through a stationary tooling pot with a pull head (see Fig. 8-6) permits broaching of parts having deeper teeth and wider faces by using longer tools.

These machines, however, must be higher than pushup machines because the upper end of the pull rod has to be retracted below the workpiece with a retriever and the lower end has to be pulled up past the top of the pot for unloading.

Most pot broaching machines are hydraulically powered and generally range in size from 1 ton (8.9 kN), 12″ (305 mm) stroke to 50 tons (445 kN), 48″ (1219 mm) stroke. Cutting speeds usually vary from 30-120 fpm (9.1-36.6 m/min), but special machines are available with speeds to 240 fpm (73.2 m/min.)

Other special broaching machines. Many other types of broaching machines are available for specific applications. One example is short-stoke vertical broaching machines with dial index tables for cutting internal or external shapes on workpieces having interference surfaces that prevent passing conventional broaches completely over or through the workpieces. Tooling stations on the index table hold a series of broaches, either punch or ring-type, and

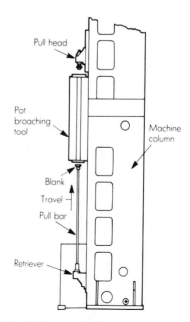

Figure 8-6 Pullup pot broaching machine

the workpiece is retained in a fixture attached to the machine ram. As each broach station is indexed under the workpiece, the ram strokes downward to cut and upward to strip the workpiece from the tool. This cycle is repeated until the last broach has completed the operation.

Most machines of this type are hydraulically powered, with ratings of 4-30 tons (35.6-267 kN) and strokes of about 6″ (152 mm). The machines can generally be furnished with automatic loaders and unloaders and lend themselves well to in-line automation.

Operating Parameters

Cutting speeds, feeds, and depths of cut used for shaping and slotting vary widely for different applications. The cutting speed depends primarily on the material to be cut (including its hardness and condition), the depth of cut and feed, and the material from which the cutting tool is made. Typical cutting speeds range from 25 fpm (7.6 m/min) or less for some high-alloy steels to 140 fpm (42.7 m/min) or more for some brasses and bronzes.

Depths of cut and feeds vary with the power capacity of the machine being used, length of stroke, rigidity of the setup, amount of stock to be removed, and surface finish requirements. Depths of cut range to 0.125″ (3.18 mm) or more and feeds from 0.008 to 0.050″ (0.20 to 1.27 mm) or more per stroke. Slower cutting speeds are generally required for deeper cuts and higher feeds.

Cutting fluids are usually not required for planing, shaping, and slotting operations because of the intermittent contact of the tools with the workpieces. Also, the chips produced generally fall clear of the tools and need not be flushed away by the application of a fluid. There are applications, however, in which the use of a cutting fluid is desirable to maintain close tolerances, produce smooth surface finishes, or minimize built-up edges on the tools. In such cases, the fluid should be directed at the cutting area and the flow maintained continuously throughout the cutting stroke.

SAWING

Sawing is a machining process in which straight, band, or circular blades having a series of small teeth are employed to cut various materials. Practically every manufacturing firm uses wire, shaped bars, tubes, pipes, extrusions, structural shapes, sheets, plates, castings, or forgings. These materials generally must be cut to required lengths for subsequent processing by machining, press forming, or assembly.

Although several methods of cutoff, sometimes called slugging, exist, sawing with power hacksaws, bandsaws, and circular saws is one of the more widely used methods.

Cutoff is also done on lathe-type cutoff machines with single-point tools. On turret lathes and automatic bar machines, workpieces can be cut from the stock with a parting tool after machining.

Another method of cutoff is gang milling using a bed-type machine with a number of side-tooth slitting saws and a side milling cutter on each end of an arbor. Flame cutting can be used in the production of slugs; however, it has only limited application because of the rough surfaces produced and possible effects of burning, hardening, or softening of the cut surfaces. Slugs used for press-forming operations are often produced by shearing, heading combined with shearing, the nick-and-break method, or blanking.

In spite of the variety of cutoff methods available, many shops find that sawing slugs for use on chucking-type automatics, as well as for other applications, is preferable because this method of cutting is often easier, faster, and less costly.

Power Hacksawing

Power hacksawing is characterized by the reciprocating action of a relatively short, straight, toothed blade that is drawn back and forth over the workpiece in much the same manner as a hand hacksaw. It differs from other sawing methods in that the back-and-forth motion of the blade makes a noncontinuous cut.

The power hacksaw was the first practical cutoff machine. Modern heavy-duty machines provide an economical and efficient means of sawing a wide range of materials and stock sizes. They are used extensively for utility needs and in smaller shops in which production requirements are not high.

Advantages

A major advantage of power hacksawing is the relatively low capital investment required. The machines themselves are moderate in cost; however, stock feeds, automatic controls, and other accessories and attachments can add substantially to the price.

Hacksawing machines are easy to set up and simple to operate. Unskilled or semiskilled help can be used, and one operator can often attend two or more machines. Tooling costs are low, and the comparatively thin blades used are inexpensive enough to make it economically feasible to throw the blades away when they become worn, rather than resharpen them. Maintenance costs also are low because of the simple design and operation of these machines.

Versatility is another important advantage of power hacksawing. The machines can handle most cutting requirements including practically all materials, a wide range of stock sizes within their capacities, and any cutoff length. Hacksawing is often more practical and economical than bandsawing for cutting large workpieces with thick cross sections, especially when cutting materials that are somewhat difficult to machine.

Accuracies maintained and finishes produced with power hacksawing range from fair to good depending on the material being sawed. Tendency for the hacksaw blades to twist or deflect is minimal. Since power hacksawing machines can provide fairly accurate cuts in hard materials, they are often preferred for cutting tough forgings, hardened tool steels, and similar materials.

Limitations

A major disadvantage of power hacksawing machines is that they are slower than bandsawing and circular sawing machines. The cutting action is noncontinuous, and only half of each reciprocating stroke is productive. Noncutting time, however, has been reduced on modern machines (discussed next in this chapter) by the development of systems for more rapid return strokes. Bundling of stock for multiple cutting also increases productivity.

The reciprocating action of hacksawing prohibits the use of blade supports close to the area of cutting. This may cause bowing of the blade and some inaccuracy. For this reason, hacksaw blades are made thicker than the bands used on bandsawing machines, thus requiring more power and producing more chips. The kerf (cut width) in hacksawing, however, is less than that in circular sawing. Kerf varies from 0.092-0.183″ (2.34-4.65 mm) with regular hacksawing blades. Power hacksawing is essentially a roughing operation, and at least 0.002″ (0.05 mm) should be left on cut surfaces for finishing.

Blade wear in power hacksawing is uneven because only part of the blade is used for cutting since the arms holding the blade obstruct use of the blade ends. Also, the necessity for stopping and reversing the direction of blade travel at the end of each stroke causes the cutting speed to vary, thus reducing efficiency.

Hacksawing Machines

Hacksawing machines consist of a supported reciprocating frame and saw blade mounted to a base for supporting the work. They are available in several basic designs. Horizontal machines are the most popular. On column or way-type horizontal machines, the supporting member (carrying the reciprocating frame and saw blade) is mounted on one or more vertical columns or uprights with ways. This supporting member is fed downward in a vertical plane on the column(s) to saw the workpiece(s). On some machines angular cuts can be made by swiveling the supporting member and columns on the machine bed.

On hinge-type horizontal machines the supporting member carrying the reciprocating frame and saw blade is mounted on the back of the machine base. Feeding produces a scissor-type motion with the reciprocating blade moving downward in an arc and a vertical plane for sawing. Small portable hacksawing machines with retractable wheels are also available.

Vertical machines have the support for the reciprocating frame and saw blade mounted on the rear of the machine base, with the frame reciprocating in a vertical plane. The supporting member is fed horizontally toward the front of the machine, and the reciprocating blade saws the fixed workpiece(s).

All hacksawing machines have means, either mechanical or hydraulic, of lifting the saw frame at the completion of the cut and keeping it raised during the noncutting return stroke. Means for adjusting the stroke length are also standard. While single-speed machines are available, most are equipped with transmissions to provide from two to six different cutting speeds. Some have infinitely variable cutting speeds with a constant, but faster, return speed.

Completely automatic power hacksawing machines perform the following steps:

1. Feed stock through the open workholding vise or fixture.
2. Gage length to required dimension.
3. Close and lock clamping vise or fixture.
4. Feed blade through the stock.
5. Raise the blade at the end of the cut.
6. Open the vise or fixture.

This automatic cycle is repeated until the final cut has been made (of a preset number of slugs or at the end of the stock), after which the machine is stopped. Figs. 8-7 through 8-11 are examples of modern power hacksaws.

Figure 8-7 BSM210/240 hacksawing machine (Courtesy of Kasto-Racine, Inc.)

Figure 8-8 BSM253 hacksawing machine (Courtesy of Kasto-Racine, Inc.)

Figure 8-9   BSM403 hacksawing machine
(Courtesy of Kasto-Racine, Inc.)

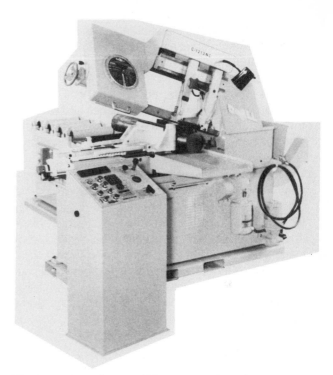

Figure 8-11   C-1213-NC automated sawing system
(Courtesy of DoAll Co.)

Figure 8-10   BSM220A hacksawing machine
(Courtesy of Kasto-Racine, Inc.)

Hacksaw Blades

Power hacksaw blades made from different materials, in a variety of sizes and pitches and with different tooth geometries, are available. Selecting the best blade for a specific application depends on many factors including the cross-sectional area and hardness of the material to be sawed, cutting speed, blade strength, tooth geometry, and tension. Practically all blades have only one cutting edge, consisting of teeth extending almost the full length of the blade. A pinhole or pinholes are provided near each end of the blade to fit over pins on the saw frame or bow of the machine.

Proper tensioning of the blades on the machines, usually accomplished with adjustment nuts, is critical to minimize blade deflection or wandering and possible failure due to buckling under heavy cutting loads. The degree of tension applied depends primarily on the blade material, length, thickness, and width; whether the machine cuts on the push or draw stroke; and the sawing results obtained. Some machines have systems to automatically sense and indicate the tension, and portable devices such as stretch gages for clamping to the blades and showing the tension on a dial indicator are available. Overtensioning can cause the premature breakage of blades.

Blades will bow (curve away from the work) under heavy cutting forces. Some bowing is allowable; however, if it results in excessive flexing, the blade tension should be increased or a stronger blade should be used. This problem can be minimized by using blades with pinholes closer to the cutting edge. With this design, the tensioned blade is bowed slightly away from the work when not cutting and straightens during sawing, thus minimizing wandering. Some machines permit the use of backup bars to provide additional support for blades.

Blade Materials: Three types of materials are generally used for power hacksaw blades. The tips of the teeth on all three types typically have a minimum hardness of R_C62. Blades made from the through-hardened tool steels are seldom used for production applications, but they are sometimes employed for cutting soft metals, for one-of-a-kind jobs, or for general utility requirements.

Blades made from high-speed steels that have only the tooth area hardened are widely used for sawing many different materials. They provide good cutting characteristics, but can present a safety hazard in that they have a tendency to shatter if they break under tension.

Composite or bimetal blades, consisting of a HSS cutting edge welded to an alloy steel body or backing, are becoming increasingly popular. This design allows the backing material to be selected for maximum resilience and fatigue resistance. These blades permit safer operation at higher speeds and feed pressures. Like blades made from the other materials, these blades have cutting edges that are hardened to a minimum of R_C62, but the hardness of the body is usually a maximum of R_C52.

Sizes of Blades: Blade size depends primarily on work and strength requirements. The length of the blade should be as short as possible—not much more than the maximum width of the work to be sawed. Blades for power hacksawing generally range from about 12-53" (305-1346 mm) in nominal length, with a usual tolerance of ± 1/16" (1.6 mm). Long, wide blades are available in segmental styles, and worn or broken sections can be selectively resharpened or replaced.

Blade widths usually vary from ⅝" (16 mm) for light-duty sawing to 4⅝" (117.5 mm) for heavy-duty applications, with a tolerance of ± 1/32" (0.8 mm). Thicknesses generally range from 0.032" (0.81 mm) for light-duty to 0.150" (3.81 mm) for heavy-duty use, with a tolerance of ± 0.003" (0.08 mm). Blades must have sufficient thickness to withstand feed pressures applied and to provide the necessary rigidity to minimize flexing. Shorter, heavier blades assure straight cuts, give more cuts per blade and per hour, and reduce blade breakage. Dimensions and tolerances of both hand and power hacksaw blades are presented in ANSI Standard B94.52-1977 "Hack Saw Blades."

Pitch of the Teeth: Pitch, the distance between adjacent teeth on the saw blade, depends primarily on the hardness of the material to be cut and the cross-sectional area of the workpiece. At least two or three teeth should be engaged with the work at all times during sawing, and as coarse a pitch as possible should be used. Blades with fewer teeth per inch and larger tooth gullets are generally preferable for softer materials and solid bars. For average sawing conditions, blades with six teeth per inch are widely used for bars 1-5" (25-127 mm) diam, four teeth per inch for bars 5-8" (127-203 mm) diam, and three teeth per inch for bars larger than 8" diam. Blades with 10-18 teeth per inch are generally used for bars less than 1" (25 mm) diam.

Power hacksaw blades are available with from 2½ to 18 teeth per inch, but pitches of 4, 6, 10, and 14 are the most commonly used. Some machine builders claim that a wide variety of materials and work sizes can be sawed with the same pitch blade because the machine controls compensate for the variables.

Tooth Geometry: The most widely used tooth geometry for power hacksaw blades is the regular or standard straight tooth design shown in view *a* in Fig. 8-12. This design has a 0° rake angle, a straight 56° back angle, and a full, round gullet for chip clearance. Another geometry sometimes used on blades with coarser pitches has a positive rake angle or undercut (generally 10°), a shallow cutting-edge clearance angle (usually 15°), and a rounder flank surface, as shown in view *b* in Fig. 8-12.

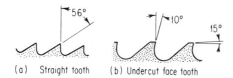

Figure 8-12 Straight tooth geometry (a) and undercut face tooth (b)

Tooth Set: Tooth set is the lateral projection of the teeth from the centerline of the blade to provide cutting clearance and prevent binding. Overall set is the total distance between the outer corners of oppositely set teeth. Overall set determines the kerf (width of cut). Three types of tooth set are:

1. <u>Alternate set</u> in which the teeth are flared alternately to the right and left (Fig. 8-13a).
2. <u>Raker set</u> in which every third tooth is straight (unset) and the succeeding two teeth are flared alternately to the right and left (Fig. 8-13b).
3. <u>Wavy set</u> in which groups of teeth (two or more) are flared alternately to the right and left. This type set is not recommended for power hacksawing and is used infrequently, only for fine-pitch blades—24 or 32 teeth per inch (Fig. 8-13c).

Another type of set, not illustrated, is the modified raker in which the conventional raker set (one tooth right, one tooth left, and one unset) is reversed in the subsequent set of three teeth.

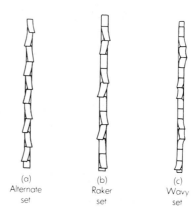

Figure 8-13 Three types of tooth set

Workholding for Hacksawing

As previously mentioned, multiple rollers for positioning and lifting large, heavy stock are desirable. Automatic machines often have roller-chain or lead-screw bar feed systems. A large and substantial swivel-type or variable position vise is often used to permit miter cutting. Presetting locators for angles commonly sawed are also useful. Some vises are designed with interchangeable jaws for special workholding requirements, and some have two movable jaws. For cutting short lengths, a vise that clamps on either side of the blade is useful. Swivel-type or variable position vises can only be used on machines with manual stock feeds. Automatic machines generally have a material sensing function, and the vise cannot be moved without affecting accuracy.

For maximum economy, as much stock should be gripped in the vise as the blade and machine will cut in one setup. Several methods of clamping multiple parts in a power hacksaw are illustrated in Fig. 8-14. Various nesting equipment, including clamps and extensions, is available for efficient bundle cutting. Bundle cutting, however, is not always practical for production applications.

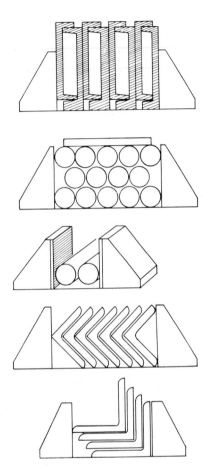

Figure 8-14　Various methods of clamping multiple parts in a power hacksaw

Recommendations for clamping various types and shapes of workpieces in conventional clamping vises include the following:

1. Thin strips should be as flat as possible.
2. Short ends of stock should be cut singly to assure proper clamping and accuracy.
3. Hexagonal stock should be laid on the plane of the bar. For multiple cutting, however, almost any arrangement is satisfactory.
4. Round bar stock, when cut in multiples, should be arranged in a square or rectangular bundle. The bars should be interlocked in layers with every other layer having one less bar than the first and last layer for more secure clamping and, more importantly, for constant contact of the saw blade with the work without interruption from layer to layer.
5. Tubing should be clamped in the same manner as round stock.
6. Multiple or nested cutting of angles, channels, and other structural shapes can be done by loading the vise as shown in Fig. 8-14.
7. In most cases, an overhead guide bar should be used when clamping workpieces for multiple cutting. When the workpieces are clamped with the movable vise jaw, the parts will readjust their positions and automatically arrest themselves against the overhead guide bar, thus being rigidly clamped from the top and side.

Operating Parameters for Hacksawing

Cutting speeds in strokes per minute are not directly proportional to cutting rates in feet per minute for all hacksawing machines because of different stroke lengths and/or methods of blade reciprocation. The maximum speed—strokes per minute (spm)—at which a machine can be operated is limited by the peak blade speed developed during the cutting stroke. The peak blade speed is limited by the characteristics of the blade. Machines equipped with fast return strokes (previously described) can operate at higher effective spm's without exceeding the peak blade speed and thereby causing blade failure due primarily to excessive heat at the cutting teeth.

Speeds for power hacksawing generally range from 25 to 165 spm, with the maximum speed employed only for cutting some carbon and free-machining steels. When the materials to be cut are hard, heat treated, and/or rough, the use of a lower cutting speed is usually more efficient and economical because blade life will be lengthened. Excessive speeds, too light a feed pressure, or dull blades can cause work hardening of some materials such as austenitic stainless steels, high-temperature materials containing nickel, and some soft, ductile, low-carbon steels.

Bandsawing

Power bandsawing, often called band machining, uses a long endless band with many small teeth traveling over two or more wheels (one is a driven wheel, and the others are idlers) in one direction. The band, with only a portion exposed, produces a continuous and uniform cutting action with evenly distributed, low, individual tooth loads. Bandsawing machines are available in a wide variety of types to suit many different applications.

The cutting action of bandsawing differs from other sawing methods in that its continuous, single-direction cutting action, combined with blade guiding and tensioning, gives it the ability to follow a path that cannot be duplicated with power hacksawing and circular sawing. The bandsaw blade or band can follow the cutting teeth along any path over which it is guided, making radii or contour cuts possible. Band teeth cut with a shearing action and tend to take a full, uniform chip.

Advantages

Versatility is one of the most important advantages of power bandsawing. The process is not limited to the use of conventional saw bands with cutting teeth; at least nine known methods of band machining exist. These methods are as follows:

1. Conventional sawing, used primarily for cutoff, contour cutting, and slotting.
2. Friction sawing, used for the high-speed cutting of hardened ferrous metals, nonferrous metals, and nonmetallic materials.
3. Diamond-band machining for cutting glass, carbide, semiconductor and graphitic materials, ceramics, and quartz.
4. Electroband (electrical discharge) machining, generally used on aluminum, copper, stainless steel, and titanium honeycomb material, as well as other fragile, cellular structures.
5. Band filing for light stock removal, particularly on internal surfaces, from a wide variety of materials.
6. Band polishing for burr removal and finishing surfaces previously sawed and/or filed.
7. Scallop-edge, wavy-edge, and knife-edge bandsawing, used primarily for cutting soft and fibrous materials that may tear, fray, or otherwise result in poor surface finishes when cut with tooth-type bands.
8. Spiral-edge bandsawing for the omnidirectional (360°) cutting of intricate patterns in thin pieces of metal, plastic, and wood.
9. Abrasive wire bandsawing, used primarily on CNC machines for the omnidirectional cutting of difficult-to-machine materials and for finishing dies, cams, and other complex-shaped parts.

Contour band machining offers several major advantages over other machining methods: rapid cutting to shape, safe and easy operation, raw material savings, and relatively low costs. All these advantages result from the way the bandsawing machine removes unwanted material in sections instead of wasted chips, thus increasing production efficiency. Less time is required to saw around a section than to produce chips, and the resulting unwanted section can sometimes be used to manufacture other products.

This ability to create fewer chips also makes the process the most material and energy efficient of the three basic types of cutoff sawing machines used to produce slugs for further processing. Bandsawing produces a smaller kerf (width of cut) than hacksawing or circular sawing for any given stock size range, thus reducing energy requirements and material losses in the form of chips. Stated another way, more slugs or workpieces can be produced from any given amount of stock. This factor becomes increasingly significant with more expensive materials and as material costs rise.

Limitations

There are few limitations to the use of power bandsawing. The versatility of the process makes it suitable for a wide variety of applications on many different materials and sizes of workpieces. Machines equipped with bimetallic bands are used to saw materials with hardnesses to 464 Bhn (R_C49). Even harder materials can be cut with friction sawing or abrasive-edge bands.

Rigidity of the band used decreases with an increase in the distance between saw guides, but the cutting rates do not decrease proportionately. Cut widths to 52″ (1320 mm) can be made in alloy steel with an unsupported 2″ (51 mm) or wider band, and cut widths to 62″ (1575 mm) can be made with a wide band having backer-bar support.

Factors which influence cutting rates when sawing wide workpieces include the pitch, width, thickness, and tension of the band; the rake angle and sharpness of the teeth; the hardness of the material being sawed; and the band speed. When sawing narrow work widths, tooth construction is the limiting factor with respect to maximum cutting rates. If a maximum cutting rate is assumed to be just under the rate that will tear out the tooth tips, the rate can be maintained for increasing work widths until the cutting edge of the band goes into compression rather than tension. Then the limiting factor becomes the beam strength of the band and feed force must be reduced to maintain a straight cut.

A reasonably accurate rule-of-thumb is that allowable feed force is inversely proportional to the span between the saw guides—double the span, half the rate. For example, if the maximum cutting rate for a narrow band when sawing a given material to 6″ (152 mm) diam is 20 in.²/min (129 cm²/min), the maximum cutting rate for 12″ (305 mm) diam would be 10 in²/min (64.5 cm²/min). Published cutting rate charts will generally not support such calculations because they rarely show maximum cutting rates for every diameter.

A typical sawing accuracy cited by many manufacturers of bandsawing machines is ± 0.002″ (0.05 mm) per inch of cut. This tolerance is fairly standard, but because of the many variables for different applications, closer tolerances can often be maintained. Surface finishes of 450-500 μ in. (11.4-12.7 μ m) are commonly produced, but smoother finishes can be obtained by using slower feeds, finer pitch bands, higher band speeds, or a combination of these variables.

While bandsawing is most often associated with the cutting of metal or wood, this process is being used for sawing a wide variety of materials ranging from asbestos to zirconium. Although bandsawing is used for operations such as filing, polishing, and others previously listed, by far the largest single application is sawing. The basic bandsawing operations are cutoff, contouring, and slotting. Practically all sawing applications consist of one or more of these operations (see Fig. 8-15).

Production cutoff operations are normally performed on semiautomatic or automatic machines designed specifically for this purpose. Contouring is nearly always done on vertical bandsawing machines, most of which have tables that tilt. A tilting table permits both straight and contour cuts to be made at angles to, as well as parallel to, flat workpieces. This three-dimensional shaping allows complicated parts to be made quickly; some examples are shown in Fig. 8-19.

Bandsawing Machines

Bandsawing machines have evolved from the simple two-wheel vertical machine on which the operator pushed a workpiece through the band into sophisticated machine tools made in many types. They are now available in two-, three-, or four-wheel versions. Contouring, vertical, horizontal, tilt-frame, angle, cutoff, plate, friction, and universal are some of the names used to designate various types. Some manufacturers offer combination vertical/horizontal bandsawing machines for light- to medium-duty cutting of a variety of materials. Figs. 8-16, 8-17, and 8-18 are examples of modern bandsaws. Fig. 8-19 illustrates the types of cuts possible on contouring-type bandsaws.

Saw Bands and Other Tools

Selecting the proper type of band tool for a specific application is of critical importance. Factors that

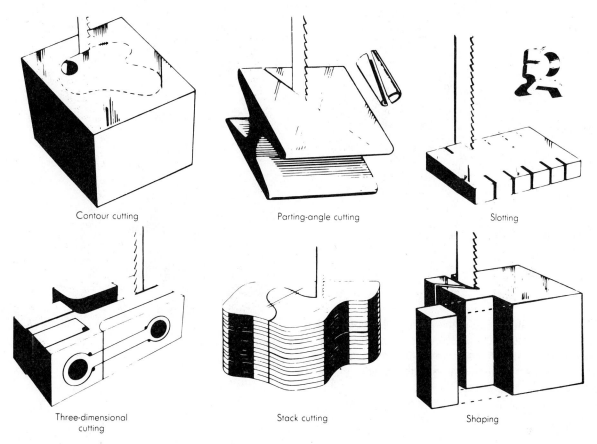

Contour cutting   Parting-angle cutting   Slotting

Three-dimensional   Stack cutting   Shaping
cutting

Figure 8-15   Bandsawing operations (Courtesy of DoAll Co.)

should be considered in band selection include the following:

1. Type and hardness of material to be cut, which determine the tooth form and composition of the band to be used.
2. Size and variations in cross section of the stock to be cut, which dictate the pitch of the teeth required.
3. Type of cut required—whether straight, contour, or both. The need to cut small radii will limit the width of the band.
4. Type and condition of the machine to be used.
5. Production requirements.
6. Whether a cutting fluid will be used.
7. Overhead costs.

Conventional Sawing: Toothed bands with different tooth geometries and hardnesses for specific applications are used for conventional bandsawing methods. Terminology generally accepted for saw bands is presented in Fig. 8-20.

Tooth geometries. There are three major types of tooth forms, generally classified as standard (regular), skip, and hook teeth, as illustrated in Fig. 8-21. The standard tooth form has a zero rake angle and a full rounded gullet with a smooth radius. Bands with standard teeth are the most versatile and are recommended for intricate contouring and straight cutoff work. They are also widely used to meet smooth finish requirements, to cut thin work, and when small radii are needed.

Figure 8-16   Tilt-frame band machine (NC) (Courtesy of DoAll Co.)

Figure 8-17   NC band sawing machine (Courtesy of Kasto-Racine, Inc.)

The skip tooth has the same form as the standard except that the gullet is lengthened by omitting every other tooth to handle larger chip loads. The skip tooth is recommended for accelerated cutting of nonferrous metals, plastics, and woods.

The hook tooth has a lengthened gullet, similar to the skip tooth form, and a positive rake angle— up to 10° depending on the manufacturer, type of band, and application. Teeth with positive rake angles tend to pull themselves into the work. As a result, they penetrate the work with less feed pressure than teeth with no rake. Bands with hook teeth permit fast cutting of all metals, plastics, and woods and are generally recommended for sawing hard materials and penetrating work-hardening metals.

Recent variations of the three major tooth forms include one having a standard tooth form except for a 5° positive rake angle instead of none. Other modifications have been introduced in an attempt to reduce the noise level on applications requiring interrupted cuts, such as with structural shapes or tubing. Bands for this purpose use a combination of pitches and/or a combination of set angles and gullet depths to prevent the buildup of sustained resonant conditions by imparting different frequencies that tend to dampen each other.

Figure 8-18   Block-bandsawing machine (Courtesy of Kasto-Racine, Inc.)

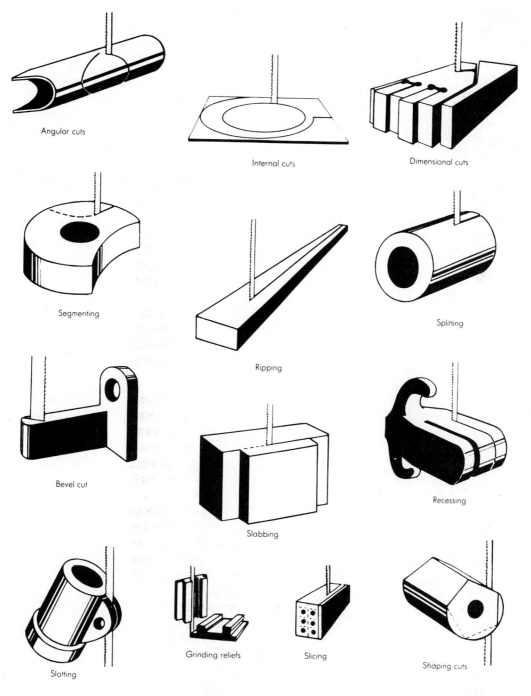

Figure 8-19   Three-dimensional cutting possible on contouring-type bandsawing machines (Courtesy of DoAll Co.)

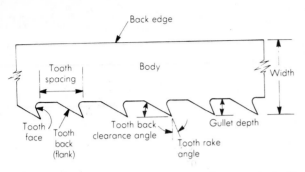

Figure 8-20   Terminology commonly accepted with respect to saw bands

Workholding and Fixturing for Bandsawing

Horizontal cutoff and tilt-frame bandsawing machines are usually equipped with from one to four sets of vises, depending on the machine size and application. The vises serve as workholders for most operations because the stock is generally long and the saw simply cuts it into shorter pieces. With three or more vises, remnants or bar ends can be minimized or reduced to lengths of 1/2″ (12.7 mm) or less. Special fixturing is available from machine manufacturers or other sources when required.

Vertical contouring machines cut many different shapes that may require special fixturing. Most

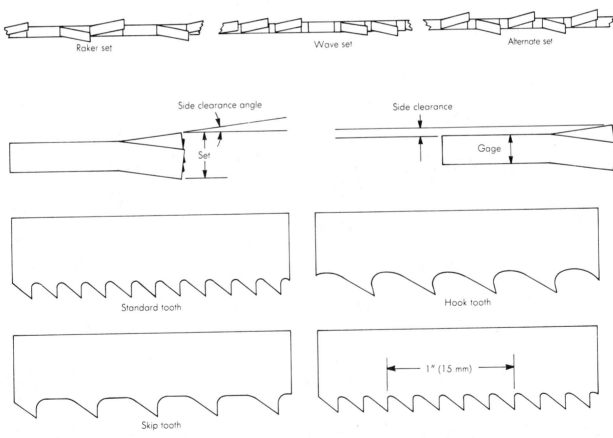

Figure 8-21   Types of tooth forms and sets widely used on bands for bandsawing

builders offer standard options such as rip fences, work squaring bars, clamps, universal vises, workholding jaws, ball transfers, table extension bars, protractor-type work stops, and other devices to accommodate many requirements.

Because the downward cutting force of a saw band tends to hold a workpiece on the machine table, elaborate holding and guiding devices are seldom needed. Simple standard attachments, such as those illustrated in Fig. 8-22, are capable of holding and/or guiding work for most operations. There are, however, reasons for using special holding or guiding devices; these include the following:

1. To hold or support irregularly shaped stock, unstable stock, or thin material.
2. To improve the accuracy and/or the repetitive accuracy of the sawing operation.
3. To facilitate the production of large quantities of identical workpieces.
4. To lessen operator fatigue.
5. To make the operation more automatic and thus faster and less costly.

Every workholding device must have at least two locating points or surfaces—called primary and secondary locators—to hold the part in place. These locators are established from a datum line in the case of castings or forgings, from a reference dimension in the case of previously machined parts, or from a predetermined layout line placed on the workpiece.

Operating Parameters for Bandsawing

When the proper band has been selected for a specific operation, it is placed on the wheels of the machine. The saw guides are then adjusted, and the band is tensioned according to the manufacturer's instructions.

Speeds and Feeds: A rule-of-thumb for conventional bandsawing is: the harder the material to be cut, the lower the band speed; the softer the material, the higher the band speed. While some aluminum alloys can be sawed at band speeds to 7000 sfm (2134 m/min), most stainless steels are sawed at 75-150 sfm (23-46 m/min).

Thickness of the material to be cut also influences the band speed to be used. Generally, thinner sections are sawed with higher band speeds than thicker sections. The recommendations of machine builders and band manufacturers with respect to band speeds and feed rates for sawing various materials should be followed.

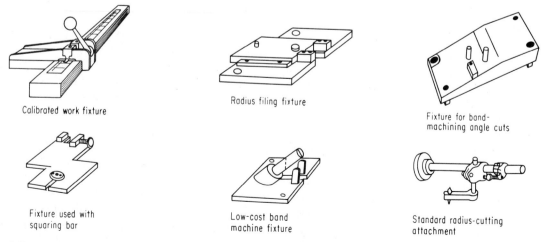

Calibrated work fixture

Radius filing fixture

Fixture for band-machining angle cuts

Fixture used with squaring bar

Low-cost band machine fixture

Standard radius-cutting attachment

Figure 8-22   Typical simple fixtures that can be used for power bandsawing

Cutting Fluids: Proper selection and use of a cutting fluid is critical to optimum sawing.

Stainless steels and some other hard alloy steels are sawed best with a sulfur-based cutting oil. Band speeds, however, should not exceed 150 sfm (45.7 m/min) when using oil because the resulting smoke may be objectionable.

Metals that are difficult or moderately difficult to machine and are sawed at speeds of 150-300 sfm (45.7-91.4 m/min) can use a soluble concentrate for the cutting fluid. One part concentrate is generally mixed with 3-15 parts water, depending on the type of concentrate and the sawing application.

Metals that are easy to moderately difficult to machine and are sawed at band speeds over 200 sfm (61 m/min) can usually be cut most successfully with a heavy-duty synthetic concentrate mixed one part concentrate to 5-10 parts water.

Application methods. In bandsawing, proper application of the right cutting fluid can mean the difference between a profitable and unprofitable operation. It is important that the cutting fluid be directed to the cutting area and that a sufficient amount be applied to carry through the entire cross section of the material being sawed. Some machine builders offer means of feeding cutting fluid through the saw guides, thus assuring that the fluid reaches both sides of the band as well as the teeth. Other means available for applying cutting fluid include nozzles, mist sprays, pressurized mist systems, and curtain applicators.

Fluid properties. Good lubrication qualities are an important requirement for the cutting fluid used to prevent chips from bonding to the tooth faces. While the bands are cooled to some extent by air as they pass around the machine wheels, a cutting fluid with good cooling properties is essential to keep the small teeth cool while they are in the cut.

Proper viscosity of the cutting fluid is also important. Thicker fluids may be desirable for some applications, but they must be thin enough to carry through long, narrow cuts—otherwise, overheating and possible softening of the teeth can occur. Sulfur-based cutting oils used for sawing may have viscosities ranging from 55-160 SSU at 100°F (38°C). Water-soluble concentrates may have viscosities to 900 SSU at 100°F, undiluted.

Circular Sawing

Circular sawing is a process employing a rotating continuous cutting blade having teeth on its periphery to cut ferrous and nonferrous metals, plastics, and other materials to required lengths. With the workpiece clamped securely, the saw blade is either fed horizontally, vertically, or on an angle into the material. The process is often called cold circular sawing to differentiate it from sawing of hot metal in steel mills and forge shops, which is beyond the scope of this discussion.

Cutting action in circular sawing is essentially the same as in milling, particularly slot milling. Each tooth removes a chip, which curls and is carried away from the cutting area in the tooth gullet, thus allowing continuous cutting. Large circular sawing machines have been used for many years to cut off billets, forgings, extrusions, bars, tubes, and similar stock. Now, smaller machines are being increasingly applied for a wide variety of parts. The process can be used to cut practically any material.

Friction sawing is a related process in which the toothed circular blade is rotated at a very high speed and heavy feed pressure is applied. Frictional heat causes the workpiece material to soften to a plastic state and to be removed by the traveling teeth. A blade with a smooth rim (no teeth) can be used to circular saw high-carbon steels (0.60-1.00% carbon content) because the rim becomes roughened on such steels. On low-carbon steels, however, the rim does not roughen, and the blade periphery must be indented to form teeth.

While circular friction sawing is fast, it has many limitations. For example, the process is limited to about 4" (102 mm) diam solid parts, and the best performance is obtained with shapes on which the length of blade contact is very short. In addition, machines with high horsepower are required, the high blade speeds require total enclosure for safety, and the high noise level necessitates soundproofing. Large burrs that are produced can be dangerous and must be removed in a secondary operation. Also, the heat-affected metals being cut develop a skin hardness due to rapid cooling. For these reasons, the use of this method has declined. The remainder of this chapter, therefore, will be devoted to conventional circular sawing.

Advantages

Major benefits of circular sawing include high production capability and high accuracy. Rigid machines and blades available permit high feed pressures. Many machine attachments and material handling systems, discussed later, are available to automate the process and thus reduce the noncutting portion of the cycle and decrease labor costs. Also, changeover time for different-sized workpieces is fast, making the process economical for both small lot sizes and high production requirements.

Accuracy is inherent in circular sawing due to the rigidity of the machines and milling-type cutters. Length tolerance for most stock feed systems is ± 0.004″ (0.10 mm). Accuracy of cut, with respect to combined squareness and parallelism, is generally ± 0.001″ (0.03 mm) per inch (25.4 mm) of material height or width in the direction of blade travel. One machine builder guarantees 0.00075″ (0.0190 mm) per inch. In the plane perpendicular to the direction of blade travel, the tolerance is ± 0.0005″ (0.013 mm).

Virtually burr-free surface finishes are produced, often eliminating or reducing the need for secondary finishing operations. For blade sizes up to about 16″ (406 mm) diam, finishes typically range from 60 to 125 μ in. (1.5 to 3.2 μ m). Usually, surface finishes as smooth as 8 μ in. (0.2 μ m) have been produced in circular sawing aluminum, and finishes as smooth as 32 μ in. (0.8 μ m) in cutting steel. The harder the material being cut, the smoother the finish usually produced.

Tooling costs are relatively low. It has been estimated that the tool cost for circular sawing of mild steels is less than one-half cent per square inch (6.45

cm²) of material removed, making it one of the least expensive methods of sawing solid metals. Because of its rigidity, there is no tendency for the blade to deflect, which could cause more wear on one side of the blade than on the other. With the resultant uniform wear rate, no loss of accuracy occurs as the blade dulls.

Operating costs are low because the simple operation of circular saws lends itself to the use of unskilled labor. Blade speed selection is normally accomplished by pushbutton. Changeover time for a modern machine to cut different types and sizes of material is only a few seconds. One blade will cut most materials and stock sizes within the capacity of the machine, and blade changing can be done quickly and easily.

Circular saws are relatively safe because of the low rotational speed of their blades. No need exists for the operator to have his hands in the cutting area, and many automatic machines have completely enclosed feeding and sawing areas.

Limitations

There are no real limitations to the use of circular saws. It is true that the initial capital investment is greater than for a hacksaw or bandsaw because a heavier, higher horsepower machine is required for comparable capacity. Increased productivity and accuracy, however, can result in a rapid write-off of the machine if sufficient work is available to keep it operating efficiently. Circular saw blades are also more expensive initially than bandsaw or hacksaw blades, but they can be resharpened many more times and reground, if necessary, to cut different materials. Long blade life generally results in lower tool cost.

Greater loss of the material being cut, because of the increased kerf (width of cut), is often cited as a disadvantage of circular sawing, but this is often not the case. Circular saw blades as thin as 0.060″ (1.52 mm) are available, but such thin tooling cannot withstand the high cutting forces and maintain the close tolerances for which circular sawing is noted. Most bar stock that is slugged into short length is 5″ (127 mm) or less in diameter. In this range, circular saw blades normally have a thickness ranging from 0.096-0.118″ (2.44-3.00 mm). With the inherent accuracy of circular sawing and the short drop (waste) ends produced, generally 2″ (51 mm) or less in length, material loss due to cutting width can be less than with other methods. Even when cutting very short lengths, it is often less expensive to produce a slightly wider kerf with circular sawing than to remove material in a secondary operation to attain the required accuracy.

Circular Sawing Machines

Circular sawing machines, having blades mounted on power-driven rotating spindles, are generally of four basic designs: (1) pivot arm, (2) vertical column, (3) horizontal travel, and (4) plate saws.

Virtually all circular sawing machines allow work to be clamped on both sides of the cut to provide a milled, practically burr-free finish. Self-adjusting clamping and various automated systems are available on many machines to maximize productivity for short-run as well as high production requirements.

Models for both ferrous and nonferrous cutting are available in high-speed steel and carbide-tipped blade versions. Cutting-speed and feed-rate ranges necessary for all materials to be cut should be specified when selecting a circular sawing machine. Speed changes can be accomplished with selective gearing, pickoff gears, pulley changes, or more often, variable-speed drives. Circular sawing machines capable of cutting material up to 86″ (2200 mm) wide by 26″ (660 mm) thick have been built. Figure 8-23 illustrates the feeding, clamping, and discharging arrangement of a tilt-arm circular saw.

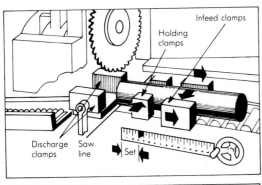
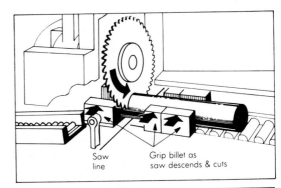
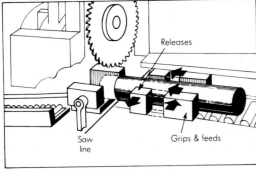
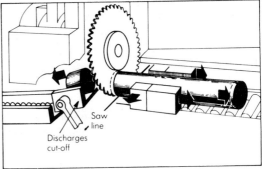

Figure 8-23 Feeding, clamping, and discharging arrangement on one type of tilt-arm circular sawing system (Courtesy of The Hill Acme Co.)

Circular Sawing Fixtures

Workpieces are generally sawed singly since this simplifies material handling. Round bars and tubes are usually held in V-blocks; square, rectangular, or other shaped material can be clamped directly on the bed, table, or supporting plate of the machine. When the stock to be cut is warped or crooked, care is necessary to assure that it is properly seated and clamped prior to sawing. Many circular sawing machines, however, have the capability of cutting two or more pieces in a single pass, and this is often done to increase productivity. Various work-clamping methods used to facilitate such gang cutting are illustrated in Fig. 8-24. Special fixtures are sometimes required to hold unusual shapes.

A typical automated system includes a magazine feed table or unscrambler, an infeed conveyor, the sawing machine, a chip removal unit, and workpiece discharge conveyor. Round stock is easily fed from a storage table having rails sloped toward the entry conveyor, with an escapement device for releasing workpieces as required. Drag-chain conveyors are often used for storing round-cornered squares and feeding them onto the infeed conveyor. An alternate device is a walking beam unscrambler unit. The entry conveyor must be synchronized with the sawing machine and should be reversible to feed into or out of the sawing area.

Circular Saw Blades

Three basic types of circular saw blades available are solid, segmental, and carbide tipped. Diameters of the blades used depend on the size of the workpieces to be sawed. Blades should have a diameter sufficient to clear through the maximum thickness of the stock in one pass.

Solid Blades: With solid blades, available from 8 through 16″ (200 through 400 mm) diam, the body and teeth are made from one solid disc of HSS, such as AISI M2 or M7, that is heat treated to a hardness

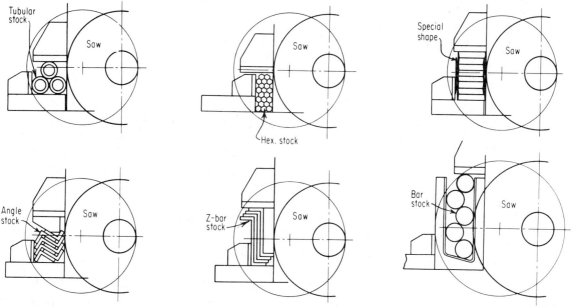

Figure 8-24   Various methods of clamping different shaped material

of R_C65. Blade bodies are made slightly concave by hollow grinding on both sides to provide clearance in the cuts. They are used to saw both ferrous and nonferrous materials, and they can be resharpened until they reach a diameter that is no longer practical for use on the machine. Thinner blades can be used for sawing nonferrous materials.

Segmental Blades: Segmental saw blades, available from 12-120″ (300-3050 mm) diam, consist of a disc-type body with toothed segments around its periphery. The blade body is produced from a high-strength, low-alloy steel capable of absorbing shock while remaining rigid. The toothed segments, tapered to provide side clearance, are made from HSS with a hardness of R_C65. Segment lengths vary with the blade diameters, ranging from 2½″ (63.5 mm) long for a 12″ (305 mm) diam blade to 5″ (127 mm) for 72″ (1829 mm) diam blades.

Most segmental-type, circular saw blades have a tongue machined around the outer periphery of the blade body. Inner surfaces of the segments are grooved to fit over the body tongue. One manufacturer produces segmental blades with grooves in the blade body and tongues on the segments. With both designs, segments are fastened to the blade bodies with rivets. Rivets are also placed outside the blade body, between mating faces of the segments, to provide lateral stability.

Segmental blades are more widely used than solid blades because of their greater ability to absorb shock. Teeth on the segments can be designed to

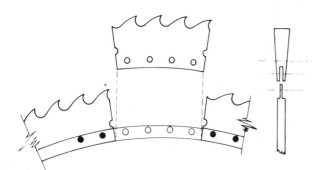

Figure 8-25   Individual segments on HSS circular saw blades

suit specific requirements. Also, when individual segments are worn or broken, they can be removed (see Fig. 8-25), resharpened, and replaced a number of times, thus reducing blade costs. However, segmental blades generally have to be thicker than solid blades, and the surface finishes produced are not usually as smooth.

Carbide-Tipped Blades: Carbide-tipped circular saw blades, available from 12-72″ (305-1829 mm) diam with kerf ranges between 0.157 and 0.430″ (4.00 and 10.92 mm), have a high-strength, low-alloy steel body, with carbide brazed to the tooth tips. These blades have been used for many years to saw aluminum, brass, and some plastics. More recently, carbide-tipped blades have been increasingly used in sawing steel, particularly to meet high production requirements and to saw large forged billets. Dramatic improvements in productivity have resulted from the use of carbide-tipped blades for such applications. Because of the critical loading of the carbide in circular sawing, today's state of the art allows economical utilization of this type of blade only for solid shapes. U.S. classification C-5 carbide (ISO P40) is widely used for carbide-tipped blades to saw ferrous metals and C-2 or C-3 (ISO K20 or K30) carbide for carbide-tipped blades to saw nonferrous materials.

Advantages of sawing large billets with carbide-tipped blades include the elimination of ragged billet ends resulting from the nick-and-break method, shear cracks sometimes caused by cold shearing, and the need for expensive, high-capacity shears required for hot shearing. Also, the flatter, more accurate end surfaces produced by circular sawing reduce rejection rates, save material, and permit easier and more economical billet handling.

Tooth Geometry: A major advantage of circular sawing is that the rigid tooling allows a wide range of materials and stock sizes to be cut with the same blade. For sawing certain materials and long production runs, however, it is generally more economical to change the few variables available for optimum performance.

Triple-chip tooth design. The most common type of tooth geometry is the triple-chip or high-low pattern illustrated in Fig. 8-26. This design essentially provides a milling-type cutter with each pair of teeth producing three chips. The first tooth in each pair, called the roughing tooth, is higher and chamfered 45° on each side so that one-third of its width remains flat and removes a single chip from the center of the cut with each pass. The second tooth in each pair, called the finishing tooth, is lower (an amount equal to 0.02 times the pitch, generally from 0.010-0.025", 0.25-0.64 mm) and flat and removes two chips per pass, one from each side of the slot produced by the preceding roughing tooth.

Tooth widths on circular saw blades must be wider than the body to prevent jamming in the cut. The roughing teeth guide the blade straight through the material, and the height differential prevents the finishing teeth from penetrating deeper than the roughing teeth due to the constant infeed. This type of geometry breaks up the chips and splits the chip load between each pair of teeth, allowing faster material removal. Material removed by the finishing teeth flows toward the slot produced by the roughing teeth; this process accounts for the smooth milled-type finish that is produced.

Triple-chip tooth geometry is recommended for most ferrous cutting applications, particularly for sawing solid stock and thick sections, because it can withstand high loads and is capable of rapid stock removal rates. This design, however, is not generally recommended for sawing thin sections, thin-walled tubing, nonferrous materials, or certain plastics. Instead, an alternate-bevel tooth pattern is usually recommended. With this design, every other tooth is beveled on an opposite side for one-half of the tooth width, with all teeth the same height; the teeth have a finer pitch than with the triple-chip design. One advantage of the alternate-bevel, equal-height design is that the blades are easier to resharpen and, therefore, simpler saw grinding machines can be used.

Straight-tooth design. Another geometry commonly used for sawing brass and aluminum is the straight-tooth design. With this design, the teeth are not beveled and they are all the same height. Other geometries are also used for specific applications. For example, some carbide-tipped blades have a different blade geometry for each tooth in sets of three teeth.

Tooth gullets allow chips to curl. The tooth gullets temporarily store the chips so that the teeth can continuously remove material from the workpiece, as shown schematically in Fig. 8-27. Design of the gullet is a function of the tooth pitch—the larger the pitch, the larger the gullet.

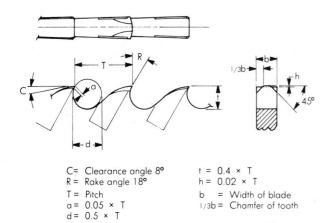

C = Clearance angle 8°
R = Rake angle 18°
T = Pitch
a = 0.05 × T
d = 0.5 × T

t = 0.4 × T
h = 0.02 × T
b = Width of blade
1/3b = Chamfer of tooth

Figure 8-26   Triple-chip tooth geometry

Figure 8-27   Tooth gullets which curl the chips produced

Rake angles on the teeth provide the wedge to shear the material being sawed, and the clearance angles permit using a constant feed rate without pushing the backs of the tooth tips into the workpiece. The easier the material is to saw, the larger the rake and clearance angles to permit fast feed rates. Large rake angles reduce the cutting forces, but also reduce the strength of the teeth. Increasing the clearance angles provides more room for chip removal, but if clearance angles are too high, tooth strength is reduced. The harder the material is to saw, the smaller the rake and clearance angles should be.

Positive rake angles of up to 18° and clearance angles to 8° are used for sawing most materials. For long production runs and special applications, however, improved productivity and longer blade life can often be obtained by using other angles.

Operating Parameters for Circular Sawing

Calculating the exact feed rate for circular sawing any given solid material is possible. However, many interdependent variables exist, including the type (HSS or carbide-tipped), diameter, pitch and gullet capacity, and tooth geometry of the saw blade; machining characteristics of the material to be sawed; workpiece size; cutting speed; and the rigidity and condition of, as well as the power available for, the machines to be used. Work material size affects both the feed rate and cutting speed to be used. Larger stock sizes require lower feed rates, but the material removal rate increases.

Cutting Speed: An inverse relationship exists between the tensile strength of the material to be sawed and the cutting speed. Lower strength materials can be sawed with higher cutting speeds, but stronger materials require lower speeds. Also, increased feed rates are used with higher cutting speeds, and reduced feeds with lower speeds. The limitation in this relationship is the strength of the teeth—the maximum allowable chip thickness decreases as the work material becomes stronger.

Materials with higher tensile strengths require more energy for chip removal, which creates additional heat and can anneal the teeth if the surface speed is too high.

Recommended cutting speeds and feed rates for circular sawing various materials are presented in Fig. 8-28. For cutting nonferrous materials, either HSS or carbide-tipped blades can be used. The lower cutting speeds in the ranges given in Fig. 8-28 are the maximum for HSS blades, while the higher speeds can be used for carbide-tipped blades. These recommendations are based on the use of modern, rigid, circular sawing machines with ample power and positive hydraulic-feed systems. A mechanical feed system, such as one with a preloaded ballscrew, can improve performance, especially for sawing high-strength alloy metals.

Cutting Fluids: The use of a cutting fluid is recommended for circular sawing all metals except brass and cast irons. Cutting fluids, however, are generally not used when cutting with carbide-tipped blades. Chips produced in circular sawing serve as effective heat sinks, and the workpieces generally stay cool. As a result, lubricity of the cutting fluid to facilitate flow of the chips over the tooth surfaces is more important than its cooling capacity.

Good results are obtained with soluble oils and synthetic or chemical water mixtures. Relatively rich mixtures, such as one part oil or synthetic fluid to six parts water, are generally recommended. Flooding of the cutting area is most often used since this helps in removal of the chips. For the cutting of nonferrous metals at high surface speeds and the traverse sawing of long plates, however, mist coolant is often applied.

KEY TERMS AND PHRASES

Bandsawing
Broaching
Carbide-tipped blade
Chip/tooth interface

Materials to be Circular Sawed	Material Tensile Strength, ksi (MPa)	Cutting Speed, sfm (m/min)	Feed Rate, ipm (mm/min)	Material Removal Rate, in.²/min (cm²/min)
Mild steels: AISI 1008-1035, 1112, 1132, & 1212-1213	50-95 (345-655)	60-100 (18.3-30.5)	4-8 (102-203)	25-40 (161-258)
Low-alloy, high-carbon steels: AISI 1040-1095, 1137-1151, 1320-1345, 2330-2517, 3115-3150, 3310-3315, 4017-4068, & 4140	85-150 (586-1034)	45-60 (13.7-18.3)	3-7 (76-178)	20-35 (129-226)
Medium to high alloy steels: AISI 4142-4161, 4317-4340, 4608-4640, 5120-5160, 52100, 6117-6152, 8615-8660, 8715-8750, 9255-9262, 9310-9317, 9437-9763, & 9840-9850	115-190 (793-1310)	30-50 (9.1-15.2)	3-6 (76-152)	15-30 (97-194)
Stainless steels:				
201-205, 301-303, 416-430, & 501-502	80-110 (552-758)	30-40 (9.1-12.2)	2-4 (51-102)	10-16 (65-103)
302-304, 316-321, 347-410, 420-440, & 430-446	90-120 (621-827)	20-30 (6.1-9.1)	1.5-3.5 (38-89)	6-12 (39-77)
17-4PH & 17-7PH	150-170 (1034-1172)	15-25 (4.6-7.6)	1-3 (25-76)	2-6 (13-39)
Cast irons:				
Soft	---	85 (25.9)	10 (254)	40 (258)
Medium	---	45 (13.7)	7 (178)	30 (194)
Chilled	---	30 (9.1)	5 (127)	25 (161)
Tool steels: M1, M2, M3, D7, T1, T2, T4, & T15	110-180 (758-1241)	15-30 (4.6-9.1)	1-3 (25-76)	3-12 (19-77)
Special alloys: Titanium, Inconels, Nimonics, Waspaloy Hastelloys, & Incoloys	125-200 (862-1379)	15-25 (4.6-7.6)	0.5-3 (13-76)	1-6 (6-39)
Nonferrous metals:				
Aluminum & its alloys	---	7000-15,000 (2134-4572)	40-80 (1016-2032)	200-2000 (1290-12 900)
Copper & its alloys	---	1200-7000 (366-2134)	20-60 (508-1524)	60-500 (387-3225)
Bronze	---	300-600 (91-183)	8-20 (203-508)	50-100 (323-645)

Figure 8-28 Cutting speeds and material removal rates

Circular sawing
Combination broach
Contouring
Cutoff
Cutting teeth
Dual-ram broaching machine
External broach
Finishing teeth
Gullet depth
Helical broach
Hinge-type horizontal hacksawing machine
Hook tooth
Horizontal hacksawing machine
Horizontal internal broaching machine
Horizontal surface broaching machine
Internal broach
Pot broaching machine
Power hacksawing
Pull broach
Pullup broaching
Push broach
Pushdown broaching
Ripping
Rotary broach
Roughing teeth
Sawing
Segmental blade
Shaping
Single-ram broaching machine
Skip tooth
Slabbing
Slicing
Slotting
Solid blade
Stock removal
Straight tooth
Straight-tooth design
Surface broach
Tooth face
Tooth rake angle
Tooth spacing
Triple-chip tooth design
Undercut face tooth
Vertical combination broaching machines
Vertical internal broaching machine

QUESTIONS FOR ADDITIONAL STUDY AND REVIEW _____

1. Explain the process of broaching.

2. List three advantages of broaching.

3. Explain the limitations of broaching.

4. Explain how broaches are classified.

5. List the types of broaches associated with each classification of broach.

6. What material are most broaches made of?

7. What are the functions of cutting fluids in broaching? *P 179*

8. Explain how broaching machines are classified.

9. Explain the following broaching processes:
   • Pushdown
   • Pullup
   • Pulldown

10. What is a pot broaching machine?

11. Describe sawing as a process.

12. What does the term *slugging* mean?

13. Describe hacksawing as a process.

14. What are the primary advantages of hacksawing?

15. What are the main limitations of hacksawing?

16. What are the three materials most commonly used for hacksawing blades?

17. What are the three types of tooth set for hacksawing blades?

18. Describe bandsawing as a process.

19. List five advantages of bandsawing.

20. What are the limitations of bandsawing?

    P193

21. List five factors that should be considered in bandsaw selection.

22. List three different types of tooth forms and sets used on bands for bandsawing.

23. Explain the functions of cutting fluids in bandsawing.

24. Describe circular sawing as a process.

25. List four types of machines used for circular sawing.

CHAPTER

Turning and Boring

MAJOR TOPICS COVERED

- The Turning Process
- Types of Lathes
- Cutting Tools for Turning
- Workholding for Turning
- Operating Parameters for Turning
- The Boring Process
- Types of Precision-Boring Machines
- Boring Tools
- Toolholders for Precision Boring
- Workholding for Boring
- Operating Parameters for Precision Boring

The Turning Process

Turning is a machining process in which a workpiece is held and rotated about its longitudinal axis on a machine tool called a lathe. Cutting tools mounted on the lathe are fed into the workpiece to remove material and thus produce the required shape. The principal surfaces machined are concentric with the longitudinal axis of the workpiece.

Turning operations are defined as the removal of material from external surfaces on rotating workpieces. Related operations on external surfaces, also performed on lathes, include facing, chamfering, grooving or necking, knurling, skiving, threading, and cutoff (parting).

Operations that can be performed on internal surfaces with a lathe include drilling, reaming, boring, threading, and recessing. Boring operations are also performed on special-purpose machines discussed later in this chapter, as well as on multifunction machines.

Lathes are one of the most versatile machine tools available. Most lathes have the capability for threading, and with attachments or NC, can cut tapered or contoured surfaces, both external and internal. Other operations that can be performed on some lathes include spinning, honing, polishing, and buffing.

Fundamentals of Lathe Operation

Many different types of lathes of varying complexity are available to suit specific applications. A number of these lathes are discussed in the next section of this chapter. The basic requirements for any of these lathes are (1) means for holding and rotating the workpieces and (2) a means for holding and moving the cutting tools.

Holding and Rotating the Workpiece:
Workpieces are held in a lathe between centers or by a chuck, collet, fixture, or faceplate. Rotation of

the workpiece is accomplished by a spindle mounted in the lathe headstock. The spindle is sometimes driven directly by an electric motor, but the drive is usually through belts and/or a gear train.

Chucks or faceplates connected to the headstock spindle are used to hold short, large-diameter workpieces. Collets are used for short, small-diameter workpieces or workpieces machined on the end of a bar or tube that is fed through the spindle and parted from the stock when completed. Between-center holding is used for long workpieces and requires that center holes be previously drilled in each end of the workpiece.

For between-center turning, a center is provided on the spindle and a tailstock is mounted on the outboard end of the bedways. The tailstock is adjustable along the ways for various workpiece lengths and is equipped with a center. The center can be replaced by a drill or reamer when required for chucking operations. Steadyrests or follow rests are sometimes placed against the workpiece at positions between the centers to minimize deflection during machining.

Cutting Tool Movements:
The carriage of a basic engine lathe consists of a carriage, cross slide, compound rest, and apron. The carriage slides longitudinally along ways on the lathe bed, thus guiding the carriage parallel to the lathe and workpiece axis. Movement of the cross slide, actuated by a feedscrew, is across the bedways (perpendicular to the lathe axis) and over slide ways on top of the carriage.

Clamped to the top of the cross slide is a compound rest that can be rotated 360° and secured at any angle with respect to the lathe axis. The compound rest has a T-slot used to clamp a toolpost or toolblock. A slide on the compound rest can be moved along the base by a feedscrew to provide movement of the cutting tool at any desired angle with respect to the workpiece axis.

An apron fastened to the underside of the carriage contains the gears and clutches for longitudinal and cross feeds. It also has a split nut to engage a leadscrew mounted on the lathe bed to drive the carriage when cutting threads (see Fig. 9-1).

Operating Variables:
Many factors influence any turning operation. The three major ones are cutting speed, feed rate, and depth of cut. These factors are discussed in detail under the section on operating parameters later in this chapter.

Cutting speed refers to the rotational speed of the lathe spindle and workpiece and can be expressed in revolutions per minute (rpm). For turning and most other machining operations, however, the cutting speed is generally given in surface feet per minute (sfm) or meters per minute (m/min), which is the rate at which the workpiece surface moves past the cutting

Figure 9-1   CNC Engine Lathe (Courtesy of The Olofsson Corp.)

tool. The surface speed equals the rotary speed (rpm) of the spindle times the circumference of the workpiece (in feet or meters).

Feed rate is the rate at which the tool advances along its cutting path. It is expressed in inches or millimeters per minute (ipm or mm/min), or in inches or millimeters per revolution (ipr or mm/rev).

Depth of cut is the thickness of the layer of material removed from the workpiece surface (the distance from the uncut surface to the cut surface), expressed in inches or millimeters. When turning cylindrical workpieces, the diameter is reduced by twice the depth of cut.

Types of Lathes

A wide variety of lathes and turning machines is available in many sizes to suit specific application requirements. They can be controlled manually, semiautomatically, or automatically. Major classifications of different types include engine lathes, contouring lathes, turret lathes, and NC/CNC turning machines. Each classification is further subdivided into specific kinds.

Other lathe-related machines such as single-spindle automatic lathes and screw machines, Swiss-type automatic screw machines, and multispindle automatic bar and chucking machines are discussed in Chapter 18.

Engine Lathes: The engine lathe is a basic, general-purpose machine tool that is used primarily to generate forms by removing material with one single-point cutting tool at a time. The tool moves parallel, perpendicular, or at an angle to the axis of rotation of the workpiece.

Through the use of attachments and accessories, a number of different operations can be performed on engine lathes. These operations include single-point threading, thread chasing, tapping, taper turning, duplicating and contouring, drilling, reaming, boring, milling, and grinding. The versatile engine lathe is widely used for producing many different parts in small quantities, as well as for toolroom and maintenance work.

Engine lathes are generally classified as either chucking or center-type machines. On chucking machines, workpieces are held in chucks or collets or on faceplates mounted on the lathe spindles. On center-type machines, workpieces are supported between centers mounted in the spindles and the tailstocks of the lathes.

Lathes are often divided into arbitrary classifications with respect to size, function, and degree of precision. Sizes of lathes are generally specified by their swings over the bed and cross slide and by the distances between centers or bed lengths, which determine the maximum diameters and lengths of workpieces that can be handled.

Every engine lathe provides a means for traversing the cutting tool both along the axis of workpiece revolution and at an angle to that axis. Beyond this similarity, lathes may embody characteristics common to several different classifications.

Engine lathes are further classified as bench lathes, regular engine lathes, toolroom lathes, manufacturing lathes, and special-purpose lathes. See Figs. 9-2 and 9-3. Figure 9-4 illustrates boring on a lathe.

Figure 9-2   CNC Manufacturing Lathe (Courtesy of The Olofsson Corp.)

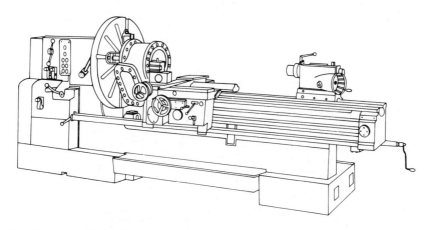

Figure 9-3 Sliding-bed type of gap lathe

Figure 9-4 Boring on a lathe using a carbide cutter (Courtesy of Kennametal Inc.)

Contouring Lathes: Contour turning is the production of three-dimensional forms on workpieces by controlling the path of the cutting tool. Most contour turning is now done on NC lathes, discussed later in this chapter. There is, however, still considerable work of this type being done on standard engine lathes equipped with tracing attachments and on automatic tracer lathes when larger production quantities are required.

Contouring on engine lathes. Movement of the cutting tool when contour turning is done on an engine lathe is controlled by a tracing attachment. With these attachments, a follower or stylus moves over the surface of a flat template, previously machined part, master, or model, thus controlling the movements of the cutting tool to duplicate the required shape.

The controls may be actuated hydraulically, electrically, electronically, electromechanically, pneumatically, or mechanically. A typical hydraulically operated tracing attachment, mounted on an engine lathe, is illustrated in Fig. 9-5. Also see Fig. 9-6.

Horizontal Turret Lathes: Horizontal turret lathes differ from engine lathes in two basic respects. A square turret is mounted on the cross slide in place of the usual compound rest of the engine lathe and is pivoted about a vertical axis to bring one of four tools into cutting position. On some lathes, a fixed toolholder is mounted on the back end of the cross slide or a separate rear cross slide. The second basic difference is that a multisided turret takes the place of the tailstock on the engine lathe. The turret usually is pivoted about a vertical axis so that, by rotating it, the tool on each side may be brought into cutting position (see Fig. 9-7).

Numerically controlled horizontal turret lathes do not always fit the above description because of the numerous turret arrangements available on NC equipment.

Horizontal turret lathes are manufactured as hand-operated, power-fed, automatic, and numerically controlled machines. The hand-operated machines require an operator to manipulate the various controls

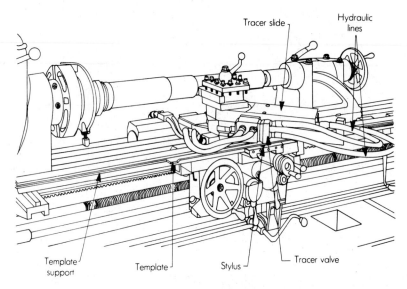

Figure 9-5 Hydraulically operated tracing equipment

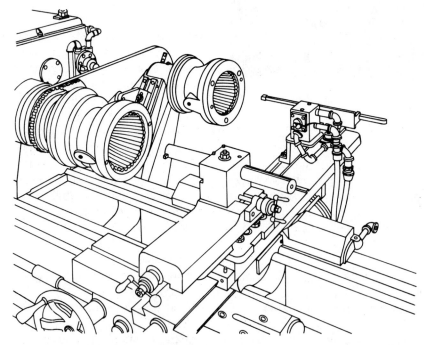

Figure 9-6 Hydraulic tracing from a rotating master

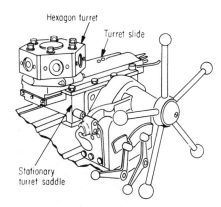

Figure 9-7 Turret construction on a ram-type machine

required for indexing and moving the turrets, changing speeds, etc. On automatic and NC turret lathes the operator places the workpiece in the chuck and starts the machine; all the machine motions are controlled automatically.

A major advantage of turret lathes, compared to engine lathes, is that the availability of more tools permits many parts to be completely machined in one setup at higher production rates. They are particularly well suited for workpieces requiring both external and internal operations. A possible limitation of turret lathes is the length-to-diameter ratio of the workpieces. Long parts have to be supported by a center in the turret because there is no tailstock. Also, it may not be economical to use power-fed or automatic turret lathes for machining workpieces that require only a few tools or for meeting production requirements of less than ten identical parts.

Automatic turret lathes. These lathes, commonly referred to as single-spindle automatic chucking machines, are used basically for the same type of work as the turret lathe fitted with chucking equipment. They generally require hand loading and unloading, but complete the machining cycle automatically.

These machines are used when production requirements are too high for hand or power-fed turret lathes and too low for multiple-spindle automatic machines to produce economically. Setup time is slightly higher than for the hand turret lathe, but

operator fatigue and error are considerably reduced. The setup time is much lower than for multiple-spindle automatic machines, and expensive tooling is not usually required. Cost reduction is also an important factor to be considered. The automatic features permit a more constant flow of production, and scrap loss is reduced by eliminating operator error. The machines are designed to permit combined cuts economically and automatically, thereby removing the responsibility from the operator. Also very important is the fact that, during the automatic machining operation, the operator is free to operate another machine or is able to inspect the finished parts completely without loss of time.

Two basic types of automatic turret lathes are available. One has the saddle mounted on the bedways and a turret which rotates around a vertical axis similar to the conventional turret lathe. The other has a turret mounted on a shaft extending from the headstock. The turret rotates around a horizontal axis parallel to the spindle centerline. It normally consists of four, five, or six tooling stations. Standard holders are available to adapt commonly used turret-lathe tooling. Cross-slide tooling stations are available in the front and rear on one long slide or on independently operated front and rear slides.

Each machine has a control unit which automatically selects the speeds, feeds, lengths of cut, and machine functions. Included under machine functions, as needed, are dwell, cycle stop, index, reverse, cross-slide actuation, and many other functions. Chip and splash guards are also standard equipment. Other units of the machine are similar to the standard turret lathe.

NC/CNC Turning Machines: Numerically controlled (NC) and computer numerically controlled (CNC) lathes and turning machines are being increasingly applied because of their capabilities for increasing productivity, reducing the cost of machined parts, and providing more production flexibility, including contouring capability.

Advantages. Higher productivity is being obtained with NC lathes because of faster setups, reduced toolchanging requirements, increased utilization (more time spent in cutting), and shorter cycles. Faster metal removal rates are the result of higher horsepower, spindle speeds, and feed rates available. These features permit taking full advantage of the improved cutting tool materials now available.

For many applications, NC lathes have at least doubled productivity, and in some cases, production has been increased four or more times over conventional methods. The availability of more tools per machine minimizes toolchanging requirements and often reduces or eliminates the need for preliminary or secondary operations. Greater accuracy, repeatability, and reliability of these machines has improved the quality of the parts produced and has reduced scrap.

Substantial cost savings can result from reduced operator skill requirements and minimal needs for special tooling, material handling, and inspection. Also, less labor may be needed since it is often possible for one operator to attend two or more NC lathes simultaneously. Shorter leadtimes provide reduced inventory costs and faster delivery of workpieces. Another advantage is that operating variables (cutting speeds, feed rates, depths of cut, tooling, etc.) can be controlled by management and part programmers rather than individual machine operators.

Types of NC lathes. A wide variety of NC lathes and turning machines is available. While some have single or multiple vertical spindles, most are of horizontal-spindle design. Horizontal-spindle machines are usually supplied in one of three basic forms:

1. Center-type machines, often referred to as shaft lathes, are used primarily for between-center work. They are equipped with a tailstock and are available with long bed lengths. High spindle speeds, a single set of slides, and turrets arranged for only OD-type tooling are common characteristics of these machines.
2. Chucking-type machines are characterized by larger and lower speed spindles, wider and heavier slides (sometimes with more than one set), turrets arranged for both OD and ID operations, short bed lengths, and either no tailstocks or optional swing-up style tailstocks for occasional shaft work.
3. Universal or combination machines are either basic center-type machines equipped with

chucking-type tooling or chucking-type machines provided with tailstocks.

Figs. 9-8, 9-9, and 9-10 are examples of modern CNC lathes.

Figure 9-8   CNC Horizontal Lathe (Courtesy of The Olofsson Corp.)

Figure 9-9   CNC Vertical Lathe (Courtesy of The Olofsson Corp.)

Figure 9-10   Twin Spindle Vertical Precision Turning Machine (Courtesy of The Olofsson Corp.)

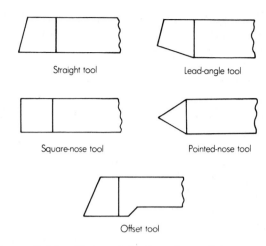

Figure 9-11   Styles of single-point tools in common use

Cutting Tools for Turning

Most material removal in turning operations is done with single-point tools. One exception is the use of form tools ground to specific shapes. A single-point cutting tool has one cutting part (tool point) and a shank by which the tool is held. The cutting part consists of the cutting edges, face, and flank.

Single-point tools are available as solid tools produced from bars of tool steel or from carbide blanks with tips brazed to a toolholder. They are also available as indexable inserts made from various cutting tool materials and clamped to holders. Indexable-insert tools have become the most widely used for turning.

Solid Single-Point Tools: Solid single-point tools for turning are produced from castings, forgings, rolled bars, or compacts made by powder metallurgy processes. The cutting tool materials used include carbon and low-alloy tool steels, high-speed steels, cast cobalt-based alloys, and carbides.

Styles of single-point tools. Several styles of single-point tools in common use are illustrated in Fig. 9-11. Another style, not shown, is the round-nose tool used extensively for turning large-diameter workpieces because it permits employing high feed rates. The straight, lead-angle, and offset tools are made in right- and left-hand types. All styles have square or rectangular shanks to fit standard toolposts and toolholders. Selection of a particular style depends primarily on the type of cut to be made.

Straight side-cutting tools. These are general-purpose tools for both rough and finish turning, facing, and boring operations. They are usually preferred for machining workpieces with thin cross sections because most of the cutting pressure is across the end of the shank, resulting in little end pressure and deflection of the workpiece. Since their side cutting edge angles are zero, such tools are suitable for machining to square shoulders. They are available with a small lead angle for light finishing cuts.

Lead-angle tools. These tools are generally used for heavier turning, facing, and boring operations, as well as for interrupted or irregular cutting. The side cutting edge angle leads the tool into the cut and eases it out again with a minimum of shock to the cutting edge. These tools can be positioned at an angle to cut to square shoulders at the ends of the turning operations.

Square-nose tools. These tools are often carried in stock to facilitate quick grinding of special styles or forms.

Pointed-nose tools. These tools are available with 60° and 80° included angles. The 60° tool is used principally for cutting 60° angle threads. Tools with an 80° included angle are designed for boring, undercutting, chamfering, and general-purpose use on lathes.

Offset tools. These tools are available in end and side-cutting types, with styles similar to straight side-turning and end-cutting types. They are used on cuts where the tool offset permits reaching surfaces that are difficult to machine with straight-shank tools. Workpieces may be turned, bored, or faced to a square shoulder with this style of tool. A lead angle may be added if desired for work not requiring a square shoulder (see Figs. 9-12, 9-13, 9-14, and 9-15).

Indexable Inserts:
Indexable inserts are the most widely used tools for turning operations. Uncoated and coated carbide inserts are by far the most predominant, but inserts made from high-speed steels, ceramics, polycrystalline diamonds, and cubic boron nitride are also used for many applications (see Fig. 9-16).

Selection of inserts. When selecting an indexable insert—whether made of high-speed steel, carbide, ceramic, polycrystalline diamond, or cubic boron nitride—seven factors should be considered. These factors are insert shape, geometry, size, thickness, radius, tolerance, and material. Variables that influence insert selection include the following:

1. Workpiece material and condition.
2. Tolerance, surface finish, and production requirements.
3. Cutting speed, feed rate, and depth of cut.
4. The machine to be used and its power capability.
5. Rigidity of the machine and setup.
6. Operations to be performed.
7. The holder in which the insert is to be used.

Form Tools:
A form tool is a cutting tool intended to produce a desired contour on a workpiece by means of a turning operation. Flat or circular form tools are available. A flat form tool (Fig. 9-17) embodies a square or rectangular cross section with

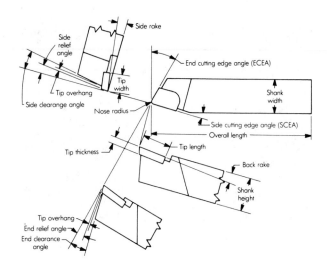

Figure 9-12 A typical single-point carbide-tipped tool

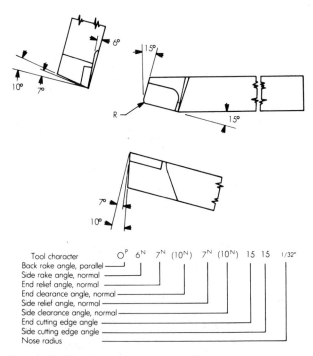

Figure 9-13 Tool character code for designating the geometry of a single-point tool in abbreviated form

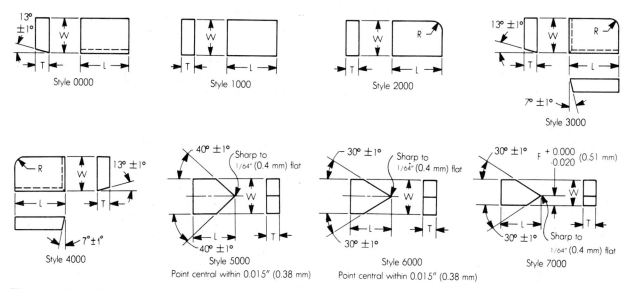

Figure 9-14 Standard styles for sintered-carbide blanks

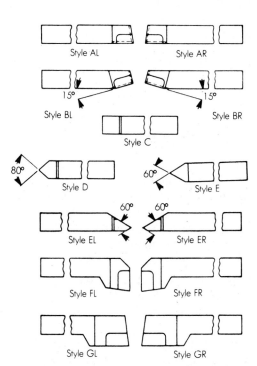

Figure 9-15 Styles of standard carbide-tipped single-point tools

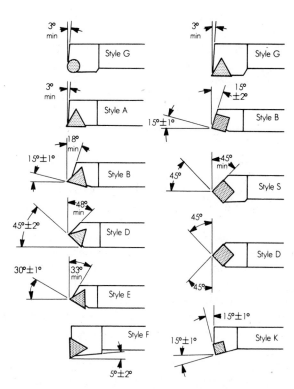

Figure 9-16 Some standard styles of holders for round, triangular, and square inserts

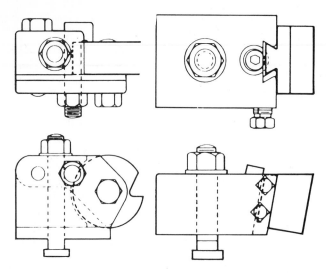

Figure 9-17   Circular form tool (left) and flat form tool mounted in their holders

the form along its end. Flat form tools may be mounted in a conventional tool post or provided with a dovetail to fit a special holder. The tools may be high-speed steel or steel shanks tipped with cast alloy cutting material or carbide. A circular form tool (Fig. 9-17) is round (disc-shaped) with the form or cutting component located on its periphery as a cutout portion. These tools are usually made of high-speed steel, but may be either carbide-tipped or solid carbide. Blanks for circular and flat (dovetailed) form tools, together with their associated mounting and clamping elements, have been standardized in ANSI B94.32-1954 (reaffirmed 1971).

The overall economic considerations of the operation should be the determining factor in deciding whether to use a flat or circular type of form tool in a particular case, but the machine tool and toolholder available for the job usually determine which type will be employed. Original costs of circular form tools are ordinarily high, but the cost per unit produced is less. Flat form tools, particularly those of the end-form kind, generally cost less, but the cost per unit produced by them frequently is higher because of a shorter tool life. The least expensive form tools to make are the end-form kind made from standard bits with the form ground in the solid.

Knurling Tools: Knurling is most commonly used to obtain decorative surfaces, serrated surfaces when components are locked together in unit assemblies, and hand-grip or nonslip surfaces. These surfaces are obtained by the displacement of the material when the knurl is pressed against the surface of a rotating work blank. Knurls are used for producing straight, diagonal, or diamond knurling, and they have teeth of uniform pitch on cylindrical surfaces. Two general methods of specifying knurls—circular-pitch and diametral-pitch—are now in use. Knurling tools with standardized diametral pitches are covered in ANSI Standard B94.6-1981.

The circular-pitch method is related to the distance between the teeth on the circumference of the work and is usually expressed in terms of the number of teeth per inch (TPI). Figure 9-18 indicates the circular pitches for the different numbers of teeth in terms of normal pitch and transverse pitch for diagonal and diamond knurling with a helix angle of 30°. Because of differences in work materials, the relationship between the work-blank diameter and the finish-knurled diameter should be established by experimentation. Also, the exact number of teeth should not be specified unless required. Various types of toolholders are used to apply either one or two knurling tools to the workpiece.

Burnishing Tools: Smooth finishes are produced on turned surfaces by roller burnishing. Roller burnishing tools consist of a series of tapered, hardened, and polished rolls positioned in slots within a retaining cage. As the rolls rotate in a cold-working operation, plastic deformation removes tool marks and surface irregularities. Burnishing can also be accomplished with diamond tools.

Cutoff (Parting) Tools: Cutoff tools are used on bar-type machines to part completed workpieces from the bar stock, pipe, or tube. A straight cutoff blade is a flat piece of tool steel generally having a cross section in the shape of a rectangle, trapezoid, or trapezium when the cross section is taken at right angles to its length. Various shapes, as shown in Fig. 9-19, are provided to fit the different holders and

TPI		Circular Pitch, in. (mm)	
Normal	Transverse	Normal	Transverse
12	10.39	0.0833 (2.116)	0.0962 (2.443)
16	13.86	0.0625 (1.587)	0.0722 (1.834)
19	16.45	0.0526 (1.336)	0.0607 (1.542)
20	17.32	0.0500 (1.270)	0.0577 (1.466)
24	20.78	0.0417 (1.059)	0.0482 (1.224)
25	21.65	0.0400 (1.016)	0.0462 (1.173)
29	25.11	0.0345 (1.016)	0.0462 (1.173)
30	25.98	0.0333 (0.0846)	0.0398 (1.011)
35	30.31	0.0286 (0.726)	0.0330 (0.838)
40	34.64	0.0250 (0.635)	0.0289 (0.734)
41	35.51	0.0244 (0.620)	0.0289 (0.734)
47	40.70	0.0213 (0.541)	0.0246 (0.625)
50	43.30	0.0200 (0.508)	0.0231 (0.587)
80	69.28	0.0125 (0.317)	0.0144 (0.366)

Figure 9-18 Diagonal and diamond knurling with 30° helix angle

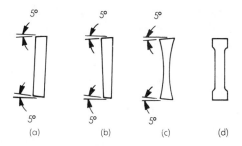

Figure 9-19 Shapes for straight cutoff blades

clamping devices in general use. The blade is furnished unsharpened, heat treated, and cut to length. These blades may be used in special holders for grooving and recessing.

Cutoff tools are also manufactured by using the carbide insert concept. These tools usually consist of a toolholder, length-adjustable support blade, and replaceable insert. The insert can be made with built-in chip control which will produce chips narrower than the slot machined in the part.

Workholding for Turning

Safe, fast, accurate, and rigid means of holding workpieces on lathes are critical requirements for successful turning. All the power required at the cutting tool must be transmitted through the workholding device to the workpiece. As a result, solid gripping of the workpiece is essential. This is especially important with the trend toward higher speed machining and the increased requirements for closer tolerances and smoother finishes.

Major types of workholding devices are faceplates and fixtures, mandrels, jaw-type chucks, step chucks, collets, and, occasionally, magnetic and vacuum chucks. The workpiece, lathe, and tooling used often dictate the type of workholding device that can be employed. In many cases, however, the use of several types is possible and judicious selection is required.

Regardless of the type used, the workpiece should be gripped on the largest diameter practical. This assures a favorable relationship between the gripping and cutting diameters to accommodate torque more easily. Workpieces should also be gripped as close to the faces of chucks as possible.

Between-Center Turning Operations:
Many workpieces, particularly shorter parts, are turned on chucking-type lathes without the use of centers. This is done with chucks, collets, or other workholding devices, or by bolting workpieces or fixtures directly to the faceplates of lathes. Some faceplates are equipped with jaws for rotating large-diameter workpieces. Many other workpieces, particularly longer ones, require support on one or two lathe centers with at least one steadyrest in between.

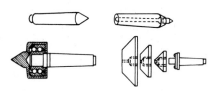

Figure 9-20 Various types of centers, live and dead, used on lathes

Types of centers. Some of the various centers, both live and dead types, used on lathes are illustrated in Fig. 9-20. Headstock centers always rotate with the lathe spindles and workpieces. Tailstock centers may be of the live type, rotating with the workpiece, or the dead type, stationary (see Fig. 9-21).

Collets for Lathes:
Collets, also called collet or bar chucks, are workholding devices used to grip workpieces or stock—including cold-drawn and centerless ground bars having smooth or machined surfaces—on smaller size lathes and other machine tools. Advantages of collets include high holding power because of their large contact area with the stock, the absence of clamping marks normally left by chucks, and relatively low cost. Also, they do not lose their gripping force due to centrifugal effects.

A collet is usually seated directly in the spindle of a lathe. In operation, the collet opens under its own spring tension to allow bar stock to be fed through it or workpieces to be placed in it. The collet is then closed to securely grip the stock or workpiece.

Collets are hollow steel cylinders generally having slots extending along most of their length, with a tapered OD at the closing end and, in some cases, ID threads at one end for mounting stock stops and

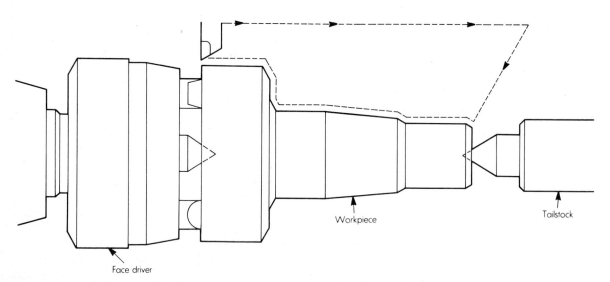

Figure 9-21 Face driver permits turning entire OD of workpiece mounted between centers in one clamping

OD threads at the opposite end for connecting to a draw bar. They are available in fractional, decimal, letter, number, and metric sizes for holding round, square, rectangular, hexagonal, and special-shaped stock. While most collets are made to hold stock on-center, they can be designed to hold stock off-center any desired distance, as is required for eccentric or odd-shaped workpieces.

Serrated, taper hole, step, plug chuck, and extended-nose collets provide additional means to grip stock. So-called emergency collets have a pilot hole that can be drilled or bored to required size. This design is useful for short production runs or when exact collet sizes are not readily available. The three basic collet styles used for metalcutting are stationary, push out, and draw in. These styles are illustrated in Fig. 9-22; the draw-in collet shown has interchangeable serrated pads (also see Figs. 9-23 and 9-24).

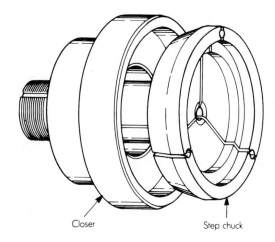

Figure 9-23   Emergency step chuck for draw-in spindle

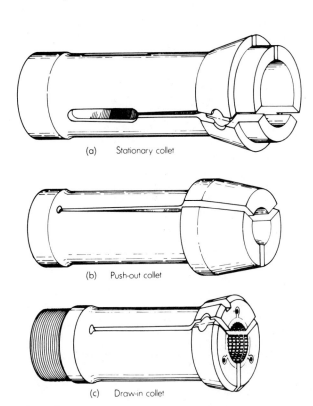

(a)   Stationary collet

(b)   Push-out collet

(c)   Draw-in collet

Figure 9-22   Three basic styles of collet

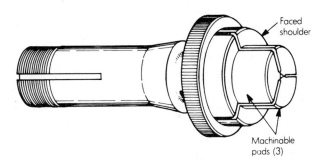

Figure 9-24   Expandable collet with machinable pads

Jaw-Type Chucks: Chucks for use on engine, toolroom, turret, and automatic lathes are designed to fit the spindle noses specified in ANSI Standard B5.9-1967 (reaffirmed 1972). Dimensions of the chucks and jaws are listed, and classifications for different types of duty are specified in ANSI Standard B5.8-1972 (reaffirmed 1979). At present, however, this standard is incomplete in that it does not cover many chuck designs now available.

Types of chucks. Lathe chucks are available in a wide variety of types and designs, and are either manually or power actuated. Manually operated chucks are generally restricted to toolroom, maintenance, or limited production requirements because the time required for chucking may take longer than for machining. Power chucks cost more, but are faster and more productive. They also permit adjusting the gripping force to suit various requirements. Major types of chucks are independent, self-centering, power, diaphragm, spring-jaw, trunnion-type, and indexing chucks. Fig. 9-25 contains dimensions for three-step, reversible top jaws for Class I chucks. Figs. 9-26 and 9-27 illustrate expander and faceplate fixtures for lathes.

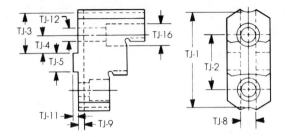

Dimension Designation		Size of Chuck					
		6 (152)	8 (203)	10 (254)	12 (305)	15 (381)	18-36 (457-914)
TJ-1:	Length of jaw	2.62 (66.5)	3.12 (79.2)	3.76 (95.5)	4.30 (109.2)	5.00 (127.0)	5.00 (127.0)
TJ-2:	Center-to-center screw holes**	1.500 (38.10)	1.750 (44.45)	2.125 (53.97)	2.500 (63.50)	3.000 (76.20)	3.000 (76.20)
TJ-3:	Cross slot to long bite end †	1.125 (28.57)	1.375 (34.92)	1.562 (39.67)	1.875 (47.62)	2.250 (57.15)	2.250 (57.15)
TJ-4:	Screw center to edge of key	0.500 (12.70)	0.625 (15.87)	0.688 (17.48)	0.875 (22.22)	1.125 (28.57)	1.125 (28.57)
TJ-5:	Width of cross key	0.499 (12.67)	0.499 (12.67)	0.749 (19.02)	0.749 (19.02)	0.749 (19.02)	0.749 (19.02)
		0.498 (12.65)	0.498 (12.65)	0.748 (19.00)	0.748 (19.00)	0.748 (19.00)	0.748 (19.00)
TJ-8:	Width of tongue slot	0.315 (8.00)	0.315 (8.00)	0.503 (12.78)	0.503 (12.78)	0.503 (12.78)	0.503 (12.78)
		0.313 (7.95)	0.313 (7.95)	0.501 (12.73)	0.501 (12.73)	0.501 (12.73)	0.501 (12.73)
TJ-9:	Depth of tongue slot	0.17 (4.3)	0.17 (4.3)	0.17 (4.3)	0.17 (4.3)	0.17 (4.3)	0.17 (4.3)
		0.15 (3.8)	0.15 (3.8)	0.15 (3.8)	0.15 (3.8)	0.15 (3.8)	0.15 (3.8)
TJ-11:	Height of cross key	0.12 (3.0)	0.12 (3.0)	0.12 (3.0)	0.12 (3.0)	0.25 (6.3)	0.25 (6.3)
		0.10 (2.5)	0.10 (2.5)	0.10 (2.5)	0.10 (2.5)	0.23 (5.8)	0.23 (5.8)
TJ-12:	Drill size for screws	0.406 (10.31)	0.406 (10.31)	0.531 (13.49)	0.531 (13.49)	0.656 (16.66)	0.781 (19.84)
TJ-16:	Counterbore for screw head	0.609 (15.47)	0.609 (15.47)	0.797 (20.24)	0.797 (20.24)	1.000 (25.40)	1.188 (30.18)

  * All dimensions are in inches (mm). Unless otherwise specified, tolerance on two-place decimals is ±0.02″ (0.5 mm).

** Holes located within 0.006″ (0.15 mm) of true position.

  † To be equal in sets within 0.0015″ (0.038 mm).

Figure 9-25   Dimensions of three-step, reversible top jaws for Class I chucks

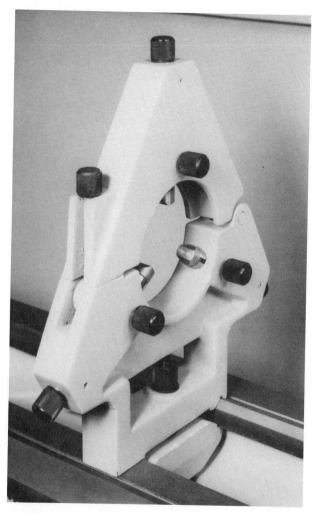

Figure 9-26   Hinge-top center of steady rest (Courtesy of DoAll Co.)

Figure 9-27   Open-sided steady rest (Courtesy of DoAll Co.)

Magnetic and Vacuum Chucks: While magnetic and vacuum chucks are more commonly used on machine tables for grinding and milling, they are also employed occasionally for light-duty turning operation. These operations are generally of the precision type and involve shallow cuts. Vacuum or magnetic chucks can be designed to hold many different odd-shaped parts and often eliminate problems of distortion when fragile thin-walled components are turned.

Magnetic chucks. Permanent magnetic and electromagnetic chucks are used on lathes. They are now available with higher holding-power ratings and the capability of providing gripping to all edges of the chucking surface. Controls to vary the holding power are available on some electromagnetic units.

Advantages of magnetic chucks include rapid loading and unloading, minimum distortion, no marking of the workpiece surfaces, and less chance of interference with the cutting tools. When required, demagnetizers are used to reverse the magnetic field and eliminate residual magnetism from the workpieces, tools, and machine components.

Vacuum chucks. Rotating faceplate-type vacuum chucks usually require a rotating union to be installed in back of the chuck, extending through the machine spindle and connecting to an air exhaust line. In some cases, the connection can be made to a rotating union mounted through the face or faceplate of the chuck. The nondistorting, nondamaging holding force of such chucks makes them suitable for thin or fragile parts.

Clamping pressure available with vacuum chucks is generally about 12 psi (83 kPa). The chucks are built with porous, pin hole, or grooved plates. Portions of the chuck face not covered by the workpiece are masked or blocked to eliminate leakage. Cone-shaped or domed vacuum chucks have been built for secondary operations on spun parts or workpieces that have been contour machined.

Operating Parameters for Turning

Variables that must be determined for any turning, facing, or related operation include power requirements and cutting speed, feed rate, and depth of cut to be used.

Power Requirements for Turning:
The following equations can be used to calculate the horsepower and power actually required by a single-point cutting tool to turn a specific material:

For U.S. customary units:
$$hp_c = (uhp)\ 12\ CV f d$$

For SI metric units:
$$P_c = U_p \bullet \frac{V}{60} \bullet C f d$$

where:
  hp_c = horsepower at the cutting tool, hp
  P_c = power at the cutting tool, kW
  uhp = unit horsepower

  U_p = unit power
  C = feed correction factor
  V = cutting speed, sfm or m/min
  f = feed rate, ipr or mm/rev
  d = depth of cut, in. or mm

Unit horsepower and unit power. For each different material to be machined, a measure of the power required is the unit horsepower (uhp) and its SI metric equivalent, the unit power (U_p). Unit horsepower, also called specific power consumption, is defined as the horsepower required to remove a material at a rate of one cubic inch per minute. Unit power is the power required to remove a material at a rate of 1000 cubic millimeters, or one cubic centimeter, per second.

Values of both unit horsepower and unit power for single-point tools are determined experimentally by measuring cutting forces with dynamometers and applying the results to the following equations:

For U.S. customary inch units:
$$uhp = \frac{F_c}{396{,}000\ f d}$$

For SI metric units:
$$U_p = \frac{F_c}{f d}$$

where:
  F_c = cutting force, lb or kN
  f = feed rate, ipr or mm/rev
  d = depth of cut, in. or mm

For multiple-tool operations, the power required by each tool must be calculated at the point in the cycle when the most power is needed. When tools are removing varying amounts of material and attachments are operating simultaneously, more than one calculation is necessary to determine the maximum power required.

Speed, Feed, and Depth of Cut:
The parameters of cutting speed, feed rate, and depth of cut control both the material removal rate and tool life in turning. Any increase in these operating parameters increases the material removal rate, but decreases

tool life. A change in any one of the three parameters has an equal effect on the material removal rate; however, each parameter has a different effect on tool life.

Depth of cut. Tool life is less affected by changes in the depth of cut than by changes in either feed rate or cutting speed. In fact, there is little effect on tool life except when the depth of cut is less than ten times the feed rate.

The consensus of most authorities in material removal is that the best method of increasing the material removal rate is to use the deepest cut possible. Depth of cut, however, is limited by the amount of stock to be removed, power capability of the machine, rigidity of the setup, tooling capability, surface finish and accuracy requirements, and sometimes by the shape of the workpiece. Also, it is generally recommended that only 50-75% of the cutting edge should be engaged with the workpiece.

Feed rate. Changes in the feed rate have a greater effect on tool life than changes in the depth of cut, but a lesser effect than changes in the cutting speed. The same investigations cited previously found that a 50% increase in feed rate results in about a 60% decrease in tool life.

Despite the sacrifice in tool life, it is generally recommended that the largest possible feed rate be used to obtain a higher production rate and a lower power requirement per volume of stock removed. Increases in feed rates, however, are limited by the ability of the machine tool, cutting tool, workpiece, and setup to withstand the cutting forces, as well as by the surface finish required on the workpiece.

Cutting speed. The cutting speed used for turning has a greater effect on tool life than either depth of cut or feed rate, and speed selection is most critical.

The use of higher cutting speeds to obtain increased material removal rates can result in costly penalties with respect to tool life and may be the least desirable means of improving productivity. Newer cutting tool materials, such as coated carbides, ceramics, polycrystalline diamond, and cubic boron nitride, however, can provide benefits because of their higher cutting speed capability. Higher speeds may also create problems with respect to vibration, the life of machine

components such as bearings, and reduced safety. Careful consideration must be given to balancing increased production and cost per part machined.

Cutting Fluids for Turning: A few turning operations, such as machining cast iron parts and some short-run applications, do not require the use of cutting fluids. Cutting fluid requirements also vary with the cutting tool material. When they are used, cutting fluids serve one or more of the following functions: cooling, lubricating, controlling or preventing a built-up edge on the tool, flushing away chips, and preventing rust.

When the metal to be machined is free cutting, permitting the use of higher cutting speeds, the most important consideration in selecting a cutting fluid is its cooling properties. When the metal characteristics require that low cutting speeds must be employed, lubricity and antiweld properties of the cutting fluid become most important.

As a general rule, the use of a water-based fluid is recommended when cutting speeds exceed about 100 sfm (30.5 m/min). A compounded cutting oil is used for lower speeds. Taking into account all the requirements and variables of a specific turning operation, there will usually be more than one type of fluid that gives satisfactory performance.

For cutting tools made of high-speed steels or cast cobalt-based alloys, good results are obtained with either soluble oil (diluted 10 to 15 parts water to one part oil) or sulfurized oil. Some heavy turning operations, however, are performed successfully with no cutting fluid.

A difference of opinion exists about the value of cutting fluids for turning with carbides. Most authorities recommend their use to reduce tool wear and friction. If a fluid is used, proper application is essential to assure flooding the tool and workpiece with a continuous, copious flow. Too little fluid can cause chipping, cracking, or failure of the tool due to thermal cycling stress.

Coated carbide tools can generally be used without a cutting fluid, but one is sometimes used to cool the workpiece and/or remove chips. Cutting fluids are generally not recommended or needed when using ceramic tools. This is because the tools remain relatively cool because of the low thermal conductivity of the ceramics and most of the heat generated is carried away in the chips. When ceramic tools are used to machine materials having a low thermal conductivity, such as stainless steel, a cutting fluid is sometimes used to reduce the temperature at the cutting edge. Cutting fluids, however, may cause thermal cracks when tools made of ceramics, as well as some carbides, are used.

Single-crystal diamond tools generally require an abundant and continous flow of cutting fluid because excessive heat will burn or crack the tools. Cooling is also important when polycrystalline diamond tools are used, and good results are obtained with a soluble oil diluted to 15 parts water to one part oil. There are successful applications, however, using single-crystal and polycrystalline diamond tools without a cutting fluid.

For cubic boron nitride tools, soluble oil (diluted 20:1) is generally recommended, but there are applications in which machining is done dry. Fig. 9-28 is a checklist for planning a turning process.

Safety in Turning: Safety requirements for the construction, care, and use of lathes are specified in ANSI Standard B11.6-1975. Common sense, good judgment, and safe work practices are required at all times because every dangerous condition or situation cannot be completely covered in any standard.

The possibility of tool failure and fragmentation is a major concern with respect to safety in machining. Tool fragments can attain high velocities, so protection of personnel and equipment is essential. This can be accomplished by the use of safety glasses and the installation of safety devices and protective shields or screens. Most modern automatic lathes have the tooling area completely enclosed by guards with access for loading and unloading by means of an interlocked door. Operation can only take place when the door is closed.

The tooling itself, the insert thickness, and the holders must be sufficiently strong to withstand the cutting loads imposed. Tool overhang should be kept to a minimum to limit deflection and chatter. Excessive overhang deflection and/or chatter can cause tool breakage.

Chip control, previously discussed, is also essential to safety. The possibility of hot, high-velocity chips being projected from the workpiece makes machine guarding and personal protective equipment mandatory. Chips should never be handled by hand, and an air hose should not be used to blow chips from a machine. It is extremely important that the machine always be stopped prior to chip removal.

Adequate means should also be provided to collect and dispose of dust, mist, and sludge produced in tool grinding. The inhalation of mist containing metallic particles can be hazardous, especially over extended periods of time. An exhaust system capable of keeping dust to a tolerable level is also recommended when cast iron is machined.

General recommendations with respect to safety include keeping the machine and work area clean, avoiding overloading, assuring proper maintenance, and staying clear of moving parts of the machine (pinch points).

The Boring Process

Boring is a precision machining process for generating internal cylindrical forms by removing metal with single-point tools or tools with multiple cutting edges. This process is most commonly performed with the workpiece held stationary and the cutting tool both rotating and advancing into the work. Boring is also done, however, with the cutting tool stationary and the workpiece rotating.

Common applications for boring include the enlarging or finishing of cored, pierced, or drilled holes and contoured internal surfaces. Related operations sometimes performed simultaneously with boring include turning, facing, chamfering, grooving, and threading.

Boring can be done on horizontal, vertical, or angular machines as long as the machine design provides the inherent rigidity and accuracy to produce

- The Workpiece:
  1. Be sure that workpiece specification factors, such as size, tolerance, finish, shape, and radii, are required for the end use of the product.
  2. When possible, try to have machining requirements allow for the use of standard tooling.

- The Machine and Setup:
  1. Select a machine with adequate power, capacity, and rigidity to satisfy requirements.
  2. Use toolholders and workholders of sufficient size and strength to assure rigidity. Keep tool overhang as short as possible to minimize deflection and chatter.

- Tool Design and Material:
  1. Use standard tooling when possible. Special grinds, sizes, or geometries are often less cost effective than the use of standard designs.
  2. Use tool designs which are simple in concept, having few component pieces, and that can be quickly changed and adjusted. Ease of replacement and required inventory of components are important considerations.
  3. Select a cutting tool material best suited for the specific application, based on the type of wear expected. A discussion of the advantages, limitations, and recommended applications for various cutting tool materials is presented in Chapter 3, "Cutting Tool Materials."
  4. When selecting a grade of tool material, pick the hardest standard grade possible first. If chipping occurs, change to a softer and tougher grade.

- Indexable Inserts:
  1. Thicker indexable inserts are stronger mechanically than thinner inserts and can absorb higher cutting forces and impact loading, as well as dissipate heat better.
  2. When using indexable inserts, be sure that the pockets in the holders are always free of chips, fragments, and debris and that insert seats are tight, flat, and not broken.

- Tool Geometry:
  1. Use negative rake tool geometry whenever possible since this design is stronger mechanically and may dissipate more heat from the cutting zone than tools with positive rake geometry. Also, in the case of indexable inserts, this design provides more cutting edges.
  2. Use a lead (side cutting edge) angle when possible to reduce impact loading when the tool enters the cut. This design also permits a gradual reduction in load as the tool leaves the cut and produces a better surface finish, compared to a tool with a zero lead angle. Use of a lead angle, however, produces slightly higher cutting forces and may cause a chip control problem when ductile materials are machined. Tools with high lead angles may cause chatter because of the direction of the cutting forces.
  3. Reducing the end cutting edge angle produces a better surface finish, but may increase heat generation because of rubbing.
  4. Use as large a nose radius or corner radius as possible. This design strengthens the tool and improves the surface finish produced. Large radii, however, may cause chatter, deflection from chip size effect, and chip control problems when ductile materials are machined.
  5. Chip control may be obtained by using mechanical chipbreakers, pressed grooves, and ground steps; by changing the rake angle, side cutting edge angle, or nose radius; and by varying the cutting speed and/or feed rate.

- Operating Parameters:
  1. Use the greatest depth of cut possible and the highest feed rate practical.
  2. Then select the highest cutting speed commensurate with balancing production rate against tool life.

- Cutting Fluid:
  1. Check for thermal shock and cracking of a tool which may be caused by an intermittent flow of cutting fluid.
  2. If necessary, filter the fluid to remove particles that can cause accelerated tool wear.

Figure 9-28 Guidelines for initial planning of a turning process

the tolerances required. Considerable boring is done on the various types of lathes previously discussed in this chapter.

Applications of boring can be divided into heavy cutting and precision operations. Heavy boring is generally done on large horizontal and vertical boring machines, including vertical turret lathes and boring, drilling, and milling machines. These machines and other machines also used for boring—such as automatic lathes, multispindle bar and chucking machines, machining centers, and transfer machines—are discussed in Chapter 18.

Precision boring is performed on machines specifically designed for this purpose. These machines generally take relatively light cuts, maintain close tolerances, and are often capable of high production rates.

Types of Precision-Boring Machines: Many types of precision-boring machines are available. Major types include horizontal single- and double-end machines, center-drive machines, vertical machines, way-type machines, and NC machines.

Since heat and vibration are major deterrents to the accuracies and finishes required in precision boring, heavy-duty rigid bases are required for the machines to minimize problems of chatter and vibration. Also, to isolate vibrations and avoid heat distortion of machine components, all electrical, hydraulic, and drive equipment is generally located external to the base. Figs. 9-29, 9-30, 9-31, and 9-32 are examples of modern boring machines.

Precision-Boring Machines

Precision-boring machines are available in a wide variety of types to suit many different applications. Configurations include single or multiple spindles arranged horizontally, vertically, or at any required angle. Selection of the type to be used depends primarily upon the size and configuration of the workpieces, operations to be performed, and production requirements.

Cutting tool or workpiece rotation for precision boring depends upon the specific application and the size, shape, and balance of the workpiece. The ability to rotate workpieces or tooling makes it possible to perform many difficult operations simultaneously or in sequence. It also assures concentric diameters and square faces, which are difficult to obtain when a workpiece is relocated for separate operations. Irregularly shaped and/or unbalanced workpieces are generally bored with rotating tools. Rotating tools and multiple spindles are also often used when several holes have to be bored in the same workpiece. Rotation of the workpiece is sometimes preferred for more complex operations.

Figure 9-29 CNC boring machine (Courtesy of Cincinnati Gilbert)

Figure 9-30 CNC boring machine (Courtesy of Cincinnati Gilbert)

Figure 9-31 CNC boring machine (Courtesy of Cincinnati Gilbert)

Figure 9-32 CNC boring machine (Courtesy of Cincinnati Gilbert)

Boring Tools

Boring operations are usually harder on cutting tools than turning operations because of the confined machining area, which can cause chip removal problems, especially from deeper and smaller diameter bores. As a result, the size, strength, and stiffness of boring tools are often limited by hole size and length of cut. If the chips nest or pack, the cutting tools take considerable abuse.

Despite these limitations, normal cutting-tool theory and the preceding discussion of turning tools in this chapter apply to tools used for precision boring. Owing to the special nature of boring operations, however, some design considerations tend to be more critical. Boring tools are available as solid tools, with tips brazed to holders, and as indexable inserts. Tooling with indexable inserts is used more extensively for boring. Figs. 9-33 and 9-34 are examples of boring tools.

Toolholders for Precision Boring

Boring tools can be divided into two main categories: rotating and fixed (nonrotating). Rotating tools are tools mounted in rotating spindles to perform various boring, facing, and related operations with the bore and toolholder on the same centerline. Nonrotating tools are of various arrangements and

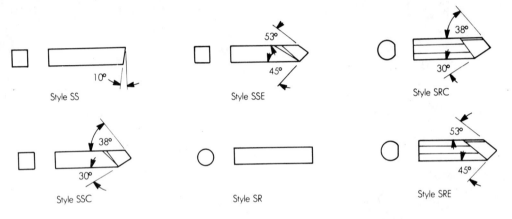

Figure 9-33 Standard solid square and round carbide boring tools and tool bits

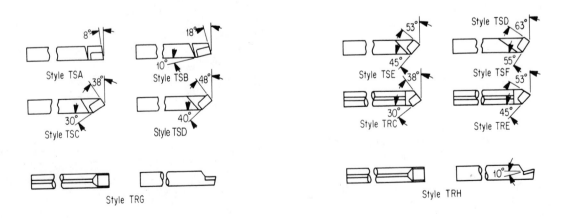

Figure 9-34 Standard carbide-tipped boring tools

are mounted to the table or cross slide of the machine to perform operations on rotating workpieces, generally not on the same centerline as the toolholder (see Figs. 9-35, 9-36, 9-37, and 9-38).

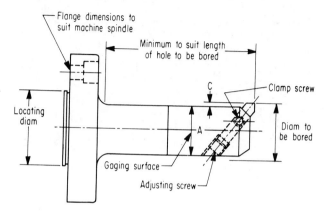

Figure 9-35   Boring bar

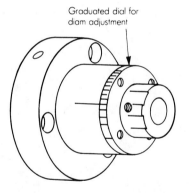

Figure 9-36   Boring-bar holder with built-in micrometer adjustment

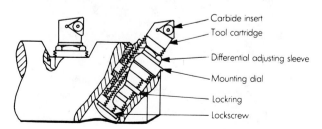

Figure 9-37   Micrometer-adjustable toolholder for boring operations

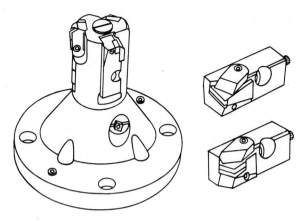

Figure 9-38   Boring bar with cartridges that hold indexable inserts

Workholding for Boring

Many of the various types of chucks and collets discussed under turning in a preceding section of this chapter are also used for precision boring, as well as for combination machining operations. Fixtures are also used extensively for precision boring.

Fixturing of workpieces for precision-boring operations is an extremely important and critical matter. When the high degree of accuracy usually demanded of the operation performed by the machine is considered, holding the part during the operation demands careful consideration of the correct locating surfaces and clamping must minimize distortions, which influence accuracy. The compromise between adequate, rigid clamping and small distortions can present a challenge in ingenuity of fixture design.

Design of the part itself can be an extremely important factor. Special provisions for locating and clamping made during part design can often prevent many problems and reduce fixture cost considerably. Adequate preparation of the part in processing prior to precision boring can also help considerably in overcoming problems in fixturing.

Fixtures can be extremely simple or complex, depending upon various factors. Low production requirements may only justify a simple approach with manual clamping. However, some low-production fixtures may demand power clamping. High production may demand a highly sophisticated, automatic clamping fixture. Regardless, fixtures should be designed with ease of loading in mind, and always with careful attention given to proper clearance for the boring bar and the removal of the chips made by the process.

Fixtures can be divided into three main categories: stationary, indexing, and rotating (see Figs. 9-39, 9-40, and 9-41).

Figure 9-40   Center drilling as a boring method

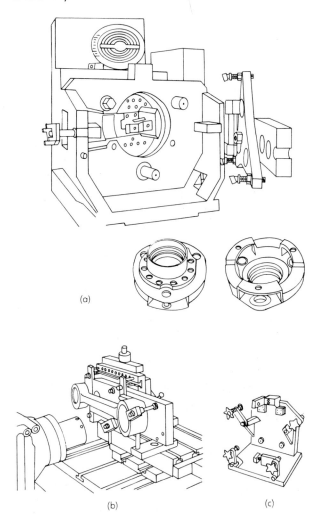

(a)

(b)   (c)

Figure 9-39   Simple stationary manually-clamped fixtures for precision boring

Figure 9-41   Drilling and reaming as boring processes

Operating Parameters for Precision Boring

Variables such as tool selection, power requirements, and cutting fluids, as well as the subjects of tool sharpening, troubleshooting, and safety, are essentially the same for boring tools as for turning tools, which were discussed in preceding sections of this chapter.

Safety in Precision Boring: Safety requirements are specified in ANSI Standard B11.8-1974, "Construction, Care, and Use of Drilling, Milling, and Boring Machines." Other recommendations presented in the preceding section "Safety in Turning" also apply to boring operations.

Extra caution should be exercised in boring when checking the cutting action of the tool because the nature of the operation tempts the operator to lean over the rotating workpiece. Care is also necessary to assure proper chip control within the bore. Long, stringy chips can accumulate within the bore, creating a hazard because of the possibility that they may whip from the hole. With workpieces, having through holes and held-in chucks, chips forced out the back of the hole may be propelled radially outward at high speed by the chuck jaws.

KEY TERMS AND PHRASES _____

Burnishing tools
Centers
CNC turning machines
Collets
Contouring lathe
Cutting fluid
Cutting tool
Depth of cut
Engine lathe
Feed rate
Fixtures
Form tools
Horizontal turret lathe
Indexable inserts
Jaw-type chucks
Knurling tools
Magnetic chuck
Parting tools
Precision-boring
Solid single-point tools
Turning process
Vacuum chuck

QUESTIONS FOR ADDITIONAL STUDY AND REVIEW _____

1. Describe the turning process.

2. Describe how the workpiece is held on a lathe.

3. Describe the cutting tool movements of a basic engine lathe.

4. What are the variables that influence a turning operation?

5. Describe the following types of lathes:

   - Engine lathe
   - Contouring lathe
   - Horizontal turret lathe

6. Describe the following types of cutting tools used in turning operations:

   - Solid single-point
   - Indexable inserts
   - Form tools
   - Knurling tools
   - Burnishing tools
   - Parting tools

7. Explain how the following workholding devices operate:

   - Centers
   - Collets
   - Jaw-type chucks
   - Magnetic chucks
   - Vacuum chucks

8. What is the formula for calculating the horsepower and power required by a single-point cutting tool? What does each element of the formula mean?

9. Explain the impact of depth of cut in turning.

10. Explain how changes in the feed rate affect tool life.

11. Explain how the cutting speed affects tool life.

12. What functions do cutting fluids serve in turning?

13. Explain how chip control is essential to safety in turning.

14. Describe the boring process.

15. What are the most commonly used types of precision-boring machines?

16. Explain how the design of a part can affect the design of a workholding fixture.

CHAPTER 10

Drilling, Reaming, and Related Processes

MAJOR TOPICS COVERED

- The Drilling Process
- Twist Drills
- Toolholders for Drilling
- Workholding Devices for Drilling
- Drilling Machines
- Drilling Feeds and Speeds
- Cutting Fluids for Drilling
- Counterboring, Spotfacing, and Countersinking
- Reaming

Drilling

The Drilling Process

Drilling is basically the production or enlarging of holes by the relative motion of a cutting tool and the workpiece, which produces chips. The cutting tool, the workpiece, or both may rotate, with the tool generally being fed. Several different methods of drilling exist, including conventional, deep-hole, and small-hole drilling. The choice of a method depends upon the size, depth, tolerance, and finish needed; production requirements; and the machines available to perform the operations.

While drilling is fast and economical, its cutting action is difficult and inefficient. Cutting speed varies from a maximum at the periphery of the tool to zero at the center of the tool, thus varying the load on the cutting edges. Both chip ejection and flow of the cutting fluid are restricted in drilling. In addition, the production of small, deep holes can create problems with respect to necessary rigidity of the tools.

Cutting Action: Drilling is a complex three-dimensional cutting operation with conditions varying along the entire cutting edge. With twist drills, the rake angle normal to the cutting lip decreases from the periphery toward the drill center and cutting action improves along the cutting edge from the axis to the periphery of the drill. While the outer edge of the drill produces chips by shearing, workpiece material under the chisel edge of the tool is subject to more severe deformation, thus requiring greater thrust forces.

The limited chip space provided by a drill makes it desirable to have the chips produced in small pieces. Coiling of the chips, especially in deep holes, causes packing of the drill flutes, interferes with chip ejection, and reduces the flow of cutting fluid to the drill tip. This causes excess heat generation and premature dulling of the tool.

Effect of workpiece material. Ductility of the material to be drilled is a major factor in chip formation. When less ductile materials are being drilled, the chips tend to break into pieces; this is desirable and generally permits the use of lower cost, standard drills. When more ductile materials are being drilled, the chips tend to bend and coil and special tool designs and geometrics must be employed to minimize this action.

Effect of feed rate. Chip thickness, which varies with the feed rate, also has a major influence on chip formation. Increasing the feed, which increases the chip thickness, minimizes the possibility of the flute clogging from coiled chips. Maximum feed, however, is limited by the structural strength of the drill and the capability of the machine. A woodpeckering or step-drilling technique—periodic withdrawal of the drill from the hole—may be required to remove chips when deep holes are being drilled, but this practice is not recommended for work-hardening materials.

Twist Drills

Drills are defined as rotary end-cutting tools having one or more cutting lips and one or more helical or straight flutes for the passage of chips and the admission of a cutting fluid. These cutting tools are made in a wide variety of types with many different forms, dimensions, and tolerances.

Twist drills are not considered to be precision cutting tools; rather, they are tools designed to produce holes rapidly and economically. When precision is required, subsequent operations such as boring or reaming are generally required. Drilling, using twist drills having tapered webs, is also generally limited to hole depths of about three to five times the hole diameter unless the woodpeckering technique of periodic tool withdrawal is employed or coolant-fed twist drills are used. See Fig. 10-1 for twist drill nomenclature.

Classification of Twist Drills: Twist drills can be classified by the material from which they are made, kinds of shank, number of flutes, hand of cut, length, diameter, and point geometry.

Based on the kind of shank, twist drills can be classified as:

1. *Straight-shank drills.* Those having cylindrical shanks which may be the same or different diameter than the body of the drill. The shanks may be provided with or without driving flats, tangs, grooves, or threads.
2. *Taper-shank drills.* Those having conical shanks suitable for direct fitting into tapered holes in machine spindles, driving sleeves, or sockets. Taper-shank drills generally have a tang to assist in driving and to permit removing the drill from the spindle or holder.

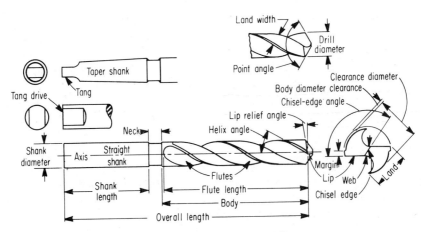

Figure 10-1   Standard terms used to describe elements of twist drills

Based on the number of flutes, twist drills can be classified as:

1. *Single-flute drills.* These tools, having only one flute, are used for originating holes and for drilling plastics.
2. *Two-flute drills.* These are the conventional type drills also used for originating holes.
3. *Three- or four-flute drills* (core drills). These are commonly used for enlarging and finishing drilled, cast, or punched holes. They do not produce original holes.

Based on hand of cut, twist drills can be classified as:

1. *Right-hand cut.* As viewed when looking toward the point of these drills, with their shanks extending away, they must be rotated in a counterclockwise direction in order to cut. Most drills are made for right-hand rotation.
2. *Left-hand cut.* When viewed from the cutting point, clockwise rotation is necessary for cutting.

Types of Twist Drills:
Twist drills are manufactured in a wide variety of types, some of which are illustrated in Fig. 10-2, and in many different sizes. To produce a hole of any given diameter, twist drills are commercially available with variations in length, flute and shank configuration, point geometry, and web thickness. In some cases, a dozen or more drills may be available to produce the same size hole.

Drills are made in many different diameter sizes — fractional, number (wire gage), letter, and metric — ranging from 0.0059″ (0.150 mm) to 3½″ (89 mm). However, data compiled by National Twist Drill, based on sales of more than 50 million standard twist drills, showed that a median 90% of all sales (5% were for larger sizes, and 5% for smaller) fall between 0.050 and 0.400″ (1.27 and 10.16 mm) diam. The most common drill size, especially for rivet holes in the aircraft/aerospace industry, is a No. 30 (0.1285″, 3.264 mm), with a ⅛″ (3.2 mm) diam a close second. Only about 1% of all twist drills sold exceed ¾″ (19 mm) diam.

For simplication purposes, many styles of drills can be classified separated into general-purpose and

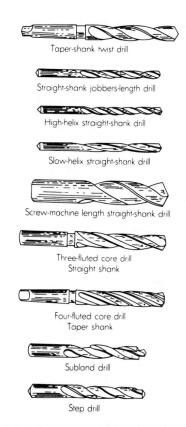

Figure 10-2 Some conventional and special-purpose twist drills

heavy-duty categories. General-purpose drills are the most widely used. Slight alterations of the original point angles sometimes improve performance for given speeds and feeds. Heavy-duty drills are designed to provide greater torsional strength and rigidity than general-purpose drills. They can be used to drill steel forgings, hard castings, and high-hardness ferrous alloys. See Fig. 10-3 for drill sizes.

Twist Drill Geometries:
Efficient drilling of the wide variety of materials encountered in industry today requires many different drill designs and geometries. Many holes can be drilled satisfactorily with standard off-the-shelf twist drills, but no one drill is best for all applications. Variations in drills being used, while maintaining required strength and sufficient room for

DRILL SIZES IN DECIMAL EQUIVALENTS

Inch	Decimal	Wire & Letter	M/M
1/64	.0156		
	.0157		.4
	.0160	78	
	.0165		.42
	.0173		.44
	.0177		.45
	.0180	77	
	.0181		.46
	.0189		.48
	.0197		.5
	.0200	76	
	.0210	75	
	.0217		.55
	.0225	74	
	.0236		.6
	.0240	73	
	.0250	72	
	.0256		.65
	.0260	71	
	.0276		.7
	.0280	70	
	.0292	69	
	.0295		.75
	.0310	68	
1/32	.0312		
	.0315		.8
	.0320	67	
	.0330	66	
	.0335		.85
	.0350	65	
	.0354		.9
	.0360	64	
	.0370	63	
	.0374		.95
	.0380	62	
	.0390	61	
	.0394		1.
	.0400	60	
	.0410	59	
	.0413		1.05
	.0420	58	
	.0430	57	
	.0433		1.1
	.0453		1.15
	.0465	56	
3/64	.0469		
	.0472		1.2
	.0492		1.25
	.0512		1.3
	.0520	55	
	.0531		1.35
	.0550	54	
	.0551		1.4
	.0571		1.45
	.0591		1.5
	.0595	53	
1/16	.0610		1.55
	.0625		
	.0630		1.6
	.0635	52	
	.0650		1.65
	.0669		1.7
	.0670	51	
	.0689		1.75
	.0700	50	
	.0709		
	.0728		1.8
	.0730	49	
	.0748		1.85
	.0760	48	
	.0768		1.9
5/64	.0781		1.95
	.0785	47	
	.0787		2.
	.0807		2.05
	.0810	46	
	.0820	45	
	.0827		2.1
	.0846		2.15
	.0860	44	
	.0866		2.2
	.0886		2.25
	.0890	43	
	.0906		2.3
	.0925		2.35
	.0935	42	
3/32	.0938		
	.0945		2.4
	.0960	41	
	.0965		2.45
	.0980	40	
	.0981		2.5
	.0995	39	
	.1015	38	
	.1024		2.6
	.1040	37	
	.1063		2.7
	.1065	36	
	.1083		2.75
7/64	.1094		
	.1100	35	
	.1102		2.8
	.1110	34	
	.1130	33	
	.1142		2.9
	.1160	32	
	.1181		3.
	.1200	31	
	.1220		3.1
1/8	.1250		
	.1260		3.2
	.1280		3.25
	.1285	30	
	.1299		3.3
	.1339		3.4
	.1360	29	
	.1378		3.5
	.1405	28	
9/64	.1406		
	.1417		3.6
	.1440	27	
	.1457		3.7
	.1470	26	
	.1476		3.75
	.1495	25	
	.1496		3.8
	.1520	24	
	.1535		3.9
	.1540	23	
5/32	.1562		
	.1570	22	
	.1575		4.
	.1590	21	
	.1610	20	
	.1614		4.1
	.1654		4.2
	.1660	19	
	.1673		4.25
	.1693		4.3
11/64	.1695	18	
	.1719		
	.1730	17	
	.1732		4.4
	.1770	16	
	.1772		4.5
	.1800	15	
	.1811		4.6
	.1820	14	
	.1850	13	
	.1850		4.7
	.1870		4.75
3/16	.1875		
	.1890		4.8
	.1890	12	
	.1910	11	
	.1929		4.9
	.1935	10	
	.1960	9	
	.1969		5.
	.1990	8	
	.2008		5.1
	.2010	7	
13/64	.2031		
	.2040	6	
	.2047		5.2
	.2055	5	
	.2067		5.25
	.2087		5.3
	.2090	4	
	.2126		5.4
	.2130	3	
	.2165		5.5
7/32	.2188		
	.2205		5.6
	.2210	2	
	.2244		5.7
	.2264		5.75
	.2280	1	
	.2283		5.8
	.2323		5.9
	.2340	A	
15/64	.2344		
	.2362		6.
	.2380	B	
	.2402		6.1
	.2420	C	
	.2441		6.2
	.2460	D	
	.2461		6.25
	.2480		6.3
1/4	.2500	E	
	.2520		6.4
	.2559		6.5
	.2570	F	
	.2598		6.6
	.2610	G	
	.2638		6.7
17/64	.2656		
	.2657		6.75
	.2660	H	
	.2677		6.8
	.2717		6.9
	.2720	I	
	.2756		7.
	.2770	J	
	.2795		7.1
	.2810	K	
9/32	.2812		
	.2835		7.2
	.2854		7.25
	.2874		7.3
	.2900	L	
	.2913		7.4
	.2950	M	
	.2953		7.5
19/64	.2969		
	.2992		7.6
	.3020	N	
	.3031		7.7
	.3051		7.75
	.3071		7.8
	.3110		7.9
5/16	.3125		
	.3150		8.
	.3160	O	
	.3189		8.1
	.3228		8.2
	.3230	P	
	.3248		8.25
	.3268		8.3
21/64	.3281		
	.3307		8.4
	.3320	Q	
	.3346		8.5
	.3386		8.6
	.3390	R	
	.3425		8.7
11/32	.3438		
	.3445		8.75
	.3465		8.8
	.3480	S	
	.3504		8.9
	.3543		9.
	.3580	T	
	.3583		9.1
23/64	.3594		
	.3622		9.2
	.3642		9.25
	.3661		9.3
	.3680	U	
	.3701		9.4
	.3740		9.5
3/8	.3750		
	.3770	V	
	.3780		9.6
	.3819		9.7
	.3839		9.75
	.3858		9.8
	.3860	W	
	.3898		9.9
25/64	.3906		
	.3937		10.
	.3970	X	
	.4040	Y	
13/32	.4062		
	.4130	Z	
	.4134		10.5
27/64	.4219		
	.4331		11.
7/16	.4375		
	.4528		11.5
29/64	.4531		
15/32	.4688		
	.4724		12.
31/64	.4844		
	.4921		12.5
1/2	.5000		
	.5118		13.
33/64	.5156		
17/32	.5312		
	.5315		13.5
35/64	.5469		
	.5512		14.
9/16	.5625		
	.5709		14.5
37/64	.5781		
	.5906		15.
19/32	.5938		
39/64	.6094		
	.6102		15.5
5/8	.6250		
	.6299		16.
41/64	.6406		
	.6496		16.5
21/32	.6562		
	.6693		17.
43/64	.6719		
11/16	.6875		
	.6890		17.5
45/64	.7031		
	.7087		18.
23/32	.7188		
	.7283		18.5
47/64	.7344		
	.7480		19.
3/4	.7500		
49/64	.7656		
	.7677		19.5
25/32	.7812		
	.7874		20.
51/64	.7969		
	.8071		20.5
13/16	.8125		
	.8268		21.
53/64	.8281		
27/32	.8438		
	.8465		21.5
55/64	.8594		
	.8661		22.
7/8	.8750		
	.8858		22.5
57/64	.8906		
	.9055		23.
29/32	.9062		
59/64	.9219		
	.9252		23.5
15/16	.9375		
	.9449		24.
61/64	.9531		
	.9646		24.5
31/32	.9688		
	.9843		25.
63/64	.9844		
1	1.0000		

TAP DRILL SIZES FOR CUT AND FORMED THREADS

TAP SIZE	Cut Thread		Formed Thread	
0 - 80	3/64	.0469	54	.0545
1 - 64	53	.0595	1.65mm	.065
1 - 72	53	.0595	1.7mm	.0669
2 - 56	50	.0700	5/64	.0781
2 - 64	50	.0700	2mm	.0787
3 - 48	46	.0810	43	.089
3 - 56	45	.0820	2.3mm	.0906
4 - 40	43	.0890	39	.0995
4 - 48	3/32	.0938	2.6mm	.1024
5 - 40	38	.1015	33	.113
5 - 44	37	.1040	2.9mm	.1142
6 - 32	34	.1110	1/8	.125
6 - 40	32	.1160	3.2mm	.1260
8 - 32	29	.1360	25	.1495
8 - 36	29	.1360	24	.1520
10 - 24	23	.1540	11/64	.1719
10 - 32	20	.1610	16	.1770
12 - 24	15	.1800	5mm	.1968
12 - 28	13	.1850	8	.1990
1/4 - 20	13/64	.2031	1	.2280
1/4 - 28	7/32	.2187	A	.2340
5/16 - 18	G	.2610	7.3mm	.2874
5/16 - 24	J	.2770	M	.2950
3/8 - 16	O	.3160	S	.3480
3/8 - 24	R	.3390	T	.358
7/16 - 14	U	.3680	13/32	.406
7/16 - 20	25/64	.3906	10.5mm	.4134
1/2 - 13	27/64	.4219	•	.466
1/2 - 20	29/64	.4531	•	.478
9/16 - 12	31/64	.4844	•	.525
9/16 - 18	33/64	.5156	•	.538
5/8 - 11	35/64	.5469	•	.584
5/8 - 18	37/64	.5781	•	.600
11/16 - 11	39/64	.6094	•	.646
11/16 - 16	5/8	.6250	•	.680
3/4 - 10	21/32	.6562	45/64	.7031
3/4 - 16	11/16	.6875		.722

NOTE   Cut thread tap drill sizes are for 2 - B threads. Formed thread tap drill sizes are for approximately 65% thread.
*Special drill sizes

Figure 10-3   Drill sizes and tap drill sizes (Courtesy of Zagar, Inc.)

easy chip ejection, include different drill points, lip relief and clearance angles, and flute construction (helix angle, web thickness, and web thinning).

Various degrees of included-point angle, with proper lip relief, and specific types of web thinning are used to perform the following:

1. Control the formation of the chips produced.
2. Control the size and shape of the chips.
3. Control chip flow along the flutes.
4. Increase the strength of the cutting lips.
5. Reduce the rate of cutting lip wear.
6. Reduce the thrust required for drilling.
7. Control the hole size and quality.
8. Control the size and amount of burrs produced.
9. Reduce the amount of heat generated.
10. Permit variations in cutting speed and feed rate for more efficient drilling.

Drill points. Since drill points form the cutting edges, their geometries are critical to tool performance. There is a variety of point styles being used today; some of the more common ones are described in this section. Proper selection, control, and use of drill points can result in substantial savings in drilling costs.

Single-angle points. Standard twist drills having conventional points with a 118° included angle are the most commonly used because they provide satisfactory results in drilling a wide variety of

materials. The cutting lips on these drills are essentially straight lines, with the heel side of each land a smooth curve (see Fig. 10-4a).

A possible limitation to the use of this conventional point is that its straight chisel edge contributes to wandering of the point, often making it necessary to first use a center drill for improved hole accuracy. Also, the sharp corners tend to break down more rapidly than some other geometries available, and there is more of a tendency to produce burrs on breakthrough. As a result, drills with this type point are generally best suited for applications for which close tolerances are not required.

As the hardness of the workpiece material decreases, improved drill performance can be achieved by reducing the included angle of the drill point to 60-90°. Drills having these more acute point angles produce thinner chips for a given feed rate and are commonly used, with low helix flutes, for producing holes in soft plastics and nonferrous materials. Drills having points with a 90° included angle are also used occasionally for drilling soft cast irons and certain woods.

Similarly, as the hardness of the workpiece material or depth of hole increases, the included angle of the drill point is increased to 135-140°. These larger point angles produce thicker and narrower chips for a given feed rate. Drills with these flatter points are generally used to produce holes in harder, tougher materials,

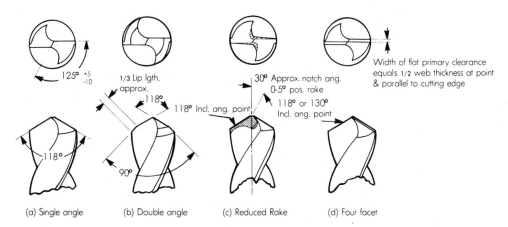

(a) Single angle   (b) Double angle   (c) Reduced Rake   (d) Four facet

Figure 10-4 Four types of drill point geometries (Courtesy of Cleveland Twist Drill Co.)

and they usually minimize burring. It is especially important to use guide bushings with drill points having higher angles because there is a tendency for the points to skid or walk on the workpiece surfaces when starting holes.

Double-angle points. Twist drills with double-angle points (see Fig. 10-4b) are generated by first grinding a larger included angle (118 or 135°) and then a smaller included angle (typically 90°) on the corners. This provides the effect of chamfers and reduces abrasive wear on the corners.

Initial applications for this style point were in drilling medium and hard cast irons as well as other very abrasive materials to reduce corner wear on the drills. More recent applications include improving hole sizes and finishes and drilling very hard materials to reduce chipping of the corners of the lips. Twist drills with double-angle points are often used for the same applications as drills with rounded-edge (radiused lip) points, discussed later in this section.

Reduced-rake points. A common and easily applied point variation is the flatted cutting lip. Both cutting edges are flatted on their flute faces, called dubbing, from the cutting lip corners to the chisel edge, as illustrated in Fig. 10-4c. This type of point reduces the effective axial rake to 0-5° positive, causing a pushing or plowing of metal rather than a shearing action. Reduced shearing action is an effective method of preventing the tools from digging in when drilling is performed on materials with low tensile strengths such as many types of brass, bronze, and some of the harder acrylic plastics such as Plexiglas. Reducing the rake also strengthens the cutting lips, and this type of point is often used in operations in which chipping of the lips has been a problem.

Four- and six-facet points. The geometry of a four-facet point (see Fig. 10-4d) is generated by grinding flat primary relief (10-18°) and secondary clearance angles (25-35°) on the end of each flute. The width of the primary relief flat is equal to one-half the web thickness, resulting in four facets on the end of the drill which subtend at a point on the drill axis and entirely remove the chisel edge. Six-facet points are produced by adding two cutting edges at the web of four-facet points.

Since these points are exactly in the middle of the drills, the tools are self-centering and accurate and straight holes can be produced. They also require less power and thrust and permit increased feed rates. Drills with these points, however, are subject to more wear on their margins, and they cannot be modified to suit drilling of various materials. Another disadvantage is the cost of resharpening with a special machine.

Four- and six-facet points have found their greatest use for solid carbide drills used to produce holes in printed circuit board materials such as fiberglass-epoxy. The points may also be used on small-diameter HSS drills that do not lend themselves to normal point-splitting techniques.

Split-points. This type of point, also called a crankshaft point, was originally developed for use on drills designed for producing small-diameter, deep holes in automotive crank-shafts. Since then it has gained widespread use for drilling a wide variety of hard and soft materials. Heavy-duty types with thicker webs are used for drilling stainless steels, titanium, tough alloys, and high temperature resistant alloys. Drills with this type of point are also employed extensively for applications in which guide bushings cannot be used, as well as for portable drilling applications.

In generating split points on drills, the clearance face of each cutting edge is given a sharp (55° typical) secondary relief to the center of the chisel edge (see Fig. 10-5), thus creating a secondary cutting lip on the opposite cutting edge. The angle between these lip segments acts as a chipbreaker when drilling is done on many materials, producing smaller chips that are readily ejected through the flutes. More importantly, however, the additional cutting edges produced and the reduction in width of the original chisel edge reduces thrust requirements (typically 25-30% compared to conventional 118° points) and improves the centering capability. A disadvantage is the need for a point-splitting grinding machine.

Helical (spiral) points. This type of point is generated by reducing the drill point from a chisel edge to a helical (spiral) point, as illustrated in Fig. 10-6. This produces an S-shaped chisel with a radiused crown effect which has its highest point at

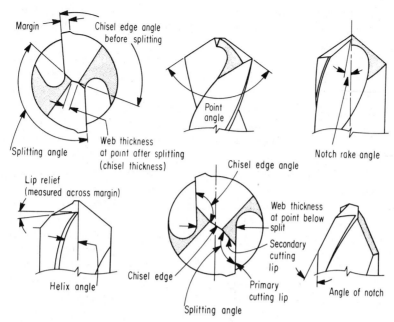

Figure 10-5 Geometry of split-point twist drills

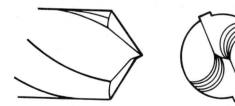

Figure 10-6 Helical (spiral) point

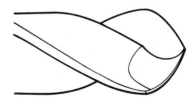

Figure 10-7 Rounded-edge point

the center of the drill axis. This S-shaped chisel creates a continuous cutting edge extending from margin to margin across the web.

Advantages of drills with a helical point include a self-centering capability and some reduction of thrust. Their use also results in better hole geometry and improved hole size.

A possible disadvantage of this type of point is that burrs are sometimes produced at hole breakthrough. Also, the S-shaped chisel is weaker than straight chisel points, resulting in faster dulling

when hard materials are drilled. Special machines are required to grind these points.

Rounded-edge (radiused-lip) points. These points are generated by grinding a blended, rounded edge (radiused corner or lip) on conventional points (see Fig. 10-7). Points such as these provide a continuously varying point angle, with the lips and margins blended by a smooth curve. Because the drill cuts on long, curved lips, there is less load per unit area and less heat generated. Since the corner is eliminated, margin wear is reduced. Breakthrough burrs are eliminated, and tool life can be lengthened compared to conventionally pointed drills when cast iron is drilled. Feed rates can also be increased because of the improved heat dissipation.

Twist drills with rounded-edge points are used when drill life is most important. Drills with these points are not self-centering and are best applied where guide bushings are used. When used on NC machines, prior center drilling is required. The time required for center drilling, however, may be more than offset by longer tool life. A possible limitation is that special grinding machines are required to produce these points. Also, when steel is drilled, these points cut closer to size, which may reduce drill life compared to that possible with conventional points because of greater corner and margin wear.

Combined helical/rounded-edge points. Drill grinding machines are available that combine features of both the helical and rounded-edge points. The point produced provides the self-centering capability of helical points and the long life, burr-free breakthrough, and higher feed capacity of rounded-edge points. These features make the drills capable of producing accurate holes on NC machines without the need for prior center drilling.

Lip relief. The lip relief angle used on a drill is also important. With inadequate lip relief, a drill will not cut freely; excessive relief will shorten the drill life. It is even more important that the relief angle on each lip be equal and that the relief surfaces be in close axial relationship to each other. The amount of hole oversize produced increases with an increase in relative lip height.

The amount of relief depends primarily upon the drill diameter, cutting edge strength, and the material to be drilled. For drilling harder materials, the angle is often reduced; for softer and nonferrous materials, it is generally increased.

Higher relief angles generally provide best results with light feeds and low-strength, nonferrous materials. Some of the plastics and cast irons also require higher relief angles because of their abrasiveness. With heavy feeds, as well as harder workpiece materials, reduced relief angles provide cutting edges with additional support to withstand the higher cutting loads.

Web thickness. Because the chisel edges are noncutting portions of drill points, the webs of twist drills are made as thin as possible, consistent with adequate structural strength. Heavy-duty drills have thicker webs (about twice the thickness of standard general-purpose drills) and often have narrower flutes to increase torsional stiffness.

Most drills are manufactured with webs which increase in thickness toward their shanks. Resharpening of a worn drill shortens the drills and increases the web thickness and chisel edge length (see Fig. 10-8). This results in increased thrust requirements, additional heat generation, and shorter drill life unless the web is thinned to its original thickness. Heavy-duty drills generally require thinning before they are used. The web thickness on some deep-hole drills, however, does not increase; the thickness is the same at the chisel end as it is at the end of the flutes and is called a parallel web.

Thrust force on a twist drill is more sensitive to changes in web thickness than is the drill torque.

Most of the drill torque results from the outer portions of the drill lips because this is where most of the material removal occurs. For a drill of regular proportions, only about 15% of the torque comes from the web. With a drill of regular design, about 50%

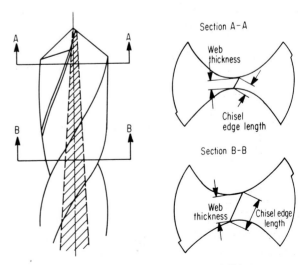

Figure 10-8   Resharpening of twist drill increases the web thickness

of the total thrust force is caused by the web. If the web thickness is doubled, the thrust force is increased by more than 60%; then, about 75% of the total thrust is caused by the web.

Web thinning. Several types of web thinning are commonly used. The type shown in Fig. 10-9a is perhaps the most common. Length A is usually one-half to three-fourths the length of the cutting lip. In this type of thinning, as well as in all others, it is important that the thinning cut extend far enough up the flute so that an abrupt wedge is not formed at the extreme point. The distance of the thinned cut varies with the amount of thinning required, but an average of one-fourth to one-half the drill diameter is usually satisfactory.

Sometimes it is advisable to extend the thinning out to the extreme edge in order to change the shape of the chip. In this type of thinning (see Fig. 10-9b), a positive effective rake is maintained the full length of the cutting edge. A third type of thinning often used results in the split or crankshaft point described previously.

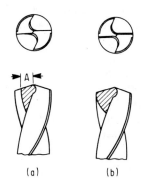

Figure 10-9 Two types of web thinnings: (a) at chisel edge; and (b) undercut thinned point

Some manufacturers offer self-thinned webs on jobbers-length twist drills. These drills have a web which is straight (uniformly thick) for one-third or more of the flute lengths and then tapers toward the shank.

Helix angles. The helix angle on standard twist drills generally ranges from 25-33°. High-helix (fast-spiral) drills with helix angles of 35-40° and low helix (slow-spiral) drills with helix angles of 15-20° are also

commercially available for drilling certain materials and special applications, as discussed previously in the section on types of drills.

Although used in Europe for many years, a relatively recent introduction to the United States is the parabolic flute twist drill that provides more open flutes for improved chip removal and cutting fluid flow while permitting heavy webs for high torsional strength. Combined with webs of constant thickness, they have proven to be ideal for deep-hole drilling in cast irons, mild steels, and aluminum alloys. For some deep-hole applications (with depth-to-diameter ratios to 12:1 or more), speeds and feeds to 100% greater than conventional drills have been reported, often eliminating the need for woodpeckering.

Toolholders for Drilling

Many different devices are used to hold drills and provide the driving connection between the machine spindle and the drill. These include sockets, sleeves, chucks, collets, and other arrangements. Selection of the proper device is critical because drills not properly gripped can be pulled from the driver by friction between the drill and workpiece when the drill is retracted.

Taper-Shank Drills: Drills with taper shanks fit directly into the spindles of drilling machines that have the same size taper as the drills. When the hole in the spindle is larger, a reducing socket or sleeve is used. Short sleeves are preferable to fitted sockets because of the increased rigidity they provide. Drifts are used to remove taper-shank drills from the sockets or sleeves.

Variations of the taper shank are sometimes used for heavy-duty operations. The most common of these is the flatted shank. The socket has a flat in its bore to match that on the drill shank, thus providing a positive drive. For larger diameter drills, a pair of flats is sometimes used. Other special variations employed occasionally include half tangs, squares, keyseats, keyways, grooves, notches, slots, threads, and knurls.

Straight-Shank Drills:
Drills with straight shanks are held in several ways, including chucks, sleeves, bushings, and collet-type holders.

Chucks. Three-jaw chucks are the most common holders and drivers for small-diameter, straight-shank drills. They are available in wrench, or key-tightening, and wrenchless (keyless) styles. These chucks are made with plain or ball bearing construction, and for taper or threaded mounting.

Each chuck holds a range of drill sizes within its capacity. Typical ranges for various chucks are 0 to ¼″, 0 to ⅜″, and 0 to ½″ (6.4, 10, and 13 mm); ⅛ to ⅝″ or ⅛ to ¾″ (3 to 16 or 19 mm); and ⅜ to 1″ (10 to 25 mm). Small-size keyless chucks have a micrometer graduation on their sleeves to facilitate changing drill sizes. These chucks depend upon friction between the jaws and drill shank for gripping. Care is necessary to assure sufficient tightening to prevent drill slippage and excessive wear. Fig. 10-10 is a chucking head.

Figure 10-10 Chucking head (Courtesy of Zagar, Inc.)

Sleeves and bushings. Tapered split sleeves are sometimes used to drive small-diameter, straight-shank drills for certain production applications. These sleeves have a taper on their OD to fit the machine spindle or socket and a straight bore to fit the drill shank. Flats or squares on the drill shanks and driving slots in the sleeves are used occasionally, particularly on multispindle machines with close centers.

A disadvantage of these drivers is that a separate sleeve is required for each size drill. Specifications for split sleeve, collet-type drivers for straight-shank drills, reamers, and similar tools are presented in ANSI Standard B94.35-1972, published by ASME.

Straight sleeves are sometimes used to hold larger diameter, straight-shank drills in machines such as turret lathes. Setscrews extending through the sleeves are generally used to hold the drills in place. These devices also have the disadvantage of requiring a different size sleeve for each drill size. The sleeves must fit the drill shanks closely to avoid misalignment when clamping, and the setscrews used often mar the drill shanks.

Collet-type holders. A major advantage of collet-type holders is their capability of gripping drills on their margins or straight shanks. In doing this, the length of the drill projecting from the collet can be varied and kept to a minimum to suit requirements for short-hole, deep-hole, or other drilling applications. Called stubbing, this method increases rigidity by decreasing the length-to-diameter ratios. Resulting benefits can include longer drill life, the capability of using higher feed rates and cutting speeds, reduction in the need for jigs and bushings, possible elimination of center drilling or spotfacing, shorter cycle times, and the ability to use broken drills.

Quick-Change Tooling:
Many types of quick-change tooling devices are available to permit changing tools in a few seconds.

The pistol grip quick-change chuck (see Fig. 10-11) is a direct replacement for the conventional ¼″ (6.4 mm) three-jaw chuck. It is operated by extending a spring-loaded sleeve and inserting a drill with an integral quick-change adapter. The chuck contains three retaining balls which engage in the detent holes of the drill adapter when the sleeve is released. These three balls provide the torque driving mechanism and serve to retain the drill in the chuck. The quick-change adapter is joined to the drill shank by either silver brazing or interference fit.

Drills can be changed seven seconds faster with the quick-change chuck than with a conventional key-type chuck. Other advantages include lighter weight, lower cost, the ability to drill in closer quarters, and elimination of damage to drills and workpieces.

The quick-change chuck system for angle drill motors eliminates the need for threaded-shank drills used previously. The operating principle of the angle motorchuck is similar to the pistol grip chuck except that the chuck collar is rotated, rather than extended, to open the chuck. The ball detent is identical to the pistol grip version.

This system eliminates the need for wrenches required for threaded-shank drills and, consequently, reduces adapter damage and tool distortion. The use of the angle motor, quick-change chuck saves over eight seconds per drill change. Lower cost and extended drill life are additional advantages (see Fig. 10-12).

Figure 10-12   Multiple-spindle head for tool changer (Courtesy of Zagar, Inc.)

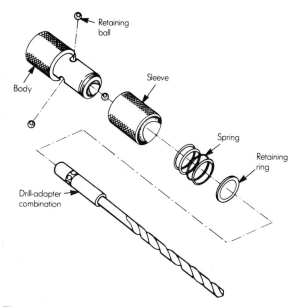

Figure 10-11   Quick change chuck

Workholding Devices for Drilling

Jigs and fixtures are precision devices used to accurately machine duplicate parts. As a general rule, jigs and fixtures are designed to hold, support, and locate a workpiece while controlling the position and alignment of the cutting tools. Good jig and fixture design can minimize tool breakage and the production of unsatisfactory workpieces.

The principle difference between a jig and fixture is the method used to position the cutting tool. Jigs securely hold and locate the workpiece while guiding the cutting tool by means of a bushing or similar device. Fixtures securely hold and locate the workpiece while referencing the position of the cutting tool by means of set blocks and feeler gages.

Although both jigs and fixtures are used for a wide vareity of machining operations, the jig is by far the most common type of device for drilling, reaming, and related operations. Regardless of the machining operation, the basic construction and function of a jig are the same for drilling and reaming.

Jigs can be divided into two broad categories: open and closed. Open jigs are generally used for machining parts on a single surface, while closed jigs are used for parts that require machining on two or more surfaces. The terms used to identify these jigs are normally directly related to the basic construction of the tool itself.

The specific size, shape, and construction details of any jig are normally determined by the workpiece to be machined. To perform their basic function, however, all jigs must adhere to certain design principles and must include the following elements:

1. Locating devices and work supports.
2. Clamping devices.
3. Tool guidance devices.

Drilling Machines

Machines designed specifically for drilling are available in many different types, sizes, and capacities. The types include light-duty (sensitive), heavy-duty upright, radial, gang, multispindle, turret, deep-hole, small-hole, and special purpose machines. In addition to drilling, many of these machines can also perform related operations, such as reaming, facing, chamfering, counterboring, countersinking, undercutting/recessing, roller burnishing, and tapping. In some cases, depending upon the design and rigidity, the machines are used for boring and milling operations.

Light-Duty, Sensitive Drilling Machines:
Machines of this type are the most common of all drilling machines. These general-purpose machines are most often used for drilling one hole at a time in small workpieces, with hole diameters to about 1″ (25 mm) diam. They are often referred to as drill presses and are employed extensively for many toolroom, machine shop, and maintenance applications, as well as for some production operations.

The typical light-duty drilling machine has a vertical, base-mounted, round column; a table that can be adjusted vertically and tilted; and a powered spindle that holds the cutting tool. The round column allows the table to be swung aside when not required. These machines are available in both floor and bench models.

Most light-duty drilling machines are manually fed with a rack-and-pinion mechanism and a hand-operated lever, but automatic feeds are available on some models. Hand feeding is the reason these machines are often referred to as sensitive types; it permits the operators to change feed rates as they sense soft or hard spots in the workpieces from the feel of the cutting action.

Upright (Vertical) Drilling Machines:
Upright or vertical drilling machines are similar to the light-duty machines just discussed, but differ in that they are more massive for heavy-duty applications. They permit the production of larger diameter and deeper holes with improved accuracy and quality. Practically all upright drilling machines are equipped with power feed. They are most suitable for workpieces that can be quickly positioned under the tool, require short cycle times, or need only a few holes per part.

Gang Drilling Machines:
A gang drilling machine consists of two or more independent, light-duty or upright drilling machines mounted on a common base or table.

Radial Drilling Machines:
Excellent versatility is an important advantage of radial drilling machines. These machines are used extensively for drilling holes in large and irregularly shaped workpieces that cannot be easily positioned or repositioned. A number of smaller workpieces can also be clamped to the base or floor plate. Flexibility of these machines permits drilling holes in workpiece surfaces that cannot be reached with other drilling machines. Time is saved by repositioning the drill instead of the workpiece for each operation.

A radial drilling machine consists of a horizontal arm, from 2-12 ft. (0.6-3.7 m) or more in length, supported by a round, vertical column. The arm can be raised, lowered, and rotated around the column axis. The drillhead mounted on the arm contains the speed-changing and power-feed mechanisms, as well as the spindle, and can be repositioned along the arm and clamped in any desired location. Some machine designs permit tilting the head to produce angular holes.

Multispindle Drilling Machines and Heads:

In addition to multispindle drillheads for use on single-spindle machines, multispindle drilling machines are available for high-production requirements. Major time savings can be realized with both heads and machines having multiple spindles by performing a number of machining operations simultaneously and minimizing the need for toolchanging. Multispindle machines are used primarily for three general types of production operations:

1. Multiple operations (drilling, reaming, chamfering, spotfacing, etc.) in a single hole. Machines used for these applications are often equipped with hand-positioned tables, shuttle tables, or rotary indexing tables.
2. One operation in multiple holes which are the same size or different sizes and on the same or different planes. Machines used for these operations may require a rotary indexing table if hole center distances are close. Multiple-plane operations are often performed with multiple-position workholding fixtures.
3. Multiple operations in multiple holes which generally require that the machine be equipped with a rotary indexing table or other type of table, especially when tapping is one of the operations to be performed.

Turret Drilling Machines:

Upright drilling machines, both bench and floor types as well as hand and power-feed types, are available with indexing drums or turrets. The turret typically has six or eight faces, although machines are available with turrets having four and ten faces. Each face has a spindle for holding a drill or other cutting tool. The turrets can be indexed manually or automatically to bring the spindles into operating position with respect to the workpiece.

Turret drilling machines permit performing a number of operations in a hole or group of holes without the need for changing tools. Various tools on the turret are sequenced into cutting position with every feed stroke of the machine. Turret drilling machines are suitable for heavier workpieces that can remain stationary, as well as for operations in which quick-change tooling is not practical. The capability of these machines can be expanded by adding indexing, rotating, or shuttling fixtures.

Deep-Hole Drilling Machines:

Deep-hole drilling with gundrilling, gunboring, trepanning, and other self-guided tools using high-pressure cutting fluids is sometimes done by converting conventional machines such as suitably designed lathes and drilling, boring, and milling machines. Most applications, however, are performed on machines specifically designed for deep-hole drilling. These machines are generally horizontal, but some, used for shorter operations on smaller workpieces, have vertical or angular spindles.

Most deep-hole drilling machines have a rotating tool that is fed into a workpiece mounted on a table at one end of the machine. Some machines, used to drill long slender parts, rotate the workpiece while a nonrotating drill is fed into it. For some precision applications, both the workpiece and tool rotate, but in opposite directions.

Small-Hole Drilling Machines:

Major problems in the mechanical drilling of small holes include compensating for the decreased rigidity of the delicate tools required, controlling chip removal, minimizing runout, and maintaining a uniform feed rate. This type of drilling can often be done on conventional machine tools such as lathes, drilling and boring machines, machining and turning centers, and transfer machines. Sensitive drill presses are used extensively for drilling small holes. They are almost always hand fed, with either a sliding quill to advance the rotating drill or an elevating table to force the work into the drill.

Automatic screw machines, especially Swiss types, are used for small-hole drilling, often with both the workpiece and drill rotating. These machines, as well as small turret lathes, permit using several tools to produce the holes. For example, a center drill can be used to start the hole, then a pivot drill to enlarge and deepen the hole, and finally a straight-shank drill to enlarge the hole further and finish it to final depth.

Special-Purpose Drilling Machines: Many

drilling machines are built in a wide variety of designs and configurations for special-purpose applications. Special-purpose dedicated machines are often used when large quantities of parts require multiple operations. These include shuttle transfer, dial index, ring index, trunnion index, and in-line transfer machines.

Special-purpose machines for drilling of pilot holes in tubes and pipes and for forming of 90° branch collars or bosses, all in one cycle, are built by T-Drill, Inc. This method eliminates the need for tube or pipe cutting and end preparation for welding T-fittings. As soon as the cutting tool penetrates the wall of the workpiece, during the downfeed stroke, two formation pins are extended. Then, with the feed reversed, the collar is formed as the rotating pins are withdrawn from the hole. Extension and retraction of the formation pins are accomplished by cam action, with lugs on the upper ends of the pins traveling in spiral grooves in an adjustment cone.

Portable Drilling Units: Considerable drilling

is done with portable tools that are powered pneumatically, electrically, or hydraulically. Such tools are used extensively, particularly in the aircraft/ aerospace and automotive industries, when workpieces cannot be easily taken to drilling machines. Drilling of fastener holes in airframes with portable tools is probably the most common manufacturing operation required in the aircraft industry, with millions of holes drilled each month.

Some portable tools are available with magnetic bases or other devices for mounting or clamping to the work. In addition to being used for drilling, portable tools are also employed for screwdrivers, nutrunners, impact wrenches, hammers, routers, and grinders, as well as for tapping, nibbling, shearing, sanding, scraping, filing, sawing, and broaching operations. See Figs. 10-13, 10-14, and 10-15 for examples of modern drilling machines.

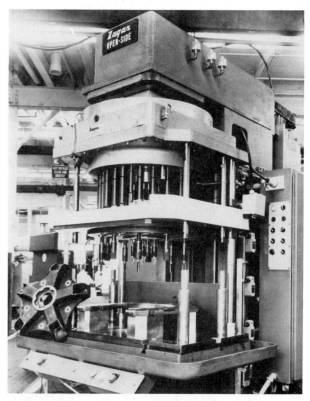

Figure 10-13   Multiple-spindle drilling machine (Courtesy of Zagar, Inc.)

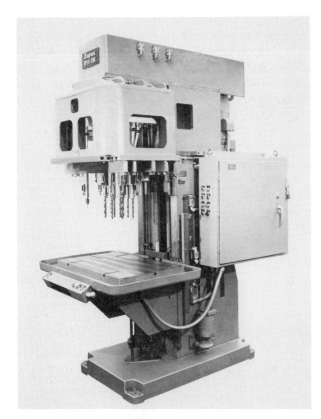

Figure 10-14   Drilling/tapping machine with adjustable spindle head (Courtesy of Zagar, Inc.)

Thrilling, Drap, and PID: Thrilling, Drap, and PID are tapping methods. Thrilling is a tapping method that uses a single tool. Threads are cut using an oscillating motion. Drapping is a tapping method that also uses a single tool, but conventional cutting motion. PID, or Proportional Integral Derivative, is software that synchronizes the tapping spindle with the motor driving the Z axis on a tapping machine. This occurs during acceleration, deceleration, and constant speeds. Fig. 10-16 is a modern single-tool tapping machine.

Figure 10-16   Single-tool tapping machine (Courtesy of Zagar, Inc.)

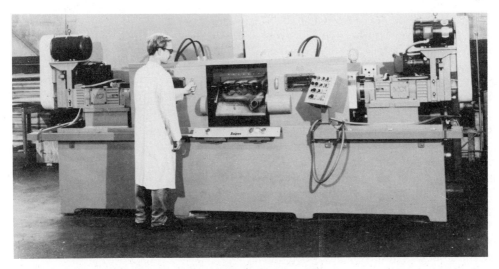

Figure 10-15   Horizontal drilling machine (Courtesy of Zagar, Inc.)

Drilling Speeds and Feeds:

Drill speed refers to a drill's peripheral or surface speed in feet per minute (sfm) or meters per minute (m/min). Drill speed is related to spindle speed (rpm) as follows:

$$sfm = 0.0262 \, d \times rpm$$

where:

   sfm = drill surface speed, fpm
   d = drill diameter, in.

or:

$$m/min = 0.00314 \, d \times rpm$$

where:

   m/min = drill surface speed, m/min
   d = drill diameter, millimeters

or:

$$rpm = \frac{3.82 \times sfm}{d}$$

where:

   d = drill diameter, in.

or:

$$rpm = \frac{3.1831 \times m/min}{d}$$

where:

   d = drill diameter, mm

Feed rate is expressed as inches per revolution (ipr) or millimeters per revolution (mm/rev), as well as inches per minute (ipm) or millimeters per minute (mm/min).

The parameters of cutting speed and feed rate control metal removal rate, hole quality, and drill life. Any increase in these parameters generally increases metal removal rate, but decreases tool life. While an increase in either speed or feed has an equal effect on metal removal rate, an increase in speed usually has a larger effect in reducing drill life than an increase in feed rate.

As a result, the highest possible feed rate should be used for drilling, with moderate cutting speeds to provide satisfactory holes and economical tool life, balanced against production requirements. Feed and speed selection depend upon many variables,

including the composition and hardness of the material to be drilled, depth and diameter of hole, type and condition of the drilling machine, rigidity of the setup, efficiency of the cutting fluid, and requirements for accuracy, surface finish, and production rates. See Fig. 10-17.

Material Drilled	Drill Diam, in.	Cutting Speed, sfm (m/min)	Feed Rate, ipr (mm/rev)
Cast irons: nodular, ductile, or malleable	13/16 to 1 1/8	165-300 (50-91)	0.004-0.008 (0.10-0.20)
	1 to 1 3/8	165-300 (50-91)	0.005-0.010 (0.13-0.25)
	1 1/4 to 1 5/8	165-300 (50-91)	0.006-0.012 (0.15-0.30)
	1 1/2 to 2 1/2	165-300 (50-91)	0.008-0.014 (0.20-0.36)
	2 3/8 to 3 1/2	165-300 (50-91)	0.010-0.015 (0.25-0.38)
Steels: 1000 series, such as 1018, 1020, etc.	13/16 to 1 1/8	300-400 (91-122)	0.003-0.005 (0.08-0.13)
	1 to 1 3/8	350-450 (107-137)	0.003-0.006 (0.08-0.15)
	1 1/4 to 1 5/8	400-500 (122-168)	0.004-0.007 (0.10-0.18)
	1 1/2 to 2 1/2	450-600 (137-183)	0.004-0.007 (0.10-0.18)
	2 3/8 to 3 1/2	500-700 (152-213)	0.005-0.009 (0.13-0.23)
Steels: case hardened unalloyed, low carbon	13/16 to 1 1/8	200-300 (61-91)	0.003-0.005 (0.08-0.13)
	1 to 1 3/8	250-350 (76-107)	0.004-0.006 (0.10-0.15)
	1 1/4 to 1 5/8	300-425 (91-130)	0.005-0.007 (0.13-0.18)
	1 1/2 to 2 1/2	330-490 (101-149)	0.005-0.008 (0.13-0.20)
	2 3/8 to 3 1/2	250-550 (107-168)	0.006-0.010 (0.15-0.25)
Steels: high carbon, alloyed, heat treated	13/16 to 1 1/8	200-300 (61-91)	0.003-0.005 (0.008-0.13)
	1 to 1 3/8	250-325 (76-99)	0.004-0.006 (0.10-0.15)
	1 1/4 to 1 5/8	300-400 (91-122)	0.005-0.008 (0.13-0.20)
	1 1/2 to 2 1/2	325-450 (99-137)	0.005-0.008 (0.13-0.20)
	2 3/8 to 3 1/2	350-500 (107-152)	0.006-0.010 (0.15-0.25)

Steels: high tensile strength	13/16 to 1 1/8	165-250 (50-76)	0.004-0.005 (0.10-0.13)
	1 to 1 3/8	195-300 (59-91)	0.004-0.005 (0.10-0.13)
	1 1/4 to 1 5/8	230-330 (70-101)	0.005-0.007 (0.13-0.18)
	1 1/2 to 2 1/2	265-390 (81-119)	0.006-0.008 (0.15-0.20)
	2 3/8 to 3 1/2	265-425 (81-130)	0.006-0.009 (0.15-0.23)
Stainless steels	13/16 to 1 1/8	230-280 (70-85)	0.003-0.004 (0.08-0.10)
	1 to 1 3/8	265-300 (81-91)	0.004-0.005 (0.10-0.13)
	1 1/4 to 1 5/8	280-345 (85-105)	0.004-0.005 (0.10-0.13)
	1 1/2 to 2 1/2	295-395 (90-120)	0.004-0.005 (0.10-0.13)
	2 3/8 to 3 1/2	300-400 (91-122)	0.004-0.006 (0.10-0.15)
Titanium alloys	13/16 to 1 1/8	100-135 (30-41)	0.003-0.004 (0.08-0.10)
	1 to 1 3/8	100-150 (30-46)	0.004-0.007 (0.10-0.18)
	1 1/4 to 1 5/8	115-165 (35-50)	0.005-0.008 (0.13-0.20)
	1 1/2 to 2 1/2	130-175 (40-53)	0.006-0.009 (0.15-0.23)
	2 3/8 to 3 1/2	135-190 (41-58)	0.006-0.010 (0.15-0.25)

Figure 10-17   Recommended starting speeds and feeds for drills with indexable carbide inserts

Cutting Fluids for Drilling: As with most other machining operations, the most important characteristics for drilling are the ability of the cutting fluid to cool and lubricate. Lubrication reduces friction between the sliding chips and the drill and also minimizes heat caused by friction between the drill and workpiece. Many drill failures are the result of excessive heat.

Cutting fluids have a direct influence on tool life, built-up edge, and hole finish. Water-based emulsified oil is the most commonly used coolant today for drilling operations. It is suitable for a wide variety of steels and some of the nonferrous materials.

Some firms specializing in drilling small holes have reported good results from using water-soluble oils in conjunction with a mist sprayer operating at a pressure of 25-35 psi (172-241 kPa). The pressurized air serves to remove chips and, together with the cutting fluid, effectively cools the drill.

When drilling high temperature resistant alloys and work hardening grades of stainless steel, tool life can be enhanced with a lubricant of sulfur-based oil or sulfo-chlorinated mineral oil.

Most abrasive nonmetallic materials such as fiberglass, ceramics, etc., are drilled without a liquid coolant. Two methods for removing the abrasive powdered chips from the hole are a jet of air, or preferably a vacuum.

Counterboring, Spotfacing, and Countersinking

Counterboring, spotfacing, and countersinking are secondary operations performed with end-cutting tools. Enlarging a hole for a limited depth is called counterboring. If the cut is shallow so that it leaves only a finished face around the original hole, it is called spotfacing. The cutting of an angular opening into the end of a hole is countersinking, sometimes referred to as chamfering. Tools of this type often present difficulty because they are among the most inefficient of cutting tools due to the distance of the cutting edge from the support.

The counterbore is defined as a rotary, pilot-guided, end-cutting tool, having one or more cutting lips and usually having straight or helical flutes for the passage of chips and the admission of cutting fluid. A spotfacer is defined as a rotary, pilot-guided, end-cutting tool, having teeth on one or both ends. Spotfacers are mounted on either straight or taper-shank pilots (drive bars) and are used to produce flat surfaces normal to their axes of rotation. Spotfacers are designed as a variation of the counterbore to reach inaccessible areas. The drive bar acts as the pilot. A countersink is a rotary, end-cutting tool which may or may not be piloted for the purpose of beveling or tapering the work material around the periphery of a hole. The surface cut by the conical tool is concentric with and at an angle of less than 90° to the centerline of the hole.

Counterbores

Six types of counterbores are in general use. They are:

1. *Solid counterbores.* These are made of one piece of tool material, including the pilot. One tool manufacturer brazes a pilot sleeve on the solid body. The two-lip construction provides good chip space while retaining the advantage of an unbroken surface on the pilot.
2. *Counterbores with interchangeable pilots.* These are counterbores having removable, mechanically held pilots.
3. *Interchangeable counterbores.* These are counterbores having end-cutting portions as well as pilots that are removable and interchangeable so that a series of cutters fit the same holder and a series of pilots fit the same cutter. These types of counterbores are generally available in standard sizes from ¼ to 5″ (6.3 to 127 mm) diam (Fig. 10-18).
4. *Inserted-blade counterbores.* These are counterbores which have replaceable, mechanically held blades. The blades may be either solid or tipped (Fig. 10-19).
5. *Indexable-insert counterbores.* These are counterbores with indexable-insert tips. They may be used in the same manner as interchangeable counterbores; however, they are more limited in application than other types (Fig. 10-20).

6. *Disposable-insert counterbores.* These counterbores or spotfacers have disposable inserts and removable pilots or pilot drills. The inserts may also be designed to chamfer the holes; depth setting remains constant when the inserts are changed.

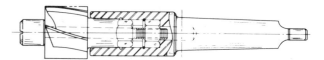

Figure 10-18   Interchangeable counterbore with removable pilot and cutting portion

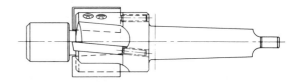

Figure 10-19   Inserted-blade counterbore

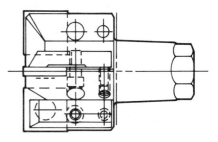

Figure 10-20   Counterbore equipped with indexable inserts

Spotfacers

A spotfacer, as its name implies, is designed for shallow machining of a surface for applications such as washers and bolt and nut heads. Fig. 10-21 shows a standard back spotfacer with drive bar. These tools are designed to reach inaccessible spots

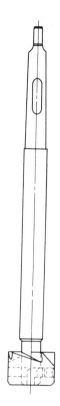

Figure 10-21   Back spotface cutter and drive-bar assembly

hole, it automatically extends due to centrifugal force. Then when the direction of spindle rotation is reversed and feed applied, the required operation is performed. With the exception of the smallest size tools, which use HSS cutters, the wings are provided with clamped carbide inserts.

The same rules apply for back spotfacing as for counterboring; however, most back spotface cutters are designed without deep flutes on the periphery and therefore are intended only for very shallow work. Designs are also available for deeper work and heavy-duty drives.

As with counterbores and countersinks, speeds and feeds for spotfacers are generally lower than those used for drilling.

As a rule of thumb the speed should be approximately three-fourths that used in drilling with feed the same penetration rate as for drilling; however, the load per tooth is less than in drilling because of the larger number of teeth used in a counterbore or similar type of tool. Because of the variations in the many jobs using this type of tooling, no hard-and-fast rules can be given for exact speeds and feeds to be used. If a hand feed is used, it is important to start the cut very carefully so that hogging does not occur with resultant breakage of the tool. It is also important to minimize backlash in the feeding mechanism of the machine.

in castings or similar workpieces. The body of the drive bar acts as a pilot, and the tool is generally run in reverse with the spindle moving toward the machine to produce the desired surface. Because of this, the standard single right-hand cutter actually appears to be a left-hand cutter when viewed in a normal manner. If the cutter is designed to spotface with a spindle feed away from the machine face, a left-hand cutter should be used. Cutters also come in double right-hand or double right-hand and left-hand types.

Automatic back spotfacing, counterboring, or back chamfering tools are also available. These tools consist of a spindle with a recess into which the cutter, called a wing, folds when the spindle enters the hole in the workpiece. When the cutter (wing) leaves the

Countersinks

Countersinks are generally classified in two general categories: (1) shank-type countersinks and (2) combined drills and countersinks. Commercially available combined drills and countersinks were discussed previously in this chapter under the subject of types of twist drills.

The types of countersinks shown in Fig. 10-22 may be broadly classified as machine countersinks. These are used mostly to produce countersunk holes for screw and rivet heads, as well as to chamfer and deburr holes. They are available with included point angles of 60°, 72°, 82°, and 90°.

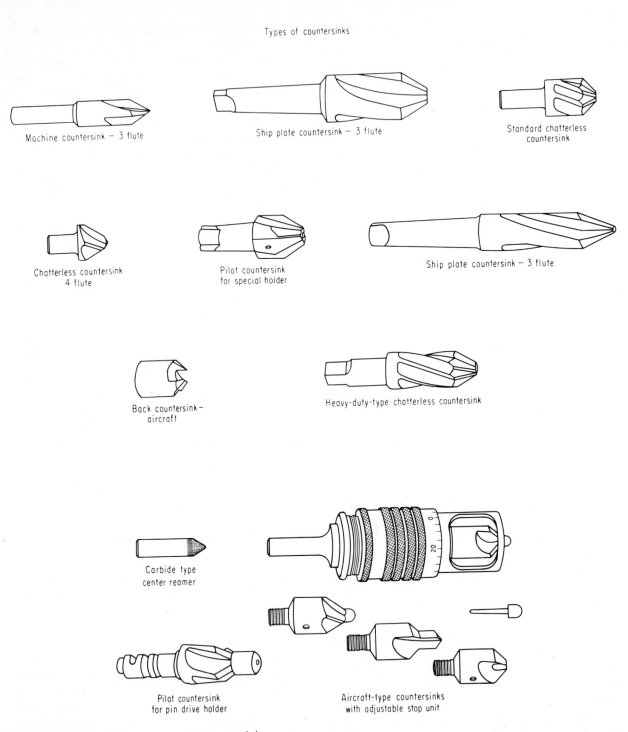

Types of countersinks

Machine countersink — 3 flute

Ship plate countersink — 3 flute

Standard chatterless countersink

Chatterless countersink 4 flute

Pilot countersink for special holder

Ship plate countersink — 3 flute

Back countersink– aircraft

Heavy-duty-type chatterless countersink

Carbide type center reamer

Pilot countersink for pin drive holder

Aircraft-type countersinks with adjustable stop unit

Figure 10-22   Various types of countersinks

Reaming

Reaming is a machining process for enlarging, smoothing, and/or accurately sizing existing holes by means of multiedge fluted cutting tools (reamers). As the reamers and/or workpiece is rotated and advanced relative to each other, chips are produced to remove relatively small amounts of material from the hole wall. Reaming may be performed on the same type of machines used for drilling. The machines used for drilling are discussed earlier in this chapter.

Accuracy of the hole and quality of finish produced by reaming depends primarily upon the condition of the starting hole, rigidity of the machine and fixture, correct speeds and feeds, a suitable and properly applied cutting fluid, and precise resharpening of dull tools.

Since stock removal is small and must be uniform in reaming, the starting holes (drilled or otherwise produced) must have relatively good roundness, straightness, and finish. Reamers tend to follow the existing centerline of the hole being reamed, and in limited instances it may be necessary to bore the holes prior to reaming to maintain required tolerances. With the proper conditions and operating parameters, reaming can produce close tolerances and smooth finishes.

Reamers

A reamer is a rotary cutting tool, generally of cylindrical or conical shape, intended for enlarging and finishing holes to accurate dimensions. It is usually equipped with two or more peripheral channels or flutes, either parallel to its axis or in a right- or left-hand helix as required. Those with helical flutes provide smooth shear cutting, are less subject to chatter, and produce a better finish. The flutes form cutting teeth and provide channels for removing the chips. See Fig. 10-23 for nomenclature.

Kinds of Reamers: Reamers are made in many different forms (Fig. 10-24), including solid and inserted-blade types, adjustable and nonadjustable; they are available for either manual operation (hand reamers) or for machine use (chucking reamers). Materials from which cutting elements of most production reamers are made include high-speed steel and cemented carbides.

Carbide reamers. These tools are being used increasingly because of their longer life, improved accuracy, and resistance.

Bore reamers. These tools combine boring and reaming in a single operation to minimize problems with respect to hole size, straightness, and finish. Single-point bore reamers, for use in applications for which guide bushings can be used, have a single-point cutting edge on the end of the tool, followed by a reaming section. Multipoint bore reamers are available for applications for which bushings cannot be used.

Coolant-fed reamers. These tools, having means (usually internal passages) for directing coolant to the cutting edges, offer advantages for some applications, particularly when reaming blind holes. In such applications, reduced friction and temperatures at the reamer/workpiece interface decrease wear and lengthen tool life. In some cases, feeds and speeds can be increased and improved accuracies and smoother finishes obtained. The initial cost of coolant-fed reamers is higher, but increased productivity and improved quality often make them economically desirable.

Reamer Holders/Drivers

Reamers are commonly held and driven by three-jaw chucks, straight sleeves and setscrews, and, for taper shanks, sleeves or sockets. Reamers with adapters for quick-change chucks are used for production applications.

When reamers must guide themselves into previously made holes, they require floating holders to maintain alignment. There are several types of floating holders. Some permit angular float, others permit a parallel (axial) float, and still others permit both angular and parallel float.

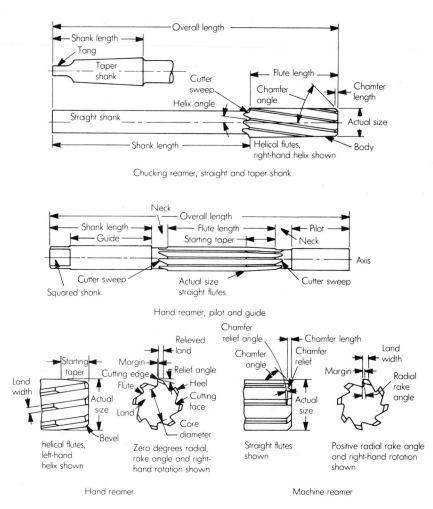

Figure 10-23 Terms applying to reamers

Floating holders have some limitations. If the reamer axis is vertical, floating reamer drives often do a good job of correcting for small amounts of misalignment. When the workpieces rotate, however, as is the case on screw machines, lathes, and some other machine tools, floating holders are sometimes inadequate. This is because relatively large amounts of misalignment are often found on these machines and because the weight of the reamer and holder tend to push the tool into an off-center position.

Some full floating holders, which compensate for both angular and parallel misalignment, are equipped with springs or other components to counterbalance the mass of the holder. A floating holder cannot generally operate both vertically and horizontally and still correct for both angular and parallel misalignment. Application details (vertical or horizontal operation and rotating or stationary tool) should be specified when a floating holder is ordered.

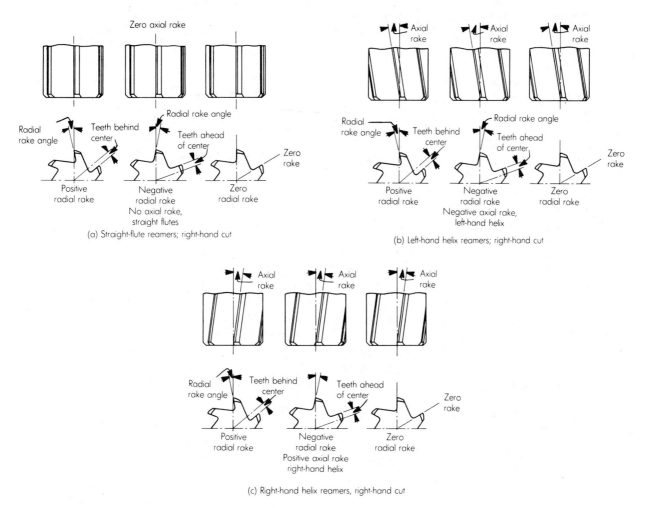

Figure 10-24 Reamers for right-hand rotation

Workholding for Reaming

Jig design and the use of bushings for reaming are essentially the same as for drilling, discussed previously in this chapter. Major functions of the jigs and bushings are accurate locating, supporting, and securing of the workpieces, and precise guiding of the tools. A difference for reaming is that closer tolerances are generally required on both the jigs and bushings.

Operating Parameters for Reaming

Factors that must be established for efficient and economical reaming include the proper cutting speed, feed rate, and cutting fluid to be used. Other important considerations are resharpening the reamers and troubleshooting the operation.

Speeds and Feeds for Machine Reaming:

Reamers are operated at slower speeds and higher feed rates than twist drills of the same diameter. In general, the speeds of reamers may be 65-75% of those for drilling the same material, and the feeds are often two to three times those for drilling. High feed rates are required so that each flute has an adequate chip load.

Reamer feeds depend upon the type of material being reamed and the size or strength of the reamer. When soft materials such as aluminum or brass are being reamed, the feeds may vary from 0.001″ (0.03 mm) per flute per revolution for small reamers to 0.005″ (0.13 mm) per flute per revolution for large reamers. For hard materials such as hard cast irons and steels with a hardness of 330 Bhn or more, the feed per flute per revolution ranges from 0.0004-0.0015″ (0.010-0.038 mm).

Speeds and feeds for machine reaming vary, sometimes slightly and occasionally a great deal, although the same material is being reamed. These variations may be due to the finish and/or accuracy required, differences in the machine setup, or the design of the workpieces.

Speeds that are too low adversely affect the productivity obtainable with reamers without offering any substantial increase in tool life. Speeds that are too high may cause the workpiece material to cling to the edges and lands of the reamer, resulting in premature dulling of the cutting edges and the production of rough holes. In reaming hard materials, a reamer can be quickly ruined if operated at too high a speed. In all cases, the cutting speed should be adjusted to eliminate any chatter. One common method of selecting a reaming speed for a given job on a specific machine is to increase the speed until chatter occurs and then reduce the speed slightly. Lack of rigidity in the setup may necessitate lower speeds. When close tolerances and a fine finish are required, it is usually necessary to finish ream at considerably lower speeds.

Reamer feeds depend primarily on the type of reamer used, the amount of material to be removed, and the finish required. The more stock to be removed, the lower the feeds should be. Too high a feed tends to produce spiral marks or a wavy finish and may reduce the accuracy of the hole. Too fine a feed allows the reamer to idle in the cut and cause excessive wear and glazing of the hole. At all times the feed must be high enough to permit the reamer to cut rather than rub or burnish.

KEY TERMS AND PHRASES

Collet-type holders
Counterboring
Countersinking
Double-angle drill point
Drilling
Feed rate
Four- and six-facet drill points
Gang drilling machines
Helical points
Left-hand cut drill
Light-duty, sensitive drilling machines
Lip relief
Multiple-spindle drilling machines
Portable drilling units
Radial drilling machines
Reaming
Reduced-rake drill point
Right-hand cut drill
Rounded-edge points
Single-angle drill point
Single-flute drill
Small-hole drilling machines
Special-purpose drilling machines
Speed
Split-points
Spotfacing
Straight-shank drill
Taper-shank drill
Turret drilling machines
Twist drills
Two-flute drill
Upright drilling machines
Web thickness
Web thinning

QUESTIONS FOR ADDITIONAL STUDY AND REVIEW _____

1. Explain the drilling process.

2. Explain the cutting action that takes place in welding.

3. Explain how twist drills are classified.

4. List five different types of twist drills.

5. Explain the following types of drill points:
   - Single-angle
   - Reduced-rake
   - Split-point
   - Rounded-edge point

6. Explain the term *lip relief* as it relates to drilling.

7. Explain the types of toolholders used for the following types of drills:
   - Taper-shank
   - Straight-shank

8. What are the three elements all workholding devices for drills must have?   P 248

9. Describe the following types of drilling machines:
   - Light-duty
   - Upright
   - Gang
   - Radial
   - Multiple-spindle
   - Turret
   - Deep-hole
   - Small-hole
   - Special-purpose
   - Portable

10. What purpose do cutting fluids serve in drilling?

11. List and explain the six types of counterbores.

12. How are countersinks classified?

13. What is a spotface?

14. Describe the reaming process.

15. List the most common types of reamers.

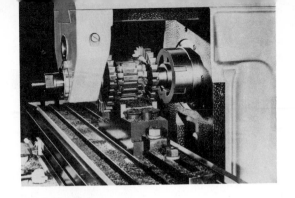

CHAPTER 11

Milling and Grinding

MILLING

Milling is a machining process for removing material by relative motion between a workpiece and a rotating cutter having multiple cutting edges. In some applications, the workpiece is held stationary while the rotating cutter is moved past it at a given feed rate (traversed). In other applications, both the workpiece and cutter are moved in relation to each other and in relation to the milling machine. More frequently, however, the workpiece is advanced at a relatively low rate of movement or feed to a milling cutter rotating at comparatively high speed, with the cuter axis remaining in a fixed position. A characteristic feature of the milling process is that each milling cutter tooth takes its share of the stock in the form of small individual chips. Milling operations are performed on many different machines.

Since both the workpiece and cutter can be moved relative to one another, independently or in combination, a wide variety of operations can be performed by milling. Applications include the production of flat or contoured surfaces, slots, grooves, recesses, threads, and other configurations.

Milling is one of the most universal, yet complicated machining methods. The process has more variations in the kinds of machines used, workpiece movements, and types of tooling than any other basic machining method. Important advantages of removing material by means of milling include high stock removal rates, the capability of producing relatively smooth surface finishes, and the wide variety of cutting tools that are available. Cutting edges of the tools can be shaped to form any complex surface.

Milling Methods

The major milling methods are peripheral and face milling; in addition, a number of related methods exist that are variations of these two methods, depending upon the type of workpiece or cutter.

Peripheral Milling

In peripheral milling, sometimes called slab milling, the milled surface generated by teeth or inserts located on the periphery of the cutter body is generally in a plane parallel to the cutter axis. Milling operations with form-relieved and formed profile cutters are included in this class. The cross section of the milled surface corresponds to the outline or contour of the milling cutter or combination of cutters used.

Peripheral milling operations are usually performed on milling machines with the spindle positioned horizontally; however, they can also be performed with end mills on vertical-spindle machines. The milling cutters are mounted on an arbor which is generally supported at the outer end for increased rigidity, particularly when, because of the conditions of the setup, the cutter or cutters are located at some distance from the nose of the spindle. Peripheral milling should generally not be done if the part can be face milled.

Face Milling

Face milling is done on both horizontal and vertical milling machines. The milled surface resulting from the combined action of cutting edges located on the periphery and face of the cutter is generally at right angles to the cutter axis. The milled surface is flat, with no relation to the contour of the teeth, except when milling is done to a shoulder. Generally, face milling should be applied wherever and whenever possible.

Chip thickness in conventional (up) face milling varies from a minimum at the entrance and exit of the cutter tooth to a maximum along the horizontal diameter. The milled surface is characterized by tooth and revolution marks, as in the case of peripheral milling cutters. The prominence of these marks is controlled by the accuracy of grinding the face cutting edge of the teeth, or by the accuracy of the body/insert combination in indexable cutters and of

mounting the cutter so that it runs true on the machine spindle. It is also controlled by the rigidity of the machine and workpiece itself. When the length of the face cutting edge is less than the feed per revolution (or the amount the work has moved in one revolution of the cutter), a series of roughly circular grooves or ridges results on the milled surface. Similar marking is produced by the trailing teeth when they drag on the milled surface of the work. This is known as heel drag.

In face milling, it is important to select a cutter with a diameter suited to the proposed width of cut if best results are to be obtained. Cuts equal in width to the full cutter diameter should be avoided, if possible, since the thin chip section at entry of the teeth results in accelerated tooth wear from abrasion plus a tendency for the chip to weld or stick to the tooth or insert and be carried around and recut. This is detrimental to surface finish. A good ratio of cutter diameter to the width of the workpiece or proposed path of cut is 5:3.

Related Milling Methods

Many other milling methods can be classified as either peripheral or face milling operations. Because of the type of workpiece being machined and/or the specific type of cutter used, however, these methods are often referred to as end, side, straddle, gang, gear, cam, or other types of milling.

End Milling: End mills have cutting edges on both their end faces and their peripheries. When used in face milling operations, the diameter of the cutter determines the maximum width of cut. In peripheral milling, the axial length of the teeth determines the maximum depth of cut.

The combinations of cuts possible with end mills are numerous. Experience has shown that, when the end of the cutter is brought in contact with the work for slot milling, the hand of rotation and the hand of the helix should be the same (right-hand cut and right-hand helix; left-hand cut and left-hand helix). The combined effect of the axial, radial, and tangential force components on the cutter may be a deflection either toward or away from the work, depending upon the respective intensities of these forces. The axial force, however, tends to pull the cutter away from the spindle, and positive means must be provided to hold it in position. When milling is done on the front face, as well as the periphery, of end mills, it may be dangerous to cut a long surface on the periphery simultaneously with right-hand rotation and right-hand helix. This is because the hand of helix forces the cutter into the workpiece and causes serious damage to the machine, cutter, and workpiece. Secure holding of the cutter can minimize possible danger.

When the end mill is used for profiling and the end of the tool is not in use, the hand of rotation and the hand of helix should be opposite (right-hand cut and left-hand helix; left-hand cut and right-hand helix). The axial force acts against the spindle, providing additional means to hold the cutter in position.

Side and Straddle Milling:
Side milling consists of machining a plane surface perpendicular to the milling machine arbor with an arbor-mounted tool called a side milling cutter. Straddle milling entails machining two or more parallel surfaces using two or more side milling cutters spaced apart on the machine arbor.

Gang Milling:
This method consists of using two or more cutters, mounted on the machine arbor, to mill multiple surfaces simultaneously. The cutters can be of various types. Care must be exercised in cutter selection to control cutting speeds within an acceptable range. Cutters made from different tool materials are sometimes used to help maintain effective cutting speeds when different diameters are being milled.

Gear Milling:
Although most gears are now produced on gear cutting machines, some spur gears are made in small quantities on milling machines. The machines must be equipped with dividing heads, and standard gear tooth cutters are used. Worm gears can be made on universal milling machines that cut gashes first and then finish the gear teeth to size with hobbing cutters.

Cam Milling:
Cams, worm threads, and other helical surfaces are produced on milling machines equipped with universal dividing heads. This is accomplished by rotating the workpiece while it is fed in the direction of the rotational axis.

Thread Milling:
With the availability of NC/CNC machines having three-axis contouring capability and advanced controls, thread milling is undergoing a resurgence in popularity. Ease of programming with canned routines, long cutter life, and high-quality threads are among the advantages of this milling method.

Plunge Milling:
Plunge milling with multipoint tooling is an alternative to the use of single-point turning tools for facing operations. The rotating multipoint facing head used for this method has a sufficient number of inserts to completely cover the area to be machined. Cutting edges of the inserts are set parallel to the workpiece surface, and as the head is advanced axially, all cutting edges simultaneously engage the face to be milled. Metal removal rates are greater than those possible with single-point tooling.

Planetary Milling:
Circular forms can be cut on planetary milling machines with the workpieces held stationary and motion confined to the milling cutter. Machines for this method are similar to planetary thread milling machines except that a no-lead master is used or a no-lead attachment is provided for use with the universal master.

Crankshaft Milling:
Milling of crankshafts, camshafts, and other unbalanced shafts has replaced the traditional turning process in some plants. Advantages of this milling method include faster production, closer tolerances, lower tooling costs, and more rapid changeover. Milling machines for both external and internal cutting of unbalanced shafts are described later in this chapter.

Diesinking:
Machining of three-dimensional contoured cavities in dies and molds, commonly

called diesinking, is done by electrical discharge machining or by milling. Diesinking is still being done on conventional milling machines, but this process is relatively slow. Conventional milling machines for diesinking must have heads that can be set at various angles and/or attachments such as rotating angular and extension heads, sine tables, and rotary indexing tables.

Most diesinking by the milling process is now done on machines with CNC or tracer control. Milling machines for copying are available with tracers operated by mechanical pantograph, air, hydraulic, electric, or combinations of these. At least one machine builder offers a copy mill having both tracer control and CNC.

Operating Parameters for Milling

There are so many variables influencing milling that it is difficult to predict results reliably. These variables include the size and shape of the workpiece; the material from which it is made (its machinability, physical properties, and condition); the kind of milling operation to be performed; the type of cutter used (its material and geometry); the machine employed (including its condition); the rigidity of the setup; and the production rate, tolerance, and surface finish requirements. Width and depth of cut, as well as the tooth entrance angle, also have a profound effect.

All these variables notwithstanding, an attempt must be made to establish at least initial parameters for any milling operation. These parameters include power and force requirements, cutting speed, feed rate, depth of cut, and cutting fluid to be used. Optimum parameters cannot be established, however, and truly reliable predictions of results cannot be obtained until the milling operation is actually performed and trial parameters are tested. Other important factors that must be considered are sharpening practices (if grind-type cutters are used), setup and application methods, troubleshooting, and safety.

Power Requirements

Two power requirements exist for any milling application. The first, by far the greater in magnitude, is the power required at the machine spindle to rotate the cutter through the workpiece. The second, lesser in value, is the power required to feed the workpiece into the cutter or the cutter into the workpiece.

Spindle Power: Several methods have been developed for calculating the power required at the machine spindle for milling. One formula, widely accepted throughout the machine tool industry as well as by milling cutter users, is as follows:

$$hp = KST [0.00549(1000A)^r]$$

where:

- hp = the approximate horsepower required at the machine spindle for milling, including a 30% dull tool allowance and a 20% machine friction allowance
- K = a machinability factor for milling different materials (see Fig. 11-1)
- S = peripheral speed of cutter, sfm
- T = average number of cutter teeth in contact with the workpiece
- A = cross-sectional area of workpiece material removed by one cutter tooth, in.^{2}
- r = a machining exponent for different workpiece materials (see Fig. 11-1)

For metric usage, the horsepower (hp) should be multiplied by 0.746 to obtain the kilowatt (kW) requirements.

Figure 11-2 shows the metal removal rates for average milling conditions, using carbide cutters and a feed rate of 0.010 ipr (0.25 mm/rev) per tooth, with milling machines of different horsepower ratings. Values given vary with the geometries of the cutters.

Factors Affecting Power Requirements: Since the spindle power requirements calculated with this formula are approximate, other factors must be considered if more accurate estimates are needed. Factors that influence power requirements include

A, in.^{2}	Values of $[0.00549 \, (1000A)^r]$ for milling:			
	Steel (r = 0.803)	Cast Iron (r = 0.865)	Cast Steel (r = 0.850)	Aluminum (r = 0.940)
0.0001	0.000862	0.000746	0.000774	0.000631
0.0002	0.00150	0.00136	0.00139	0.00121
0.0003	0.00209	0.00194	0.00198	0.00177
0.0004	0.00262	0.00249	0.00251	0.00232
0.0005	0.00315	0.00301	0.00305	0.00287
0.0006	0.00365	0.00353	0.00356	0.00340
0.0007	0.00413	0.00404	0.00406	0.00393
0.0008	0.00459	0.00453	0.00454	0.00445
0.0009	0.00505	0.00501	0.00502	0.00497
0.001	0.00549	0.00549	0.00549	0.00549
0.002	0.00966	0.0100	0.00988	0.0105
0.003	0.0133	0.0142	0.0139	0.0154
0.004	0.0167	0.0182	0.0178	0.0202
0.005	0.0200	0.0202	0.0218	0.0249

Material Milled	Material Factor, K	Material Milled		Material Factor, K
Cast irons, with Bhn of:		Aluminum, with Bhn of:		
140-190	0.83	50-75		0.42
190-230	1.3	110-145		0.67
230-320	1.7			
		Bearing babbitt and bronze		0.72
Nodular irons, with Bhn of:		Steels:		
200-270	0.83	AISI No.	Bhn	
240-300	1.3	1010	110-130	1.5
270-350	1.7	1020	140-160	1.6
		1045	220-235	2.5
Malleable irons, with Bhn of:		1137	180-190	1.7
		3140	220-240	2.7
110-145	0.56	4140	190-230	2.2
150-200	0.74	4820	100-230	2.7
200-240	0.83	5140	175-230	2.3
		8620	170-220	2.1
		6140	190-230	2.8

Figure 11-1 Values and factors for calculating power requirements in milling

cutting speed, undeformed chip thickness, cutter geometry, and machine efficiency.

Cutting speed. When most common materials are milled, the power requirement per unit of material removed decreases as the cutting speed increases up to a critical value, which varies for different materials. Further increases above the critical value do not significantly affect power requirements.

Chip thickness. Increasing the undeformed chip thickness by increasing the feed per tooth or insert results in an increase in power consumption. The increase in power consumption, however, is proportionately smaller than the increase in metal removal rate.

Since the undeformed chip thickness is constantly changing in a milling operation, the position of the

	Rated Power Capacity of Machine Spindle, hp (kW)										
	5 (3.7)	7.5 (5.6)	10 (7.5)	15 (11.2)	20 (14.9)	25 (18.6)	30 (22.4)	40 (29.8)	50 (37.3)	75 (56)	100 (74.6)
Material Milled	Metal Removal Rate, in.^{3}/min (cm^3/min)										
Aluminum alloys	15 (246)	25 (410)	35 (574)	55 (901)	80 (1311)	100 (1639)	120 (1966)	170 (2786)	220 (3605)	330 (5408)	450 (7374)
Brass	6.5 (107)	10 (164)	14 (229)	22 (361)	30 (492)	38 (623)	45 (737)	62 (1016)	80 (1311)	120 (1966)	170 (2786)
Bronze	5.5 (90)	8.6 (141)	12 (197)	19 (311)	25 (410)	32 (524)	36 (590)	52 (852)	65 (1065)	110 (1803)	150 (2458)
Cast irons:											
soft, 150-180 Brinell	8.5 (139)	13 (213)	18 (295)	29 (475)	36 (490)	45 (737)	54 (885)	72 (1180)	92 (1508)	142 (2327)	200 (3277)
medium-hard, 180-225 Brinell	5.5 (90)	8.6 (141)	12 (197)	19 (311)	25 (410)	32 (524)	36 (590)	52 (852)	65 (1065)	110 (1803)	150 (2458)
malleable, soft to hard	5.5 (90)	8.6 (141)	12 (197)	19 (311)	25 (410)	32 (524)	36 (590)	52 (852)	65 (1065)	110 (1803)	150 (2458)
hard, 225-350 Brinell	3.5 (57)	6 (98)	9 (147)	15 (246)	20 (328)	25 (410)	30 (492)	40 (655)	55 (901)	90 (1475)	130 (2130)
Cast steels, soft to hard	3.2 (52)	5.2 (85)	7.5 (123)	12 (197)	16 (262)	20 (328)	24 (393)	32 (524)	43 (705)	68 (1114)	95 (1557)
Steels:											
100-150 Brinell	3.5 (57)	6 (98)	9 (147)	15 (246)	20 (328)	25 (410)	30 (492)	40 (655)	55 (901)	90 (1475)	130 (2130)
150-250 Brinell	3.2 (52)	5.2 (85)	7.5 (123)	12 (197)	16 (262)	20 (328)	24 (393)	32 (524)	43 (705)	68 (1114)	95 (1557)
250-350 Brinell	2.8 (46)	4.5 (74)	6.5 (107)	10 (164)	14 (229)	17 (279)	21 (344)	28 (459)	37 (606)	60 (983)	85 (1393)
350-450 Brinell	2.5 (41)	4 (66)	5.5 (90)	9 (147)	12 (197)	15 (246)	18 (295)	24 (393)	33 (541)	54 (885)	80 (1311)

Figure 11-2 Sample metal removal rates

(*Valenite Div., Valeron Corp.*)

milling cutter (Figs. 11-3 and 11-4) must be considered in determining average undeformed chip thickness. When the cutter axis intersects the workpiece, the maximum undeformed chip thickness equals the feed per tooth or insert. Whenever the cutter axis overhangs the workpiece, the undeformed chip thickness during milling is always smaller than the feed per tooth or insert.

Cutter geometry. The element of milling cutter geometry that has the greatest effect on power consumption is the true rake angle (see Fig. 11-5). As the true rake angle is increased (made more positive or less negative), cutting forces are reduced and power consumption is decreased. Increasing the true rake angle, however, causes each tooth or insert to be placed in a weaker cutting position. When negative cutting rakes are used, up to 30% more power may be required.

Machine efficiency. The simplified formula above is for calculating power required at the milling machine spindle. It does not take into account the power required to overcome friction and inertia within the machine. The efficiency value of a machine tool is equal to the percentage of rated motor power that

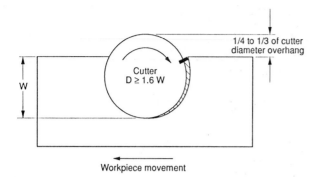

Figure 11-3   Proper cutter positioning

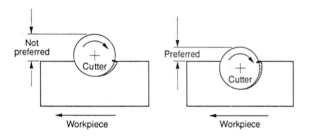

Figure 11-4   Preferred entry angle for milling

is available at the spindle. Available power varies with machine types and construction and between different machine manufacturers. This efficiency depends primarily upon its construction; type of bearings; number of belts or gears driving the spindle, carriage, or table; and other moving parts.

Determining Power More Accurately:
Taking these factors (speed, chip thickness, cutter geometry, and machine efficiency) into consideration, a detailed discussion of determining a reasonably accurate estimate of power required at the motor and spindle, or the maximum metal removal rate possible with a certain size of motor, is presented in the *Milling Handbook of High-Efficiency Metal Cutting*. An accurate power monitor on the machine is the best method of determining actual power consumed.

Tangential Load: The tangential load is a force which serves as a basis for making several design decisions in milling applications. This force is tangent to the effective cutting radius of the cutter, as illustrated in Fig. 11-6. Direction of the force can be derived by a simple graphic vector summation of the individual cutting forces of each tooth or insert engaged in the workpiece. For continuous cuts, the direction of force lies on a line between the point of tooth entry and the point of tooth exit.

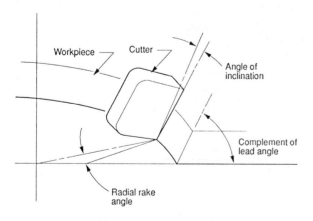

Figure 11-5   Relationship of angles in milling

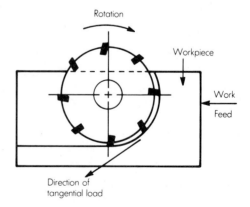

Figure 11-6   Tangential load for face milling cutter

Once the cutter power has been calculated, the tangential load can be derived from it with the formula:

$$T = \frac{126,000 \times hp}{D \times rpm}$$

where:

T = tangential load, lb
hp = horsepower required at the cutter
D = cutter diameter, in.
rpm = rotational speed of the cutter

This formula for tangential load assumes constant load on the cutter, which may not be the case. For metric usage, pounds (lb) should be multiplied by 4.448 to obtain the tangential force in newtons (N).

Feed Force: The tangential load has a direct relationship to the force required to feed the work into the cutter or vice versa. The tangential load for a plain milling cutter used in a climb or down milling application tends to pull the workpiece into the cutter. This results in a small feed load. The action also produces a downward force which increases the load on the table ways of a horizontal milling machine. This increased frictional load, however, is usually minimal, and its effects are more than offset by the pulling action. For such applications, the force required to feed the work into the cutter can be low and may represent only that force necessary to overcome the weight of the workpiece, fixture, and table, plus the friction of the table ways and the feed drive train. In some cases, the cutter may overcome the resistance and pull the workpiece into itself with possible disastrous results.

Conventional or up milling with a plain milling cutter tends to lift the workpiece off the table of a horizontal milling machine; the tangential load directly opposes the direction of table feed. For such applications, it is usually safe to assume that the force required to feed the table will not exceed the value of the tangential force created by the cutter, nor will it exceed any other allowances required for table and feed drivetrain friction.

Face milling applications can be analyzed in much the same manner. Depending upon the direction of cutter rotation in relation to the direction of feed, as well as the location of the area being milled, such applications produce either positive- or negative-feed loads. However, since climb milling is almost always preferred, the tendency is to pull the work into the cutter. As is the case with the previously explained plain milling applications, this results in minimal or negative loads.

Resultant components of the tangential force can be calculated from the formulas:

$$A = T \cos \alpha$$

and

$$S = T \sin \alpha$$

where:

A = resultant force along feed axis, lbf
S = resultant force at 90° to feed axis, lbf
T = tangential force produced by cutter, lbf
α = angle between tangential force line and feed axis, degrees

Angle α is difficult to estimate because it varies with the workpiece material, cutter design, cutting fluid, and operating parameters.

For metric usage, pound-force (lbf) should be multiplied by 4.448 to obtain force in newtons (N).

Feeds and Speeds For Milling

The two factors, in addition to depth and width of cut, that have the greatest effect on productivity and forces acting upon the cutter, machine, workpiece, and fixture in milling are the feed rate and cutting speed. Together, these factors determine the stock removal rate, which provides the basis for the power and force calculations just discussed.

Milling Feed Rates: The feed rate for milling cutters is generally expressed in inches per minute (ipm) or millimeters per minute (mm/min) and is normally established by selecting an appropriate feed per tooth (fpt), blade, or insert. In selecting feed per tooth, it should be noted that there is a minimum chip thickness, which varies for different materials, that must be maintained in order to produce good cutter life. At the other extreme, the maximum chip thickness is usually limited by the power available; the strengths of the cutting teeth, workpiece, and fixture; and other factors such as available chip space between the cutter teeth and finish desired.

Chip thickness varies from zero to the same as the feed per tooth with deep peripheral cuts, while the maximum chip thickness is less than the feed per tooth with shallow peripheral cuts. Feed per tooth (fpt) in inches or millimeters, inches per revolution (ipr), or millimeters per revolution (mm/rev), and feed rate in inches per minute (ipm) or millimeters per minute (mm/min) are all interrelated. Selection starts with the feed per tooth. Formulas for calculating ipr, ipm, and fpt are:

$$ipr \ (\text{or } mm/rev) = \frac{ipm \ (\text{or } mm/min)}{rpm}$$

or:

$$ipr \ (\text{or } mm/rev) = fpt \ (in. \text{ or } mm) \times number \ of \ teeth$$
$$ipm \ (\text{or } mm/min) = ipr \ (\text{or } mm/rev) \times rpm$$
$$fpt \ (in. \text{ or } mm) = \frac{ipr \ (\text{or } mm/rev)}{number \ of \ teeth}$$

Changing the machine spindle speed while the table feed rate is held constant causes the feed per tooth to change. If the feed per tooth is considered optimum, any change in cutting speed should be accompanied by a change in table feed rate.

Chip thickness or load per tooth varies depending upon the lead angle and the relationship of the tooth to the centerline of the cutter.

Cutting Speeds:
Milling cutter speed refers to its peripheral or surface speed expressed in feet per minute (sfm) or meters per minute (m/min). It is the straight-line distance that a point on the cutter OD would travel in one minute at a specified rotary speed (rpm). The cutter speed is related to machine spindle speed (rpm) as follows:

$$sfm = 0.262d \times rpm$$

where:

sfm = milling cutter surface speed, ft/min
d = cutter diameter, in.

or:

$$m/min = 0.00314d \times rpm$$

where:

m/min = milling cutter surface speed
d = cutter diameter, mm

or:

$$rpm = \frac{3.82 \times sfm}{d}$$

where:

d = cutter diameter, in.

or:

$$rpm = \frac{318.31 \times m/min}{d}$$

where:

d = cutter diameter, mm

Relationship Between Speed and Feed:
Whenever any one of the variables—the cutting speed, feed per tooth or insert, or width or depth of cut—is increased while the others are held constant, the metal removal rate increases. A change in any of these operating parameters has an equal effect on the metal removal rate.

Increasing the speed, feed, or cutting depth reduces cutter life, but the amount that cutter life is reduced depends upon which operating parameter is increased. In general, cutter life is less affected by changes in depth of cut than by changes in either speed or feed. As a result, the depth of cut should be as high as possible for the most favorable compromise between cutter life and metal removal rate.

Feed per tooth has a greater effect on cutter life than the depth of cut, but the change in cutter life is much smaller than would result from an equal increase in cutting speed. Consequently, most experts recommend using the highest feasible feed per tooth to optimize the trade-off between machining time and cutter life.

Cutting speed has a much greater effect on cutter life than either depth of cut or feed per tooth. As a result, selecting a speed is the most critical variable when operating parameters are being established. Since most workpiece materials can be successfully machined within a broad range of cutting speeds, the speed should be selected to maximize the production rate or minimize the total cost per piece milled for the specific operation.

Available machine power sometimes limits the metal removal rate that can be achieved in a milling operation. For such limited power applications, the depth of cut and feed rate should still be as high as possible, with the cutting speed set so that power requirements are within the limits of the machine. The cutting speed, however, should never be set so low that chip welding to the cutter teeth occurs. Some experts feel that the best way to compensate for lack of power is to change the width of cut, keeping the cutting speed in the most efficient range for the cutting tool material used.

Milling Cutters

A milling cutter is a rotary tool provided with one or more cutting edges which intermittently engage the workpiece and remove material by relative movement of the workpiece and cutter. Milling cutters can be classified by styles or uses, construction characteristics, and methods of mounting. Methods of mounting cutters are discussed in a subsequent section of this chapter.

Cutter Styles and Uses

Many different milling cutters are available for various applications. They are sometimes classified or described by terms which refer to their use, purpose for which they are made, shape or position of their cutting edges, or shape of the workpiece produced. Some of the most common types of milling cutters, illustrated in Fig. 11-7, are plain, form, or side milling cutters, shaped profile cutters, and face or end mills.

Plain (peripheral or slab) milling cutters. These tools are cylindrical in shape and have straight or helical cutting edges only on their circumferences. They are used for peripheral cutting of straight surfaces.

Form milling cutters. These are modifications of plain milling cutters that have cutting edges shaped to perform specific applications. They include convex, concave, corner rounding, chain sprocket, gear, and many special cutters.

Side milling cutters. These tools have cutting edges on their peripheries and on one or both faces. Those with cutting edges on only one face are called half-side milling cutters. Those having alternate cutting edges aligned in different directions are called staggered-tooth side milling cutters. Side milling cutters are also available in shell mill types.

Shaped profile cutters. These are similar to form milling cutters and are available in various styles including single angle, double angle, thread, T-slot, dovetail, keyseat, and special forms.

Face mills. These tools are designed to machine surfaces parallel to the face of the cutter. They have teeth that cut on the circumferential surface and on one side in much the same way that a half-side milling cutter cuts. The maximum width of cut on which a plane surface can be produced by a face mill is determined by the effective cutting diameter, although full width of cut is seldom recommended. Step cutters, having a tier of inserts stepped both radially and axially in a single body, permit deep cuts without the long engagement length normally involved when deep cuts are taken.

End mills. These are a variety of shank-type side milling cutters. They are used for facing, slotting, profiling, diesinking, and engraving operations.

Dimensions and tolerances of various types and sizes of milling cutters and end mills are presented in ANSI Standard B94.19-1977, published by ASME.

Construction of Milling Cutters

Three basic types of construction exist for milling cutters: solid, inserted or brazed blade, and mechanically clamped, indexable insert. Both the solid and blade types can be resharpened and are often referred to as grind-type cutters. While indexable-

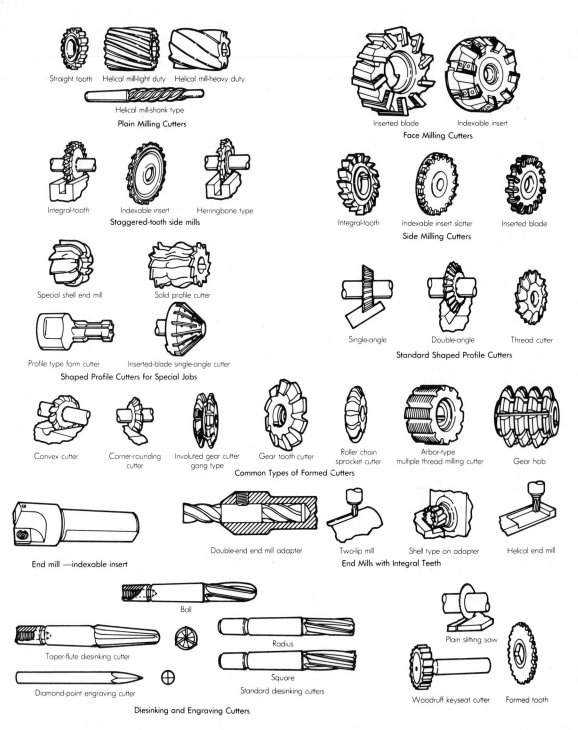

Straight tooth   Helical mill-light duty   Helical mill-heavy duty

Helical mill-shank type

Plain Milling Cutters

Inserted blade   Indexable insert

Face Milling Cutters

Integral-tooth   Indexable insert   Herringbone type

Staggered-tooth side mills

Integral-tooth   Indexable insert slotter   Inserted blade

Side Milling Cutters

Special shell end mill   Solid profile cutter

Profile type form cutter   Inserted-blade single-angle cutter

Shaped Profile Cutters for Special Jobs

Single-angle   Double-angle   Thread cutter

Standard Shaped Profile Cutters

Convex cutter   Corner-rounding cutter   Involuted gear cutter gang type   Gear tooth cutter   Roller chain sprocket cutter   Arbor-type multiple thread milling cutter   Gear hob

Common Types of Formed Cutters

End mill —indexable insert

Double-end end mill adapter   Two-lip mill   Shell type on adapter   Helical end mill

End Mills with Integral Teeth

Ball

Taper-flute diesinking cutter

Radius

Diamond-point engraving cutter

Square

Standard diesinking cutters

Diesinking and Engraving Cutters

Plain slitting saw

Woodruff keyseat cutter   Formed tooth

Figure 11-7   Common types of milling cutters

insert cutters are widely used, grind-type cutters are still required by some companies for certain applications. One advantage of grind-type cutters is that their geometry can be tailored to suit a wide variety of milling applications; in addition, runout can be controlled more closely than with other types of cutters (see Figs. 11-8 and 11-9).

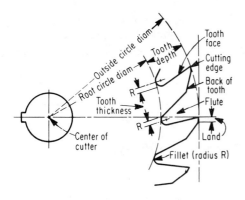

Figure 11-8   Parts of teeth of a solid plain milling cutter

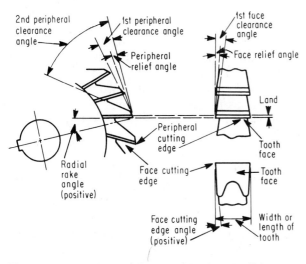

Figure 11-9   Nomenclature of teeth on solid-type side milling cutter

Milling Cutter Nomenclature

Full nomenclature for milling cutter teeth is given in ANSI Standard B94.19-1977, published by ASME. Figures 11-8 and 11-9 generally illustrate most standard terms; additional terms that are frequently used are as follows:

clearance The additional space provided behind the relieved land of a cutter tooth to eliminate undesirable contact between the cutter and workpiece.

cutting edge The leading edge of the cutter tooth.

cutting edge angle The angle which a cutting edge makes with an axial plane at any given point. A constant lead produces a constant cutting edge angle on a cylindrical cutter and a varying cutting edge angle on a tapered cutter. A varying lead can be used to produce a constant cutting edge angle on a tapered cutter.

entrance angle The angle formed between a centerline on the cutter which is perpendicular to the direction of feed and a radial line through a point on the cutting edge at which the tooth first contacts the workpiece.

heel 1. The back edge of the relieved land; 2. the inner end of a facing cutting edge.

helix angle The cutting edge angle which a helical cutting edge makes with a plane containing the axis of a cylindrical cutter.

land The narrow surface of a profile-sharpened cutter tooth immediately behind the cutting edge.

lip angle The included angle between a tooth and a relieved land.

rake The angular relationship between the tooth face, or a tangent to the tooth face at a given point and a given reference plane or line. Various rake angles are illustrated in Fig. 11-10.

helical rake Applies to helical teeth only (not angular). The helical rake at a given point on the flute face is the angle between the tool axis and a tangent plane at the given point.

hook A concave condition of a tooth face. The rake of a hooked tooth face must be determined at a given point.

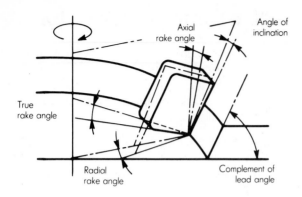

Figure 11-10 Relationship between various angles of milling cutter insert

positive rake Describes a tooth face in rotation whose cutting edge leads the surface of the tooth face.

radial rake The angle between the tooth face and a radial line passing through the cutting edge in a plane perpendicular to the cutter axis.

resultant rake The angle between a tangent to the tooth face at a given point on the cutting edge and a radial line to this point measured in a plane perpendicular to the cutting edge. Descriptive of cutter geometry alone, it is the resultant rake contained on a cutter due to the combination of radial rake or hook, axial or helical rake, and a corner angle or corner radius.

relief The result of the removal of tool material behind or adjacent to the cutting edge to provide clearance and prevent rubbing (heel drag).

axial relief The relief measured in the axial direction between a plane perpendicular to the axis and the relieved surface. It can be measured by the amount of indicator drop at a given radius in a given amount of angular rotation. (Axial relief is preferred to the term end relief.)

concave relief A relieved surface behind the cutting edge which is concave.

eccentric relief A relieved surface behind the cutting edge which is essentially convex.

flat relief A relieved surface behind the cutting edge which is essentially flat.

primary relief The relief immediately behind the cutting edge.

relief angle The angle formed between a relieved surface and a given plane tangent to a cutting edge or to a point on the cutting edge.

radial relief Relief in a radial direction measured in the plane of rotation. It can be measured by the amount of indicator drop at a given radius in a given amount of angular rotation.

secondary relief See preferred term "clearance."

Mounting of Milling Cutters

Milling cutters are mounted on arbors, in the machine spindle, or on the spindle nose, often with the use of adapters. Regardless of the mounting method, the cutters must be rigidly held to withstand the high interrupted forces of milling and to run true both radially and axially.

To facilitate accurate mounting of cutters, most milling machine spindles are provided with a tapered bore, an OD, and a face perpendicular to the spindle axis, all precisely ground. The spindles usually have four threaded holes for holding clamping screws and two keys for driving cutters, adapters, or arbors. Essential spindle dimensions, tool shanks, and draw-in bolt ends for milling machines are presented in ANSI Standard B5.18-1972, published by ASME.

Mounting Shank-Type Cutters

Small-diameter face milling cutters, generally with a diameter of 2″ (51 mm) or less, and almost all end mills have a straight or tapered integral shank to fit an adapter or the spindle bore. Common styles of integral shanks used on such cutters are illustrated in Fig. 11-11.

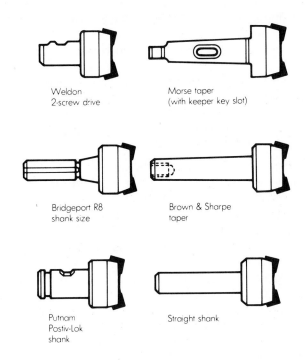

Weldon
2-screw drive

Morse taper
(with keeper key slot)

Bridgeport R8
shank size

Brown & Sharpe
taper

Putnam
Postiv-Lok
shank

Straight shank

Figure 11-11 Common shank styles used on end mills

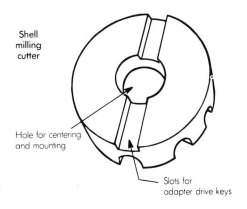

Shell
milling
cutter

Hole for centering
and mounting

Slots for
adapter drive keys

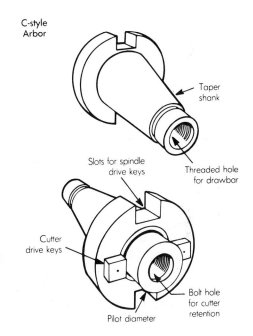

C-style
Arbor

Taper
shank

Threaded hole
for drawbar

Slots for spindle
drive keys

Cutter
drive keys

Bolt hole
for cutter
retention

Pilot diameter

Figure 11-12 Shell milling cutters

Mounting Shell Mills

A wide range of small-diameter face milling cutters are available as shell mills. Shell mills are identical in function to face milling cutters, but have hollow bodies. They are mounted on C-style arbor adapters (see Fig. 11-12). The adapter is centered by the internal taper of the machine spindle and is retained by a drawbar. Precision drive keys on the spindle face engage keyslots in the arbor which in turn has drive keys that engage the cutter body. The shell mill is positioned by the pilot diameter on the end of the arbor and held in place by a single lockscrew.

C-style arbors are available to fit most machine spindle noses. They are also made with special shank designs for NC/CNC machines with quick-change tooling systems and for machining centers with automatic toolchangers.

Mounting Larger Face Mills

Face milling cutters larger than about 8″ (200 mm) diam are available for either of two popular mounting methods: the flat-back drive and the National Standard drive, also called the National Machine Tool Builders (NMTB) drive (see Fig. 11-13).

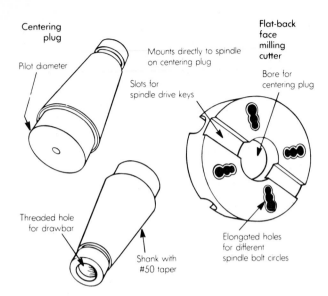

Figure 11-13 Flat-back mounting for face milling cutters

Milling Machines

Machines designed specifically for milling are available in many different types, sizes, and capacities to suit specific requirements. Types of milling machines include knee, bed, tracer, program-mable, computer numerical control (CNC), and special machines. They range from versatile machines that can perform many different operations to dedicated designs for production applications.

Many operations previously done on milling machines are now being performed on machining centers, as well as on other multifunction machines such as automatics and boring, drilling, and milling machines. Some milling is also done on lathes with attachments and heavy-duty drilling machines.

Machine Control Systems

Milling machines are available for manual, semi-automatic, and automatic operation. Numerical and computer numerical control (NC and CNC) are used on general-purpose machines for milling dies and molds; on dedicated machines such as skin and spar mills, described later in this section; and even more extensively on horizontal boring mills, machining centers, and other machine tools.

Types of Milling Machines

Because of the wide variety of milling machines available, only the more common types are discussed in this section. These include hand, knee, bed, tracer, programmable, NC/CNC, and special milling machines. Most types are available with horizontal or vertical spindles. The choice between a horizontal or vertical machine depends primarily upon the workpieces to be milled. Relatively flat workpieces are generally milled on vertical-spindle machines. Cubic or odd-shaped parts usually require a horizontal-spindle machine. Horizontal machines are also generally used for slotting, side milling, and similar operations (see Fig. 11-14).

On horizontal-spindle machines, an arbor holding the cutter(s) is mounted horizontally on an axis parallel to the machine table. On vertical-spindle machines, the cutter axis is normally perpendicular to the machine table, but can often be tilted to perform angular cutting.

Dimensions, areas, and general features of horizontal and vertical knee-type milling machines and horizontal bed-type milling machines are presented in ANSI Standard B5.45-1972, published by ASME. The purpose of this standard is to facilitate the interchange of tooling and fixturing between machines. This interchange results in increased flexibility, more rapid changeover with minimum tool-ing modifications, and reduced obsolescence. Dimensions of spindle noses and tool shanks for milling machines are tabulated in ANSI Standard B5.18-1972, also published by ASME.

Hand-Fed Milling Machines: These small milling machines, mounted on pedestals or benches, are still employed for some toolroom or light-duty operations. Such machines are desirable for milling workpieces having large variations in stock removal requirements because necessary changes in feed rate can be sensed by hand pressure. Their application, however, appears to be declining.

Hand-fed milling machines generally have a rotating cutter mounted on a horizontal spindle. Feed is generally by means of a hand lever, but power feed can be applied to these machines.

Knee-and-Column-Type Milling Machines:

Knee-and-column-type machines, in the horizontal version, have the spindle mounted in the column at a fixed height and have the capability of positioning three sliding motions. Vertical motion is obtained by sliding the knee member up and down on the central stationary column. Cross motion is generally obtained by sliding a saddle member in and out across the top of the knee. Longitudinal motion (right or left) is obtained by sliding the workholding table on the saddle at a right angle to the cross motion. Machines with a vertically mounted spindle generally have a fourth sliding motion which is up and down in the same direction as the knee.

On most machines, all three or four motions can be used to feed the workpiece during a cut; however, table motion is usually preferred. Basically, knee-and-column machines are numbered or sized from 1 through 6 in accordance with the table travel: No. 1, 22" (559 mm); No. 2, 28" (711 mm); No. 3, 34" (864 mm); No. 4, 42" (1067 mm); No. 5, 50" (1270 mm); and No. 6, 60" (1524 mm).

Bed-Type Milling Machines:

Bed-type machines, more commonly called fixed-bed-type machines, are characterized by the extremely rigid construction afforded by a rectangular-shaped bed casting or weldment. These units are supported and leveled along their entire length, which can vary from 3-30 ft (0.9-9 m) or more.

For the larger bed sizes, the unit is usually secured to the floor with anchor bolts to ensure even greater stability. The bed supports and guides a work-carrying table which is moved in a longitudinal direction only (right to left) by various means such

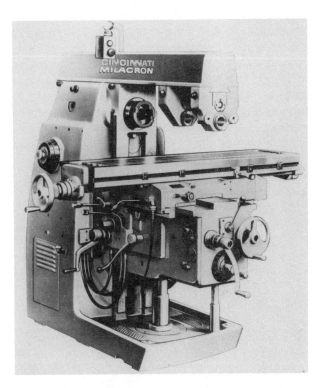

Figure 11-14 Modern horizontal milling machine *(Courtesy of Cincinnati Milacron)*

as a rack and pinion, Acme screw and nut, ball screw and nut, or hydraulic cylinder.

This type of bed permits heavy cutting loads on large or heavy workpieces and can be used with various other machine elements to form a wide variety of fixed-bed machines, some of which are referred to as manufacturing types. Machines of this type can be further classified as horizontal, vertical, or planer types or as boring, drilling, and milling machines. Beds on these machines provide space for a self-contained cutting fluid reservoir and usually have adequate space for collection of the major portion of chips formed during cutting cycles.

The fixed-bed-type milling machine, whether having a horizontal or vertical spindle, has many features that benefit the user. Machine size is usually governed by the horsepower rating of the spindle carrier, which in most cases can be anywhere from 1-50 hp (0.7-37 kW) or more, depending upon the machine type and the manufacturer. The range of machine sizes available permits light to heavy cutting and either up (conventional) or down (climb) milling with high-speed steel, carbide, ceramic, or diamond cutters. Most manufacturers offer wide ranges of spindle speeds and table feed rates that accommodate the majority of cutting requirements and permit correct chip-per-tooth loads for all types of cutters and work materials (see Fig. 11-15).

Figure 11-15 Bed-type milling machine *(Courtesy of Cincinnati Milacron)*

Fixed-Bed Saddle-Type Machines:
Fixed-bed saddle-type milling machines with vertical spindles provide greater rigidity than knee-and-column-type machines. As a result, higher power cuts can be taken with more accuracy for a given size machine. Another advantage of machines of this design is the ability to counterbalance the vertical slide, thus providing sensitive vertical motions.

Tracer-Controlled Milling Machines:
Milling machines with tracing capabilities are used to produce parts with complex shapes economically, for either single-piece or mass-production requirements as well as for diesinking operations. One or more types of tracing functions may be used simultaneously to generate the desired complex surfaces. By coordinating the paths of the milling cutter and

tracing element, as determined by the master or model, a milling machine which is tracer-controlled may operate under one of the following systems: mechanical, manual hydraulic, manual electric, automatic hydraulic, automatic electric, electric-spark contact, or optical (light-beam, with electric-eye sensor) contact.

Nomenclature given to various types of tracing functions is illustrated in Fig. 11-16.

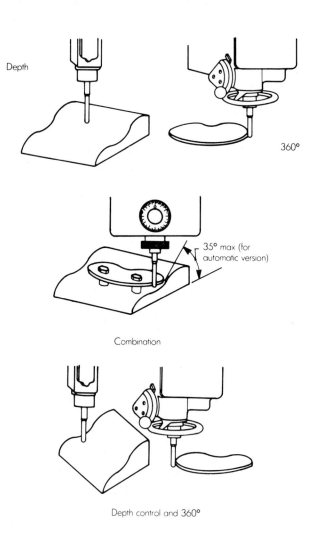

Figure 11-16 Four types of functions performed on tracer-controlled milling machines *(Courtesy of Cincinnati Milacron)*

Milling machines with depth-tracing functions are known as diesinkers and may have the following variations:

1. Power and hand feed to the machine slides, without feed-rate modifications to the feeding slides. The operator varies the feed rate by hand according to the contour of the master or model. These machines are known as hand diesinkers.
2. Power and hand feed to the machine slides, with feed-rate modification, automatic feed reversal, and pick feed or progression. Automatic feed-rate modification produces a constant feed rate between the cutter and the surface being generated. Machines with these features are known as automatic diesinkers. These machines may also be operated as hand diesinkers, making it possible to remove large amounts of material quickly when the workpiece is being roughed out.
3. Depth-tracing functions may also be arranged to use a roller following a template as the model. Feed rate to the table is automatically modified to maintain a constant feed rate between the cutter and the surface being generated. A variable-feed-rate attachment is also available for high-production jobs in which a great variation of stock is to be removed.

Programmable Milling Machines: Programmable milling machines feature pushbutton programming by means of manual data input (MDI). These machines bridge the gap between standard and NC milling machines. They provide the flexibility of many standard machines with the production capabilities of NC machines, without the need for NC coded part programming. Major applications of these machines include tool and die, prototype, and short-run operations, but they are used less frequently in shops that have programming capability for other machines. Programmable milling machines are available in horizontal- and vertical-spindle models (see Fig. 11-17).

NC/CNC Milling Machines: In addition to mechanical-electrical, mechanical-hydraulic, and mechanical-electrical-hydraulic controls, numerical

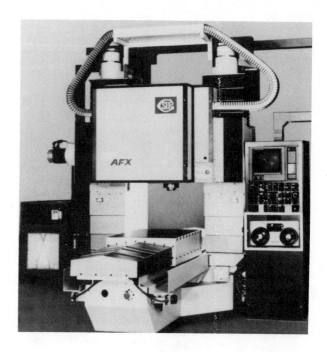

Figure 11-17 Programmable boring and milling machine *(Courtesy of American SIP Corporation)*

control and computer numerical control (NC/CNC) are being applied to milling and other machine tools requiring complex cycles. In some cases, both tracer and numerical control are provided with the option for NC or CNC retrofit at a later date. Automatic toolchangers are also available on some NC machines (particularly machining centers).

An NC/CNC milling machine provides control for at least two axes of simultaneous motion, with three or four axes under tape control being quite common. Some machines are provided with five or more axes under NC. In addition to the conventional longitudinal, transverse, and vertical movements, some machines have the column and spindle carrier mounted in circular swivel ways to permit the spindle to swivel in the horizontal and vertical planes. An NC/CNC system with continuous-path capabilities is desirable for most applications, and circular interpolation is frequently used when curved surfaces and contours are to be milled (see Fig. 11-18).

Figure 11-18   CNC milling machine *(Courtesy of Bridgeport Machine Division, Textron, Inc.)*

Special Milling Machines: In a general sense, a special milling machine is any milling machine designed and built to machine a specific part or family of parts. Usually a basic standard machine that is specially modified is considered a special milling machine if the modification results in approximately 50% or more change in the basic design.

Special milling machines can take the form of any of the standard milling machines, such as horizontal or vertical spindle, fixed bed, knee type, fixed or moving table, fixed or traveling column, ram type, or almost any other conceivable configuration. The type of machine control can also be highly varied. Controls from straight manual to direct computer control are available for special machines. Special milling machine configurations can vary considerably, depending upon the job for which the machine was designed.

Attachments for Milling Machines

Many different attachments are available for milling machines. Attachments are standard or special auxiliary devices intended to be fastened to or joined with one or more components of a milling machine to augment the range, versatility, productivity, or accuracy of operation. Some attachments are required to perform certain operations. These accessories may be cutter or workpiece holding and driving mechanisms. Attachments enable the cutting axis or the workpiece to be oriented differently or to be moved along specific geometric paths. Also, they may be precision measuring devices. The cutter holding and driving attachments are usually made to be used on standard horizontal knee-type machines.

Many attachments are built and offered by milling machine builders. However, the long existence and general acceptance of knee-and-column machines have made it possible for other suppliers to market attachable items for every well-known milling machine.

Vertical Milling Attachments: These attachments are used to convert horizontal machines to swivel-head vertical types. They permit the cutting-spindle axis to be oriented with reference to a graduated circular base and to be held in any angular position in the vertical plane parallel to the column face. One such attachment (see Fig. 11-19) is mounted against the column face and driven by the machine spindle. Quill-type and fixed spindles are available. Speeds are the same as the machine speeds or at some ratio to them.

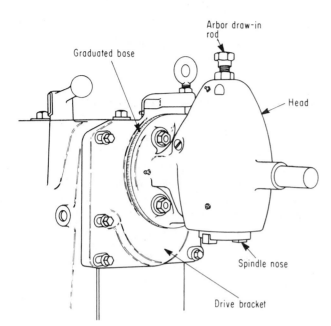

Figure 11-19 Swivel-head vertical milling attachment

Universal Milling Attachments: Similar to a swivel-head vertical attachment but having two swivel axes and associated graduated circular bases at right angles to one another, a universal milling attachment permits the cutting-spindle axis to be held at practically any angle. These attachments are made in a variety of sizes, spindle-speed ratios, spindle-nose tapers, and work capacities, with or without axially adjustable spindle quills.

High-Speed Milling Attachments: Such attachments are driven from the horizontal machine spindle with a speed ratio greater than 1:1, which makes it possible to operate small-diameter cutters at high speeds. Generally, the spindle head is extendable some distance across the table and may contain one or two swivel arrangements for angular milling.

Rack-Milling Attachments: This type of attachment is mounted on the machine column, is driven through gears by the machine spindle, and has a horizontal cutting-spindle axis at right angles to that of the machine. In conjunction with appropriate

form cutters and workholding means (usually a rack-milling vise and a rack-indexing attachment), this equipment permits racks or cross-slotted pieces of considerable length to be cut. A plain knee-type machine is used for straight racks, and a universal machine for slanted or skew racks.

Thread-Milling Attachments: This type of mechanism is similar to the rack-milling attachment, but it projects an adjustable distance from the column face so that the cutter is normally directly above the center of the swivel saddle of a universal knee-type machine. It uses thread-milling cutters in conjunction with a dividing head and lead attachment to produce any of the regular forms of external straight, tapered, or worm threads and many special threads, including internal threads when size limitations permit. An adjustable follower rest can be used when necessary on long workpieces. A universal milling attachment having sufficient clearance for this kind of work can also be used for milling threads on a plain knee-type machine.

Slotting Attachments: This equipment, mounted on the machine column and driven by the machine spindle, converts rotary motion into reciprocating motion of adjustable stroke length. The mechanism is mounted on a graduated circular swivel base, permitting reciprocating motion at any angle in the vertical plane parallel to the column face. One end of the sliding ram accepts single-point slotting tools of any practical form. Among other things, this attachment is used for cutting internal or external keyways, splines, serrations, blind holes, cavities, or gears, particularly in inaccessible locations such as those adjacent to large-diameter shoulders.

Crane and Parking Attachments: Much of the previously mentioned equipment is too heavy for a person to lift easily, or it creates a storage problem. To alleviate this situation, various parking attachments, attachment cranes, and parking brackets, which can be fastened to a machine either permanently or temporarily, are available. They facilitate the mounting or dismounting of a heavy attachment; or when the attachment is not in use, they store or park it someplace on the machine.

Rotary Tables: Rotary tables or circular-milling attachments, capable of rotary movement about a vertical axis, are made in a variety of diameters and may be manually or power driven. Manual drive with a handwheel and a graduated dial or an indexing unit enables an operator to position a workpiece for cuts at various angles or to index equal or unequal divisions of a circle in spacing or slotting operations. A rotary table, by virtue of its design, is rigid and can accommodate large workpieces. Power can be applied through a lead attachment in cutting a continuous spiral scroll or through a power-drive unit (which rotates the rotary table at various rates while the machine table remains stationary) in radii milling or continuous rotary milling. On CNC machines these attachments can often be controlled by a fourth axis or a shared third axis drive.

Arbors: Some cutters can be centered on and bolted directly to the spindle nose or if equipped with an integral tapered shank centered in the spindle-nose taper and held in place by a draw-in bolt. Cutter holders are discussed in a subsequent section of this chapter. However, many cutters (especially the peripheral-milling variety) cannot be held in this way and must be mounted on or in intermediate holding, locating, or adapting devices or arbors (see Fig. 11-20). Arbors are available in many diameters, lengths, styles, and standard spindle-nose tapers, the most commonly used being Nos. 40 and 50.

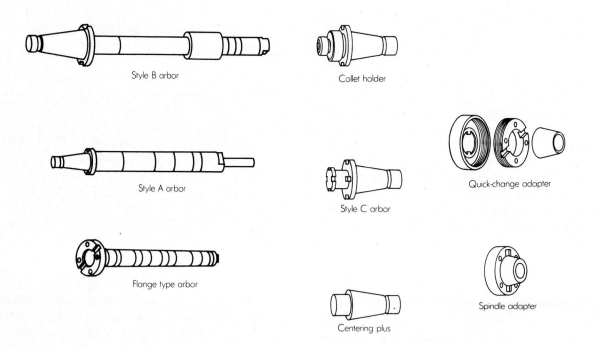

Style B arbor

Collet holder

Style A arbor

Quick-change adapter

Style C arbor

Flange type arbor

Spindle adapter

Centering plus

Figure 11-20 Arbors and adapters used on milling machines

Vises: Milling-machine vises (Fig. 11-21), keyed and bolted to the table, provide a convenient method of securely handling and accurately orienting a workpiece. Plain and swivel-type vises are commonly obtainable in 5, 6, 7, 8, and 9″ (127, 152, 178, 203, and 229 mm) nominal sizes, specified according to jaw length. Plain vises adapted for attachment to platens or for use as fixture parts are available, as well as cam-clamping vises. Universal or toolmaker's vises are made with either two or three swivel settings, permitting a workpiece to be set at any desired angle.

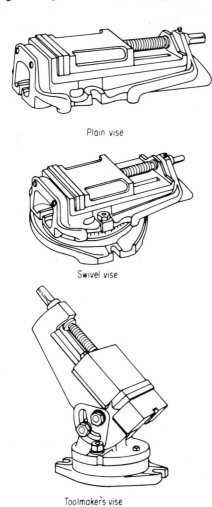

Plain vise

Swivel vise

Toolmaker's vise

Figure 11-21   Common types of vises used on milling machines

Rack-milling vises are used to hold relatively long slender workpieces and are usually used in conjunction with a rack-milling attachment for cutting racks or cross slots. Many simple workholding devices can be made by removing the vise jaws and modifying the flat surfaces to any desired shape for gripping or part orientation.

Index Bases: For production milling, an index base placed on the machine table can accommodate duplicate or progressive fixtures at each end. One fixture can be unloaded and reloaded during the cutting cycle. The index table is unclamped, pivoted 180°, and clamped in position by manual means or by power from electric, pneumatic, or hydraulic sources.

Chucks: Chucks in many styles and with various numbers of jaws are used to hold workpieces by gripping either an external or an internal cylindrical surface. They are mounted directly on the machine table, a rotary table, or a dividing head. Chucks also may be mounted with an adapter on a machine-spindle nose, for use in holding and rotating a workpiece which is to be turned or milled.

Safe Operating Procedures

The machine should be shut off and spindle rotation stopped before cutters are changed, inserts are indexed or changed, chips are removed, workpieces are loaded or unloaded, measurements are made, or hands are placed near the cutting zone for any reason. The work area should be kept clean and free of obstacles, and flammable materials should be removed from the area before beginning a milling operation.

Cutting fluids, if used for milling or cutter grinding, should be kept as clean as possible, and the chance of fire must be considered if oils are used. Adequate ventilation is also important.

GRINDING

Grinding is the most widely used single method of all the different categories of metalworking processes, when basing the comparison on the number of machine tools in use. In this respect, grinding exceeds even such basic processes as turning or drilling.

Grinding is an abrasive process, thereby distinguished from most other metalworking processes. These latter processes are considered metalcutting because they operate by removing chips from the worked metallic part by means of distinctly shaped cutting edges of the tool. Grinding, however, removes the work material by means of abrasive grains. These grains, although not having distinct edge forms, also penetrate into and remove workpiece material elements the, while irregular in size, resemble in their shapes that chips produced by material removal operations.

The often superior quality of the produced work surfaces and several other properties of ground parts have significant positive merit in many applications. The manufacturing engineer should consider abrasive methods as a potentially promising alternative to other methods. This is true even in applications beyond those for which grinding and other abrasive methods are now recognized as the proper or only feasible metalworking procedure.

Grinding Wheels and Discs

The proper selection of grinding wheels probably is the most important component of planning an efficient and economical grinding operation. The task of selecting the correct wheel or disc is made difficult by the fact that there are thousands of wheels and discs, each with specific characteristics. Charts and tables, such as those presented in subsequent sections of this chapter, provide guidelines for selecting a grinding wheel for the job at hand. For special applications and difficult-to-grind materials, it is best to work with the grinding wheel supplier. It is also advisable to maintain a good working relationship with the local representative to keep current with respect to new developments.

Wheel Composition

Grinding wheels and discs are composed of selectively sized abrasive grains held together by a bonding material. Five distinct elements must be considered when selecting a wheel for a specific application. These elements are:

1. Abrasive—the grinding agent used in the wheel. Chemical composition, physical properties, and particle shape affect performance.
2. Grain size—the particle size of the abrasive grains, which influences stock removal rate and surface finish generated.
3. Bond—the bonding materials that hold the abrasive grains together to form a grinding wheel. Chemical composition affects strength, resilience, and other physical properties of the wheel.
4. Grade—the strength of the grinding wheel, usually controlled by varying amount of bonding material. This is frequently referred to as the hardness of the wheel.
5. Structure—the proportion and arrangement of the abrasive grains and bond. The porosity of the grinding wheel is affected by both the structure and the grade.

Wheel Specification

A standard marking system, defined by the American National Standards Institute as ANSI Standard B74.13-1977, is used by all grinding wheel manufacturers. This marking system involves the use of letters or numbers in each of seven positions, as indicated in Fig. 11-22. When necessary to show special grain combinations, manufacturers may add an additional symbol to the regular grain-size number. A similar marking system is used by most grinding wheel manufacturers to designate diamond wheels and CBN wheels. This marking system involves the use of letters or numbers in each of seven positions, as indicated in Fig. 11-23.

Types of Grinding Wheels: Figure 11-24 illustrates the various shapes of standard peripheral

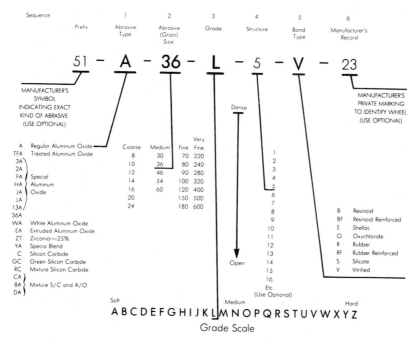

Figure 11-22 Standard bonded-abrasive wheel-marking system (ANSI Standard B74.13-1977)

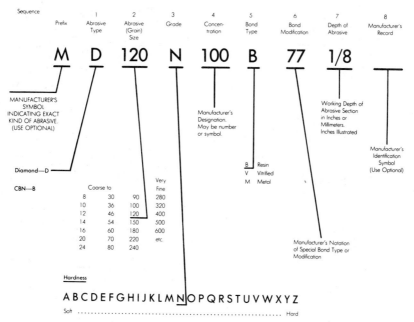

Figure 11-23 Wheel-marking system for diamond and cubic boron nitride wheels (ANSI Standard B74.13-1977)

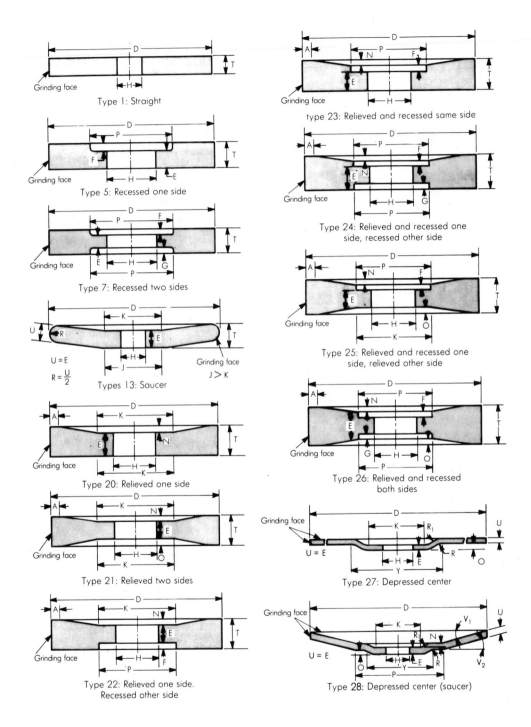

Figure 11-24   Standard shapes of peripheral grinding wheels (ANSI Standard B74.2-1974)

grinding wheels in use today. Missing numbers in this list of standard shapes pertain to wheel geometries that have been dropped in standards but are usually available as specials. Figure 11-25 illustrates the various shapes of standard side or face grinding wheels in use today.

Wheel Balance

Particular attention is needed to make sure that a wheel is in balance before it is used for grinding. Balance is not entirely dependent on the wheel itself, but is also affected by the machine spindle and the means of tightening the wheel on the machine. Consequently, the machine/wheel system should be in balance before the wheel is operated.

An out-of-balance wheel sets up excessive vibration, produces faster wheel breakdown, poor finishes, or chatter and can be dangerous. Wheels generally should be statically balanced before putting them on the machine. They then should be dressed into concentricity, taken off, rebalanced, and put on the grinder and operated. Today equipment is available that will balance the wheel while it is running on the machine.

Trueing and Dressing Wheels

Trueing means removal of abrasive material from the cutting face of the wheel so that the OD will run concentric with the ID. It also means bringing the sides of the wheel parallel to each other and perpendicular to the spindle. *Dressing* means removing the glaze from a dull wheel, removing loaded material from the face, restoring a wheel to its original geometry, and conditioning the wheel to do a specific job. Grinding

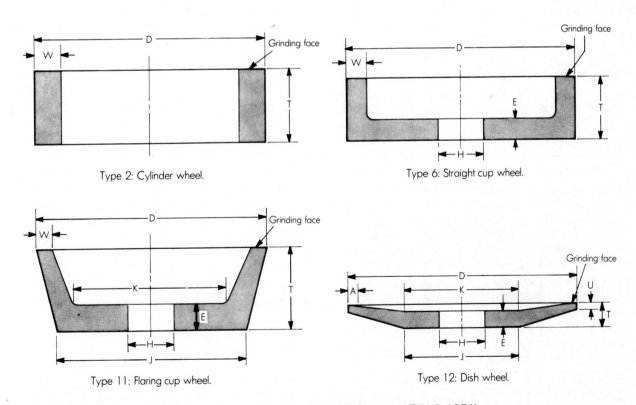

Type 2: Cylinder wheel.

Type 6: Straight cup wheel.

Type 11: Flaring cup wheel.

Type 12: Dish wheel.

Figure 11-25   Standard side or face grinding wheels (ANSI Standard B74.2-1974)

wheels can be made to act harder and finer, or softer and coarser, by means of wheel conditioning.

Kinds of wheel dressers available include metal cutters, abrasive sticks, abrasive wheels, single-point diamonds, single-set and matrix diamond dressers, rotary and stationary diamond rolls, and crushing rolls. Each has specific advantages in its field of usage.

Grinding Wheel Safety

Grinding wheels and machines should always be used in accordance with guidelines and mandatory regulations of the Occupational Safety and Health Act of 1970 (OSHA). Grinding operations, which are covered in Section 1910 Subparts O and P of the act, are based on ANSI Standards B7.1-1978 and B11.9-1975. These standards should be consulted for detailed recommendations not covered specifically in the act.

Wheel Guarding: State and federal safety regulations mandate that, with few exceptions, safety guards must be used on grinding machines. Surveys show unguarded grinding wheels to be the most violated safety regulation and one of OSHA's top 20 citations. Unfortunately, the numerous grinding wheel injuries that have occurred could have been prevented had the wheel been properly guarded.

Abrasive wheels, 2″ (50 mm) diam and smaller, attached to steel mandrels do not require guarding. Since the abrasive portion of the mounted wheel is basically a solid mass (except for the shallow recess in one side to accept the mandrel), the ultimate centrifugal bursting strength of the abrasive is quite high and usually exceeds the critical speed of a steel mandrel. ANSI B7.1 lists the standard mounted wheel maximum speed at 10,000 sfm (51 m/s), provided the strength of the steel shank and overhang are adequate.

Of course, other protective equipment such as goggles, face shields, and protective clothing are positive ways to guard against flying sparks and swarf.

Grinding Fluids

Many fluid formulations used to cool and lubricate cutting operations are also used to perform similar functions in grinding operations. However, the grinding process by its nature exhibits several unique characteristics which make it significantly different from conventional cutting processes. For this reason, special considerations must be given to the functions, selection, and use of grinding fluids.

Functions of Grinding Fluids

Grinding fluids perform virtually the same functions as cutting fluids. They lubricate the chip/grit and grit/workpiece interfaces, reducing the power required to remove a given volume of material and thereby reducing the heat generated in the grinding operation. Secondly, they cool and prevent or minimize heat buildup in the parts being ground.

In metalcutting the energy necessary to deform metal to form a chip is approximately twice that required to overcome friction between the tool/workpiece and the chip/workpiece interfaces. In grinding, the force necessary to overcome friction is approximately the same as that necessary for chip formation. Consequently, friction forces are much more important in grinding than in cutting, making lubrication in grinding critical, not only from the standpoint of power, wheel life, and surface finish, but also in relation to heat development and possible damage to the ground surface.

Grinding Machines and Fixtures

There are numerous types of grinding machines and fixtures to go with them. The more widely used are those that perform the following types of grinding: cylindrical grinding, center hole grinding, jig grinding, high-speed grinding, and deep and creep-feed grinding.

Cylindrical Grinding

Cylindrical grinding is performed to remove stock, create precise geometry, and obtain desired surface finishes on external or internal surfaces of round workpieces. The term cylindrical grinding generally refers to outside diameter (OD) grinding. Internal grinding generally is the term used to refer to the grinding of the internal surfaces, or internal diameter (ID), of workpieces. These surfaces (OD or ID) are usually cylinders, shoulders, or tapers, but they may include fillets, grooves, or other formed surfaces of revolution.

A special type of external cylindrical grinder, the thread grinder, produces precise helical surfaces. Another special grinder called a roll grinder produces crowned cylinders with mirror finishes.

Workholding Methods in Cylindrical Grinding: The most commonly used workholding devices for general-purpose cylindrical grinding are centers, chucks, mandrels, collets, and faceplates (see Figs. 11-26, 11-27, and 11-28).

Cylindrical grinding fixtures are similar in design to lathe turning fixtures. There are, however, several unique features of grinding that must be considered when designing a cylindrical grinding fixture. These considerations include the following:

1. Since grinding is essentially a finishing operation when dimensions are held to very close tolerances, accuracy of the fixture is a prime concern.
2. In most cases only a relatively small amount of material is removed; consequently, grinding fixtures do not require the bulk characteristics of machining fixtures.
3. Locating parts properly is very important. However, since most parts to be ground have already been machined, a relatively accurate surface should be available to hold and locate the part.

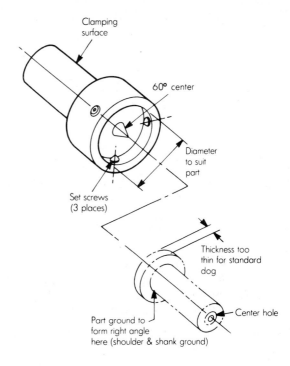

Figure 11-26   Grinding fixture for parts to be mounted between the workhead center and the center in the fixture

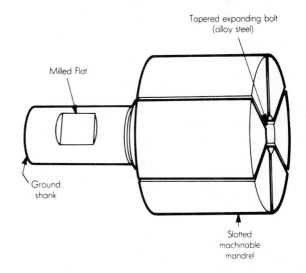

Figure 11-27   Expansion mandrel for use in either a chuck or collet

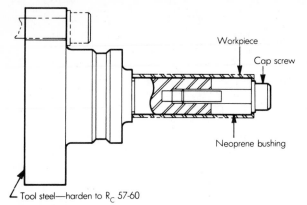

Tool steel—harden to R_C 57-60

Figure 11-28 Nut mandrel for thin-walled workpieces

4. Thin workpieces cannot be permitted to deflect during grinding. If necessary, auxiliary work supports (steady rests, etc.) must sometimes be used in addition to the fixture to prevent distortion.

5. Heat build-up should be controlled with a proper application of fluid.

6. Grinding fluid nozzles should be selected to deliver a large volume of fluid with minimum pressure. The contact line between wheel and work must be well flooded with fluid.

7. Fixtures must be designed to permit easy removal of fluid and sludge. All pockets in which these materials can accumulate must be eliminated or the balance of the fixture could easily be affected.

8. Fluid nozzles should never inhibit the movement or operation of the fixture.

9. Wheel dressing and trueing should be performed without removing the fixture or without seriously reducing the grinding time.

10. Fixtures that are intended to rotate must be balanced. If the fixture cannot be balanced internally, an auxiliary counterweight must be selected and positioned to ensure dynamic balance.

Fixtures used for cylindrical grinding are normally classified by the grinding process they perform or by the type of grinding machine with which they are used. In addition, fixtures may also be classified by their basic construction characteristics.

Center Hole Grinding

The accuracy of center-type turning and grinding operations is heavily dependent upon the accuracy of the workpiece centers. Rough machining or grinding operations in which accuracy is not particularly critical may require only drilled center holes. However, in precision operations, center holes must be ground accurately. For example, grinding of center holes may be required after heat treating because heat treating of workpieces may seriously distort center holes and the resulting oxidation and scale may create location problems in precision operations.

Properly ground centers must be round and ground at the precise angle. A true conical form must be generated, and the surfaces of the center hole must be free of ridges for proper location. In addition, concentricity is an important consideration (see Fig. 11-29).

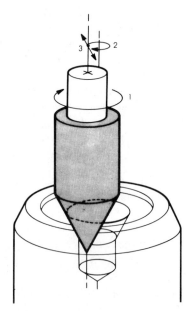

Figure 11-29 Center holes ground on generation-type grinders

Jig Grinding

Jig grinding machines (Fig. 11-30) were originally designed to grind holes accurately to size and to coordinate location in hardened steel, as required for the manufacturing of press tools. These machines utilize the same principles of rectilinear-positioning control employed in jig borers. They are commonly used as companion machines to the jig borer. Modern jig grinders can generate vertical surfaces contoured in the X-Y plane as well as internal and external diameters.

Jig grinding machines differ from jig borers in that the machine spindle is replaced by a more complex unit offering the following capabilities:

1. Means for adjusting the radial offset of the grinding spindle to accommodate various diameters or radii.
2. Provisions to drive the grinding spindle in a planetary orbit at controlled speeds.
3. Fine adjustment of the radial offset engineered to function while the main machine spindle is operating.
4. An automatic vertical reciprocating feed motion for the grinding spindle with provisions for control of its rate and traverse range.

Figure 11-30   Numerical control grinding machine *(Courtesy of Cone/Blanchard Machine Co.)*

5. Means for generating the vertical surfaces of workpieces at set angles, producing tapered diameters and contoured surfaces as required for clearance in press tools.
6. Provisions for controlling the angular direction of the planetary offset for the grinding spindle relative to the machine's slide motion.
7. An engineered system for transmitting and controlling power to the machine spindle and the grinding wheel, both simultaneously and independently.
8. Provisions for interchanging a variety of grinding spindles as required for universal application.

Particular attention is given in the design of the jig grinder to provide protection for the vital components of the machine from the harmful effects of abrasive particles produced while operating.

High-Speed Grinding

The theory of high-speed grinding, a relative newcomer to metalworking, suggests that, under certain conditions, grinding wheel speeds can be increased significantly beyond normal wheel speeds to effect proportional increases in material removal rates without significant changes in chip geometry, grinding forces, energy required per unit volume of material removed, surface finish, or residual stresses in the workpiece. The theory of high-speed grinding dictates that dressing the grinding wheel can be used to control normal grinding force, surface finish, and wheel wear.

Deep and Creep-Feed Grinding

Creep-feed grinding originated in Europe in about 1958, when the first prototype creep-feed grinder was developed by ELB-Schliff of West Germany. Within five years, several production-type creep-feed grinding applications surfaced. Today, several machine tool builders, both domestic and overseas, offer special creep-feed grinding machines. Particular interest recently has been centered around creep-feed machines which feature both conventional grinding and creep-feed capabilities.

Creep-feed grinding is generally used to describe a surface grinding operation performed in a single pass with an unusually large depth of cut. The term deep grinding is used in Europe to describe creep-feed operations in external cylindrical grinding such as tool, thread, and gear grinding.

Generally, the creep-feed grinding process is marked by a special mode of operation. As illustrated in Fig. 11-31 in contrast to the conventional grinding technique, the depth of cut per pass or revolution is increased 1000-10,000 times and the work speed is decreased in the same proportion. Thus, it is possible to grind profiles with a depth of 1.0-30.0 mm (0.04-1.2″) or more in one pass, using work speeds from 0.25-0.75 m/min (9.8-30 ipm), and to reduce machining times 50-80%. Figures 11-32, 11-33, and 11-34 are examples of modern grinding machines.

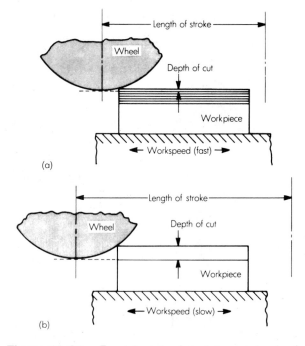

Figure 11-31   Feed, length of stroke, and depth of cut for a) conventional surface grinding; and b) creep-feed grinding

Figure 11-32   Modern grinding machine *(Courtesy of Litton Industrial Automation Systems)*

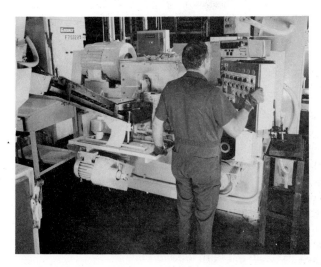

Figure 11-33   Modern grinding machine
(Courtesy of Litton Industrial Automation Systems)

Figure 11-34   Reciprocating gun-type grinding
machine *(Courtesy of Litton Industrial Automation
Systems)*

KEY TERMS AND PHRASES

Abrasive
Arbors
Bed-type milling machine
Bond
Cam milling
Center-hole grinding
Chucks
CNC milling machine
Crane attachments
Crankshaft milling
Cutting speed
Cylindrical grinding
Deep and creep-feed grinding
Diesinking
Dressing
End milling
End mills
Face milling
Face mills
Feed force
Fixed-bed saddle-type machine
Form milling cutter
Gang milling
Gear milling
Grade
Grain size
Grinding
Grinding fluid
Hand-fed milling machine
High-speed grinding
High-speed milling attachments
Index bases
Jig grinding
Knee-and-column milling machine
Peripheral milling
Plain milling cutter
Planetary milling
Plunge milling
Rack-milling attachments
Rotary tables
Shank-type cutters

Shaped profile cutter
Shell mills
Side milling cutter
Slotting attachments
Spindle power
Straddle milling
Structure
Thread milling
Thread-milling attachments
Tracer-controller milling machine
Trueing
Universal milling attachments
Vertical milling attachments
Vises
Wheel balance

QUESTIONS FOR ADDITIONAL STUDY AND REVIEW

1. Describe the following milling processes:
   - Peripheral milling
   - Face milling

2. Describe the following related milling methods:
   - End milling
   - Side milling
   - Gear milling
   - Cam milling
   - Plunge milling
   - Diesinking

3. Explain four factors affecting power requirements for milling machines. p266~267

4. Explain the term *feed force.*

5. Explain the relationship between *speed* and *feed.*

6. Describe the following milling cutter styles:

    • Plain cutter
    • Form cutter
    • Side cutter
    • Shaped profile cutters
    • Face mill
    • End mill

7. Explain how shell mills are mounted.

8. Describe the following types of milling machines:

    • Hand-fed
    • Knee-and-column
    • Bed-type
    • Fixed-bed saddle-type
    • Tracer controlled
    • Programmable
    • CNC

9. What is a *rotary table*?

10. What is an *arbor*?

11. Explain the five elements used in selecting grinding wheels.   P 284

12. What problems will an out-of-balance grinding wheel cause?

13. Describe the process of trueing and dressing grinding wheels.

14. What functions do grinding fluids serve?

15. Describe the following grinding processes:

    • Cylindrical grinding
    • Center-hole grinding
    • High-speed grinding
    • Deep and creep-feed grinding

CHAPTER 12

Nontraditional Machining

MAJOR TOPICS COVERED

- Hydrodynamic Machining
- Ultrasonic Machining
- Rotary Ultrasonic Machining
- Ultrasonically Assisted Machining
- Electromechanical Machining
- Electrochemical Grinding
- Electrochemical Honing
- Hone-Forming
- Electrochemical Machining
- Shaped Tube Electrolytic Machining
- Electron Beam Machining
- Electrical Discharge Machining
- Electrical Discharge Wire Cutting
- Electrical Discharge Grinding
- Laser Beam Machining
- Plasma Arc Machining
- Chemical Milling
- Photochemical Machining
- Nontraditional Machining of Nonmetals

The designation "nontraditional machining" is applied to a wide variety of mechanical, electrical, thermal, and chemical material removal processes developed mostly after about 1940. These alternate manufacturing processes have evolved in response to increasing demands in industry for better, more consistent workpiece quality and higher production efficiency in the processing of hard, tough materials,

workpieces with unusual finishing requirements, and parts with complex shapes that require processing beyond the normal capabilities of the traditional machining processes.

Originally, the nontraditional machining designation was applied to emerging processes or to processes that have not been used extensively heretofore. Today, however, this definition is somewhat misleading. Although many of the nontraditional machining processes were conceived and developed to solve special processing problems in the aerospace industry in the late 1950s and 1960s, today, many of these same processes have found wide application in varied industries over a broad range of production jobs.

Nontraditional machining, as a classification of manufacturing operations, includes literally scores of processes; some are applied on a large scale, while others are not much more than laboratory curiosities. The purpose of this chapter is to present a discussion of the more commonly used nontraditional machining processes as well as a discussion of those processes which hold the most promise of increased usage. In this chapter, treatment is limited to nontraditional processes which offer an alternative to traditional mechanical or abrasive removal processes. Only brief treatment for definitive purposes is given to the many other nontraditional machining processes that are not fully developed for production use, are proprietary, or are applied in extremely isolated instances.

In general, nontraditional machining processes are characterized by higher power consumption as a function of material removal rate as compared with traditional machining processes. Although notable exceptions exist, the stock removal rate of nontraditional machining processes is usually less than that attainable with conventional machining techniques. In most nontraditional machining processes, however, increased throughput is of secondary concern. Rather, users select a unique machining approach to overcome the problems that an unusual part configuration might present to traditional methods. In addition, experience has shown that many nontraditional processes can successfully contribute to special surface integrity in the areas of surface roughness, maximum depth of plastic deformation, hardness alteration, cracks, residual stress, recrystallization, metallurgical transformations, heat-affected zones, etc. Nontraditional machining processes are typically employed when conventional methods are incapable, impractical, or uneconomical because of special material properties, workpiece complexities, or lack of inherent rigidity.

Mechanical Processes

The purpose of this section is to provide an overview of the various nontraditional machining processes that use mechanical energy as the primary source of energy for material removal. These mechanical processes include: Hydrodynamic machining (HDM), Ultrasonic machining (USM), Rotary ultrasonic machining (RUM), Ultrasonically assisted machining (UAM), and Electromechanical machining (EMM).

Hydrodynamic Machining (HDM)

Hydrodynamic machining removes workpiece material and produces a narrow kerf by the cutting action of a fine, high-pressure (usually up to 60 ksi,

414 MPa), high-velocity stream of water or water-based fluid with additives. A lower pressure (usually about 250 psi, 1.7 MPa) version of the process called water jet machining (WJM) is used primarily as a deburring or finishing process.

In HDM, the water used for cutting is pressurized by a hydraulically powered intensifier. An accumulator is used to eliminate pulsation as shown in Fig. 12-1. The relationship between nozzle and workpiece in HDM is illustrated in Fig. 12-2. View *a* defines the standoff distance, penetration depth, and rake angle. View *b* shows the configuration of positive rake in relation to nozzle feed.

Applications: HDM is effective in slitting and contour cutting many nonmetallic materials, such as wood and paper, asbestos, plastics, gypsum, leather, felt, rubber, nylon, fiberglass, and fiberglass-reinforced plastics. Some very thin workpieces of soft metal can be cut effectively by the process; steel sheet (0.005", 0.13 mm thick) and aluminum sheet (0.020", 0.51 mm thick) are processed, but water pressure in excess of 100 ksi (690 MPa) is usually required. Equipment that operates at these higher pressures is not commercially available. The cutting of hard metals using HDM remains mostly experimental.

Practical experience and experimental research has shown that, in some cases, brittle materials such as glass, acrylic, ceramics, and crystal do not appear suitable for cutting by the HDM process because

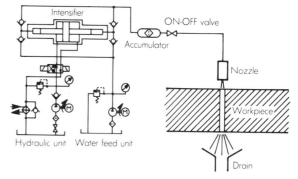

Figure 12-1   Hydrodynamic machining (HDM) operation

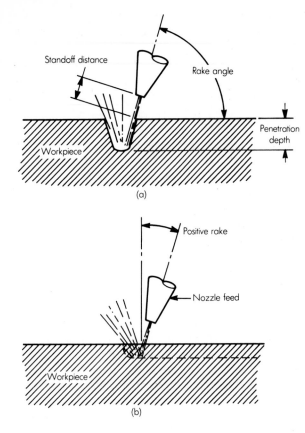

Figure 12-2 Relationship of nozzle and workpiece in HDM

which workpiece material is removed and an exact shape is imparted to the workpiece surface via the cutting action of an abrasive slurry that is driven by a tool vibrating at high frequency in line with its longitudinal axis. As shown in Fig. 12-3, the cutting tool is attached to a vibrating horn. The tool is shaped in the exact configuration to be ground in the workpiece. In this way, the vibration of the tool forces the cutting action of the abrasive grits in the slurry. The slurry is recirculated in the space between the tool and workpiece. In most applications, the slurry is automatically cooled in the recirculation cycle.

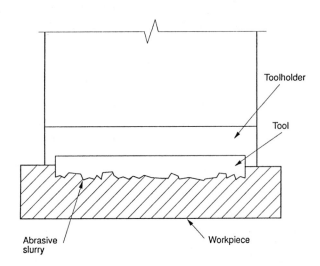

Figure 12-3 Magnified view of tool/workpiece configuration in USM

these materials tend to develop severe cracks and may break under processing conditions.

Typically, soft materials are cut easily using HDM, and friable materials can be cut with good edge quality.

At its present stage of development, the industrial use of HDM is limited to the processing of relatively thin materials. When thicker materials are cut, stream lines increase significantly causing poor edge quality.

Ultrasonic Machining (USM)

Ultrasonic machining, sometimes called ultrasonic abrasive machining or impact machining, is a mechanical nontraditional machining process by

Applications: USM is used to produce blind and through holes, slots, and irregular shapes, limited in complexity only by the configuration of the tooling. However, in some applications, tool wear and/or taper in the cut may discount the process's effectiveness. Depth-to-width ratio of the cut is usually less than about 3:1. Current practice is limited to 3.5″ (89 mm) diam tools machining cavities up to about 2.5″ (64 mm) deep.

Rotary Ultrasonic Machining (RUM)

Rotary ultrasonic machining consists of several similar types of nontraditional machining processes in which tools rotating at high speeds (up to about 5000 rpm) and vibrating axially at high frequency (about 20 kHz) are used to effect drilling, cutting, milling, or threading operations on difficult-to-work materials. There are three primary differences between rotary ultrasonic machining (RUM) and ultrasonic machining (USM): (1) RUM drives the tool with a dual motion—axial, high-frequency vibration and axial rotation (in some RUM operations the workpiece is revolved to effect the rotary motion)—while USM employs only high-frequency vibration at the tool; (2) RUM uses diamond tools while USM employs tools made of tough, ductile materials such as steel or Monel; and (3) RUM uses the abrasive properties of the diamond tool to remove stock while USM uses the tool to drive an abrasive slurry which actually performs the cutting; in this way, the tools used for cutting in RUM actually contact the workpiece while the tools used in USM only drive the slurry— no actual tool/workpiece contact is made.

Applications: The applications of RUM are currently limited by tool size. The horn/tool assembly must have a resonant (natural) frequency of about 20 kHz, so tool size is limited. Any variance in tool weight changes the natural frequency of the horn/ tool assembly; too heavy a tool increases horn/tool assembly frequency beyond the resonant frequency of the transducer and power supply causing the tool not to vibrate. Today, the largest vibrating horn feasible is about 1.5″ (38 mm) diam. Practical limit to tool weight is about 1.4 oz (40 g).

RUM is used widely in prototype work as well as production applications. The process is effective in producing prototypes because it can make precise parts which can be used to make molds for large-volume production runs.

The process is particularly effective in the machining of sintered materials such as ceramic and ferrites. Conventionally, these materials are machined and drilled in the "green" state—prior to firing. When fired, the materials experience as much as 16% shrinkage which destroys the accuracy created during machining. RUM is used to machine materials such as these after firing and close tolerance relationships are maintained. Some applications include the machining of precision ceramic components, drilling small holes in ceramic printed circuit boards, and drilling small-diameter, deep, intersecting holes in quartz for laser development.

Other applications of RUM include machining precision glass components, nuclear reactor materials, laboratory glassware, ferrite computer parts, plasma-sprayed coatings, and drilling composite aircraft skins. In the electronics field, RUM is used to successfully drill aluminum substrates for microelectronic circuits.

Drilling. RUM is used in drilling small-diameter, deep holes in extremely hard materials. With traditional tooling used on these materials, the drill sometimes wanders making it difficult to closely control hole straightness. In addition, traditional drilling of hard materials often requires backoff of the tool to allow cutting fluid, which is fed through the tool's center, to flush away chips. This procedure is eliminated through the use of RUM; consequently, RUM can significantly improve accuracy and eliminate the time required for tool backoff. The axial ultrasonic vibrations of the diamond drill reduce the friction between the tool and workpiece to provide faster and smoother cutting, eliminate binding, and enable cutting at lighter tool pressures. The combination of reduced friction and lower tool pressure increases tool life and permits machining of delicate components without cracking. Also, shelling at the points of tool entry and breakthrough are minimized. Figure 12-4 shows the relative improvement in drilling time and the number of holes drilled using RUM versus conventional drilling without ultrasonics.

Core drilling. Hard materials can also be core drilled to attain deep holes using RUM. With traditional core-drilling methods, cores sometimes jam in the base of the tool, especially in deep-hole drilling operations. If this occurs, the machine must be

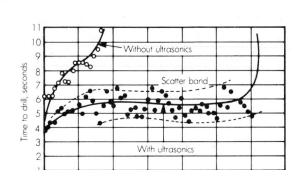

Figure 12-4   Improvements in drilling time using rotary ultrasonic drilling (RUM)

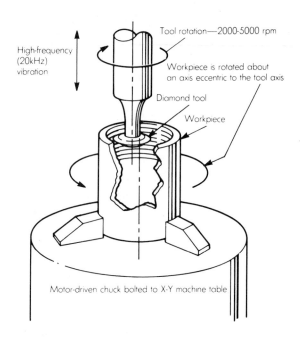

Figure 12-5   Internal threading using RUM

stopped and the tool must be extracted so that the core can be removed. This is less of a problem with RUM because the diamond tool is ultrasonically vibrated, and even in extremely deep holes, the core is generally left loose in the hole after the drill is withdrawn. It has been reported that the use of RUM in core drilling operations produces an increase in cutting efficiency, allowing hard materials to be cut faster than is possible by conventional means.

Milling. RUM is used to machine hard materials using special diamond milling cutters. Successful operations have been performed on both vertical and horizontal-spindle machines. The use of RUM in milling operations is not as prevalent as in drilling operations, however.

Internal threading. As shown in Fig. 12-5, internal threading using RUM is performed on materials of extreme hardness. For internal threading, the workpiece must be rotated about an axis eccentric to the tool axis. The tool remains stationary except for axial vibration and rotation. For these applications, the tool must be smaller in diameter than the bore to be threaded. The diamond tool must be larger in diameter than the tool shank. Generally, the shank should be greater than about 3/32″ (2.4 mm) diam to withstand side forces during cutting and to withstand stresses generated by ultrasonic vibration.

External threading. When RUM is used for external threading, the horn/tool assembly is rotated about 2000-5000 rpm and is vibrated at high frequency—about 20 kHz, as shown in Fig. 12-6. The tool remains stationary except for these motions. The workpiece is mounted on an X-Y machine table and is rotated at up to 4 rpm. In this way, the movements of the table are used to effect the generation process for thread formation. The workpiece is raised or lowered one thread width for each revolution of the chuck motor. Thread depth is controlled by adjusting the distance between the tool axis and chuck axis.

Ultrasonically Assisted Machining (UAM)

Ultrasonically assisted machining consists of coupling an outside source of vibrating energy to the standard drills or toolholders and insert assemblies that are used in traditional machining processes such as drilling and turning. UAM has evolved over the

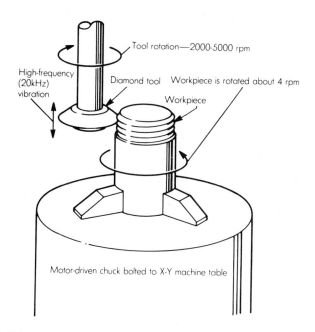

Figure 12-6   External threading using RUM

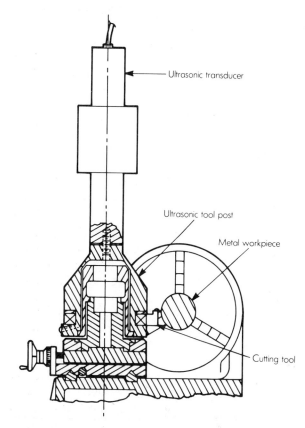

Figure 12-7   Typical setup for ultrasonically assisted lathe turning *(Courtesy of Sonobond Corp.)*

last several years in response to the need for increased cutting quality and speed in the processing of hard, tough materials. The characteristic that distinguishes UAM from other nontraditional processes which employ ultrasonic vibratory energy is that UAM is traditional in every way except that the vibratory energy is applied to the tool bit to enhance the ability of traditional machining processes. Since no special tools or cutting fluid is required, with the proper acoustic interface, traditional drilling machines and lathes are readily adaptable for ultrasonic assistance with a minimal capital expenditure.

Ultrasonic Lathe Turning: Under certain conditions, ultrasonic lathe turning (Fig. 12-7) has been shown to increase cutting rates by factors of four in aluminum, two to three in 9310, 4340, 17-4 PH steel and in 6A1-4V and Ti-3A1 titanium alloys, and five in cutting ESR 4340 steel. Nonmetallic materials have also shown marked increases in cutting rates when UAM is used. Alumina can be machined two times faster, and magnesium silicate can be machined up to four times faster in some cases, according to manufacturers of UAM equipment.

Some materials that are too brittle to machine traditionally can be machined effectively with UAM. For example, in one test, low-porosity mullite was machined with a good cut by applying ultrasonic vibrations to the tool post and carbide-tipped tool, but when ultrasonic power was turned off, the workpiece immediately shattered.

Some tests have shown that UAM reduces turning forces in some materials as much as 30-50% as compared to traditional turning methods. In the same tests, it was shown that surfaces produced by UAM exhibited a matte finish, evidence of more complete shearing of the chips from the workpiece. This phenomenon is in sharp contrast to traditional machining which often produces a glossy surface as a result of tearing, material enfoldment, and burnishing. Subsurface tearing and plastic flow are reported to be all but eliminated by UAM.

Ultrasonic Gundrilling:

A traditional gundrill consists of a single, V-shaped cutting tool brazed onto a single, fluted shank with an oil hole and a driver with a spindle adaptor or a stationary holder. One pass of the gundrill through the workpiece produces an accurate hole of high tolerance and finish.

During army-sponsored tests, an ultrasonic system was installed on a Pratt and Whitney deep-hole gundrill used for drilling 30-caliber machine gun barrels comprised of 4340 steel. Ultrasonically assisted drilling increased the production rate by 3.7 without sacrificing the concentricity adherence, surface finish, tool life, or chip formation. The surface finish found on the ultrasonically drilled barrels was comparable to the finish experienced on the conventionally drilled barrels produced at the lower feed rate. Similarly, the tool life experienced on the ultrasonically assisted drill bit was comparable to the tool life found on the traditional setup drilled at the reduced feed rate. Figure 12-8 illustrates a setup for ultrasonically assisted gundrilling.

Ultrasonic Twist Drilling:

In twist drilling applications, UAM has been shown to reduce thrust and torque in some cases. Thrust reductions of 30% were experienced when copper and cast iron were drilled, and 54% when titanium was drilled. Torque reductions of 25% were experienced for mild steel, 50% for titanium, and 65% for aluminum alloys.

Chip packing is said to be less of a problem when UAM is used in twist drilling applications. For this reason, periodic retraction of the drill is not required as frequently as in traditional drilling. For example, drill depth in titanium is normally limited to two to four times the drill diameter; with UAM, depths up to eight times the diameter have been successfully obtained without drill retraction. Depths of 20 times the drill diameter have been achieved before drill retraction when aluminum was drilled using UAM techniques [⅛″ (3.2 mm) holes drilled to a depth of 2.5″ (63 mm)].

Experiments indicate that the tool wear on ultrasonically assisted drill bits exhibit a different wear pattern than on conventionally powered drill bits. After equivalent periods of ultrasonic and nonultrasonic cutting, traditionally applied bits were worn at the outer periphery while drills applied with ultrasonics were worn evenly along the cutting edge.

Electromechanical Machining (EMM)

Electromechanical machining is an experimental nontraditional process that enhances the capabilities of traditional machining operations such as drilling and turning. Metal removal is effected in a conventional manner using standard equipment and tooling except that the workpiece is electrochemically polarized. A controlled voltage is applied across the interface of the workpiece and an electrolyte. In drilling operations, the workpiece is submerged in a bath of electrolyte; in turning operations, the surface of the workpiece is flooded with electrolyte.

The principle of EMM is that when the applied voltage is closely controlled and the electrolytic solu-

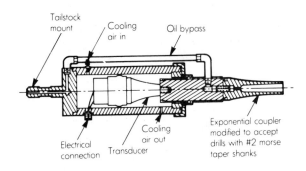

Figure 12-8   Ultrasonically assisted gundrilling equipment *(Courtesy of Sonobond Corp.)*

tion is matched to the workpiece material, the surface of the workpiece can be changed to achieve favorable characteristics which will enhance machining performance. When the variables in the process are controlled, the workpiece surface can be changed from passive (oxide film on the surface) to active dissolution (surface being slowly dissolved) to hydrogen reduction (surface is discharging hydrogen ions).

The theory behind EMM is that relatively soft and work-hardenable materials are more easily cut when the work surface is passive. In this state, the workpiece surface is hardened by the presence of oxide film which also minimizes cutting friction. On the other hand, hard materials are more easily cut when the workpiece surface is in the active dissolution region in which the material is softened.

EMM is considered to be in the early stages of development. The limited feasibility of electromechanical turning (EMT) and electromechanical drilling (EMD) has been demonstrated in both laboratory and plant settings. The limited testing conducted to date indicates advantages of surface finish, tool wear, hole tolerance, and chip configuration. However, maximum improvement is tied closely to the optimization of electrolytes, and it has been shown that the electrolytes should be modified through the use of inhibitors to minimize corrosion of machine tool components.

Electrical Processes

The purpose of this section is to provide an overview of the various nontraditional machining processes that use electrical energy as the primary source of energy for material removal. These electrical processes are sometimes called electrochemical or electrolytic processes because chemical fluids (electrolytes) are used in combination with electrical energy to effect a "cutting" action.

Electrochemical Discharge Grinding (ECDG)

Electrochemical discharge grinding, sometimes called electrochemical discharge machining (ECDM), is a combination of two processes: electrochemical grinding (ECG) and electrical discharge grinding (EDG).

In ECDG, a-c or pulsating d-c is passed from a conductive "wheel" made of bonded graphite to a positively charged workpiece. Electrolyte is pumped between the gap. No mechanical contact is made between the workpiece and wheel, although some separation force is developed as a result of the electrolyte being compressed in the gap between the wheel and workpiece. With ECDG, most of the workpiece material is removed by the action of ECG: The oxides that form as a result of this process are removed effectively by the intermittent random-spark discharges of EDG (see Fig. 12-9). Relatively high-amperage, low-voltage current is employed in the process.

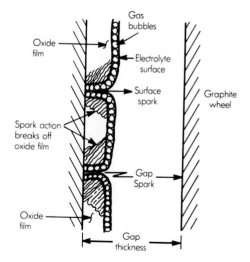

Figure 12-9   Electrochemical discharge grinding (ECDG)

Applications: The production uses of ECDG are somewhat limited although certain applications exist that are routinely performed, mostly in the grinding and sharpening of carbide tooling. Nearly any electrically conductive material can be processed, but careful comparison of the relative advantages and disadvantages of ECDG versus processes such as ECG and EDG should be made before specifying the process. For example, ECDG can remove material five times faster than EDG, but uses up to 15 times the current used in EDG. Typical production tolerances of ± 0.001″ (0.03 mm) are achieved with ECDG.

Current successful applications of the process include grinding and sharpening of carbide inserts, generation of delicate profiles using form grinding, grinding of honeycomb materials, and grinding of carbide thread chasers.

Electrochemical Grinding (ECG)

A special form of electrochemical machining, electrochemical grinding employs the combined actions of electrochemical attack and abrasion to rapidly remove material from electrically conductive workpieces, usually hard, tough materials.

The operating principles of ECG are the same as those of ECM except that ECG employs a rotating grinding wheel. Direct current is passed through an electrolyte which is pumped in a small gap, about 0.001″ (0.03 mm), between the wheel (cathode) and workpiece (anode). In ECG, the majority (95-98%) of the material is removed by electrochemical attack; significantly less (2-5%) of the workpiece material is removed by the abrasive action of the wheel. The protruding abrasive particles in the wheel serve to remove electrochemical oxidation on the workpiece surface (see Fig. 12-10).

ECG can be compared to electroplating, but with major differences. ECG deplates material from the work and deposits it in the electrolyte; however, it does not plate material from the work onto the wheel.

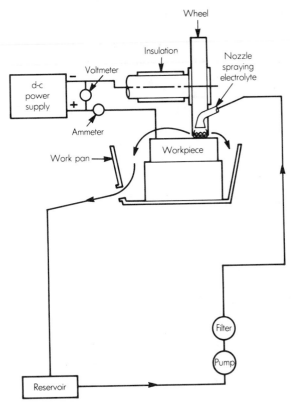

Figure 12-10   Typical setup for electrochemical grinding (ECG)

Applications: In operations in which ECG can be applied, it produces results far beyond those that conventional grinding methods can provide. In many cases it can reduce abrasive costs up to 90%. This reduction is most easily observed in connection with diamond wheels and carbide grinding. However, it is also significant with respect to steel and alloy steel grinding with nondiamond wheels.

Also, because it is a cool process, ECG can be used to grind any electrically conductive material without damage to it from heat. Therefore, ECG can simplify fracture-inspection procedures or entirely eliminate scrap due to grinding-heat fractures. In addition, this process can grind steel or alloy steel parts without generating any burr. Thus, the costly operation of subsequent deburring is automatically eliminated.

ECG has found many applications in the aerospace, automotive instrumentation, textile, and medical manufacturing industries, among others. The process is most frequently used to grind hard, tough materials. Because ECG is performed with significantly less wheel wear than conventional grinding, the process is sometimes more desirable than conventional grinding, or even milling. The process has proved effective in grinding turbine blade "Z" notches, in grinding honeycomb seal rings, and in slotting piston rings. Surgical needles and thin-wall tubing are cut effectively due to the low forces generated in the ECG process. See Figs. 12-11 and 12-12.

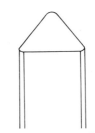

On-end stock removed 0.060" (1.5 mm) grinding time of top end was 62 s.

Square indexable insert. Users report they are regrinding the two sides of these inserts inexpensively.

Triangular indexable insert. These inserts were reground in 27 s per side. The three chipbreaker grooves were reground in a total of 42 s.

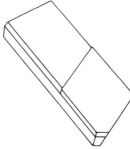

Face mill blade. Stock removed 0.010" (0.25 mm) from the top surface of carbide and 0.004" (0.10 mm) from the steel. Grinding time in one operation for both surfaces was 14 s.

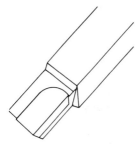

Single point tool. ECG grinding of these is common. Stock removal approx. 0.030-0.060" (0.76-1.52 mm) per minute depending on grade. Average chip breaker ground in 20 s or less.

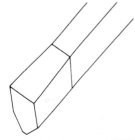

Grooving tool. Stock removed 0.010" (0.25 mm) Top face of carbide was ground flush with shank in 15 s.

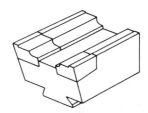

Dovetail form tool. Stock removed 0.125" (3.17 mm). Grinding time of front face of the carbide was 150 s.

Circular form tool. Stock removed 0.082" (2.08 mm) from each top surface. Grinding time of each surface was 60 s.

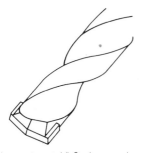

Masonry impact drill. Stock removed 0.015" (0.38 mm) from each side of carbide tip. Grinding time for both sides was 40 s. The two surfaces of point also ground by ECG.

Figure 12-11 Electrochemical grinding (ECG) applications on carbide

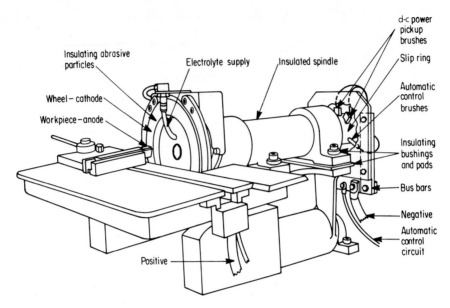

Figure 12-12   Simple electrochemical grinding (ECG) machine

Electrochemical Honing (ECH)

Electrochemical honing is similar to electrochemical grinding (ECG) in that both processes combine electrolytic metal removal with abrasive cutting action. With ECH, metal is removed by introducing an electrolyte into a gap between a cathodic honing tool body and an anodic workpiece, as illustrated in Fig. 12-13. The honing stones are nonconductive; the difference in potential is developed across the gap between the tool body and the workpiece. Direct current is passed across the gap, and the tool is stroked through the bore with the same generating motions of conventional honing. Several rows of small holes in the tool body enable electrolyte to be introduced directly between the tool and work surface. Conventional flooding is also used.

Bonded-abrasive honing stones are inserted in slots in the tool. These stones are forced out radially by the wedging action of the cone in the tool. This expansion is controlled by an adjusting head or fluid power cylinder in the spindle of the machine. The stones, which must be nonconductive, assist in the

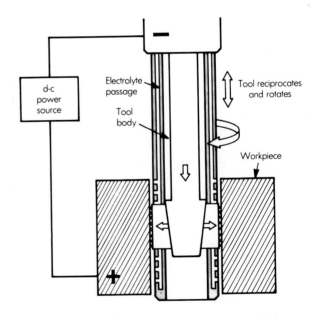

Figure 12-13   Electrochemical honing (ECH)

material-removal action and generate a round, straight cylinder. They are fed out with equal pressure in all directions so that their cutting faces are in constant contact with the cylinder's stones; they cut most aggressively on the high or tight areas and remove the geometric errors. The removal of approximately 90% of the metal in ECH operations is accomplished via electrolytic action; the honing stones maintain size and surface finish and continuously expose clean workpiece metal to the electrolytic process.

Applications: To be processed by ECH, workpieces must be conductive. The process is most effective when used to hone hard, tough metals and is well suited for the processing of parts that are susceptible to heat distortion. Electrochemical honing causes little heat buildup and no significant stresses, and automatically deburrs the workpiece. The process is particularly effective for parts that require fast stock removal with good surface finish control.

The size of cylinder that can be processed using ECH is limited only by the amount of current and electrolyte that can be supplied to the workpiece and by practical limits on honing tool size. With currently available equipment, bores from ⅜ to 6″ (9.5 to 150 mm) diam can be electrochemically honed.

Stock removal in ECH operations is usually five to ten times the rates achievable in conventional honing, and four times the rates achievable using internal grinding. Typical tolerances in production are ± 0.0005″ (0.013 mm) in diameter. Straightness can be held to 0.002″ (0.005 mm).

Cast tool steels, high-alloy steels, carbide, titanium alloys, Incoloy 901, 17-7 pH stainless steel, Inconel, and gun steel have been processed using ECH. Overall, however, the process is very limited in production applications.

Hone-Forming™ (HF)

A reversed modification of the electrochemical honing (ECH) process, Hone-Forming is a trade name used to describe a combination honing and electroplating process developed in the early 1970s by Micromatic Industries, Inc. The process is used to simultaneously abrade the workpiece surface and deposit metal.

With Hone-Forming, controlled abrading (honing) generates accurate dimensional tolerances, shape, and surface finish characteristics, and simultaneous electroforming adds metal to produce surfaces with specific metallurgical characteristics such as hardness, wear resistance, and density (see Fig. 12-14). The tool motions involved in the Hone-Forming process are the same as required in conventional honing or electrochemical honing (ECH)—rotation and reciprocation of a honing tool body through the workpiece. Metal is deposited at rates up to 50 times those achievable with conventional plating methods. Since metal is deposited only on the surface that is honed, it is unnecessary to mask surfaces that are not to be plated. Preparation of the surface by acid etching and associated washing operations are eliminated. Also eliminated is the need to put a "strike" of one metal (such as copper) on the workpiece surface prior to the HF operation.

Applications: In HF applications, the workpiece must be conductive. To date, most materials used in HF are copper, bronze, tin, nickel, cobalt, or chromium-plated and are hone-formed on workpiece materials such as iron, steel, stainless steel, and bronze. Theoretically, any surface that can be honed

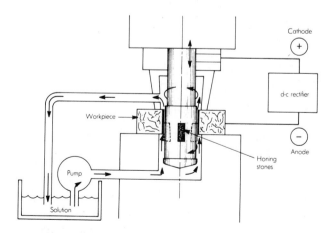

Figure 12-14 Schematic of Hone-Forming (HF)

can be processed with HF. Potential applications of the process include salvaging out-of-tolerance parts, reconditioning worn surfaces, and production manufacturing operations (see Fig. 12-14).

Electrochemical Machining (ECM)

The term electrochemical machining is often used to describe a broad classification of nontraditional machining and finishing metal removal processes that employ electrolytic action. In this section, coverage is limited to "cavity-type" ECM operations. Related processes, such as electrochemical turning (ECT), are covered in later sections of this chapter.

Electrochemical machining is a widely employed method of removing metal without the use of mechanical or thermal energy. Electric energy is combined with a chemical to form a reaction of reverse plating. Direct current at relatively high amperage and low voltage is continuously passed between the anodic workpiece and cathodic tool (electrode) through a conductive electrolyte. At the anode surface, electrons are removed by the current flow, and the metallic bonds of the molecular structure of the surface are broken. These surface atoms go into solution as metal ions. Simultaneously, positive hydrogen ions are attracted to the negatively charged surface and emitted at the cathode surface to form hydrogen atoms, which combine to form hydrogen molecules. Dissolved material is removed from the gap between the work and tool by the flow of electrolyte, which also aids in carrying away the heat and hydrogen formed. Exposure of the workpiece to hydrogen is thus reduced. As shown schematically in Fig. 12-15, ECM operations require:

1. A cathode tool prepared with an approximate mirror image of the configuration to be machined into the workpiece (with compensation for overcut).
2. A workpiece and means to hold and locate it in close proximity to the tool. (In the case of ECM sinking operations, a means of feeding the tool into the workpiece while maintaining a proper gap is required.)

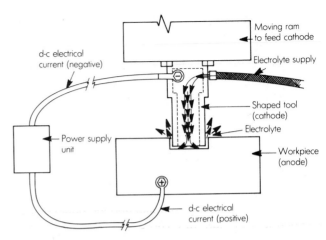

Figure 12-15   Schematic of electrochemical machining (ECM)

3. A means of supplying the gap between the tool and workpiece with pressurized, flowing, conductive liquid (electrolyte).
4. A carefully controlled source of d-c electrical power of sufficient capacity to maintain a current density between the tool and workpiece.

Applications: ECM is used in a wide variety of industries to machine many different metals. Typically, the process is used to machine hard metals, but theoretically it can be used on any electrically conductive metal. Experience has shown, however, that not all materials can be machined successfully (to acceptable metal removal rates and surface finish) using the ECM process. For example, some high-silicon aluminum alloys, such as cast alloys with a substantial silicon content, sometimes cannot be machined with acceptable surface finish. Some troublesome experiences have been documented with SAE 332 aluminum pistons with 10% silicon, for example.

External shaping. Nearly any external shape can be generated with ECM; however, the tooling may be difficult to develop. The production of turbine blades from a solid disc is a typical example of external shaping. Some shops use ECM to produce odd-shaped gear teeth for unusual applications. The use of ECM in external shaping is often desirable when workpieces are in a hardened state. The process is effective for these parts because ECM allows the user to machine after heat treating. Reverse-flow electrode technology is often preferred for external shaping (see Fig. 12-16).

Internal shaping. The preferred electrode technology for generating internal shapes is forward-flow electrode technology (see Fig. 12-17).

Wedge cutting or broaching. When combined with reverse-flow technology at rates exceeding cavity sinking rates, a tapered electrode face will machine when the front or leading edge of the electrode is not engaging metal and the angle of the wedge is less than 45°. The smaller the angle, the faster the feed rate. This method can be likened to finish boring or broaching (see Fig. 12-18).

Sawing. Electrochemical machining is sometimes used as a sawing process for cutting large billets of hard-to-machine alloys. This process is sometimes used to remove test samples and specimens from large billets prior to their being converted into forgings or rolled out into some other finished product. The design of ECM sawing tools calls for a series of holes to be drilled in a piece of tubular-shaped material

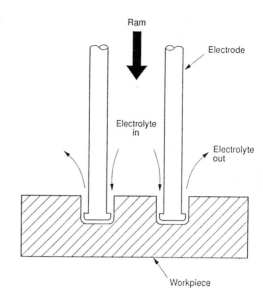

Figure 12-17 Internal shaping electrochemical machining (ECM)

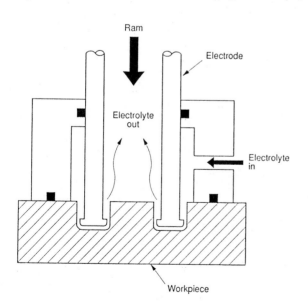

Figure 12-16 External shaping electrochemical machining (ECM)

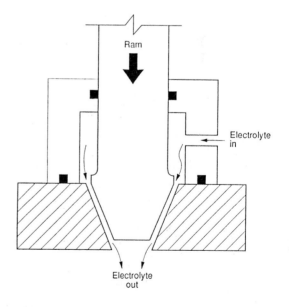

Figure 12-18 Electrochemical broaching (Westinghouse Patent) or ECM wedge cutting

to allow distribution of the electrolyte across the leading edge of the tool. In cases involving sawing large workpieces, the tool is backed up by a stiffening member to prevent its deflection under the load caused by the electrolyte forces acting on it, as shown in Fig. 12-19.

Wire cutting. Electrochemical machining is used in a wire cutting mode as shown in Fig. 12-20. The use of wire cutting is effective because it takes advantage of the inherent capability of the process to cut fast with wires.

Trepanning. Figure 12-21 shows a typical ECM trepanning tool halfway through the workpiece. The tool somewhat resembles a round hole tool except that in this case, the electrolyte is free to flow to an area inside, as well as outside, the tool. The trepanning technique is not confined to producing round holes, but can be applied to almost any shape. Trepanning also offers a short cut to producing large holes by not requiring all the material in the slug to be dissolved, thus allowing faster completion of the hole.

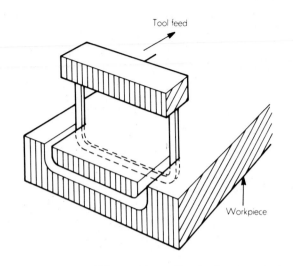

Figure 12-20 Wire cutting with electrochemical machining (ECM)

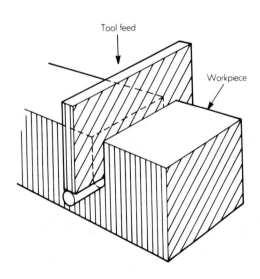

Figure 12-19 Sawing with electrochemical machining (ECM)

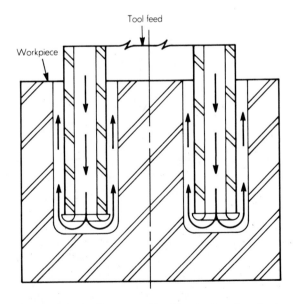

Figure 12-21 Trepanning with electrochemical machining (ECM)

Surfacing. Electrochemical machining can be used to perform operations in much the same way as a single-point tool is used to perform work on a planer. The difference is that the ECM tool can be made as wide as necessary to cover the intended area and can accommodate almost any shape. Holes are provided in the end of the tool to disperse electrolyte, and the tool is fed into the work in the same way as its traditional counterpart, as shown in Fig. 12-22.

When surfacing with ECM, the tool is used for multiple passes, removing a small amount of stock on each pass. It is not unusual that the bottom surface of the tool is slightly curved rather than flat.

Surfacing with ECM is typically used in operations in which a small amount of stock must be removed from extremely hard workpieces.

Residual stresses caused by conventional processing (grinding, planing, etc.) may cause distortion and warping. In cases such as these, surfacing with ECM can be used effectively because the process imparts insignificant stresses in the workpiece.

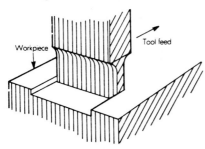

Figure 12-22   Surfacing with electrochemical machining (ECM)

Drilling. Electrochemical drilling is used to produce multiple holes in workpieces. Holes can be produced with close center spacing and no turns. The process is particularly effective for drilling small, deep holes. Variations of ECM called STEM™ (shaped tube electrolyte machining) and Electro-Stream™ are specially designed electrolytic processes for producing holes. Both processes are covered in subsequent sections of this chapter.

Turning. Electrochemical turning (ECT) is covered in a subsequent section of this chapter.

Deburring. One of the largest uses of ECM is in deburring of conductive workpieces.

Typical workpieces. A comprehensive presentation of the many types of workpieces processed by ECM and related processes is beyond the scope of this coverage. However, Fig. 12-23 presents some of the different types of workpieces that are machined using ECM (see Fig. 12-24).

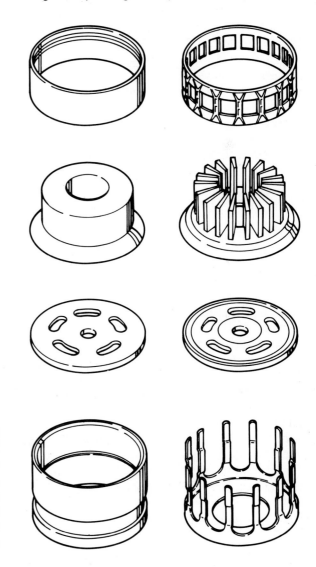

Figure 12-23   Typical workpieces machined using electrochemical machining (ECM)

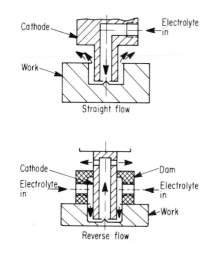

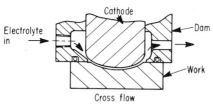

Figure 12-24 Methods of supplying electrolyte to the gap in ECM

Safety Considerations: Some electrolytes (such as acids) are very corrosive, and some (chlorates and nitrates) are combustible when dry. In addition, the effluents from ECM can cause environmental problems. Careful planning and chemical handling are recommended. Hydrogen gases evolved during ECM are mostly carried away with the electrolyte, but adequate venting provisions are needed at the proper point in the flow. Hydrogen removal in some applications is a severe problem. It is absolutely essential that this problem be considered in every ECM application.

Electrochemical Turning (ECT)

Electrochemical turning is a special application of electrochemical machining (ECM). The principles of ECM are applied in the process to electrolyti-cally machine rotating workpieces. Peripheral cuts and face cuts are accomplished as illustrated in Fig. 12-25.

Electrochemical turning is distinguished from a related process, electromechanical machining (EMM), in that ECT employs a noncontacting tool and all metal removal is accomplished via electrolytic action. In contrast, EMM is a traditional machining process in every way except that electrolyte is flooded over the workpiece surface to soften it prior to mechanical metal removal by traditional tools (EMM is covered in an earlier section of this chapter).

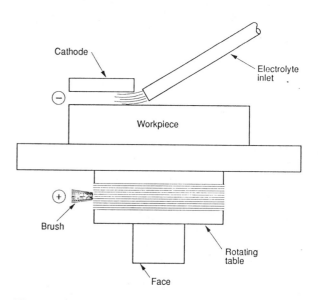

Figure 12-25 Peripheral and face cuts using electrochemical turning (ECT)

Applications: Large disc forgings are machined using ECT. In some cases, full-face electrodes are plunged into a rotating disc. Bearing races have been finished, with close tolerances and with surface roughness held to less than 5 μin. (0.13 μm) R_a. Another application, AISI 316 stainless steel workpieces (2.5", 6.35 mm diam), are electrochemically turned, using an electrolyte of NaCl and NaNo$_3$ (2:3), to a surface finish of less than 10 μ in. (0.25 μm) R_a with out-of-roundness of less than 0.0002" (0.005 mm) TIR.

Shaped Tube Electrolytic Machining (Stem™)

Shaped Tube Electrolytic Machining, a "drilling" process developed by General Electric Co. Aircraft Engine Group, is a variation of electrochemical machining (ECM). The process is used to drill small shaped or round roles (0.025-0.250″, 0.64-6.35 mm diam) in electrically conductive materials, usually difficult-to-machine alloys.

Like conventional ECM, the STEM process employs a negatively charged tool, electrolyte, and a positively charged workpiece. A major difference between STEM and conventional ECM, however, is that STEM uses an acid electrolyte. Workpiece material is dissolved into solution in the electrolyte instead of forming a sludge which could clog small drilled holes during processing.

Small-diameter, acid-resistant, metal tubes coated with an enamel-type film are used as electrodes in STEM. This insulation permits only the exposed end to perform frontal cutting. The electrolyte is pumped through the electrode tubes and exits via the narrow gap between the electrode tube and ID of the hole being drilled.

Multiple electrodes with various diameters and shapes can be used simultaneously. The electrodes are plunge fed into the workpiece at a constant rate consistent with the metal removal rate. In this way, a constant gap thickness is maintained. The electrodes are guided by a guide plate which functions similarly to a bushing plate used to guide multiple conventional drills.

During drilling, the voltage is periodically reversed for a moment (about 0.3 s) to remove metal buildup from the tube electrodes. This voltage reversal is performed just long enough to clean the tube tips, but not so long as to alter the geometry of the tubes.

Applications: STEM is used to drill small holes in hard, tough materials such as 300 and 400 series stainless steels, alloy and tool steels, nickel, Inconel, Incoloy, tungsten, and Hastelloy alloys. Although holes up to 24″ (610 mm) deep with length-to- diameter ratios of up to about 300:1 can be produced using STEM, the process has not been widely applied since its introduction in the late 1960s. Experience has shown that irregular-shaped holes should have a minimum width of about 0.020″ (0.51 mm). Oval-shaped holes and holes that are similar to them should have a major-to-minor axis ratio of no more than 3:1. Up to 100 holes can be drilled per cycle.

Electro-Stream™ (ES)

Extremely small holes (0.008-0.040″, 0.20-1.02 mm) are "drilled" using the Electro-Stream process, an electrolytic operation developed by General Electric Co.'s Aircraft Engine Group. A stream of acid electrolyte flows through a glass insulated nozzle containing a metallic cathode and is ejected against the workpiece to transform the positively charged workpiece into solution at the point of acid impingement. High voltages are used to produce holes up to 0.75″ (19.0 mm) deep. The use of an acid electrolyte eliminates the formation of sludge that occurs when using salt-based electrolytes.

Applications: In general, any electrically conductive material can be processed with ES, although the operation is usually used to produce holes in hardened or tough materials such as 300 series stainless steels, Rene, Inconel, Incoloy, and Hastelloy alloys. The process has been used successfully in the drilling of holes in the leading edge of a superalloy gas turbine vane.

Holes can be drilled effectively at angles as low as 10°, and up to 100 holes can be drilled simultaneously. Depth-to-diameter ratios of drilled holes are usually less than 50:1.

Other Electrical Processes

A number of nontraditional electrical processes are not used or, are used on an extremely limited basis. Some processes of this type are proprietary or are not fully developed for production use and, consequently, are beyond the scope of this presentation. These processes include:

- Electrolytic belt grinding (EBG)
- Electrolytic end milling (EEM)
- Electro ream (ER)
- Electro-Stream chemical milling (ESCM)
- Electro-Stream milling (ESM)
- Zero force machining (ZFM)
- Stationary Electro-Stream (SES)
- Magnetic field machining (MFM)
- Glow discharge machining (GDM)

Thermal Processes

Nontraditional thermal machining processes use thermal energy as the primary source of energy for metal removal. These processes include electron beam machining (EBM), electrical discharge machining (EDM) and related processes, laser beam machining (LBM), and plasma beam machining (PBM).

Nontraditional thermal machining processes are characterized by high temperatures and high thermal energy densities. These processes typically produce significantly different physical and metallurgical effects as compared to traditional and other nontraditional processes. Much study in recent years has been aimed at attaining a better understanding of how the effects of the nontraditional thermal processes influence workpiece metallurgy and/or functional performance.

Electron Beam Machining (EBM)

Electron beam machining uses electrical energy to generate thermal energy for removing material. A pulsating stream of high-speed electrons produced by a generator is focused by electrostatic and electromagnetic fields to concentrate energy on a very small area of work. High-power beams are used with electron velocities exceeding half the speed of light. As the electrons impinge on the work, their

kinetic energy is transformed into thermal energy and melts or evaporates the material locally.

Electron beams are concentrated on spots as small as 0.0002" (0.05 mm) diam. The process is usually performed in a vacuum, as shown schematically in Fig. 12-26. A vacuum is used both to prevent collisions of electrons with gas molecules, which would scatter or diffuse the beam, and to protect the workpiece from oxidation and other atmospheric contamination. Lead shielding is required to protect the operator from X-ray radiation produced by the electron beam.

This section is dedicated to coverage of electron beam machining—drilling small holes and cutting narrow slots or contours in thin materials to close tolerances. Electron beams are also used for welding and heat treating.

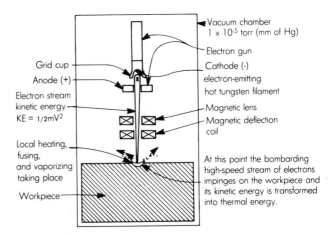

Figure 12-26   Elements of an electron beam machine

Applications: Any known material, metal or nonmetal, that will exist in high vacuum can be cut, although experience has shown that diamonds do not cut well. Holes with depth-to-diameter ratios up to 100:1 can be cut. Limitations include high equipment costs and the need for a vacuum, which usually necessitates batch processing and restricts workpiece size. The process is generally economical only for small cuts in thin parts.

Typical applications of EBM include:

1. Drilling gas orifices for pressure-differential devices, in which closely dimensioned holes must be drilled through the part. These holes regulate the amount of gas that flows in a given amount of time.
2. Producing wire-drawing dies, light-ray orifices, and spinnerets to produce synthetic fibers.
3. Producing metering holes, either round or profile shaped, to be used as flow holes in sleeve valves, rocket-fuel injectors, or injection nozzles on diesel engines.

Electrical Discharge Machining (EDM)

Electrical discharge machining, sometimes referred to as spark machining, is a nontraditional method of removing metal by a series of rapidly recurring electrical discharges between an electrode (the cutting tool) and the workpiece in the presence of a dielectric fluid. Minute particles of metal or chips, generally in the form of hollow spheres, are removed by melting and vaporization, and are washed from the gap by the dielectric fluid which is continuously flushed between the tool and workpiece.

Use of electric sparks for cutting imposes several special requirements, shown schematically in Fig. 12-27, not normally associated with more conventional machine tools. The workpiece, which constitutes one of the electrodes between which the sparks occur, must be of electrically conductive material. The other electrode (tool), which also must be made of electrically conductive material, is located in close proximity to, but not in contact with, the workpiece during cutting. In cavity-type EDM, shaped electrodes are mounted on a machine ram and are fed into the workpiece to achieve three-dimensional machining. This section describes cavity-type EDM; other sections of this chapter are dedicated to electrical discharge grinding (EDG), electrical discharge wire cutting (EDWC), and electrical discharge machining using orbital electrodes.

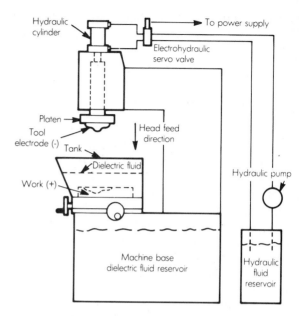

Figure 12-27   Components of an electrical discharge machine (EDM)

Applications: General considerations. The application of EDM is limited to the machining of electrically conductive workpiece materials, but the process has the capability of cutting these materials regardless of their hardness or toughness. Nonconductors such as glass, ceramics, or plastics cannot be machined using EDM techniques. Machining of hardened steel using EDM eliminates the need for subsequent heat treatment with possible distortion. Complex shapes can be cut in hardened steel or carbide without costly sectional construction being necessary.

The EDM process is most widely used by the mold-making tool and die industries, but it is increasingly applied to make prototype and production parts, especially in the aerospace and electronics industries in which production requirements are relatively low. Production of stamping dies is a major application of this process because of the favorable economics afforded by using EDM to match one portion of the die made conventionally. Extruding, heading, drawing, forging, and die casting dies, as well as molds for plastics, are also made using EDM techniques.

Electrical discharge machining is particularly well suited for parts which are made from materials that are difficult to machine and/or contain small or odd-shaped holes, a large number of holes, holes having shallow entrance angles, intricate cavities, or intricate contours. Miniature parts and parts made from material too thin or fragile to withstand conventional, mechanical cutting forces are also good applications. Round or irregular-shaped holes as small as 0.002″ (0.05 mm) diam can be produced with length-to-diameter ratios of about 20:1. Narrow slots as small as 0.002-0.012″ (0.05-0.30 mm) wide are cut routinely.

Burr-free cutting is characteristic of EDM. Many features of modern EDM equipment, such as multiple electrodes, automated dressing, and NC motion control, contribute to broaden process applicability. The scope of EDM applications ranges from tool and die cavity work to automated transfer line operations. See Fig. 12-28.

Electrical Discharge Wire Cutting (EDWC)

Sometimes called traveling wire EDM, electrical discharge wire cutting is a process that is similar in configuration to bandsawing, except in the case of EDWC, the "saw" is a wire electrode of small diameter. Material removal is effected as a result of spark erosion as the wire electrode is fed (from a spool) through the workpiece. In most cases, horizontal movement of the worktable, controlled by CNC on modern machines, determines the path of cut, as illustrated in Fig. 12-29. However, some EDWC machines move the wire horizontally to define the path of cut, leaving the part stationary. On both types of machine configurations, the wire electrode moves vertically over sapphire or diamond wire guides, one above and one below the workpiece. The electrode wire is used only once, then discarded because the wire becomes misshapened after one pass through the workpiece. A steady stream of deionized water or other fluid is used to cool the workpiece and electrode wire and to flush the cut area.

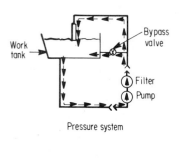

Pressure system

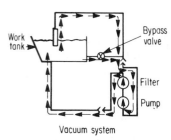

Vacuum system

Figure 12-28 Pressure and vacuum systems used to distribute dielectric fluid in electrical discharge machining (EDM)

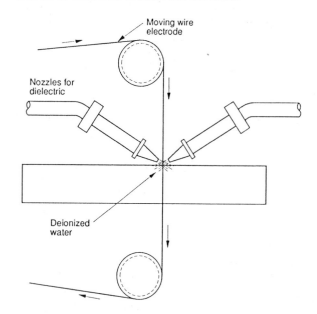

Figure 12-29 Electrical discharge wire cutting (EDWC)

Viewed from above, the electrode wire cuts a slot or "kerf." The width of the kerf is the wire diameter plus EDM overcut, as illustrated in Fig. 12-30.

Starter or threading holes are required. In steel or other material, a drilled hole suffices; for carbide, the hole may have to be produced by EDM.

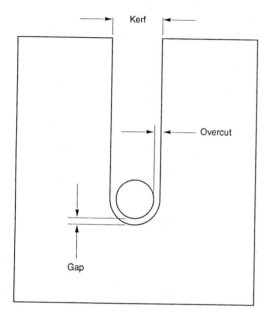

Figure 12-30   Definition of kerf in electrical discharge wire cutting (EDWC)

Applications:
As is the case with any electrical discharge process, EDWC requires that the workpiece be electrically conductive. The cut produced by the process is free of bellmouth or flaring and is controllable to produce small radii. Workpieces up to about 6″ (152 mm) in thickness can be processed using standard equipment; workpiece stacking effects greater productivity.

Stamping dies. Normally produced from hardened metals such as tool steel, stamping dies are routinely cut using EDWC. The process facilitates cutting after heat treatment, thereby eliminating distortion. The use of EDWC in the manufacturing of dies affords significant savings. By conventional methods, dies are sometimes split into two or more sections to facilitate grinding with an optical projection form grinder. Usually, after the contour has been ground in the split sections, the sections are fitted in a holder or adapter. This time-consuming and costly process is eliminated when EDWC is employed to produce the dies. Some experts claim that tool components such as dies can be produced in less than one third the time required by conventional methods.

Prototype manufacturing. Using the EDWC process, complex-shaped blanks can be cut quickly and easily and, as mentioned earlier, layers of sheet metal can be stacked and gang-cut to produce dozens or hundreds of parts in a single pass. A distinct advantage of EDWC in prototype work is that NC programming used to produce the prototype can be used for production parts, often with only minor modifications. The flexibility afforded by the use of NC in the process greatly speeds the production of blanks for test forming in blank development work.

Molds. Manufacturing of molds of all types is most often accomplished using EDM cavity-type sinking units. Expensive electrodes for these machines normally employ slight tapers and extremely accurate size requirements and provide an excellent application for EDWC. Mold work demands exceptional electrode surface finish quality, which is usually obtainable using the EDWC process. Mold inserts, as well as two-piece molds, can be cut with the process. This "step backward" in construction technique can provide significant savings when sections are complex and cavity-type EDM is difficult.

Lathe tools. The OD plunge and grooving-form types of lathe tools are normally manufactured in a grinding operation. In recent years, however, EDWC has made significant inroads in these areas. The ability of EDWC to cut an accurate tapered form is critical to these applications as tapered front and side relief keeps the tools from dragging during cutting operations. The EDWC process eliminates many costly, tedious hours of optical or form grinding—one setup produces the tool.

Lathe tools consisting of carbide brazed on a steel shank are usually ground using costly diamond wheels or other processes. The steel shank is usually prepared by milling. The steel shank is machined to provide clearance for the shape to be cut. Then, the carbide is brazed into position and diamond form grinding is used to complete the production process. With EDWC, this expensive process is eliminated.

Some lathe tools feature complex, highly accurate shapes with side "pitch" and front relief angles. Tools of this type are employed in the cutting of hobs and formed circular milling cutters. These special lathe tools can be cut using specially built EDWC machines. The application is handled by rigidly fixturing the electrode wire at both angles and servo-controlling the cut while the tool is held stationary. Special software in the EDWC machine programming system allows for the "ellipse" form of cutting due to this compound angle. By using EDWC to produce these lathe tools, significant savings over optical projection form grinding can be achieved. New, exotic forms can be achieved due to the "free-form" attributes of the EDWC process, and lathe tool breakage is reportedly reduced because the EDWC surface is said to be more stable than a ground surface.

Special form inserts. Carbide, diamond, or other nonstandard form inserts are cut using the EDWC process. The material must be electrically conductive to be cut with the process. New materials created and/or demanded by space age technology sometimes cannot be economically cut using conventional cutting tools. Special, super-hard materials, normally quite expensive, are required. Synthetic diamonds or diamond compounds that are almost impossible to grind are very expensive, but are cut effectively by EDWC. The process wastes little workpiece material due to its small kerf size, and the process cuts accurate, specially shaped pieces.

Pot and wobble broaches. Broaches for cutting outside forms on rods or shafts are referred to as pot broaches. Cutting of these tools is an excellent application for EDWC. The material used for broaches is usually hardened steel, and generally a series of rough, semifinished, and finished broaches

is required. Slightly different cutting sizes for each tool are accomplished with the use of wire offset or compensation.

A similar tool to a pot broach is a wobble broach. Wobble broaches are mounted in lathe compounds at a slight angle. The tool is fed into a slowly rotating shaft. The broaching cut expires into an undercut against a shoulder. Nonferrous connector forms are an example of this application. The EDWC process is used in these applications in the same way it is used in pot broaching applications.

Pot or wobble broaches are normally sectioned, split, and ground—a costly, skill-intensive process. The EDWC process eliminates much of the skill required to produce these broaches and produces an accurate angular relief around the form.

Extrusion dies. Sawing and filing have traditionally been used to manufacture extrusion dies for vinyl and aluminum. This skill-intensive process is eliminated by the use of EDWC. A side benefit of using the process when machining graphite is cleanliness. Graphite is extremely dirty to grind or mill—this problem is eliminated with EDWC.

Templates. The uses of templates range from large tracer lathe applications to miniature precision contour gage applications. Steel rolling mills use templates to control roll-turning tracer lathes and to check the finished parts for size and accuracy. Building aircraft engines requires many airfoil-shaped templates to control tracer machines, construct prototype models, and check final shapes. Without EDWC, these templates would be laid out by a skilled layout man, then sawed and filed to shape. A considerable number of attempts may be required before the final shape is approved. This hand process is both tedious and marginally repeatable from an accuracy standpoint.

Electrical discharge wire cutting can cut templates accurately, quickly, and without the need for highly skilled labor. A further benefit is that changes can be effected quickly by simple NC tape alterations and, possibly more important, any number of templates can be produced identically when NC is employed. See Fig. 12-31.

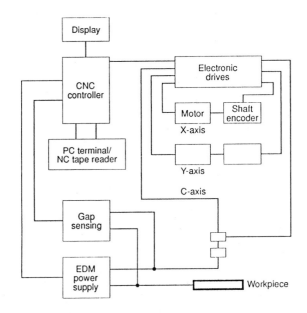

Figure 12-31 Schematic of electrical discharge wire cutting system (EDWC)

Electrical Discharge Grinding (EDG)

Electrical discharge grinding is similar to electrical discharge machining (EDM), which is covered in a previous section of this chapter, except that the electrode is a rotating wheel, generally graphite but sometimes brass. Positively charged workpieces are immersed in or flooded by a dielectric fluid and fed past the negatively charged wheel by a servo-controlled machine table, as shown schematically in Fig. 12-32. Metal is removed by intermittent high-frequency electrical discharges passing through the gap between the wheel and work. The reverse of the form on the wheel face is transferred to the workpiece surface. Chips are flushed away by fluid carried through the cutting area by the wheel rotation. The wheel never comes closer to the workpiece than the preset length of spark (usually 0.0005-0.003″, 0.013-0.08 mm).

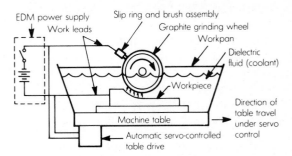

Figure 12-32 Components of an electrical discharge grinding machine (EDG)

Applications: Electrical discharge grinding is generally used for operations such as the following:

1. Grinding steel and carbide at the same time without wheel loading.
2. Grinding thin sections on which abrasive-wheel pressures might cause distortion.
3. Grinding brittle materials or fragile parts on which abrasive materials might cause fracturing.
4. Grinding through forms for which diamond-wheel costs would be excessive.
5. Grinding circular forms in direct competition with abrasive-wheel methods.

Electrical discharge grinding is used to grind hard materials such as carbide form tools, hardened steel gear racks, or tungsten carbide inserts. The process is also used to grind hardened lamination dies. Cast iron workpieces are usually not processed using EDG because sand inclusions can damage the graphite grinding wheel. See Fig. 12-33.

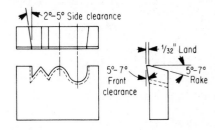

Figure 12-33 Typical full-form tool used to dress EDG wheels

Laser Beam Machining (LBM)

The use of lasers in part manufacturing for cutting, drilling, slotting, welding, scribing, and heat treating operations has increased dramatically in recent years. The purpose of this section is to provide an overview of the use of lasers for machining operations such as drilling and cutting.

Principles of Operation: Laser beam machining is based on the conversion of electrical energy into light energy and then into thermal energy. Although several types of lasers exist, all lasers produce (emit) an intense, coherent, highly collimated beam of single wavelength light. In material processing applications, this narrow beam is focused by an optical lens to produce a small, intense spot of light on the workpiece surface. Optical energy is converted into heat energy upon impact, and temperatures generated can be high enough to melt and/or vaporize any material.

The term "laser" is an acronym for "light amplification by stimulated emission of radiation." Many types of lasers exist which are capable of producing highly directive beams of visible, infrared, or ultraviolet radiation. Lasers can be classified as solid state, gas, or liquid lasers.

In a typical laser system, electrical energy is converted into light via excitation of a lasing medium. Solid state and liquid lasers are excited by xenon, krypton, or tungsten-halogen flashlamps which illuminate the lasing medium as shown in Fig. 12-34. Gas lasers are driven by direct electrical (d-c, a-c, or RF) excitation of the gas, usually at low pressure (see Fig. 12-35).

In the case of a CO_2 laser, the lasing medium is a mixture of CO_2, N, and He gases; the lasing medium used in an Nd:YAG laser is neodymium-doped, yttrium aluminum garnet (Nd:YAG). Chromium atoms are the lasing media in a sapphire crystal which constitutes a ruby laser. An Nd:glass laser employs glass plus 2-6% Nd (in a glass tube) as the lasing medium.

In a CO_2 laser, electrical energy creates an ionized discharge that excites CO_2 molecules; in an Nd:YAG laser, Nd:glass laser, and ruby laser, electrical energy

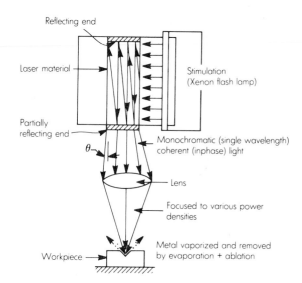

Figure 12-34 Solid state laser beam machining (LBM)

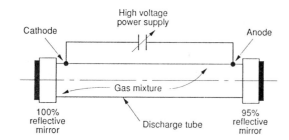

Figure 12-35 Typical gas laser configuration

is discharged into a flashlamp which emits an intense flash of light. This intense flash is focused on the solid state material, exciting the ions in the glass or crystal rod.

Light radiated by the excited lasing medium is inphase and in the same direction as the beam which initiated the reaction. As the intensified light travels through the lasing medium, it is reflected back and forth upon itself between reflective ends of the cavity so that more and more of the excited material is stimulated into giving up stored energy. The intensity of the light's swinging back and forth builds with extreme rapidity as does the portion of the light which is allowed to escape through a partly reflective surface at one end of the chamber.

Depending upon the application, lasers are operated continuously or pulsed, with pulses as short as a few billionths of a second. Pulse durations of about 17 billionths of a second are employed for range finding and similar operations; pulse durations of about 0.6 ms are typically employed in industrial applications. In general, different pulse shapes are used for different material processing applications.

The narrow spiked pulse is excellent for drilling because it instantaneously vaporizes the material being worked, thereby minimizing thermal distortion, melting, and avoiding cracking of the workpiece. This type of pulse is also effective in cutting operations.

A broad pulse with an initial spike is desirable for welding applications: the spike causes quick, efficient absorption of energy while the lower energy, flat portion of the pulse generates the welding action.

In laser cutting, material is removed by the simultaneous actions of an intense laser beam and the flow of a stream of gas, usually oxygen or less often nitrogen, argon, air, or helium. Figure 12-36 illustrates a typical setup for trepanning-type laser cutting.

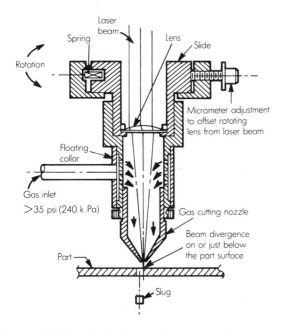

Figure 12-36   Typical setup for trepanning-type laser cutting

Applications: Any industrial application of the laser should be based on one of three criteria: (1) It can perform a superior job in terms of quality and cost over existing methods, (2) it is the only tool capable or available for the specific job, or (3) it allows restructuring of the manufacturing process, resulting in lower total cost. The cost of using laser systems falls into two categories: (1) the capital investment for the laser system and (2) the operational cost. At present both the equipment and the direct operational costs of a laser are higher than those of comparable conventional equipment and methods.

Because of the laser's ability to melt or vaporize any known metal and operate in any desired atmospheric environment, it is sometimes preferred over EBM (electron beam machining) which requires a vacuum chamber for certain applications. Other advantages include (1) the ability to machine areas not readily accessible and extremely small holes, (2) the fact that no direct contact exists between the tool (laser) and the workpiece, (3) small heat-affected zones, and (4) easy control of beam configuration and size of exposed area.

Cutting. Cutting a material with a laser generally is done by initiating a hole through the material and then moving either the focused beam or the workpiece as the laser is operated. Pulsed lasers are fired repeatedly so that each successive focused spot overlaps the previous one, resulting in the speed of cutting being determined by the maximum repetition rate of the laser. Continuous or CW (continuous wave) lasers are simply turned on and moved along the cut path. When metal is being cut, a jet of gas is normally employed to blow the partly melted, partly vaporized material out of the cut. Failure to do so results in a cut that is welded shut instead of the desired cut. Some metals, typically carbon steels, are generally cut using oxygen as the assisting gas because it reacts chemically with the iron in the steel, permitting faster and deeper cuts to be made. Cut speeds are determined by material thickness and the power available from the laser.

Drilling. One of the most attractive production applications of LBM has been the drilling of cooling holes in jet engine components. Here, the laser must compete with the electrical discharge machining and electrochemical machining processes. Most jet engine manufacturers are using pulsed lasers for production or engineering development activities.

The pulsed laser drilling process becomes economically attractive as more holes are required at a variety of compound angles on a single part. Holes of less than 0.010″ (0.25 mm) diam can easily be drilled through nickel and cobalt-based super-alloys. It is expected that the laser drilling process will continue to advance as nonconductive materials come more into use for jet engine parts.

Other laser machining applications. Pulsed lasers are also being used to balance parts dynamically as they rotate at their designed operating speeds; this affords faster balancing and increased accuracy. In this application, the part need not be stopped prior to removing the material. Conventional sensing equipment is integrated with the laser system, and the laser's output pulse is synchronized with the sensing equipment.

Lasers are also being used in a service function to vaporize electron-microscope apertures that are clogged with foreign material. Two techniques are used to accomplish this task: (1) A spot larger than the aperture is used to clean out the foreign particles and (2) on large apertures, a small spot is focused directly onto a specific spot to vaporize it. See Fig. 12-37.

Laser Safety: The following discussion presents a partial list of ways in which the hazards associated with the laser machine tool and the workpiece can be controlled.

High electrical power. The National Electrical Code prescribes safe techniques for handling electrical power. Many laser experts believe that the most important aspect of laser safety is the danger of injury by the high voltage (1200 V) and current (1000 A) required to energize the flashlamps. Interlocked covers and shields should be an integral part of the delivered laser.

Thermal problems—tool and work. Shielding, thermal insulation, and spatial separation are the most effective means of avoiding potential burns. For example, a hot surface on a laser power supply could be thermally insulated, or a shield could be placed over it, far enough away that the shield temperature would not harm skin for the duration of a normal pain response (about one-quarter second). A continuous line of metal workpieces, coming hot from a welder or cutter, should be fenced, so that no one can pick up a piece while it is still hot. Molten drops of work material can be collected in metal or ceramic trays. Small drops or sparks, particularly those projected by the flowing gas stream, should be collected on a screen or shield.

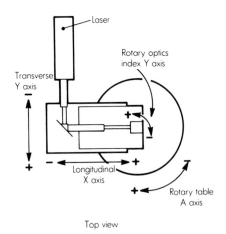
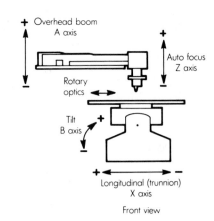

Figure 12-37   Universal laser machining center

A special note on the laser tool: The laser power should be interlocked to proper coolant flow so that the laser does not overheat if cooling is lost. Most modern laser machine tools are equipped with such an interlock system.

Beta rays and X rays. Shielding of beta rays is relatively easy: 2 cm (0.78″) of air or 0.75 cm (0.29″) of aluminum will absorb 30 kilovolt electrons. The thickness of the shield for other voltages scales directly as the square of the ratio of the voltages. X rays are not as readily shielded. Film badges can be used to measure the integrated exposure of personnel to X rays. Shields are incorporated in most modern laser machine tools, as delivered.

Toxic materials. A laser operating with a toxic laser medium should be designed so that failure of the toxic medium container would shut down the laser and so that a secondary backup container will contain the toxic material.

Toxic materials generated by chemical change of the workpiece can be collected with an exhaust system, diluted, and treated or discharged into the atmosphere. (All local, state, and federal regulations should be checked.) If the toxic effect is cumulative, then the effluent might require chemical treatment to remove it totally.

Detection of concentrations of gases, for example, can be done using electronic instruments. This procedure is essential if the operator is unable to detect the toxic material alone.

Mechanical motion. A moving part of the laser tool or of a workpiece holder should be designed so that its impact hazard is minimized: Small, slow motions are preferable; sharp corners and edges should be cushioned; and barriers and shields should be installed to prevent access to dangerous points such as automatically operated workpiece holders and positioners.

Ultraviolet radiation. The laser covers are normally adequate to contain the ultraviolet radiation generated in the gas discharge or from flashlamps in solid state lasers. The "sniff test" will quickly reveal whether ozone is being created in the laser.

Ultraviolet radiation from a plasma of work material is more of a problem. If the process is automatic,

then operator inspection is not required; in this case, an opaque shield is the best solution. If operator inspection is required, eye and skin protection can be effected by using glasses to absorb ultraviolet rays.

Noise. A noise problem from capacitor discharge or blower motors (in the case of CO_2 lasers) can be alleviated by application of acoustical insulating material or by ear protection.

Fire hazard. The normal precaution of maintaining appropriate fire extinguishers close to a high-power laser tool is quite appropriate. Fire or smoke detectors might be useful.

The need for inspection at the cutting edge. Providing the operator with an image of the work at or near the laser focus is best done by using a closed-circuit television system. Visible beam, infrared, and ultraviolet-absorbing shields are used to shield the operator from accidental exposure. Interlocks verifying that the shield is in place can be included to prevent accidental exposure of eyes or skin to the radiation while the work is being placed or removed.

When conditions are less severe, light-absorbing shields and eye protection goggles can be provided.

Very commonly, the reflection and scattering of the laser beam from the work is the chief problem. Calculations on required optical attenuation can be made using the instructions, tables, and formulas contained in the ANSI document, "Safe Use of Lasers." This document has been recently reissued, with revised maximum permissible exposures and simplified calculation methods. Example exposure calculations are presented.

Particularly when the operator is an integral part of the laser control logic circuit, a dump for unused laser beam power must be provided. Its design should account for minimum scattered and reflected radiation, as well as for heat absorption without major damage to itself for the expected unused beam duration.

Personnel training. Training of operator and maintenace personnel in the laser and work-related hazards and control measures adopted go a long way toward making the use of the laser tool accident free.

Plasma Arc Machining (PAM)

Plasma is defined as a gas that has been heated to a sufficiently high temperature to become partially ionized and therefore electrically conductive. The term plasma, as employed in physics, means ionized particles. This phenomenon may be likened to a streak of lightning which ionizes the gases of the atmosphere and heats them to incandescence. The temperature of plasma may reach as high as 50,000°F (27,800°C).

Various devices utilizing an electric arc to heat gas to the plasma state have been in existence since the early 1900s. However, the development of such apparatus into commercial plasma arc equipment for metalcutting applications dates back to only about 1955.

The plasma arc produced by modern equipment is generated by a plasma torch that is constructed in such a manner as to provide an electric arc between an electrode and workpiece. A typical plasma torch consists of an electrode holder, an electrode, a device to swirl the gas, and a water-cooled nozzle. The "swirler," which may be ceramic, encircles the lower portion of the electrode, serving to stabilize the gas flow and thus preventing gas turbulence. The geometry of the torch nozzle is such that the hot gases are constricted in a narrow column.

Primary gases, such as nitrogen, argon-hydrogen, or air, are forced through the nozzle and arc and become heated and ionized. Secondary gases or water flow are often used to help clean the kerf of molten metal during cutting.

The stream of ionized particles from the nozzle can be used to perform a variety of industrial jobs. The plasma arc, as an industrial tool, is most heavily employed in sheet and plate cutting operations as an alternative to more conventional oxy-fuel torches or other cutting tools. Plasma arc is routinely used as an integral component of some modern punching machines.

Plasma arc methods are also employed in special applications to replace conventional machining operations such as lathe turning, and to a much lesser extent, milling and planing. The purpose of this section is to provide an overview of plasma arc machining and cutting.

The ionized plasma gas is usually inactive to protect the electrode from combustion and ensure long life. When oxygen is added as either the plasma ionized gas or the secondary enveloping gas, the speed of cutting steel is increased. Use of a secondary envelope of gas improves the kerf wall appearance on certain metals and assists in removing dross, especially in grooving operations. This envelope also acts as a protective shield for the nozzle during extensive piercing operations. Depending upon equipment design, the enveloping gas may be independently controlled at various velocities.

A major improvement in mechanized plasma arc cutting occurred in recent years with the development of so-called "water injection." When the water injection technique is employed, the arc is constricted by a flow of water around the arc. This injection of water has many advantages, including:

1. A square cut can be made.
2. Arc stability is increased.
3. Cutting speed can be increased.
4. Workpieces are heated less.
5. Less smoke and fumes are generated.
6. Nozzle life is increased.

Figure 12-38 illustrates the principle of water swirl injection.

Applications: Cutting. With appropriate equipment and techniques, the plasma arc can be employed to make cuts in electrically conductive metals. The process is employed in a variety of cutting operations including straight line, circle, shape, level grooving, gouging, and stack cutting. Plasma arc techniques are also used for ripping, squaring, plate piercing, trimming, and plate edge preparation for welding. Figure 12-39 illustrates the general setup for cutting using a plasma arc torch.

Hole piercing. Reproducible, high-quality holes are made rapidly in a variety of materials with the plasma arc. The size and quality of the pierced holes are determined by arc current, arc duration, gas flow rate, gas composition, nozzle shape, and nozzle standoff. Holes can be pierced much faster than they can be drilled.

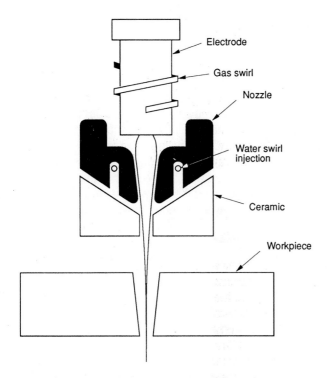

Figure 12-38   Principle of water swirl injection in plasma arc machining (PAM)

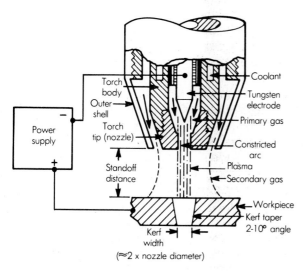

Figure 12-39   Plasma arc torch for cutting operations

Plasma arc hole piercing is performed with conventional plasma arc cutting equipment that has been modified to produce a short, carefully controlled arc operating time, suitable arc current programming during the short operating cycle, and effective slag ejection.

Almost instantly after ignition the arc rapidly penetrates through the plate forming a hole approximately the same size as the diameter of the arc stream. Allowed to dwell for a few seconds, the flame melts away the taper of the hole, creating a cylindrical shape. Continued plasma exposure increases the size of the hole to four or five times the arc stream diameter. A small amount of surface flash may form around the top of the hole during piercing; however, surface flash is easily removed by wire brushing. Selection of optimum cutting parameters reduces and sometimes eliminates dross from occurring on the bottom edge of the hole. Larger holes can be produced by moving the torch or workpiece in a circular motion.

Stack cutting. Plasma can effectively stack-cut stainless steel and aluminum. Plasma stack cutting of thin carbon steel tends to weld the layers making them difficult to separate after cutting.

During cutting, the layers should be clamped firmly enough to minimize gaps, but loose enough to permit slippage between layers due to differential expansion. The upper layer may buckle if clamping does not allow slippage.

Gouging and grooving. The plasma cutting torch is suitable for machine gouging and grooving. Gouging is accomplished by using lower power or faster speed than that required for full penetration cuts, with the torch angled approximately 45° into the direction the torch is traversed.

The following general considerations are applicable to gouging and grooving with the plasma torch:

• The angle of the torch affects the quality of the gouge. The flatter the torch to the work, the smoother is the gouged surface and the shallower the depth.

• Deep gouges can be made with multiple passes in multiple pass gouging; subsequent passes tend to have a smoother surface and remove less metal than the initial pass.

- Deeper gouges produce a shape similar to two butted "J" grooves; shallower gouges tend to be half-round shaped.
- Larger nozzle sizes produce wider gouges.

Plate edge preparation (bevel cutting). Plasma arc cutting can be used for beveling plate edges prior to welding. Metal plates have been beveled on all four edges before being rolled into shape for welding into cylinders. Edges have been prepared by plasma arc cutting for welding in longitudinal and circumferential joints.

Edge configurations may involve a single bevel, a single bevel with a nose, a double bevel, or a double bevel with a nose. Bevel cuts up to 45° are readily made. Bevel cuts in excess of 45° may involve additional care to prevent rounding of the knife edge. For bevel cutting, power settings and nozzle sizes should be selected that are compatible with the thickness of the cut face resulting from the bevel since this is the actual amount of penetration into solid metal. Multi-face edge preparations can be made in multiple passes with a single torch or in one pass or two by using multiple torches.

Machining. The plasma arc can be used for "machining" or removing the metal from the surface of a rotating cylinder to simulate a conventional lathe or turning operation. The process is shown schematically in Fig. 12-40. As the workpiece is turned, the torch is moved parallel to the axis of the work. The torch is positioned so the arc will impinge tangentially on the workpiece and remove the outer layer of metal. Cutting can be accomplished with the workpiece rotating in either direction relative to the torch, but best results are obtained when the direction of rotation permits use of the shortest arc length for cutting. The flow of molten metal being removed must be in such a direction that it does not tend to adhere to the hot surface that has just been machined.

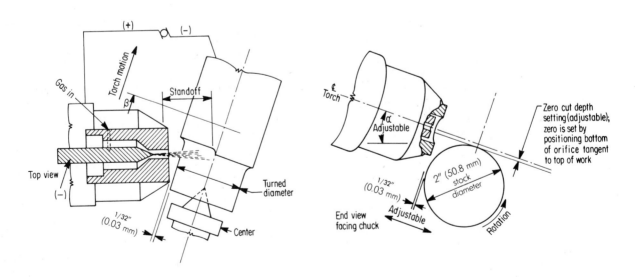

Figure 12-40   Torch-to-work geometry in plasma arc machining (PAM)

Chemical Processes

Chemical nontraditional machining processes are classified as those processes which employ chemical energy as the primary source of energy for material removal. The use of chemicals to remove metal is an old art. The industrial use of chemicals for metal removal, however, surfaced in a major way shortly after World War II when North American Aviation initiated a program using chemicals to remove unwanted metal from aircraft parts. Shortly thereafter, the company patented and licensed the Chem-Mill process which constituted the first volume production use of chemical material removal.

At about the same time, chemicals began to be used to remove unwanted copper from copper-insulator laminates in the field of printed circuits. The use of chemicals to "chemically blank" functional parts from thin metal sheet, now called "photochemical machining," was initiated in the same period.

The purpose of this section is to provide an overview of the use of chemical milling and photochemical machining or blanking.

Chemical Milling

Chemical milling is the process used to shape metals to an exacting tolerance by the chemical removal of metal, or deep etching of parts, rather than by conventional mechanical milling machining operations. The amount of metal removed, or depth of etch, is controlled by the amount of immersion time in the etching solution. Location of the unetched or unmilled areas on a part is controlled by masking or protecting these areas from the action of the etchant solution. The process consists of five main steps: cleaning, masking, scribing, etching, and demasking.

Applications: In general, chemical milling is used to:

- Remove metal from a portion or the entire surface of formed or irregularly shaped parts such as forgings, castings, extrusions, or formed wrought stock.

- Reduce web thicknesses below practical machining, forging, casting, or forming limits.
- Taper sheets and preformed shapes.
- Produce stepped webs, resulting in consolidation of several details into one integral piece.
- Remove the decarburized layer from low-alloy steel forgings.
- Remove up to 0.125″ (3.2 mm) per surface of metal to remove decarb and also create finished dimensions of die forgings.
- Improve surface finish.
- Remove surface cracks, laps, and other defects of forgings.
- Remove alpha case from titanium forgings.
- Improve surface finish and control dimensions of aluminum forgings.

Photochemical Machining

Photochemical machining or chemical blanking is the process of producing metallic and nonmetallic parts by chemical action. Basically, the process consists of placing a chemical-resistant image of the part on a sheet of metal and exposing the sheet to chemical action which dissolves all the metal except the desired part. Most parts produced in this way are similar to thin-gage stampings and are generally flat and of complex design.

Applications: Photochemical machining has a number of applications wherein it provides unique advantages. Some of these include:

1. Working on extremely thin materials when handling difficulties and die accuracies preclude the use of normal mechanical methods.
2. Working on hardened or brittle materials when mechanical action would cause breakage or stress-concentration points. Chemical blanking works well on spring materials and hardened materials which are relatively difficult to punch.
3. Production of parts which must be absolutely burr free.
4. Production of extremely complex parts for which die costs would be prohibitive.

5. Producing short-run parts for which the relatively low setup costs and short time from print to production offer advantages. This is especially important in research and development projects and in model shops.

The use of photochemical machining is generally limited to relatively thin materials, from 0.0001 to 0.050″ (0.003-1.27 mm) thick. The limit on material thickness is generally a function of the tolerance desired on finished parts. Common variables which affect the etching tolerances are type of metal being etched, size of panel, equipment being etched, equipment being used, and yield required. Other factors which affect tolerance are: (1) accuracy of initial artwork, (2) accuracy of photographic processing, (3) compensation of artwork for undercut, and (4) nonuniformities in processing such as nonuniform printing, developing, and etching.

Photographic-Resist Processing Fundamentals:
The photographic-resist process of photochemical machining is by far the most common one in use today. Figure 12-41 shows the process steps involved.

Cleaning. Metal can be chemically cleaned in numerous ways including degreasing, pumice scrubbing, electrocleaning, or chemical cleaning.

Coating. The cleaned metal is coated with photographic material which, when exposed to light of the proper wavelength, will polymerize and remain on the panel as it goes through a developing stage. This polymerized layer then acts as the barrier to the etching solution applied to the metal. Methods of coating the metal with the photoresist are dipping, spraying, flow coating, roller coating, or laminating. The type of resist used and the part's physical form determine which method is most applicable.

Prebake. After being coated with resist, the panel must usually be baked prior to being exposed. This "prebake," as it is called, is used to remove all solvents from the resist in a simple drying operation. Care must be taken not to overbake the photoresists, since most of them are sensitive to heat prior to exposure.

Exposure. Artwork that has been drawn and photographically reduced is used to expose the

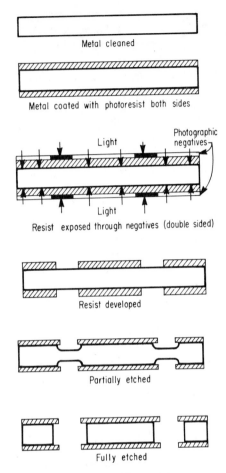

Figure 12-41 Photographic-resist process of photochemical machining

photographic resist. The negatives are generally used in matched pairs so that a minimum amount of undercut is achieved and so that the final part has straight sidewalls. The metallic-coated panel is placed between sets of negatives (either film or glass) and is clamped by either vacuum or pressure. Exposure times depend upon light intensity, the type of resist being used, and the amount of sensitizers present in the resist. Typical exposure times of from 10 to 30 s are generally required.

Equipment used for printing ranges from very simple, single-sided, graphic-arts types of vacuum frames (such as those used by photoengravers) to extremely complex automatic equipment for printing of continuous strips. The exposed image can be developed by a number of methods. Each photoresist has its own developing solution, which may be water, alkaline solution, hydrocarbons, solvents, or proprietary developers. In most cases the image is developed either by immersion followed by subsequent wash off or by spray equipment. Developing is always followed by a washing operation to ensure that no residual resist is left on the panels in the areas to be etched away.

Postbake. Certain resists require an additional baking operation following development. This "postbake" is necessary to drive out residual solvents or cause further polymerization, which improves the chemical resistance of the resist image. Postbaking is not as critical as prebaking in regard to time and temperature, but it is generally tailored to the specific resist used and the depth of etching to be obtained. Infrared lamps, conveyorized infrared ovens, or circulating air ovens are used for postbaking. In isolated instances, induction heating equipment has been used on ferrous materials. Following postbaking, it is generally advisable to cool the resist prior to etching.

Processing. The next step is etching to remove the unwanted metal that is not protected by the photoresists. A large number of etchants are available for different materials. Many materials can be attacked by a number of etchants, with the deciding factors being cost, quality, and speed of material removal. Etchant may be applied to the workpiece by immersion, splash, or spray. Less commonly used techniques are air-driven mists or fogs, and gaseous-medium etching. Following etching, the workpiece is generally washed and dried if resist removal is not required. When removing the resist is necessary, the removal can be accomplished manually or by machines either with spray-on removal compounds or with the use of mechanical action in addition to chemical action.

Screen-Printed Resist Processing Fundamentals:
Most of the steps involved are identical when using a screen-printed resist rather than a photographically printed resist. Cleaning for screen resists is generally not as critical as it is for photographic resist because the screen resists have better adhesion and their adhesion is less dependent upon the surface cleanliness of the material on which they are printed. The clean panel is placed in either a manual or automatic screen printer, and acid-resistant ink is screened onto the part. Following printing, the resist must be dried and quite often it is necessary to print the reverse side of the panel if higher accuracy or thicker materials are to be chemically blanked.

After printing is complete and the acid resist has been properly dried or baked, the part is etched in the normal manner. Following etching, the screen resists are generally removed by either chemical action or a combination of chemical and mechanical action. Because of the inherent limitations of screen printing, high-tolerance work cannot be done with currently available screen-printing equipment. However, the cost of screen printing is so much lower than the cost of photographic printing that, when tolerances permit, the former technique should be used. Generally, the cost of screen printing is only 20% of the cost of photographic printing on a per-unit-area basis.

Tooling for Photochemical Machining:
The tooling required for photochemical machining consists of the artwork and negatives used to produce the acid-resistant image. As with any product, the quality of the finished item depends upon the final part desired, the process, and the quality of the tooling. The actual artwork design depends upon the final part desired and the process used to produce the part. Artwork for photochemical machining should be made on dimensionally stable materials such as Mylar, glass, or metallic-based materials. For best tolerances, scribing or strippable coatings should be used to take advantage of process capabilities. Less accurate work can be done with normal drafting techniques using a true black ink on a stabilized Mylar drawing film.

Since artwork is generally drawn oversized, the tolerances that can be held on a particular part depend upon the size of the part. Tighter tolerances can be held on smaller parts, which can be drawn many times oversize and then photographically reduced, than they can be held on larger parts, which can be drawn only a few times oversized. A competent draftsman with proper equipment can work to a tolerance of 0.005-0.010″ (0.13-0.25 mm) over a 20″ (510 mm) area. Beyond a certain point, it is better to use high-accuracy drawing equipment, such as coordinatographs, and work the artwork 1:1. With extreme care, it is possible to produce 1:1 artwork that is accurate to ± 0.003″ (0.08 mm) over large areas, for example, 48 x 48″ (1.2 x 1.2 m).

Undercut and Tolerances:

As the etchant eats into the surface of the exposed metal, to a lesser extent it also etches away underneath the resist image. When the part is completely blanked through, there is a noticeable reduction in dimension from the acid-resist image orginally placed upon it. The term "undercut" has been applied to this phenomenon; it is expressed as a ratio of the depth of cut to the amount of undercut and varies for different metals and methods of etching. An etch factor of 3:1 means that, for every 0.003″ (0.076 mm) of etch depth, 0.001″ (0.025 mm) of undercut occurs. If the etch factor for a particular metal and etchant is known, then it can be used as a means for compensating the artwork by allowing for dimensional reduction so that accurately shaped parts can be produced.

Proper artwork compensation is one of the most important phases because, without it, there is little hope of holding required tolerances. If, for instance, it has been determined that 0.002″ (0.05 mm) of undercut will occur on a part to be etched from metal that is 0.006″ (0.15 mm) thick, then the part OD at the artwork stage must be increased by 0.002″ (0.05 mm) all around. Conversely, the ID would have to be decreased by the same amount.

Because of inherent undercut, a minimum size limit exists for slots, holes, and other piercings that can be produced. Expressing the thickness of the sheet stock to be blanked at T, the following blanking limitations on slots, holes, etc., are characteristic: 0.7 T for copper alloys, 1.0T for steel alloys, and 1.4T for aluminum alloys and stainless steel. Thus the smallest hole that can be chemically pierced into 0.010″ (0.25 mm) brass and still provide a near-vertical wall would be 0.007″ (0.18 mm).

As a general rule, internal corners develop radii equal to plus or minus the stock thickness. External corners can be held much sharper, generally equal to approximately one-third the stock thickness. However, the addition of small fillets to the artwork is of great value in reducing radii in certain cases.

Processing Multiple Parts:

Where a large number of parts are to be produced, it is desirable to have multiple images on the same film after photographic reduction. This is generally accomplished with automatic machines which can take a single image and generate a large number of images very simply.

It is usually necessary to produce accurate matching inverse images on two sheets of film or glass plates so that double-sided printing can be accomplished. It is generally desirable to produce both images—the original and the mirror image—from a single master drawing so that accurate registration is assured. Photographic methods for producing these images are well established. After the two images have been generated, it is necessary to register them accurately, one relative to the other, so that the images on the metal are in proper register.

Part Holding Methods:

Further tooling considerations involve the method in which the parts are held in the sheet during photochemical machining. The two common methods are dropping out and tabbing. While both these methods are acceptable procedures for part retention, each has its advantages and limitations.

Drop out. This method is, of course, limited to equipment designed to catch or reclaim parts that have been completely blanked out. The artwork used in this method should be designed so that an opaque border completely surrounds the part on subsequent negatives. Etching then occurs on all areas around the part, and hence the part will "drop out" onto a screen for subsequent overetching. The major advantage of the drop-out method is that parts are ready for use immediately after resist removal. This is advantageous for larger parts, but when several thousand small parts are involved, it creates quite a handling problem and tolerance allowances must be greater.

Tabbing. When this method is used small connectors or "tabs" are added to the artwork in such a manner as to tie all parts together in the final sheet. From a processing point of view, the tabbing method has the major advantages of handling ease and one-step etching in high-speed, conveyorized systems. However, the one major disadvantage is that subsequent cutting and finishing operations are necessitated by the use of tabs.

Nontraditional Machining of Nonmetals

The nontraditional machining processes described so far are used primarily with metals. Two nontraditional processes that are especially useful with nonmetals are water jet machining and abrasive water jet machining.

Water jet machining (also called fluid jet machining) can be used with plastics, composites, ceramics, glass, and wood. Abrasive water jet machining is particularly effective for use with brittle and/or heat-sensitive materials including glass, titanium, composites, and plastics.

Water jet machining forces a jet of highly pressurized fluid against the surface of the workpiece. This thin jet of fluid slits the material (see Fig. 12-42). Abrasive water jet machining works in a similar manner, but with the addition of an abrasive substance to the water jet. The abrasive enters the jet after the pressurized fluid passes through the nozzle (see Fig. 12-42).

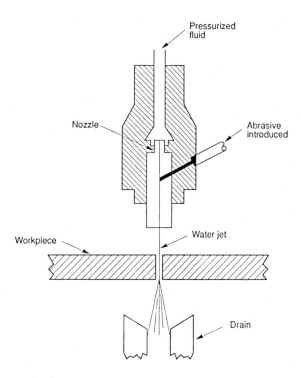

Figure 12-42   Abrasive waterjet machining

KEY TERMS AND PHRASES

Beta rays
Chemical milling
Core drilling
Deburring
Electrical discharge grinding
Electrical discharge machining
Electrical discharge wire cutting
Electrochemical discharge grinding
Electrochemical grinding
Electrochemical honing
Electrochemical machining
Electrochemical turning
Electrolytes
Electromechanical machining
Electron beam machining
Electro-Stream

External threading
Hone-Forming
Hydrodynamic machining
Internal threading
Laser beam machining
Masking
Perforation
Photochemical machining
Plasma arc machining
Pot and wobble broaches
Prototype work
Rotary ultrasonic machining
Shaped Tube Electrolytic Machining
Stamping dies
Stripping
Trepanning
Ultrasonically assisted machining
Ultrasonic gundrilling
Ultrasonic machining
Ultraviolet radiation
X rays

QUESTIONS FOR ADDITIONAL STUDY AND REVIEW

1. Describe the HDM process.

2. What are the most common HDM applications?

3. Describe the USM process.

4. What are the most common applications of RUM?

5. Describe the UAM process.

6. What is ultrasonic gundrilling?

7. Describe the EMM process.

8. What are the most common applications of ECDG?

9. Describe how the abrasive wheel functions with ECG.

10. What are the most common applications of ECH?

11. Describe the HF process.

12. Describe the ECM process.

13. Describe the STEM process.

14. List and briefly explain four thermal processes.

15. Describe the EDM process.

16. List five applications of EDG.

17. Explain the safety precautions for controlling the following potential safety hazards in laser beam machining:

    • Beta rays
    • Ultraviolet radiation

18. Explain the advantages of water injection in plasma arc machining.

19. What are five widely used applications of chemical milling?

20. Describe the photochemical machining process.

CHAPTER 13

Control of Working Processes

MAJOR TOPICS COVERED

- Sequence Controllers
- Programmable Logic Controllers
- Numerical Control (NC)
- Fundamentals of Computer Numerical Control (CNC)
- CNC System Elements
- Fundamentals of Direct and Distributed Numerical Control (DNC)
- NC Machine Configurations
- Computer-Assisted NC Part Programming
- Computer-Assisted NC Part Programming Languages
- Adaptive Control

MACHINE CONTROLS

The evolution of machine tool technology has been paced by dramatic increases in machine control capability, particularly within the past 25 years. In fact, many machine tool experts credit major improvements in manufacturing productivity and enhancements in workpiece quality over the last several decades to the fast-paced growth of capability of machine tool controls. The basic configurations of many machine tools (lathes, for example) have not changed significantly for many years; but the advent of numerical control, computer numerical control, and related enhancements has spurred important changes in the methods employed in manufacturing and has shown great impact on manufacturing cost.

The purpose of this chapter is to provide an overview of the various types of machine controls, including sequence controllers, programmable controllers, numerical control, computer numerical control, direct numerical control, and adaptive control.

Sequence Controllers

Sequence controllers are a class of electromechanical and electronic devices used to control the operation of a machine tool or other equipment in a predetermined step-by-step manner. Characteristic of these devices is the method of establishing the desired control sequence and the manner in which the controller functions. The more common types of sequence controllers available today are electromechanical stepping-drum programmers, perforated wide-paper-tape programmers, and diode-matrix pinboard programmers.

In the drum programmer, the desired control sequence is commonly established by inserting pins into appropriate rows in the surface of a cylinder. Mounted over one row of the cylinder surface are momentary contact switches so that, as each row moves into position under the switches, the pins in that row activate the switches corresponding to the position of the pins present. As the cylinder rotates or steps to the next row, the pins in that row cause the connection of certain input devices, such as pushbuttons, limit switches, and timer contacts, to the logic section of the controller. The logic section, as a result of the inputs, causes the closure of circuits to output devices such as solenoids and motor starters. When the logic section senses that selected inputs in that row are in the proper condition, the controller then advances, or "steps," the cylinder by rotating it to the next row. The pins in the next row then present the next set of input conditions to the controller and cause the closure of the corresponding desired output circuits.

In a perforated wide-paper-tape programmer, the desired control sequence is established by the pattern of holes which are punched into the tape. The operation of this type of device is similar to the operation of the familiar old player piano. In the diode-matrix pinboard programmer, the desired control sequence is established by inserting small plastic pins (each containing a diode) into a plugboard. Alteration of the desired control sequence is accomplished by changing the positions of the plastic plugs, the pattern of holes, or the position of the diode pins. All types of sequence controllers are typically used for applications having a fixed sequence of operation for a large number of repetitions.

Programmable Logic Controllers

A programmable logic controller (PLC) is a solid-state device used to control machine motion or process operation by means of a stored program. The PLC sends output control signals and receives input signals through input/output (I/O) devices. A PLC controls outputs in response to stimuli at the inputs according to the logic prescribed by the stored program. The inputs are made up of limit switches, pushbuttons, thumbwheels, switches, pulses, analog signals, ASCII serial data, and binary or BCD data from absolute position encoders. The outputs are voltage or current levels to drive end devices such as solenoids, motor starters, relays, lights, and so on. Other output devices include analog devices, digitial BCD displays, ASCII compatible devices, servo variable-speed drives, and even computers.

Programmable controllers were developed (circa 1968) when General Motors Corp. and other automobile manufacturers were experimenting to see if there might be an alternative to scrapping all their hardwired control panels of machine tools and other production equipment during a model changeover. This annual tradition was necessary because rewiring of the panels was more expensive than buying new ones.

The automotive companies approached a number of control equipment manufacturers and asked them to develop a control system that would have a longer productive life without major rewiring, but would still be understandable to and repairable by plant personnel. The new product was named a "program-mable controller."

The processor part of the PLC contains a central processing unit and memory. The central processing unit (CPU) is the "traffic director" of the processor; the memory stores information. Coming into the processor are the electrical signals from the input devices, as conditioned by the input module to voltage levels acceptable to processor logic. The processor scans the state of I/O and updates outputs based on instructions stored in the memory of the PLC. For example, the processor may be programmed so that if an input connected to a limit switch is true (limit switch closed), then a corresponding output wired to an output module is to be energized. This output might be a solenoid, for example. The processor remembers this command through its memory and compares on each scan to see if that limit switch is, in fact, closed. If it is closed, the processor energizes the solenoid by turning on the output module.

The output device, such as a solenoid or motor starter, is wired to an output module's terminal, and it receives its shift signal from the processor. In effect, the processor is performing a long and complicated series of logic decisions. The PLC performs such decisions sequentially and in accordance with the stored program. Similarly, analog I/O allows the processor to make decisions based on the magnitude of a signal, rather than just if it is on or off. For example, the processor may be programmed to increase or decrease the steam flow to a boiler (analog output) based on a comparison of the actual temperature in the boiler (analog input) to the desired temperature. This is often performed by utilizing the built-in PID (proportional, integral, derivative) capabilities of the processor.

Because a PLC is "software based," its control logic functions can be changed by reprogramming its memory. Keyboard programming devices facilitate entry of the revised program, which can be designed to cause an existing machine or process to operate in a different sequence or to respond to different levels of, or combinations of, stimuli. Hardware modifications are needed only if additional, changed, or relocated input/output devices are involved. Figures 13-1 and 13-2 are PLCs.

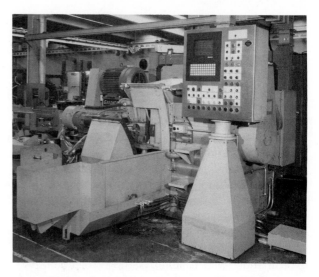

Figure 13-2   Another view of a programmable logic controller (PLC) *(Courtesy of Litton Industrial Automation Systems)*

Figure 13-1   One view of a programmable logic controller (PLC) *(Courtesy of Litton Industrial Automation Systems)*

PLC vs Computer

There are a few key characteristics which make the PLC unlike a computer or other types of controllers. First, the PLC is designed to communicate with the outside world (the process to be controlled) directly. That is, inputs from the process and controlling outputs to the process are wired directly to the PLC system. The PLC recognizes these inputs and outputs by means of a unique fixed address assigned to each I/O.

The second difference between PLCs and computers or other controllers is the relative ease of programming. The PLC uses relatively simple programming techniques that a plant technician or electrician easily can understand with minimal training. Some programmable controllers use a simple relay ladder diagram programming concept. In such cases, knowledge of Fortran, PAL, or any other computer language is not required; nor is the use of Boolean or other logical expressions required, although these can be converted into a relay ladder diagram format when necessary. The programming can be accomplished on-line with a portable programming panel or a CRT programmer in many cases.

An important point to note about PLCs is that a good PLC can be reprogrammed "on-line"; that is, while the process is running. Such operations are satisfactory and safe if, and only if, complete ladder rungs are operated on by the processor. Furthermore, on-line programming is successful only if the I/O structure is unaffected. An on-line program change could be hazardous for unproved programs. On-line programming capability can be a valuable feature in some process industries when shutting down a production line can be prohibitively expensive. The on-line feature allows certain portions of a program to be changed with minimum disruption of processing. However, the program or changes to a program should be debugged prior to use in a production situation.

The third and perhaps most important difference when PLCs are compared to computers is that PLCs are designed for an industrial environment. A well-designed PLC should allow the user to locate a PLC in a relatively high-noise, high-vibration, high-temperature, high-humidity (noncondensing) environment without affecting its operation.

Numerical Control

Numerical control (NC), computer numerical control (CNC), and direct and distributed numerical control (DNC) have given the manufacturing industry the capability to exercise a new and greater degree of freedom in the designing and manufacturing of products. This new freedom is demonstrated by the ability to automatically produce products requiring complex processing with a very high degree of quality and reliability. Furthermore, products which previously were impossible to manufacture economically can now be made with relative ease using NC machines.

The advances in product design and machines have been parallel; each advance in NC machines not only allows designing of products previously not practical, but suggests additional improvements in machines which would permit more complexity in product designing. Thus machine/product designing is a continuing cycle. The complexity of design of the product is reflected in the machine that produces it. Although many basic NC machine tools are currently available from various manufacturers, specialty applications of NC provide a fertile field for new machines. Retrofitting conventional or standard tools for NC has proved practical and popular; however, very sophisticated systems are usually designed and built specifically for NC.

Numerical control is applicable to a wide variety of industrial tasks. In evaluating the applicability of NC to a particular job, the heaviest weight should be given to jobs which include:

1. A long series of operations in which an error in the sequence would destroy the value of the operations.
2. A wide variety of different sequences of operation which must rapidly and frequently be set up on the same piece of equipment.
3. A relatively complex sequence of operations to be performed.
4. An operation in which it is impractical for a human being to operate in the environment required. Some NC machines run unattended by an operator; however, this benefit usually is associated with the use of robots which load and unload NC and non-NC equipment grouped to form a robotized machining cell.

Advantages of NC in Manufacturing

Numerical control has been shown to be one of the most significant advances in part manufacturing since the development of methods for interchangeable parts production. Over the past 20 years, NC has demonstrated the ability to improve in dramatic ways such things as:

- Planning, flexibility, and scheduling.
- Setup, lead, and processing time.

- Machine utilization.
- Tooling cost.
- Cutting tool standardization.
- Accuracy, efficiency, and productivity.
- Interchangeability of work, tools, etc.
- Safety.
- Cost estimating.

Fundamentals of Computer Numerical Control (CNC)

Computer numerical control (CNC) by Electronic Industries Association (EIA) definition is an NC system in which a dedicated stored-program computer is used to perform some or all of the basic NC functions in accordance with control programs stored in the read-write memory of the computer. Computer numerical control and soft-wired NC are synonymous terms. Computer numerical control is the dominant type of machine control being manufactured today. On the soft-wired control, the 110-volt a-c outputs are wired directly to the electromechanical devices on the machine (solenoids, for example). Likewise, switches and sensors on the machine are wired directly to the inputs. This contrasts with conventional hard-wired controls in which logic functions are wired together in a fixed, preengineered arrangement.

The key element of the soft-wired controller is a microprocessor or minicomputer. Because a computer is involved, there is a tendency to confuse the soft-wired controller and its application to computer numerical control (CNC) with direct and distributed numerical control (DNC). There are, however, several differences between the two.

Computers supporting DNC are used to disseminate manufacturing data to, and collect product information from, several machine controllers. Soft-wire controllers, on the other hand, generally support only one machine or a very small number of machines. Also, DNC computers may be remote from the machine tools, whereas soft-wired controllers are normally in close proximity. In addition, the software supporting DNC is usually written to support overall manufacturing activity, i.e., machine loading, productivity, and efficiency trends. Software for soft-wired controllers, however, is written specifically for a particular machine/device and its required fixed sequences.

Soft-Wired Controls

A soft-wired CNC system incorporates a programmable control unit—usually a general-purpose computer (mini or micro) with a read-write memory. The computer and memory replace much of the general-purpose fixed-logic circuitry of the hard-wired NC with programmable logic that is stored in the computer's memory. This stored logic, together with stored computer instructions, is called an "application software program."

This software program can be thought of as the mechanism for converting a general-purpose computer to a machine control system for a specific machine tool—for example, a two-axis lathe with a 12-tool turret. The term "soft-wired" is applicable because the functions created to control the specific machine tool result from the application software program rather than from any physical wiring of a group of logic elements.

The application software program permits flexibility in features and changes in a given machine tool (in addition to the ability to revise the software for different machines) basically without changes in physical wiring or hardware. This flexibility, however, is not unlimited in that certain options or changes may require additional hardware (switches, input/ output boards, etc.) or additional memory may be required to achieve the desired results.

As a result of the ability to change the application software program, soft-wired controls have a built-in resistance to obsolescence. But it must be pointed out that this feature (and such others as superior diagnostics and the ability to tailor a standard control for specific applications) does have a price. These features must be designed into the control. Engineering is still a requirement. Figure 13-3 lists the characteristics of soft-wired NC units.

CNC System Elements

The basic elements of a computer numerical control system are shown in Fig. 13-4. The control is the heart of the system. It processes information received from the operator and machine interface. This information is interpreted and manipulated with

hardware logic and computer programs (software). Memory provides the means to store programs and manipulate input data. Based on the information received, the control outputs data back to the operator interface and machine.

The operator interface consists of devices which send, receive, and interpret information. Since the operations performed by NC systems are defined by the software, interface devices are needed to input the various programs from memory. Paper tape input is the most common. The operator station(s) is the other major operator interface element. It contains all the switches, pushbuttons, displays, etc., required to operate and monitor machine activities.

Machine devices are regulated by the control. Based on information supplied by operator interface

Flexibility	Options can be added in the field by software revision and hardware augmentation in standard building blocks. Less costly to tailor CNC for each shop's unique problems and practice.
Field addition of new options	Newly developed options can be added after installation. Hardware and software are needed, but are easier than changes in hard-wired NC. Equipment cn be upgraded as new options become available. Premature obsolescence is minimized by this feature.
Variable tape format	Part programs for earlier NC machines can be used on CNC machine with software change. Eliminates need to reprogram existing tape library. Must be tailored for individual user.
Inch/metric conversion	Allows inch or metric tapes (switch provided) without need for separate feedback device. Facilitates machining under both systems during conversion.
Machine-language editing	Simplifies geometry changes and feed/speed optimizataion during tryout. Generate new tape at machine. Speeds program debugging. Increases available production time. Speeds cycle time. Improves programmer efficiency.
Part-program storage	Part program is stored in mini-computer memory. Tape reader, used for loading only, can be eliminated in DNC. Useful in repetitive production. Tapereader maintenance reduced or eliminated. Reader speed does not limit short block execution. No time required for tape rewind. With DNC, facilitates file maintenance (use of updated programs only).
Fewer types of print circuit boards	CNC design greatly reduces the number of boards required. Board types are common for different machine types. Reduces inventory of spare boards for single CNC unit or several, even if different machines are involved.
Board-level diagnostics	Design feature permitting fault and malfunction isolation to board. Minimizes production downtime. Allows ordinary maintenance and troubleshooting by less-skilled personnel.
Building-block approach to manufacturing automation or DNC	Flexibility of CNC allows better integration within total system than hard-wired NC. Step-by-step implementation of overall system. Part-program storage at CNC machine level improves system reliability, reduces data-rate requirement from central computer. Fits variety of DNC configurations. Allows later addition of plant data feedback and monitoring.

Figure 13-3   Advantages of soft-wired computer numerical control (CNC)

devices and feedback from various machine devices, the control turns on and off machine outputs and controls machine motion.

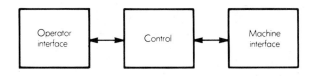

Figure 13-4   Elements of a CNC system

The Control

The control performs "real-time" decisions on a process that is in operation at the same time. There are several types of control systems; however, each can be broken down into the same functional units. Each unit performs specific functions, and all units function together to execute the programmed instructions. Figure 13-5 shows the five major functional units of a control. The dashed lines with arrows represent the flow of timing and control signals. The solid lines with arrows represent the flow of data.

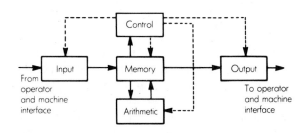

Figure 13-5   Five major functional units of a CNC system

Input Unit: All instructions and data are fed into the control through the input unit. Software, such as the system operating program, part programs, and diagnostics are input by means of paper tape,

magnetic devices, etc., and are stored in memory until needed. The status of machine and operator station devices are input in the form of a-c, d-c, and analog signals. Analog signals are converted to digital signals (A/D converter) in order to be understood by the control. Input signals are sent to memory, where they are used by the control and arithmetic units to arrive at output decisions.

For systems with many a-c or d-c inputs, a scheme called multiplexing may be used. With this scheme, the state of many devices can be monitored on a single channel. This reduces wiring without restricting real-time operation.

Memory Unit

The memory unit stores instructions and data received from the input. It also stores the results of arithmetic operations and supplies information to the output. The size of the programs and space required to manipulate data determine the amount of memory required. Basically, there are two types of memory—Random Access Memory (RAM) and Read Only Memory (ROM).

RAM. Random Access Memory provides immediate access to any storage location point in memory. Information may be "read" or "written" in the same very fast procedure. Part programs are usually stored in RAM memory to enable editing. While there are many types of RAM, only certain types (i.e., core and bubble) are able to retain data during a power loss. Complementary Metal Oxide Semiconductor (CMOS) memory is retentive if it has battery backup.

ROM. Read Only Memory stores information permanently or semipermanently. Information can be "read," but cannot be altered. Only fixed programs such as the system operating program and diagnostics should be stored on ROM. "Programmable" ROMs are referred to as PROMs, and electrically erased PROMS are called EPROMs.

Arithmetic Unit: The arithmetic unit performs calculations and makes decisions. The results are sent to the memory unit to be stored.

Control Unit: The control unit takes instructions from the memory unit and interprets them one at a time. It then sends appropriate instructions to other units to cause instruction execution.

Output Unit: The output unit takes data from memory when commanded. Outputs are in the form of a-c, d-c, and digital signals. Digital signals used as axis drive commands are first converted to analog (D/A converter). Output signals are used to turn on and off devices, display information, position axes, etc.

Operator Interface

The operator interface consists of all devices, exclusive of the machine, which send and receive control information.

Machine Interface

The machine interface consists of all devices used to monitor and control the machine tool. Extreme travel limits, miscellaneous position locations, hydraulic and air pressures can be monitored. Additionally, solenoids for hydraulic and air control as well as motor control are provided. Outputs are usually a single d-c and a-c level or a d-c output with remote a-c switching devices.

Several systems employ a multiplexing scheme which greatly reduces hardware requirements. Since multiplex cycles are usually less than 50 μs, few reliability problems are encountered. Figure 13-6 depicts some of the more common machine devices.

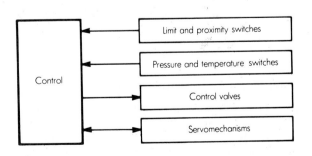

Figure 13-6   NC interface devices

Fundamentals of Direct and Distributed Numerical Control

Direct numerical control (DNC) is a system connecting a group of numerically controlled machines to a common computer memory for part-program storage, with provision for on-demand distribution of machining data. Typically, additional provisions are available for collection, display, or editing of part programs, operator instructions, or data related to the NC process.

Changing Concepts

The original DNC concept was forwarded (circa 1965) as a means of reducing NC control costs through use of one powerful controller for a group of machines, rather than a separate controller for each machine tool. The cost of electronic control equipment was much higher in the early 1960s than it is today; so high that the DNC concept was driven by a need to reduce control costs.

Proponents of the DNC concept believed that punched paper tape and tape readers at the machine tool could be completely eliminated by driving the NC machines directly from the memory of a central computer. Because NC machines of the day typically were not equipped with memory, the central computer would drive the machines in real time—that is, the computer would send NC data to the machine tools in sequence or pulse form during the actual machining operation. By operating in this manner, it was expected that maintenance costs of tape readers at the machine tool could be eliminated and that input errors caused by improper operation of tape readers at the machine tool could be avoided.

In addition, the original DNC concept promised simpler management of NC programs and an elimination of a need for costly libraries of punched paper tape. It was believed that by storing NC programs and monitoring NC machines using a central computer, the optimization of NC programs and simulation of numerical control functions (verification of tool path using a plotter, for example) would be more easily performed. Also, it was thought that collection and reporting of system operating data such as downtime, production, and maintenance information would be more easily accomplished.

The original concepts of DNC worked reasonably well in a few isolated applications; however, some of the promises of DNC never were realized on a broad scale. For example, the thought that DNC could eliminate the need for tape readers or other input devices at the machine tool proved unrealistic. Tape readers or other alternate input devices at the machine tool were found to be useful in the early DNC systems as backups to the computerized system. Such manual backup was required because occasional downtime of the central computer caused the entire DNC system to go down, sometimes idling a dozen or more expensive NC machine tools.

With the advent of computer numerical control came the availability of relatively inexpensive computer memory at the machine tool. The nature of the DNC concept was altered as a consequence. With computer memory at the machine tool, it is no longer required that the CNC machines of a DNC network be driven in real time. Instead, NC programs can be downloaded in total from the memory of the central computer to the memory of the computer at the machine tool; the connection between the central computer and the individual machine tools in the system need only be maintained for a short period of time—the time necessary to transmit the NC program. In this way, the uptime of individual machine tools is less dependent upon the uptime of the central computer and, because the machines are not driven in real time by the central computer, program editing at the machine is made much easier. This concept, known as distributed numerical control, is growing in usage. In fact, the acronym DNC, originally defined as direct numerical control, is now used by many experts in the controls industries to describe *distributed numerical control*, Fig. 13-7.

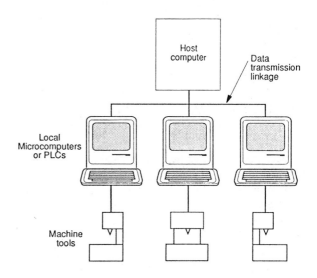

Figure 13-7   Distributed numerical control (DNC)

Applications

In general, two areas of application exist in which DNC has shown specific advantages. First, the DNC concept is often justifiable in applications that have large amounts of control information which must be managed, stored, and distributed—many NC programs or very complex programs. DNC facilitates the management of large numbers of NC programs and helps to sidestep the possibility of using the wrong NC program or using a program that is not the latest version. With DNC, lengthy NC programs can be loaded quickly, eliminating the costly nonproductive time often associated with the loading of complex programs via punched paper tape or other mechanical input media. The payoff is achieved in increased uptime and greater machine tool efficiency.

The DNC concept is also employed as the heart of the control system for so-called flexible production systems in which a number of numerically controlled machine tools are linked by means of electronic data communication and mechanical automation. Often employed to machine families of parts, such systems are equipped with a central computer which directs the flow of parts through the system and operates in a DNC mode, downloading NC programs to the member machine tools as required. In such systems, the central computer is also used to collect operating data.

DNC Operating Guidelines

Experience has shown that NC part programs which are to be stored and distributed via a DNC network should contain certain introductory information. Information of this type should include the part number of the workpiece to be machined, the drawing number, and any special processing-related information such as a list of fixtures or clamping devices that will be required to facilitate the machining of the workpiece. Special machining instructions should also be listed according to a standard format and a list should be included of the machine tools on which the part can be processed, including machine numbers and descriptions.

Part programs of a DNC system should be protected via an automated security system. Each part program should contain an authorization code at the beginning of the program which can be read by the central computer. Such a code can be employed, if necessary, to block the transfer of an NC program to a machine tool that is unauthorized for machining of the part. In this way, the use of specific machine tools for workpieces can be easily controlled.

In a DNC system, the part programs should be managed and classified in a logical fashion. Some of the classification breakdowns that have proven useful include access and reporting by program number or program name (workpiece name), machine tool authorization codes, date of program preparation, and date of change.

Experiences of users familiar with the operations of a DNC system indicate that the call-up of NC programs from the system should be sufficiently simple so that users who are not data processing professionals can call up programs without difficulty. Experience has also shown that a DNC system should be capable of downloading the same program to different machine tools simultaneously. This capability is particularly important and may have significant impact on the operating efficiency of a flexible production system, for example.

The system employed for data transmission is the heart of any DNC installation. System reliability and performance is often dictated by the viability of the data transmission network. Operating performance of the communication system in a DNC network is optimal if it does not present constraints causing one or both of the following conditions to occur:

- Machine is idled while waiting for transmission of data.
- Operator's time is wasted while waiting for responses from the DNC computer.

The operating baud rate or even the effective throughput rate is not of much concern when a part program is being downloaded if, for example, the CNC can accept the data to memory while another part program is running to produce parts.

The differences among the various CNC machines in the DNC system must be accounted for in the design of the system. For example, some CNC units may have limited internal storage. In cases in which the NC program length is larger than the internal memory capacity at the machine tool, the DNC system must have the capability to automatically download only portions of the program that are within the capacity of the machine tool. The capability should be built-in from the start.

Often, NC programs are optimized by the machine tool operator during the first several production runs of a new part. An efficient DNC system should be capable of accepting optimized NC programs from the CNC machine tools in the network; however, a system should be established that prevents the revised program from being used in place of the original program before the changes are approved by the programmer.

The possibility of downtime of the central computer must be considered in the design of the DNC system. In many cases, short periods of downtime of the central computer will not stop production because current DNC systems generally do not drive machine tools in real time; a number of programs may be stored at the machine tool so that production can continue even when the central computer is down. In emergencies, NC programs can be downloaded to machine tools via a storage disk (a disk containing the programs for a day's production) and a portable disk reader. These and other provisions for emergency operation of the system are extremely important and should be considered in the design phase of any DNC system.

The printing of certain lists is an invaluable feature of DNC which should be designed to be compatible with current management style and reporting systems. The following are a few examples of the lists which can be printed using the capabilities of the central computer of a DNC system:

- Production schedules.
- Running times of programs.
- Tools required to machine a specific part.
- Instructions for the operator.
- NC programs contained on a disk.
- Block programs.
- Data on when each program was used last.

The ability of a DNC system to collect and report machine related data is also important in some applications. Such data can be used to structure useful management reports. The following are examples of some data which can be collected using the central computer of a DNC system:

- Meantime between failures.
- Duration of downtime and causes.
- Machine utilization reports.
- Machine loading.

NC Machine Configurations

Numerical control is employed effectively with a wide range of machine tools and with many machines that are used for operations other than metal removal.

The number of axes or machine motions to which numerical control is applied commonly ranges from two to five. In general, NC machines are grouped into two classes: positioning machines and contouring machines. The functional capabilities of both types of machines are explained in the following sections.

The two axes of a representative point-to-point or positioning system are the straight-line movements of the longitudinal and cross or transverse slides, these two machine motions occurring at 90° to each other. They are respectively X and Y axes, and these motions position the workpiece by positioning the table or surface on which it is mounted according to rectangular coordinates. Two-axis control, if provided with contouring capability, could be used for two-dimensional contouring.

A third axis may be added by applying numerical control to the up and down movement of the spindle of a vertical milling machine or of an upright drill, for example. This becomes the Z axis. These axis designations are diagrammed in Fig. 13-8.

In contouring systems, the third axis provides three-dimensional control—for milling cavities in dies or molds or for milling other contours in three dimensions.

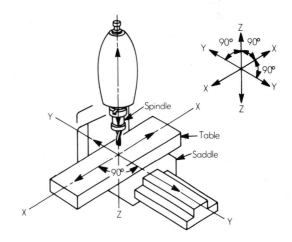

Figure 13-8 Diagram of a vertical spindle machine showing the axes

Positioning Machines and Systems

In its simplest form, the positioning machine is provided with NC dimensional control of the slide position only. Slide feed rates and spindle-rotating speeds, for example, may be selected manually. However, most modern NC positioning machines provide tape control of feeds and speeds, coolant on-off, turret indexing, etc. The method of handling these functions varies considerably from one manufacturer to another and cannot be generalized sufficiently to depict in diagrams.

Point-to-Point: A point-to-point machine (sometimes called a positioning machine) is one that moves the slides until a specific point on the workpiece is at the exact position at which the machining operation can begin. In some machines, the table slides move the workpiece to a specific location under the tool so that machining can start. In other machines, the table and workpiece remain stationary and the tool is moved to the desired location in relation to the workpiece. Certain machines can position both part and tool simultaneously.

In the first instance, each slide attempts to move at its maximum traverse rate to the new location, ignoring the status of other slides in the system. Because the slides operate independently of each other, the tool path between operations can be predicted only roughly. The path is affected by the distance between points, acceleration or deceleration, and the maximum traverse rate of each slide. The lack of linearity of the tool path between locations is of little consequence since the tool is not in contact with the workpiece during the traverse sequence.

Straight-Cut: The positioning machine operating in the manner described previously would be useful as a "hole-making" machine, that is, drilling, tapping, or boring holes at different locations on a workpiece. Such equipment would be more useful if it could machine (i.e., mill) between adjacent points; however, milling cannot generally be accomplished at maximum traverse rates. Straight-cut systems are capable of moving the cutter at a controlled feed rate along paths parallel to one or more of the machine axes.

A milling machine, for example, might be designed for a maximum error of 0.0005″ (0.013 mm) when making a cut. That is, the machine slide, which is stationary during the cut, would be required to hold its position to within 0.0005″ (0.013 mm) as the maximum allowable error in order for the cut to be within tolerance. The slide would be required to have the rigidity necessary to maintain position under the loads imposed by the cutting tools. The moving slide would travel at the speed required for the cut. Many such methods of rate modification have been devised; thus, straight-cut positioning machines have been developed.

Because traverse rate is controlled on a per-axis basis and the path described by the tool between adjacent points in a multiaxis system is unpredictable, the straight-cut-positioning machine is usually limited to milling along a principal axis of the machine. Its path is very predictable because it is as linear as the guide surface (ways) of the machine.

Two-Axis Systems: A two-axis machine is capable of drilling, milling, boring, and counterboring. In a point-to-point machine of this type, the table and workpiece are moved in both the X and Y axes by NC and positioned beneath the spindle. Spindle feed is controlled manually by the operator because NC of the third (Z-axis) slide is not provided. However, such a machine can be of substantial economic benefit because once it is set up, the operator is concerned only with spindle feeds and speeds and toolchanging.

Three-Axis Systems: A three-axis positioning machine requires an additional servoloop to control the Z-axis machine slides, connected in parallel with the X and Y axes. Since the machine has a turret, which is indexed by tape control, a workpiece requiring as many as eight different tools can be machined without stopping the cycle for a tool change. This type of machine also provides tape control of feeds and speeds, and a tape-controlled dwell cycle.

This three-axis machine may also be equipped with a tool-length compensator. This permits the operator to index to each turret position manually, and advance the turret slide to the workpiece with the rapid-advance control. Using a thickness gage, the operator can then preset each tool to compensate for variances in tool length and the programmer can program actual hole depths. Once a machining cycle is started, the cycle can continue under tape control without interruption.

The rapid-approach-and-retract and the machining-to-depth operations involve movement of the Z-axis slide. Thus the analog principles of the servoloop section of the NC system are applied in the same manner as for a single-slide system.

Special Positioning-Machine Functions: Some manufacturers of positioning NC systems have devised methods, sometimes proprietary, for controlling the slides simultaneously to produce angular movements. These methods have good economic reasons for existing in that they have greatly reduced the programming effort, have reduced the tape length, and have reduced the need for higher speed readers. Some of the angular cuts, or "slopes," produced by these methods are not exact; however, this "slope" potential has many advantages if close tolerances are not required. The machining of a chamfer, when the chamfer does not have to mate with another surface, is a good example of this application.

No matter how sophisticated a positioning machine is, it should not be confused with a contouring machine. A true continuous-path contouring machine must include both interpolation and buffer-storage elements. Positioning systems have been built with buffer storage in cases when the "read time" without buffer storage was considered excessive, that is, when the amount of data to be read or the rate at which the data should be read consumed too much of the total cycle time.

Contouring Machines and Systems

Milling machines, skin mills, spar mills, lathes, and other machines can cut very complex shapes through the use of NC contouring control systems. Some examples of other machines which employ contouring or continuous-path capability are flame cutting or plasma torch cutting systems, welding machines, drafting machines, filament winders, tape laying equipment, foam/gasket dispensers, and articulated robots. Discussions in this chapter are limited to configurations of machine tools. In such systems, the tool path is maintained by controlling the simultaneous position of multiple axes. In cutting a flat plate into a circular dish, for example, a profiling machine must be able to maintain the circular dimensions with the required accuracy and surface finish. This is achieved by designing the machine control system so that very small increments such as 0.0001″ (0.003 mm) can be attained. The tool could then theoretically have a maximum error from the desired position (ignoring the effects of machine stiffness) of only about 0.00001″ (0.0003 mm) at any point on the circumference of the circle. This type of accuracy would require the use of a position transducer system that has a resolution of 0.0001″ (0.003 mm) with no error over the range required. Practical problems have precluded achieving production systems with this kind of performance, however.

Since it is impractical to provide input data on every incremental movement of each slide, interpolators are designed into contouring machines to reduce the amount of information required and yet produce essentially the same results as if each position were individually programmed. Linear, circular, and parabolic interpolation are the most common types of interpolation applied to contouring machines. Linear interpolation is the simplest. Curved surfaces can be approximated by straight lines, and the error between the actual path and the desired path can be made as small as desired (within practical limits) by taking successively smaller straight-line segments between program-defined points. The limit, of course, is the smallest possible programmable movement of the slide. Figure 13-9 is a CNC machine tool.

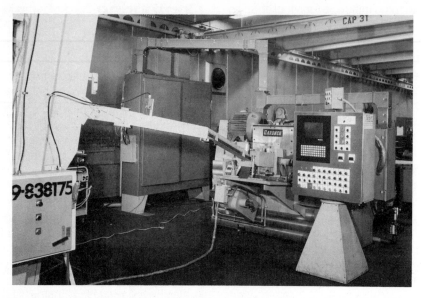

Figure 13-9 CNC machine tool *(Courtesy Litton Industrial Automation Systems)*

Computer-Assisted NC Part Programming

Advantages of Computer-Assisted Programming

The principal benefit of computer-assisted programming is increased productivity. Increased productivity results from two factors: (1) a reduction in the user's part programming time and (2) improved utilization of the numerically controlled machine tool. Computer-assisted programming reduces part programming time by:

- Reducing and simplifying the mathematical calculations which the part programmer must perform. This is especially important for more complex parts.
- Reducing the time spent correcting errors introduced by manual part programming and mathematical calculations made by hand.

- Providing a standardized input method that reduces the need to worry about varying tape formats or about forms of instruction accepted by different machine tools or machine tool controls.
- Allowing for the use and reuse of stored sets of instructions and repeated machining patterns.

Reduced part programming time can result in lower part programming labor costs and shorter lead times for part production. The degree of savings will depend on the capabilities of the selected computer-assisted system and the applicability of the system to the type of machining for which it is intended. The applicability of a system is covered later in this chapter.

Computer-assisted programming systems also increase productivity by improving utilization of the machine tool. The NC machine tool is a major capital investment; the machine pays for itself by manufacturing parts. Computer assistance helps to produce parts more quickly, and therefore to produce more parts, by allowing for the following:

- Part program error detection and feedback prior to a machine tool trial run.

- Graphic (visual) representation of the programmed part or the machine tool cutting path.
- Easy editing of a part program without involving the machine tool control.
- Optimization of machine tool movements (such as more accurate calculation of the time and place to accelerate to rapid motion).
- Automatic selection of the most efficient path for multiple operations such as pattern drilling or punching.
- Potential reduction in machine downtime for repairs caused by programming errors that result in cutter/workpiece/fixture collisions.

Small savings in machine cycle time can have a large impact on machine production. The savings can be calculated as follows:

Savings per job = savings in machine cycle time/part × cost of machine time × number of parts

Obviously the number of parts produced has a major effect on savings. For large production runs, even very small savings in machine cycle time per part can significantly reduce the total time the machine is used during the full production run.

Savings in part programming time and machine cycle time are the essential factors used to justify an investment in a computer-assisted programming system. An additional advantage of such a system may be its ability to handle more complex parts.

Elements of a Computer-Assisted Programming System

A computer-assisted system to aid part programming can consist of any number of components. The most obvious elements are the visible ones: computers and computer terminals; hardware devices for input, output, and storage of part programs; NC tape punches and readers; and the like. Less obvious, but perhaps more important, are the hidden elements of the system: part programming languages and the computer programs that convert the part programmer's input to appropriate machine instructions. Both the hardware and software

elements of computer-assisted systems are discussed in this section. Figure 13-10 is an illustration of how the elements of a computer-assisted system are related.

Processors, postprocessors, and their languages comprise the software elements of a computer-assisted system. They are the means by which computing power is put to work. Although software cannot be readily seen or touched, it is the heart of the computer system.

The remaining elements of a computing system are the devices that allow for input, processing, output, and storage of information generated during computer-assisted NC part programming.

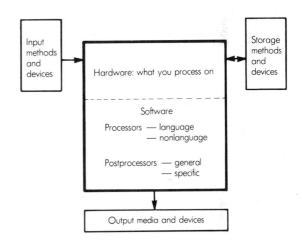

Figure 13-10 Elements of a computer-assisted NC programming system

Computer-Assisted NC Programming Procedures

The way in which a computer-assisted system is used to help in writing part programs varies according to the type of system used. In general, however, the use of such systems requires that the following steps be taken:

1. Determine how to make the part.
2. Select the appropriate programming method.

3. Write part geometry and machining statements (if using a language).
4. Process source statements and correct errors.
5. Perform a machine trial run.

Workpiece Processing: Computer-assisted NC programming does not eliminate the need for experienced manufacturing know-how. All parts require the development of some form of plan for their manufacturing. The development of this plan is called "process planning." Process planning requires knowledge of the physical capacity of available machines, the proper sequence of machining steps or operations that need to be performed, and the most efficient ways of producing the part using the company's available resources. Computer-assisted process planning (CAPP) systems are available to assist in this activity.

Computer-assisted "group technology" systems are also available to help establish more efficient ways to manufacture similar parts. Such "families of parts" can be grouped according to similarity of part geometry of machining process. This allows for retrieval of previously developed manufacturing plans, designs, or NC part programs for new parts that might be similar to part produced earlier. Group technology also helps the manufacturer to develop "manufacturing cells," organized to integrate the flow of parts, machinery, and labor in the most efficient manner.

On a very limited scale, computers may be used to assist the planner in determining how to operate machines (automatically determining correct feeds and speeds) for the manufacturing of specified parts from known stock materials. This method of computer-assisted programming, called "workshop technology," might, for example, be used to automatically determine the correct feeds and speeds for a specific machining operation. Workshop technology was first introduced in Europe in the early 1970s.

In determining how to manufacture a part, an experienced manufacturing engineer, process planner, or part programmer usually has to personally weigh such issues as the quality standards for the finished part, the profitability requirements of the company, and the optimal use of available machines.

Programming Method: After planning how to make a part, a decision must be made as to whether or not computer-assisted programming methods should be used. Factors that enter into this decision include the following:

- How complex is the part?
- How many times will the manufacturer be likely to receive new orders for this part or similar parts?
- What programming skills do programming personnel already have, and what skills would require special training?
- What will it cost to use computer-assisted versus manual programming methods?

Write Part Geometry and Machining Statements: The way in which the user defines part geometry and writes machining statements depends on (1) the information on the part drawing and (2) the programming method that will be used. These two factors must normally be considered simultaneously, because the capabilities of the programming method may or may not be well-suited to the kind of information that the design engineer chose to include on the part print.

To help describe how a part program is written, Fig. 13-11 shows a simple part (U.S. customary units) and the kinds of programming statements that might be written for it. In this example, the part description and machining sequence are shown using normal English statements for purposes of illustration. Actual programming language statements are usually written in a more abbreviated form. The written statements in this example are the source statements that, when written in a part programming language, would be sent to the computer for processing.

Example:
Part Description (see Fig. 13-11)

- Construct a line called 1 which passes through the reference location (⊕) and is parallel to the Y axis.

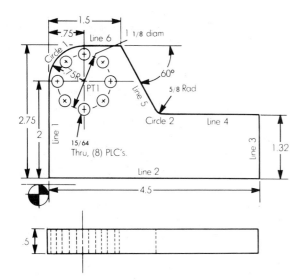

Figure 13-11   Example of simple part geometry

- Construct a line called 2 which passes through the reference location (◑) and is parallel to the X axis.
- Construct a line called 3 which is parallel to the Y axis and is located 4.5 units from the reference location.
- Construct a line called 4 which is parallel to the X axis and is located 1.32 units from the reference location.
- Construct a line called 5 which passes through a point located 1.5 units in the X direction and 2.75 units in the Y direction from the reference location, and whose angle is 60°, measured clockwise from the 3 o'clock position.
- Construct a line called 6 which is parallel to the X axis and is located 2.75 units from the reference location.
- Construct a point called 1 which is located 0.75 units in X, 2 units in Y and 0.5 units in Z from the reference location.
- Construct a circle called 1 whose center lies on point 1 and whose radius is 0.75 units.
- Construct a circle called 2 which is tangent to line 5 and line 4 and whose radius is 0.625 units. The circle center is to the right (XLarge) of line 5 and above (YLarge) line 4.

- Construct a bolt circle called SET1, whose center lies on point 1 and has a diameter of 1⅛ units. There are 8 equally spaced holes, starting at 0° and proceeding in a counterclockwise direction.

Machining Sequence (see Fig. 13-11)

- Drill the bolt circle (SET1), each hole 15/64″ (0.234″) diam, right through a plate 0.5 units thick.
- Using a 1″ diam tool, position to the left (XSmall) of line 1 and 0.1 units below (YSmall .1) line 2.
- Cut to the tangency point of line 1 and circle 1, maintaining the cutter offset to the left.
- Contour around circle 1 in a clockwise direction until the 270° position is reached (12 o'clock). At this point the tool is directly above line 6.
- Cut in a direction parallel to line 6 until the tool is past line 5.
- Cut to the tangency point of line 5 and circle 2, keeping the tool center to the right of line 5.
- Contour inside circle 2 in a counterclockwise direction until the tangency point of circle 2 and line 4 is reached. At this point the tool is directly above line 4.
- Keeping the tool in contact with line 4, cut past line 3.
- Keeping the tool to the right of line 3, cut past line 2.
- Keeping the tool below line 2, cut past line 1.

Process Source Statements and Correct Errors:
After a manuscript of part programming source statements has been prepared, the data is entered into the computer for processing. Batch or interactive processing may be used.

Feedback on the results of the processing (called "error diagnostics") may consist of English words or numerical codes representing errors that were encountered in the input source statements. The advantage of English-like statements is their ease of interpretation; numerically coded error messages require that a document cross referencing the numerical codes and their meanings be used.

The kinds of errors that might typically be encountered include:

- Typographical errors (misspelled words or incorrect punctuation).

- Syntax errors (proper words or punctuation used incorrectly in the source statements).
- Geometric incongruities (geometry elements that do not make sense; the tool is unable to follow the part shape or complete a movement).
- Machine-specific errors detected by the post processor (machine limits and speed and feed rates are exceeded).

In batch mode, these kinds of errors may be part of a long list of errors returned to the programmer after one or more passes through the batch processor. (It should be noted that a completely correct first manuscript is very rare.) In interactive mode, each line of the source statement manuscript is processed individually, with the processor reporting any errors in finds in each line at the time the line is entered by the user.

Error corrections can be made on-line while connected to an interactive system or off-line with either an interactive or batch system. On-line, interactive editing offers immediate error correction, but may tend to use more time at the computer terminal. Off-line, batch mode error correction allows for the use of cheaper computer time, but may introduce an unwanted time interval between each pass of processing and error correction.

Computer-assisted systems differ in their ability to recognize or tolerate part program errors. No system can check for all possible programming errors, particularly those which represent possible (but correct) geometry or machining. It is here that the programmer may look to additional proofing devices, such as CRTs that have graphics capability or plotters. Such devices can graphically represent the accepted part program so that the programmer can make a final, visual check of the part geometry or tool motion that has been specfied.

Machine Trial Run:
The purpose of a machine trial run is to provide a final verification of the part program before the program is used to start making production parts.

The trial run may consist of a simple run of the tape at the machine with the cutting tool mounted at a relatively large offset and without stock. By watching the machine movements, which during the trial run are generally run at block-length intervals, the operator can check for problems that might result in damage to the machine or the workpiece. As a further check, the operator might mount a substitute tool (a pen, for example) in the toolholder and check the path that the real tool would take. Sometimes scrap material or a cheap substitute for the part stock, such as wood or Styrofoam, can be mounted and cut for a more realistic final check of machining.

A trial run helps to reduce excess costs that could result from the production of incorrect parts (a waste of both material and machining time) or from broken tools or damaged machine components. Replacing damaged equipment is expensive, and repairs may require extensive machine downtime, which can be very costly.

Errors detected during the trial run can be fixed by producing a new edited NC tape. It is important that any changes made during trial or production runs be noted on the part program so that errors do not reoccur in subsequent production runs.

The Production Run:
After the machine tape is verified as being correct, it is mounted at the control and NC production can begin. Few changes are likely to occur if the tape is correct to begin with. However, the machine operator may find it necessary to make tooling changes at a given NC machine or may decide to run the production on a different NC machine for better results. Finished surfaces on the parts may indicate that slight adjustments to machine speed or feed rates are needed. The operator may observe ways to further optimize machine tool movements. (For example, the operator may find that he can use rapid tool motion in places or to tolerances that were not originally programmed.)

A computer-assisted programming system cannot automatically record what an operator does manually at the NC machine to improve the machining process. The operator must inform the part programmer of whatever modifications are made so that the program accurately reflects the final and successful machining operation.

Computer-Assisted NC Part Programming Languages

There is a wide variety of general-purpose and specialized part programming languages from which to choose, and the number and types of these languages are increasing rapidly. Because these languages are continually evolving, it would not be useful to discuss specific, specialized languages in this presentation.

Definition of Language

Although many different kinds of computer-assisted NC part programming languages exist, they all share certain features. Each language consist of a "vocabulary" of words and/or numbers with special meanings or definitions. To communicate with the computer, and eventually with the machine tool, these "words" must be combined to form meaningful sets of instructions called statements. Each language has its own set of rules, or syntax, that governs the way in which words can be arranged to make statements. (These rules are similar to the rules of grammer in "natural" noncomputer languages like English or French.) A part programmer, usually working from a design drawing of a part, uses the vocabulary and syntax of a language to write statements that control the cutting operations of a machine tool for a specific part. The part programmer writes several basic types of statements. These include geometry statements describing the physical dimensions of a given part, tool motion statements describing the relative movement of the tool and part, and other kinds of auxiliary statements, such as those specifying speed and feed rates. These statements can be written by the programmer, and they serve as the "source statements" that are entered into the computer for processing.

A second feature of all language systems is the processor, which is a set of instructions (or a program) that enables the computer to process and evaluate the source statements entered by the part programmer. After these source statements are processed, the data must usually be further modified to meet the requirements of the specific machine tool that is to be used. The additional processing that is required to modify the data is called "postprocessing." The part programmer writes special statements to define parameters for the type of postprocessing required for the machine tool being used. In some languages, the language input is first processed by the computer to produce "cutter location data" that contains intermediate tool location and motion data. This data is then postprocessed. Other languages perform both processing and postprocessing simultaneously.

In addition to these shared features of languages, processor and postprocessor language systems can also be distinguished according to the number and type of applications for which they were designed. A programmer may select a specialized language designed to be used only by a specific type of machine tool or for a specific machining application, or he may select a general-purpose language that can perform a wide variety of machining functions on any number of machine tools. The programmer's selection of a general-purpose or specialized language will be based on many factors. A summary of the advantages of each type of language system follows.

Advantages of General-Purpose Languages: There are many advantages to the use of general-purpose part programming languages. Among these are:

- Reduced programming time.
- Permanent source documentation.
- Standardization of parts and machining processes.
- Ability of the program to be easily read and understood by other users.
- Protection against changes in machine control technology.
- Broad application of programming skills among a wide variety of machines.

- Availability of trained personnel in the marketplace.
- Adaptability of programming to "family of parts" processing techniques.

Advantages of Specialized Languages:
Specialized languages also have many advantages. Among these are:

- Reduced learning time.
- Reduced complexity of software and programming.
- Reduced programming time.
- Usability on small computers.
- Reduced complexity, or elimination, of postprocessor.
- Permanent source documentation.
- Standardization of parts and machining processes.
- Protection against changes in machine control technology.
- Adaptability of programming to "family of parts" processing techniques.

Processing the Language

Languages can be processed in either interactive or batch mode. In the interactive mode, individual statements are processed line by line; with some general-purpose languages, they are processed and postprocessed simultaneously line by line. This processing method provides immediate feedback and diagnostics and permits the part programmer to correct errors and perform other editing functions before proceeding. In batch mode, the entire part program is entered and then processed. A list of error messages is produced for the entire part program; these errors must then be corrected and the entire program again processed. This step must be repeated until all errors are corrected. Although batch processing is generally less expensive than interactive processing, savings may be reduced or eliminated because of the time involved in reprocessing the batch program to produce an error-free tape.

Some general-purpose languages require two or more processing steps; for example, one step for editing syntax and another for correcting machining statement errors. This type of processing is called "multiple-pass" processing. Other languages are able to perform all processing steps in a single pass. These languages are said to use a "single-pass" processor.

Language Capabilities

Languages differ in the way they decribe the physical dimensions or geometry of parts and the machining needed to produce those parts.

General-purpose languages are capable of machining a wide variety of parts, although some of these languages may be more efficient than others in handling more complex part shapes. Specialized languages, on the other hand, may be written for a specific type of machining application and/or part description. Specialized languages exist for drills, lathes, mills, punch presses, and the like.

There is a third group of languages, called "parts generator" or "parametric" languages, that is limited to one type of part and a specific type of machine tool. A language from this group might be used to machine a cam that requires a large number of discrete tool motions for it to be machined within acceptable tolerances.

In general, because the more specialized types of languages perform a relatively small set of NC programming functions, they require smaller computers; are more easily learned; and if designed for a specific machine tool and control, may not require a separate postprocessor. However, general-purpose programming languages can be more versatile in shops that use a variety of machine types; once learned, they can be applied to a wide variety of functions and can be more easily adapted to new technologies as they become available. Figure 13-12 may be used to evaluate language systems.

Adaptive Control

In general, adaptive control (AC), sometimes referred to as automatic adaptive control (AAC), is a type of system which automatically and continuously identifies on-line performance of an activity (a

Business, operational

How long has the vendor been involved in NC programming service or product business?

How many employees are assigned to these activities?

How many NC programming service/product customers does the vendor have?

What manuals are provided? cost?

How good is the programmer's manual?

What training courses are provided? where? how long are they? cost?

What consulting services are offered? cost?

Is it a local or remote processing service? batch or time-shared?

Local Processing:

What host computer is required? terminals? other equipment?

What peripherals are used: plotters, printers, readers, punches?

Who maintains the equipment?

What types of terms are offered?

Who provides and maintains the software for local systems?

Does the vendor develop and maintain postprocessors?

Does the vendor give support for failure reports from users?

Remote Processing:

Where is the nearest regional center?

How is the center contacted for programming work?

What is the host computer? what terminals are required at user site?

Who maintains the user terminals? cost?

What postprocessors are available? cost?

Technical capability

Is this a 2D, 2½D, or 3D system?

Does it control two, three, four, or five-axis machine tools?

How many axes can be controlled for simultaneous movement?

Does it control point-to-point, straight-line cutting, contouring?

What definitions may be used for points? for lines? for circles? for mathematically defined curves? for tabulated curves?

What definitions for planes may be used? for cylinders? cones? spheres? toroids? for other solids?

How are patterns of points defined?

Can patterns be transported? rotated? mirror-imaged? scaled?

Can points in patterns be omitted?

Can the cutting sequence of points in patterns be changed?

What canned cycles or subroutines are available:

For lathe work: automatic roughing, profile finish cutting, single-point threading, tap and die threading, plunge cutting, drilling, boring, reaming, other?

For milling work: straight-line cutting, contour cutting, change of plane selected for contouring, automatic face finishing, automatic pocket milling, sculptured surface cutting, control of fourth and fifth-axis motion, other?

Can it compute feeds and speeds from material specifications?

Cost elements

Local processing system?

Host computer purchase or lease if used only for NC Programming?

Host computer, variations in charges for time of day and turnaround time?

Terminals, purchase or lease?

Terminals, connection cost if terminal is remote from host?

Plotter(s), purchase or lease?

Additional memory units and memory controller?

Printers, punches, readers, hard copy units, purchase or lease?

Supplies, cards, tape, paper?

Maintenance of hardware, terms, and warranty period?

Software, operating and communication systems, initial and service charges?

Software, processors of all sorts, initial terms, maintenance, service?

Documentation costs?

Training costs, per pupil, special courses?

Consulting service, cost arrangements?

Programmer salaries plus fringes?

Supervision and overhead?

Office space, environmental controls?

Stabilized power supply?

Telephone charges for calls to vendor for advice and help?

Hardware maintenance technician?

Remote Processing Systems:

Connect time charges to computer?

CPU-use charges?

Variations in the above with time of day?

Storage charges for postprocessors, etc.?

License fee for system?

Telephone tolls to remote site?

Terminals, purchase or lease?

Plotters, purchase or lease?

Printers, punches, readers, hard copy units, purchase or lease?

Maintenance of terminals, peripherals?

Documentation costs?

Training cost per pupil, special courses?

Consulting services, cost and arrangements?

Postprocessor costs and maintenance charges?

Programmer salaries plus fringes?

Supervison and overhead?

Office space, environmental controls?

Supplies, cards, tape, paper?

Security for proprietary information?

Note: Hardware may be purchased, leased, or rented through the vendor or through a third party.

Figure 13-12 Checklist for evaluating computer-assisted NC programming language systems

process or operation, for example) by measuring one or more variables of the activity; comparing the measured quantities with other measured quantities, calculated quantities, or established values or limits; and modifying the activity by automatically adjusting one or more variables to improve or optimize performance.

Automatic adaptive control was conceived nearly 30 years ago and has applicability in a variety of industries and operations, ranging from control of navigation systems in aircraft to process control in the petroleum, chemical, and metals industries. To a somewhat limited extent, AC has also been applied to the control of machine tool performance; however, the application of AC to improve performance of the many machining processes has proved difficult because of the large number and relative unpredictability of variables which play roles in establishing machining performance.

Adaptive Control Classifications

Although much controversy exists relative to the exact definition of AC, particularly as it is applied to control of machining operations, some experts consider it to have two primary classifications— adaptive control for optimization (ACO) and adaptive control for constraint (ACC).

Adaptive Control for Optimization: With

ACO, the performance of an operation is optimized according to a prescribed index of performance (IP), sometimes called the figure of merit or performance criterion. The IP or criterion of performance is usually an economic function, such as minimum machining cost or maximum production rate. Part quality is used as the criterion of performance in some investigations. In many cases, the IP is usually a characteristic which is not directly measured, but is calculated from several variables.

Systems which employ ACO require three functions: identification, decision, and modification, as

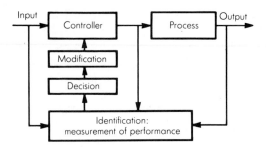

Figure 13-13　Three functions required for optimization type adaptive control

shown schematically in Fig. 13-13. The identification function compares the process performance (output) with the IP value, thus evaluating how well the system is performing. The decision function consists of using this evaluation to determine what should be done to improve the performance of the operation (improve the IP). The modification function involves implementing the changing of process parameters as dictated by the decision function.

Adaptive Control for Constraint: With

ACC, machining conditions such as spindle speed and/or feed rate (usually only feed rate) are maximized within prescribed limits of machine and tool constraints such as maximum horsepower, torque, or force. This type of adaptive control is the most common in metalworking.

Trends and Applications

Sophisticated ACO systems have been developed and have shown some viability in laboratory work; however, most productive applications of AC are of the less-sophisticated ACC type and usually involve control of a single operation through feed rate adjustments on a stand-alone machine tool.

The impetus for development of AC systems initially came from the aircraft and aerospace industries. Early investigative work resulted in very complex and sophisticated systems that continuously sensed many variables and varied both spindle speed and feed rate. In recent years, both machine tool manufacturers and users have moved from these sophisticated, expensive systems to simpler, lower cost, and more reliable AC systems, some of which measure only a few variables and vary only the feed rate of a machining operation.

Today, most successful applications of AC continue in the aircraft and aerospace industries, although little if any reliable information is available regarding the number of AC installations. Expertise in CAD/CAM, which is common in these high-technology industries, complements and often parallels the work required to successfully implement an AC system—development of advanced computer techniques and structuring of complex data bases. Additionally, workpieces in the aircraft and aerospace industries are unusually complicated, often requiring a great deal of machining time, long NC programs, and relatively small production runs, thus making conventional methods of optimizing tapes unjustifiable. In some cases, dimensional variations in large forgings used by these industries create variable machining conditions which must be programmed conservatively, thus significantly reducing overall machining productivity. Experience has shown that such workpieces are ideally suited to AC.

In general, it has also been shown that adaptive control is most appropriate for machining operations on complex workpieces of hard-to-cut alloys and operations characterized by significant variations in machining parameters, such as workpiece hardness or machinability, or changes in the dimensions of cut during the machining operation.

Adaptive control, in its current state of development, is often difficult to justify economically for high-production operations, such as those in the automotive industry, where materials typically exhibit fairly consistent properties and relatively uniform stock removal allowances. This is especially true in cases when feeds and speeds have been optimized to provide a reasonable compromise between maximum production and minimum costs. Some experts believe that, overall, the benefits of AC decrease as lot sizes increase, although ACC may have a beneficial effect on tool life and workpiece quality.

Although research and development efforts concentrating on building reliable ACs for machine tools have been underway for many years, acceptance, overall, has been relatively slow; consequently, the use of AC has not grown as rapidly as first expected. This is true even though advancements in related computer hardware and software have taken place at a dramatic rate. Several reasons have been forwarded for this lack of growth. High costs, complexity, and lack of reliability are cited by experts as major roadblocks to wide acceptance. In the mid-1960s, sophisticated ACO systems were developed that were very expensive. Today, lower cost ACC systems are available which can be retrofit to existing machines; but such systems usually do not guarantee an optimum material removal rate. Tool wear rates and time required for tool changes heavily influence the effective material removal rate, but generally they are not controllable with such AC systems.

Another obstacle to wide acceptance of AC systems is the investment required to develop a suitable data base. Expensive and time-consuming experiments and metalcutting tests are employed to develop these data bases; extensive testing is required to collect the data necessary to establish maximum and minimum allowable values (constraint limits) for measured process variables for a given tool-workpiece combination. One solution to this objection is the development of so-called "trainable" AC systems. The system consists essentially of automatic inspection of a workpiece characteristic (surface finish, for example) of a completed part and the supplying of the output resulting from this inspection to a system which trains the performance measuring system of the adaptive loop. Many experts believe that such systems hold great promise in future AC applications.

The development and use of AC systems depends heavily upon a thorough understanding of the nature of specific cutting processes; because such knowledge is limited, satisfactory algorithms are difficult to develop and computer simulation may be very complicated. The problems involved with AC system development are further compounded by the fact that many machining processes typically exhibit great variability in characteristics and strategies to deal with this process variability are not easily structured.

Probably the greatest stumbling block on the road to AC application is the lack of reliable sensors that can be used in harsh production environments. Some potential users of AC cite higher maintenance costs as a major reason for avoiding AC systems. Certainly, the relatively poor success experienced by early users of AC systems has scared off many potential users.

Justification of Adaptive Control

Reduced to its essential, AC means making adjustments in a machining operation to accommodate changes. Automatic AC, or ACC, eliminates the need for decision making by the operator in much the same way as NC allows the operator to play a less critical role in process planning. The decline in availability of skilled labor and the increased need for improved part quality highlight the need for such systems as AC.

The problems of economic justification notwithstanding, the concept of ACC is thought by many experts to be the most feasible approach to maintaining optimum feeds and speeds in machining. Proven benefits include increased productivity and sometimes longer cutter life; reduced machining costs and reduced scrap rates; improved product quality; greater machine utilization; and better protection of the machine, tool, and workpiece from damage. Improved and simplified programming and reduced dependence on operator skill are cited as further advantages.

Other economic advantages are considered attainable through the use of ACC, including reduced interest cost on capital tied up in in-process inventory. This savings is often significant when large workpieces are involved that require a great deal of machining time.

As an example of how ACC is used to increase machining productivity, Fig. 13-14 illustrates a milling operation and machining data which shows the difference between conventional milling and milling with ACC. This operation is a straight-cut, finish-

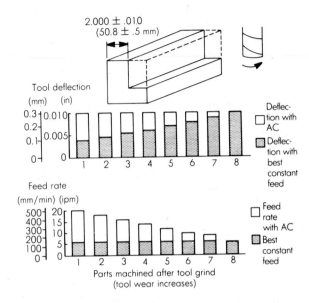

Figure 13-14   Average feed rate with adaptive control is more than double the best constant feed rate possible in this finish-milling operation

milling operation in which deflection of the end mill (1″ diam x 3″ flue length, 25.4 mm x 76.2 mm) must not exceed 0.010″ (0.25 mm). When the cutter is sharp and cutting forces are low, feeding at 20 ipm (508 mm/min) is no problem. However, when the cutting tool is dull, the forces increase and the feed rate has to be limited to about 5 ipm (127 mm/min). A feed rate which is safe for all conditions must be selected, so the NC programmer would choose 5 ipm (127 mm/min). However, with the use of ACC, the feed rate can start at 20 ipm (508 mm/min) with a sharp tool and gradually decrease to 5 ipm (127 mm/min) as the tool becomes dull. The average feed rate with ACC is more than double the best constant rate.

Adaptive Control Systems

Many different types of AC systems are now available, ranging from simple automatic tool compensation systems to sophisticated computer-driven systems which monitor and control a multitude of machining variables. Increasingly, the proven systems are being offered as standard equipment or as options on modern CNC equipment and other machinery.

Automatic Dimensional Control:

Automatic tool compensation in the pure sense is generally not considered a form of AC, although many experts consider it somewhat related. Automatic gaging and cutting tool compensation systems are used for turning and boring operations and other processes on many types of machine tools, including transfer equipment. In boring operations, for example, an automatic tool compensation system consists of a gage and feedback circuit that automatically sends a signal to a pneumatically or hydraulically operated tool adjustment mechanism when the tool wear is great enough that the bore size falls out of a set of prescribed "compensate" limits. Upon command, the cutting tool is automatically fed an appropriate amount to bring the bore back to nominal size. Such systems are commercially available and have been used successfully for more than 15 years.

One such system compensates for cutter wear in boring or turning operations. An electronic gage probes a bored hole or turned surface and sense the size difference between the gaged dimension and predetermined limits. If the size falls outside prescribed limits (usually set well within actual blueprint limits; typically 10-30% of part print tolerance), a signal is sent to an amplifier and relayed to an electronic controller, as shown in Fig. 13-15. The controller energizes a compensation module which actuates a rod through the revolving spindle to move the cutting edge to the correct setting. Tool cartridges, mounted on the machine spindles, rest on the precisely tapered ends of the rods. The rods are moved in or out of the spindles by stepping motors with hydraulic or electric drives to push the tool out or in for required adjustments. Adjustments of the cutting edges can be made in increments of 0.0001" (0.0025 mm). To eliminate drag-out marks, the cutting tools are automatically retracted 0.005" (0.13 mm) after each cut and then reset.

Other systems are also designed to compensate for dimensional variations in machining operations.

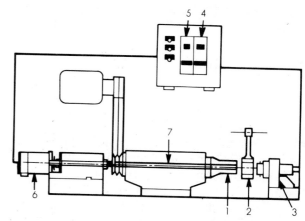

Figure 13-15 A cutting tool (1) bores the workpiece (2). The gage (3) then probes the bore and sends a signal to the gage amplifier (4) which compares the present size with the required size preset in the control panel. If adjustment is required, a signal is relayed from the compensator panel (5) to a stepper motor (6) to adjust a micrometer stop assembly which controls the motion of a drawbar (7) that adjusts the cutting tool to the corrected setting—ready for the next part.

For example, means of compensating for dimensional variations in machine tool components due to variations in temperature are employed in isolated applications. One such system employed on an NC machine features spindle growth compensation. The system automatically offsets the spindle axis and adjusts the NC commands by the amount of the offset.

In grinding, automatic in-process gages have been used for many years to continuously measure workpiece size during grinding. Such gages are interfaced with the machine controls. On some systems, this arrangement is used for automatic wheelhead positioning and retracting, controlling the feed rate (both roughing and finishing), stopping the feed for sparkout and workpiece size control, and compensating for wheel wear. Such controls are ordinarily employed for high-production, plunge grinding operations where the use of an in-process gage is justifiable. More advanced systems have been developed for controlling grinding operations, as discussed in the following sections.

Sensor Technology:
Sensor technology, often the key to AC advances, has lagged behind improvement in computer hardware and software, although considerable research and development work has been and continues to be devoted to the subject of sensors for AC. High cost and questionable reliability of sensors are the obstacles most difficult to overcome. Some important machining parameters such as tool wear and surface quality cannot be measured practically and accurately during cutting under production conditions with the current state-of-the-art technology. More reliable and economical sensors are required which are suitable for use in a production environment. They should be easy to retrofit, recalibrate, and replace and should not alter any of the machining parameters. Response speed should be compatible with the AC system, and output signals should be linear over a wide range of input values and stable over temperature variations encountered in production.

Laser and electro-optical methods hold some promise of solving problems related to sensor technology as applied to AC. Simple, low-cost gas lasers can provide a convenient noncontact method of optically measuring a wide range of workpiece dimensions on-line. This method, operating in isolated production applications, requires a well-collimated beam of high intensity light which can give a high signal-to-noise ratio. The originating beam can easily be split into several beams, which is the basis for accurately identifying workpiece edges. The effect of reflected and diffracted light in measuring the diameters of cylindrical surfaces can be eliminated with an adjustable system developed in Japan. The system is shown schematically in Fig. 13-16. The workpiece edge is projected by the optical system and sensed by a position detector.

Surface Roughness:
Surface roughness is another important quality parameter which has been of great interest for AC application in recent years. Some investigations suggest that in-process sensing of surface finish can be used as an indirect method

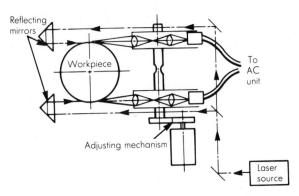

Figure 13-16 Laser beam can be split and reflected to measure workpiece diameter on this adjustable system for adaptive control

of measuring tool wear. No practical methods of sensing surface roughness during machining are available at this time for production applications. Several electro-optical sensing methods have been proposed. One method developed in Germany involves microscopic measurements of a projected small light slit on surfaces being turned, using a photodiode array.

Another method of measuring surface roughness during machining involves measuring the intensity of reflected laser light, as shown in Fig. 13-17. This type of sensing device is thought to be suitable for specific operations where the surface pattern does not change. The relationship between the intensity of the reflected light and surface finish is affected by many parameters including the type of surface (which varies with the operation) and material reflectivity.

A method of automatically controlling surface roughness by changing infeed rate in cylindrical plunge grinding operations has been developed by Braunschweig Technical University in West Germany. The experimental ACO system employs a tracing stylus that follows a peripheral line on the rotating workpiece and that is excited to vibrations in its natural frequency by the roughness of the surface. These vibrations generate an electrical signal correlating to centerline average and height of peak-to-valley of the surface profile. The measuring device may be used to monitor wheel life, as well as to control the infeed rate to maintain workpiece size.

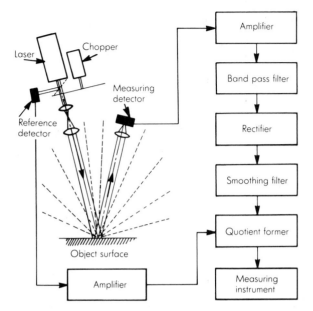

Figure 13-17   Measurement of surface finish involves detecting the intensity of reflected laster light

Tool Wear: Several sensing methods have been developed for both direct and indirect on-line sensing of tool wear. Several indirect methods are being used in production applications of AC, but most direct methods are still confined to the laboratory. Indirect methods of sensing tool wear include measuring cutting forces, torque, power, temperature, resistance between tool and workpiece, vibrations, and noise.

Forces can be measured with relative ease, but correlation with tool wear may be questionable. Correlation is difficult because cutting forces are affected by tool geometry, cutting conditions, and the work material. Also, an increase in cutting force due to an increase in flank wear can be compensated by crater wear, causing a decrease in measured force.

Cutting temperature (as an indirect measurement of tool wear) can be sensed directly by infrared radiation or indirectly by thermocouple, although experiments with the latter have caused problems of noisy signals, complicated setups, and stringent calibration requirements. Sensing of thermal emf (electromotive force) seems to give a poor correlation with the size of the worn area. However, evaluation of the slope of the emf vs. the cutting speed may indicate machinability changes for the specified tool-workpiece combination. A survey of the literature by the University of Michigan led to the conclusion that temperature measurement alone would not be adequate for many applications of AC, but that it might be feasible when combined with measurements of cutting forces. Recommendations include consideration of imbedded thermocouples as a means of temperature measurement, and provision of sensors for all major components of cutting force.

Power control is the widely used form of AC systems; often it is used in conjunction with other sensed parameters to determine operating efficiency, to prevent damage to the tool or workpiece, and to indicate amount of tool wear. One commercially available system is said to measure true horsepower of a-c or d-c motors to within 2%. Such solid state instruments are supplied by numerous vendors. In one system, Iso-watt power transducers in the motor-control panel monitor the voltage and current of the motor (or any electrical load), and output signals are converted to hp or kW measurements. The measurements are displayed and continuously compared to a present limit, which if exceeded can be used as a signal to stop the machine or to signal the operator. Power readings are also available as an analog and binary-coded decimal output suitable for interfacing with a recorder, printer, or data acquisition system for AC.

In one lathe system developed in Japan, spindle-motor current is compared with database information in real time. Feed rate adjustments are performed automatically to compensate for workpiece inconsistencies or tool wear.

Sophisticated milling machines manufactured in Switzerland employ strain gages in the spindle bearings to monitor cutting forces. Feeds and speeds are adjusted automatically as the machine operates.

Direct sensing of tool wear remains mostly experimental. Tool wear can be indicated by measuring the change in distance between the tool and machined surface. In a method tested in Japan, two mechanical feelers and a differential transformer are employed. The primary detector contacts the work surface, and a secondary detector (to compensate for thermal expansion and deflection) contacts the tools. The sensor must be adjusted for different tools, and there is the risk of possible damage from chips. Ultrasonic transducers and pneumatic gages have also been tested for measuring the distance between tool and work, but have not proven practical.

Pneumatic gages for scanning flank wear have been tested, but this method is rather slow and built-up edges on the tools affect the measurements. Small radioactive spots have also been placed on tools, just below the cutting edges; when detectors sense tha the spots have worn off, the tools are changed. This work remains highly experimental.

KEY TERMS AND PHRASES _____

Adaptive control
Arithmetic unit
Computer numerical control (CNC)
Computer-assisted NC part programming
Contouring machine
Control unit
Direct numerical control (DNC)
Distributed numerical control (DNC)
EPROM
General purpose languages
Limit switch
Machine interface
Numerical control
Operator interface
Output unit
Part geometry
Positioning machine
Programmable logic controller (PLC)
PROM
Proximity switch
RAM
ROM
Sequence controllers
Servo-mechanism
Soft-wired controls
Source statements

QUESTIONS FOR ADDITIONAL STUDY AND REVIEW _____

1. What is a *sequence controller?*

2. What is a *PLC?*

3. How does a PLC differ from a computer?

4. List five advantages of numerical control. *P 336*

5. What is a *soft-wired CNC system?*

6. What are the three elements of a CNC system? *P 330*

7. What are the five functional units in a CNC system?

8. Define the following terms:
   - RAM
   - ROM
   - PROM
   - EPROM

9. Name four different types of NC interface devices.

10. Define and distinguish between direct numerical control and distributed numerical control.

11. Name four types of data that can be collected and used for management purposes with a DNC system.

12. Define and distinguish between positioning machines and contouring machines.

13. List three advantages of computer-assisted part programming.

14. What are the main elements of a computer-assisted NC programming system?

15. List four advantages of general purpose part programming languages.

16. List four advantages of specialized part programming languages.

17. Define the term *adaptive control.*

CHAPTER 14

Welding, Cutting, and Mechanical Fastening

MAJOR TOPICS COVERED

- Oxyfuel Gas Welding and Cutting
- Arc Welding and Cutting
- Electroslag Welding
- Resistance Welding
- Electron Beam Welding and Cutting
- Laser Beam Welding and Cutting
- Thermit Welding
- Diffusion Welding
- Friction Welding
- Ultrasonic Welding
- Explosive Welding and Cladding
- Cold Welding
- Coextrusion Welding
- Pulsed Magnetic Welding
- Vibration Welding
- Welding Plastics and Nonmetals
- Mechanical Fastening of Metals
- Mechanical Fastening of Nonmetals

WELDING AND CUTTING

Welding is a materials joining process in which localized coalescence (joining) is produced along the faying surfaces of the workpieces. Coalescence is produced either by heating the materials to suitable temperatures, with or without the application of pressure, or it is produced by the application of pressure alone.

With some welding processes, filler material is added during welding.

There are more than 50 different welding processes, some of which are listed in Fig. 14-1. Most of these are discussed in detail in this chapter. The processes can be classified as either fusion or solid-state (nonfusion) methods.

Fusion welding processes, in which the workpieces are melted together at their faying surfaces, are the most commonly used processes. Arc, resistance, and oxyfuel gas welding are the predominant fusion processes. Filler metals often used with the arc and oxyfuel gas welding methods have melting points about the same as or just below those of the metals being joined.

In solid-state welding, the workpieces are joined by the application of heat and usually pressure, or by the application of pressure only. However, with these processes, the welding temperature is essentially below the melting point of the materials being joined or if any liquid metal is present it is squeezed out of the joint. No filler metal is added during welding.

Fusion Methods	
Arc welding (AW):	Resistance welding (RW):
shielded metal arc welding (SMAW)	resistance spot welding (RSW)
submerged arc welding (SAW)	resistance projection welding (RPW)
gas metal arc welding (GMAW)	resistance seam welding (RSEW)
flux-cored arc welding (FCAW)	upset welding (UW)
gas tungsten arc welding (GTAW)	flash welding (FW)
plasma arc welding (PAW)	percussion welding (PEW)
electrogas welding (EGW)	high-frequency resistance welding (HFRW)
carbon arc welding (CAW)	
gas carbon arc welding (CAW-G)*	Electroslag welding (ESW)
shielded carbon arc welding (CAW-S)	Electron beam welding (EBW)
bare metal arc welding (BMAW)*	
atomic hydrogen welding (AHW)*	Laser beam welding (LBW)
stud arc welding (SW)	Thermit welding (TW)
Oxyfuel gas welding (OFW):	
oxyacetylene welding (OAW)	
oxyhydrogen welding (OHW)	
air-acetylene welding (AAW)*	
pressure gas welding (PGW)	
Solid-State Methods	
Diffusion welding (DFW)	Cold welding (CW)
Friction welding (FRW)	Forge welding (FOW)
Ultrasonic welding (USW)	Coextrusion welding (CEW)
Explosion welding (EXW)	Hot pressure welding (HPW)

* Obsolete or seldom used processes.

Figure 14-1   Welding processes

Oxyfuel Gas Welding and Cutting

Oxyfuel gas welding (OFW) is a group of welding processes that produce coalescence by heating materials with an oxyfuel gas flame or flames, with or without the application of pressure, and with or without the use of filler metal. In these processes, the base metal, as well as filler metal, if used, is melted by the flame from the tip of a welding torch.

Oxyfuel gas cutting is a group of cutting processes used to sever or remove metals by means of the chemical reaction of oxygen with the base metal at elevated temperatures. In the case of oxidation-resistant metals, the reaction is facilitated by the use of a chemical flux or metal powder.

Oxyfuel Gas Welding

The three most commonly used oxyfuel gas welding processes are:

- Oxyacetylene welding (OAW). In this process, heating is done with a gas flame or flames obtained from the combustion of acetylene with oxygen. The process may be used with or without the application of pressure and with or without the use of filler metal.

- Oxyhydrogen welding (OHW). In this process, heating is done with a gas flame or flames obtained from the combustion of hydrogen with oxygen. The process is used without the application of pressure and with or without the use of filler metal.
- Pressure gas welding (PGW). In this process, co-alescence is produced simultaneously over the entire area of abutting surfaces by heating them with flames obtained from the combustion of a fuel gas with oxygen. The process entails the appli-cation of pressure, but without the use of filler metal.

A fourth oxyfuel gas welding process, air-acetylene welding (AAW), uses heating obtained from the combustion of acetylene with air, without the appli-cation of pressure and with or without the use of filler metal. However, by using air instead of oxygen, the resulting available heat is lower. As a result, the AAW process is obsolete or seldom used.

In a few cases, methylacetylene-propadiene stabilized (MPS), butane, ethylene, natural gas, pro-pane, or other petroleum derivatives or mixtures are used as fuel gases. These gases, however, are generally limited to welding some metals having lower melting temperatures because of the lower flame temperatures and are used more extensively for oxyfuel gas cutting discussed later in this section. Because acetylene in combination with oxygen pro-duces a flame with the highest temperature, acetylene is the fuel gas used most extensively for welding.

Advantages and Applications: Oxyfuel gas welding offers considerable flexibility because the operator can control the rate of heat input, the tem-perature in the weld zone, the rate of filler metal deposition, and speed, making it suitable for joining most metals. Other advantages are that no power source is required, and the equipment can also be used for related operations such as bending and straightening, preheating and postheating, and torch brazing. A limitation is that the process is slower than most other welding methods on thicker metals.

The equipment required for oxyfuel gas welding is comparatively simple, compact, usually portable, and inexpensive, making it especially useful for maintenance and repairs, odd job-shop work, and certain types of tube and pipe welding. It is the preferred process for welding of lead, and it is also preferred in many cases for cast iron when a joint defect of any considerable magnitude is to be repaired. Oxyhydrogen welding is generally restricted to aluminum or lead alloys. Pressure gas welding has been used for uniting links of rail and pipe, for making rings, and for similar applications where bar or pipe sections of essentially similar cross sections are to be joined. Although it has some highly specialized favorable applications, its use is generally on the decline (see Figs. 14-2 and 14-3).

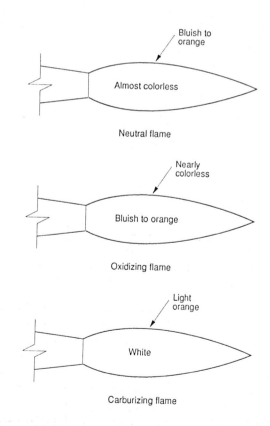

Figure 14-2 Types of oxyacetylene flames

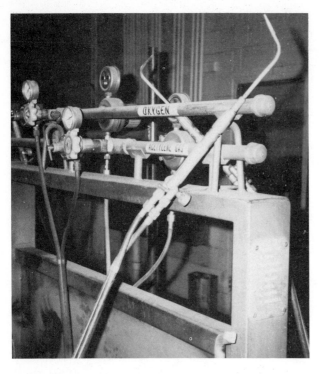

Figure 14-3   Typical oxyacetylene welding torch

Oxyfuel Gas Cutting

Oxyfuel gas cutting is the most widely used thermal cutting process. It has been given many names, such as burning, flame cutting, oxygen cutting, and flame machining. The process can be performed with equipment ranging from lightweight, inexpensive, handheld cutting torches to costly, computer-controlled, multitorch cutting machines. Although the process has been used to cut steel up to 8′ (2.4 m) thick, the majority of material cut is under 2″ (51 mm) in thickness.

Advantages and Limitations: Oxyfuel gas cutting is a versatile process that can be used to cut straight lines or continual change of direction lines because the cutting oxygen stream acts as a tool with a 360° cutting edge. Cuts can be started at the edges of workpieces or piercing can be used to start a cut at any point on the work surface. With proper conditions, edge quality is good. Two or more pieces can be cut simultaneously by stack cutting, and edges can be bevel-cut for weld joint preparation. In addition, the process can operate in any axis with equal facility.

The process is fast compared to machining and slow compared to plasma arc cutting, but the speed can be increased by the use of multiple torches, cutting machines, and stack cutting. Heat-affected zones can be large with oxyfuel gas cutting, and workpieces can be distorted, especially if they are made from thin metals (see Figs. 14-4 and 14-5).

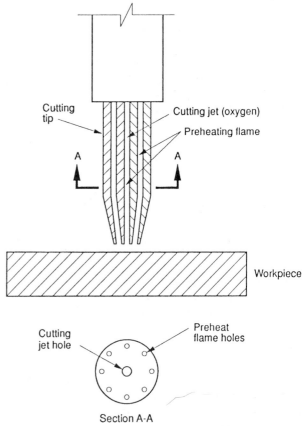

Figure 14-4   Nomenclature for oxyfuel gas cutting

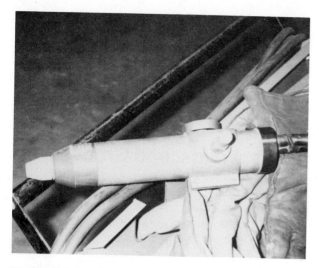

Figure 14-5   Oxyfuel gas cutting torch

Arc Welding And Cutting

Arc welding (AW) involves a group of fusion welding processes that produces coalescence (joining) of metals by heating them with an electric arc, with or without the application of pressure and with or without the use of filler metal. Gas-shielded arc welding is a general term used to describe gas metal arc welding, gas tungsten arc welding, and flux-cored arc welding when gas shielding is used.

Arc cutting is a group of cutting processes that melts the metal to be cut with the heat of an electric arc between an electrode and the metal. The processes used extensively in industry are plasma arc cutting and air-carbon arc cutting, discussed subsequently. Other arc cutting processes that are not used extensively or are used only for special applications are described briefly at the end of this section.

Fundamentals of Arc Welding

By the application of intense heat during arc welding, the base metals at the joint are melted and caused to intermix either directly or, more commonly,

with a molten filler metal. Upon cooling and solidification, a metallurgical bond results. Because the joining takes place by melting together one part with the other part, with or without a filler metal of suitable composition, the welded joint may have strength properties similar to those of the base metals. This is in contrast to nonfusion processes of joining that use a separate filler, such as soldering, brazing, or adhesive bonding, in which the mechanical and physical properties of the base materials cannot be duplicated at the joint.

In arc welding, the intense heat needed to melt metals is produced by an electric arc. The arc is generally formed between the work to be welded and an electrode that is manually or mechanically moved along the joint, or the work may be moved under a stationary electrode. The electrode may be a carbon or tungsten rod that conducts the welding current to the electric arc between the hot electrode tip and the workpiece. Also, it may be a specially prepared rod or wire that not only conducts the welding current and sustains the arc, but also melts and provides filler metal to the joint.

If a carbon or tungsten electrode is used and the joint requires added filler metal, that metal is added from a separate filler metal rod or wire. Most welding in the manufacture of steel products where filler metal is required, however, is accomplished with consumable electrodes—those that supply filler metal as well as conduct the welding current.

Basic Welding Circuit: The basic circuit for shielded metal arc welding is illustrated in Fig. 14-6.

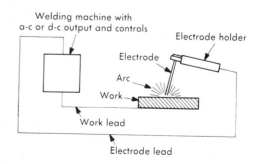

Figure 14-6   Basic arc welding circuit

An a-c or d-c power source, equipped with appropriate controls, is connected by a cable to the workpiece and by a cable to an electrode holder that makes electrical contact with the welding electrode. When the welding circuit is energized and the electrode tip is momentarily touched to the workpiece and then withdrawn a short distance, an arc is created between the electrode and the work. The arc produces a temperature at the tip of the electrode more than adequate for melting most metals.

Arc Shielding: Use of the heat of an electric arc to join metals, however, requires more than the moving of the electrode with respect to the weld joint. Metals at high temperatures react chemically with the main constituents of air, oxygen, and nitrogen to form oxides and nitrides. Upon solidification of the molten weld pool, the oxides and nitrides reduce the strength and ductility properties of the welded joint. For this reason, the various arc welding processes provide some means for covering the arc, electrode tip, the arc, and the molten weld pool with a protective shield of gas or slag. This is referred to as arc shielding.

Figure 14-7 illustrates the shielding of the welding arc and molten weld pool with a covered electrode. The extruded covering on the filler metal rod, under the heat of the arc, generates a gaseous shield that displaces the surrounding air from the molten weld metal. It also supplies ingredients that react with deleterious substances on or in the metals, such as oxides and other compounds, and ties these sub-

stances up chemically in a slag. The slag, being lighter than the weld metal, rises to the surface of the molten weld pool and solidifies with the weld metal. This slag, after solidification, has a protective function; it protects the hot solidified metal from air.

Joints, Welds, and Grooves

The relationship between joint design and the production welding process is significant when arc welding is used. Much of the inherent cost advantage of welding can be lost through poor design, as well as through poor procedure control. Factors to be considered in designing for welding include performance requirements, location of welds, stress distribution, and joint placement.

Types of joints are illustrated in Fig. 14-8. Groove and fillet welds (see Fig. 14-9) are the common types produced by arc welding. Major factors in the selection of the types of joints and welds are application requirements and costs. Combinations of fillet and groove welds are used for some joints, depending on the loading conditions.

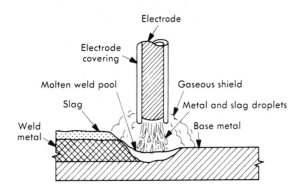

Figure 14-7 Arc shielding *(Courtesy Lincoln Electric Company)*

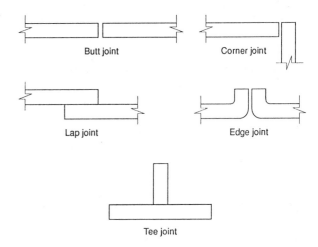

Figure 14-8 Types of weld joints

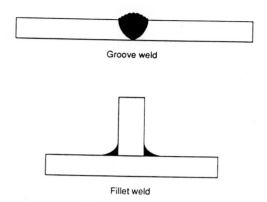

Figure 14-9 Groove and fillet welds

Fillet Welds: Fillet welds are more economical than groove welds but they sometimes require more weld metal. Simple or no edge preparation is necessary, but some surface cleaning may be required. Fillet welds are generally preferred when stresses are low, when designs permit, and when required weld sizes are less than about 5/8″ (16 mm).

When feasible from the strength standpoint, intermittent fillet welding is used instead of continuous welding for greater economy and distortion control. Fillet weld size should be limited to that required; doubling the size of a fillet requires four times as much weld metal and increases the amount of distortion.

Single-fillet welds. These welds are generally limited to low loads. When the loading is not too severe, single-fillet welds are suitable for joining plates of all thicknesses. If fatigue or impact loads are to be encountered, however, stress distribution must be carefully studied. Loading on the joint must not place the root of the weld in tension because of the stress concentration.

Double-fillet welds. These welds are suitable for more severe load conditions than can be met by single-fillet joints. Smaller double-fillet welds are generally preferable to larger single-fillet welds. The two fillet welds are generally made the same size, but one fillet weld can be smaller than the other for some applications.

Groove Welds: Groove welds are of several types (see Fig. 14-10). A general classification is according to groove preparation: square, V, bevel, J, and U-shaped grooves. All groove welds should be designed for minimum cross-sectional area and most economical edge preparation. Shearing and flame cutting of the groove faces are common; machining of the faces is generally the most expensive method, but can result in the highest quality joints. Savings can often be realized by using simulated grooves. These consist of consumable backing materials, such as square or round rods, placed between the straight edges of the weldment components. The use of simulated grooves eliminates the need and cost for machining or cutting the component edges. For joining thick sections, double-groove welds require considerably less weld metal, but they require welding from both sides.

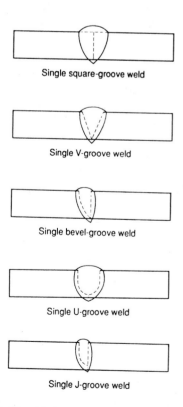

Single square-groove weld

Single V-groove weld

Single bevel-groove weld

Single U-groove weld

Single J-groove weld

Figure 14-10 Various groove welds

Square-groove welds. Edge preparation and welding costs are generally lower for these welds than other types of groove welds. Square-groove welds are suitable for all type loads, but joint strength depends on the amount of joint penetration. Complete fusion and complete joint penetration are generally necessary for most welds, particularly when the load is cyclic or intermittent in nature. The base metal for this type of weld must have good weldability because a portion of the base metal in the joint area is melted during welding.

V-groove welds. Edge preparation costs are higher for these welds than for square-groove welds, and more filler metal is used in welding. Double V-groove welds require only about half as much filler metal as single V-groove welds, but edge preparation costs are higher, and the weldment may require manipulating to weld both sides. Cost of edge preparation should be weighed against the cost of welding when selecting the joint design.

Both single and double V-groove welds are suitable for all load conditions. Double V-groove welds are used to join plates of greater thickness where the work can be welded from both sides. Both types of V-groove welds are generally most economical when the depths of the grooves do not exceed 3/4" (19 mm). As with square-groove welds, strength depends on the depth of penetration. Angular distortion of double V-groove welds can be reduced by alternating the beads—welding on one side and then the other to keep the joint aligned during welding.

Bevel-groove welds. Less joint preparation and filler metal are needed for these welds than for V-groove welds. Single bevel-groove welds are used, in most cases, for welding plates 1/2" (13 mm) or thinner in work welded from only one side.

Double bevel-groove welds are suitable for longitudinal or transverse shear loads when welding can be done from both sides. The welds are generally most economical when the depths of the grooves do not exceed about 3/4" (19 mm). Joint thickness should usually be 1 1/2" (38 mm) or less for complete joint penetration.

J-groove welds. These welds have characteristics similar to bevel-groove welds. However, they are generally more economical for joining thick sections because less weld metal is required. Single J-groove welds are generally applied to plates 1" (25 mm) and more in thickness. Double J-groove welds are often used for plates 1 1/2" (38 mm) and more in thickness when welding can be done from both sides.

U-groove welds. These welds are used for applications similar to J-groove welds. Edge preparation costs are generally higher, but complete fusion is easier to obtain. Double J-groove welds require less weld metal than single U-groove welds, but edge preparation costs are higher, and the welds have to be made from both sides.

Other groove welds. Other types of groove welds used with the arc welding processes include V-groove welds with backing and flared V-groove and flared bevel-groove welds.

Automated Arc Welding: Automated arc welding is welding with equipment that performs the entire operation without human observation or adjustment of controls. The process was developed to meet increasing demands for improved productivity and higher quality welds. It makes use of microprocessor memories, sensing devices, and programmable and adaptive controls. Sensing devices may continuously monitor the operation and feed back information to the control system, which modifies welding parameters or motion patterns to provide necessary changes. Quality welds are produced even when the weldment conditions are less than optimum, such as poorly fitted joints. Programs for automated welding can be recorded, stored, and reused when required.

Shielded Metal Arc Welding

Shielded metal arc welding (SMAW) is an arc welding process that produces coalescence (joining) of metals by heating them with an arc between a covered (or coated) metal electrode and the work (see Fig. 14-11). Shielding is provided by decomposition of the electrode covering. Pressure is not used, and filler metal is obtained from the electrode. The SMAW process is commonly called stick-electrode or manual welding.

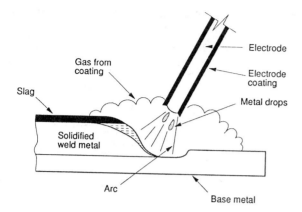

Figure 14-11   Shielded metal arc welding

Applications: The shielded metal arc method is one of the oldest and the most widely used of the various arc welding processes. It is basically a manual process used by small welding shops, home mechanics, and farmers for the repair of equipment. The process also has extensive application in industrial fabrication, structural steel erection, weldment manufacture, and other commercial metals joining operations.

Advantages: Major advantages of shielded metal arc welding include application versatility and flexibility and the simplicity, portability, and low cost of the equipment required. The process is capable of welding thin and thick steels and some nonferrous metals in all positions. Power-supply leads can be provided over long distances, and no hoses are required for shielding gas.

Limitations: Required periodic changing of the electrode is one of the major disadvantages of shielded metal arc welding for production applications. This decreases the percentage of time actually spent in welding. Another disadvantage is the limitation placed on the current that can be used. High amperages, such as those used with semiautomatic guns or automatic welding heads, are impractical because of the long and varying length of electrode between the arc and the point of electrical contact in the jaws of the electrode holder.

Welding current is limited by the resistance heating of the electrode. The electrode temperature must not exceed the breakdown temperature of the covering. If the temperature is too high, the covering chemicals react with each other or with air and therefore do not function properly at the arc. As a result of limited temperatures, deposition rates and efficiency are low.

With the development of processes, such as semiautomatic, self-shielded, flux-cored arc welding, having similar or even superior versatility and flexibility, there is less justification for using shielded metal arc welding in applications requiring substantial amounts of weld metal.

Gas Tungsten Arc Welding

Gas tungsten arc welding (GTAW) is an arc welding process that produces coalescence (joining) of metals by heating them with an arc between a tungsten (nonconsumable) electrode and the work (see Fig. 14-12). Shielding is obtained by an envelope of an inert gas or gas mixture. Pressure and filler metal may or may not be used. The GTAW process is also known as TIG (tungsten inert gas), Heliarc, argon arc, and tungsten arc welding.

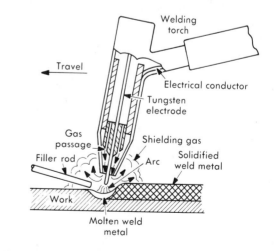

Figure 14-12   Gas tungsten arc welding *(Courtesy Lincoln Electric Company)*

Applications: While a wide range of metal thicknesses can be welded, the gas tungsten arc method is especially adapted for welding thin metals where the requirements for quality and finish are exacting. It is one of the few arc welding processes that is satisfactory for welding such tiny and thin-walled objects as transistor cases, instrument diaphragms, and delicate expansion bellows. Gas tungsten arc welding is also used to join various combinations of dissimilar metals and for applying hard-facing and surfacing materials to steel. The process is performed manually, semiautomatically, or automatically.

Advantages: An important advantage of the gas tungsten arc process is that it is suitable for welding most metals, both ferrous and nonferrous, and producing high-quality joints. It is generally not used, however, for metals that melt at low temperatures, such as tin and lead. Materials weldable by the process include most grades of carbon, alloy, and stainless steels; aluminum and most of its alloys; magnesium and most of its alloys; copper and various brasses and bronzes; high-temperature alloys of various types; numerous hard-surfacing alloys; and such metals as titanium, zirconium, gold, and silver.

Another advantage is that this process does not produce weld spatter because no filler metal crosses the arc. Also, because no fluxing agents are used, cleaning after welding is seldom required. Welding is possible in all positions.

Limitations: A possible limitation to the use of the gas tungsten arc process is that it is slower than consumable-electrode arc welding processes. Also, this method requires an externally supplied inert shielding gas or a gas mixture, adding to the cost of welding. Any transfer of tungsten particles from the electrode to the weld causes hard, brittle contamination.

Gas Metal Arc Welding

Gas metal arc welding (GMAW) is an arc welding process that produces coalescence (joining) of metals by heating them with an arc between a continuous,

solid (consumable) electrode for filler metal and the work (see Fig. 14-13). Shielding is provided by an externally supplied gas or gas mixture. The GMAW process is also known as MIG (metal inert gas), MAG (metal active gas), CO_2, short-circuit arc, dip transfer, and wire welding.

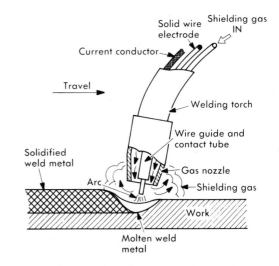

Figure 14-13   Gas metal arc welding *(Courtesy Lincoln Electric Company)*

Applications: Gas metal arc welding is performed using either a handheld gun or mechanical welding head or torch to which the electrode is fed automatically. The process is used extensively for high-production welding operations.

Advantages: The major features of gas metal arc welding are (1) the capability of obtaining high-quality welds in almost any metal, (2) the small amount of postweld cleaning it requires, (3) the visibility of its arc and weld pool to the welder, (4) its all-position capability, (5) its relatively high speed and economy, and (6) its elimination of slag entrapment in the weld. In addition, variations of the process have special advantages.

The gas metal arc process may be used to weld all of the major commercial metals, including carbon, alloy, and stainless steels, as well as aluminum, magnesium, copper, iron, titanium, and zirconium. It is a preferred process for the welding of aluminum, magnesium, copper, and many of the alloys of these reactive metals. Most of the irons and steels can be satisfactorily joined by this process, including the carbon-free irons; the low-carbon and low-alloy steels; the high-strength, quenched, and tempered steels; the chromium irons and steels; the high-nickel steels; and some of the so-called superalloys.

Limitations: As with the gas tungsten arc process previously discussed, gas metal arc welding requires an externally supplied inert shielding gas or a gas mixture, adding to welding costs. Equipment required is complex and costly, and not readily portable. The welding gun must be kept close to the work to ensure adequate shielding, making it difficult for hard-to-reach joints.

Flux-Cored Arc Welding

Flux-cored arc welding (FCAW) is an arc welding process that produces coalescence (joining) of metals by heating them with an arc between a continuous, consumable, tubular filler-metal electrode and the work. In self-shielded flux-cored welding, shielding is provided entirely by the constituents of the tubular electrode. In gas-shielded flux-cored welding, shielding is provided from an externally supplied gas or gas mixture.

Self-Shielded Flux-Cored Welding: The

self-shielded flux-cored arc welding process is an outgrowth of shielded metal arc welding. The versatility and maneuverability of stick electrodes in manual welding stimulated efforts to mechanize the shielded metal arc process. Developments consisted of making an electrode with self-shielding characteristics in coil form and feeding it mechanically to the arc (see Fig. 14-14), thus eliminating welding time lost in changing electrodes and the material lost as electrode stubs. The result of these efforts was the development of the semiautomatic and fully automatic processes for welding with continuous, flux-cored, tubular electrode "wires." Such fabricated wires

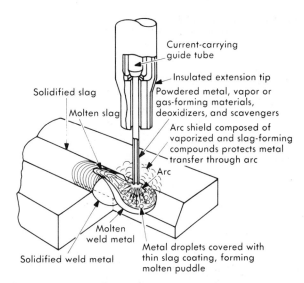

Figure 14-14 Self-shielded flux-cored arc welding *(Courtesy Lincoln Electric Company)*

contain in their cores the ingredients for fluxing and deoxidizing molten metal and for generating shielding gases and vapors and slag coverings.

Advantages. One of the advantages of the self-shielded flux-cored arc welding process is the high deposition rates possible with handheld semiautomatic guns. High deposition rates, automatic electrode feed, and elimination of lost time for changing electrodes have resulted in substantial production economies wherever the semiautomatic process has been used to replace stick-electrode welding. Decreases in welding costs as great as 50% have been common, and in some production welding, deposition rates have been increased as much as 400%. The process permits the use of long electrode extensions (the lengths of the unmelted electrodes extending beyond the ends of the contact tube during welding), which increase the deposition rate for a given voltage and current.

Another advantage of the process is its tolerance for poor fitup, which often reduces rework and repair without affecting final product quality. The tolerance of the semiautomatic process to poor fitup has expanded the use of tubular steel members in structures by making possible sound connections where perfect fitup would be too difficult or costly to achieve.

Electrogas Welding

Electrogas welding (EGW) is an arc welding process that produces coalescence (joining) of metals by heating them with an arc between a continuous filler-metal (consumable) electrode and the work. Molding shoes span the gap between parts being joined and confine the molten weld metal for vertical position welding. The electrodes may be either flux-cored or solid, and shielding may or may not be obtained from an externally supplied gas or gas mixture. There are two basic variations: one uses the solid consumable electrode wire and externally supplied shielding gas, normally CO_2 (see Fig. 14-15), and the second utilizes flux-cored electrode wire and does not ordinarily use an external shielding gas because shielding gases are formed as the flux-cored electrode wire is consumed in the arc.

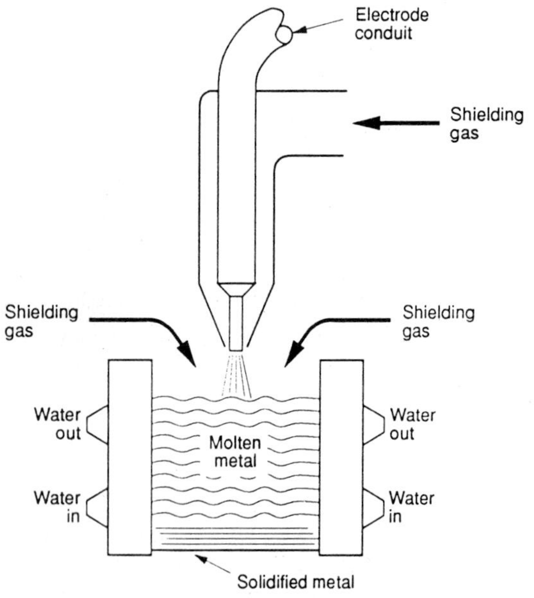

Applications and Advantages: Metals welded by the electrogas process include low-carbon steels, low-alloy high-strength steels; medium-carbon steels, and certain stainless steels. The process can also be used for welding quenched and tempered steels providing that the correct heat input is maintained for the type of steel being welded. The major use of electrogas welding has been for the field erection of storage tanks for oil, water, and other liquids. Another use is in the shipbuilding industry for joining shell plates.

Limitations: The major limitation of the electrogas process is with respect to welding position, which is generally vertical. The process should not be used if the joint is at an angle in excess of 15° from the vertical. Also, the length (height) of the weld produced is limited by the length of the elevating mechanism for moving the weld head vertically.

Submerged Arc Welding

Submerged arc welding (SAW) differs from other arc welding processes in that a blanket of fusible, granular material—commonly called flux—is used for shielding the arc and the molten metal (see Fig. 14-16). The arc is struck between the workpiece and a bare, consumable wire electrode, the tip of which is submerged in the flux. Because the arc is completely covered by the flux, it is not visible, and the weld is produced without the flash, spatter, and sparks that characterize open arc processes. Pressure is not used. The nature of the flux is such that very little smoke or visible fumes are developed.

The process is either semiautomatic or fully automatic, with the electrode(s) fed mechanically to the welding gun, head, or heads. In semiautomatic welding, the welder moves the gun, usually equipped with a flux-feeding device, along the joint. Flux feed may be by gravity flow through a nozzle concentric with the electrode, from a small hopper atop the gun, or it may be through a concentric nozzle tube connected to an air-pressurized flux tank.

Flux may also be applied in advance of the welding operation or ahead of the arc from a hopper run along

Figure 14-15 Electrogas welding process

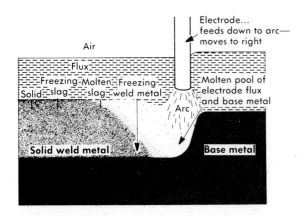

Figure 14-16   Submerged arc process *(Courtesy Lincoln Electric Company)*

the joint. In fully automatic submerged arc welding, flux is fed continuously to the joint ahead of or concentric to the arc. Fully automatic installations are commonly equipped with vacuum systems to pick up the unfused flux left by the welding head or heads for cleaning and reuse.

Applications: With the proper selection of equipment, the submerged arc process is applicable to a wide variety of welding requirements by industry. It can be used with all types of joints and permits welding a full range of carbon and low-alloy steels, from 16-gage [0.063″ (1.69 mm)] sheet to the thickest plate. It is also applicable to some high-alloy and heat-treated steels, as well as stainless steels, and is a favored process for rebuilding and hard-surfacing. Any degree of mechanization can be used, from handheld semiautomatic guns to boom or track-carried and fixture-held multiple welding heads. The submerged arc process is used extensively in ship and barge building, railroad car building, pipe manufacture, and in fabricating structural beams, girders, and columns where long welds are required. Automatic submerged arc installations are also key features of the welding areas of plants turning out mass-produced assemblies joined with repetitive short welds.

Advantages: The high quality of submerged arc welds, high deposition rates, deep penetration, adaptability of the process to full mechanization, and the comfort characteristics (no glare, sparks, spatter, smoke, or excessive heat radiation) make it a preferred process in steel fabrication. The high deposition rates attained by the use of high currents are chiefly responsible for the economies achieved with the process. Cost reductions when changing from the manual shielded metal arc process to submerged arc are frequently dramatic. For example, a hand-held submerged arc gun with mechanized travel may reduce welding costs more than 50%. With fully automatic multiarc equipment, it is not unusual for the costs to be only 10% of those with stick-electrode welding.

Welds made under the protective layer of flux have good ductility and impact resistance, and uniformity in bead appearance. Mechanical properties at least equal to those of the base metal are consistently obtained. In single-pass welds, the fused base metal may greatly influence the chemical and mechanical properties of the weld. For this reason, it is sometimes unnecessary to use electrodes of the same composition as the base metal for welding many of the low-alloy steels.

Limitations: Except for special applications, the submerged arc process is limited to welding in the flat and horizontal positions. As a result, workpieces must be flat or nearly flat. Flux, flux handling equipment, and workholding fixtures are required. Many joints also require the use of backing plates.

Because of its high penetration, the submerged arc process requires less deposited metal and, therefore, a change in joint design. Generally, for automatic welding, V-grooves should be wider than they are deep. The groove is used primarily to prevent buildup of the weld rather than to secure penetration. The vee should be made within 10% of expected bead width and only as deep as required to eliminate unnecessary buildup.

If a deep, narrow groove, such as that designed for hand welding, is used, internal bead cracking may result from internal shrinkage unless low currents are used. If the arc voltage used is too high with such a narrow groove, there will also be a possibility of slag inclusion and incomplete fusion at the bottom of the vee. With low voltage, an undercut may appear at the edge of the bead. The arc being deep in the groove, there may also be a tendency to wander to one side, resulting in a weld being off the seam. A good rule to follow is to have the weld 1½ times as wide as it is deep, as shown in Fig. 14-17.

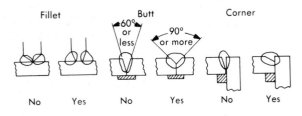

Figure 14-17   V-grooves for submerged arc welding

Stud Welding

Stud welding (SW) is an arc welding process that produces coalescence (joining) by heating with an arc between a metal stud or other fastener and base metal. When the abutting surfaces to be joined are heated to the proper temperature, they are brought together under pressure for solidification to take place. Shielding gas may or may not be used.

Applications: Studs are attached to only one side of workpieces, thus eliminating the need to have access to the reverse sides of assemblies. Stud-welded fasteners are used in place of rivets, drilled and tapped holes, and manually arc-welded fasteners.

Applications for stud welding incude the attaching of insulation to ductwork, truck cabs, and bulkheads. Other applications include attachment of handles to cookware, heat transfer studs in boilers, heat radiation fins in motors, assembling electronic panels, securing electrical and hydraulic lines, and the attachment of panels in the automotive industry. Stud welding is being used extensively in shipbuilding, in the automotive industry, in both large and small appliance industries, and other industries where fasteners must be attached.

Stud and base materials are the same as those joined by other arc welding processes. Metals most frequently stud welded are low-carbon steels, ferritic and austenitic stainless steels, low-alloy steels, titanium, nickel alloys, aluminum, and copper alloys. In addition, zinc die castings, magnesium alloys, and zirconium alloys are stud welded (see Figs. 14-18 and 14-19).

Advantages: Stud welding is a rapid process. Up to 20 studs per minute can be welded by handheld equipment, while up to 50 studs or more can be welded utilizing automatic, capacitor-discharge stud welding equipment. Robotic systems with automatic feeds have been developed for stud welding.

Base plates can be as thin as 0.015″ (0.38 mm) when using the capacitor-discharge process, while the base plate thickness for arc stud welding should normally be no less than one-third of the stud diameter to achieve maximum strength.

Studs of various cross-sectional shapes, such as round, square, rectangular, and hexagonal shapes, are commonly welded. Stud welds are generally made to plane surfaces, but with appropriate accessories, studs can be welded to curved surfaces such as tubes and pipes.

Stud welding eliminates the need for drilling and tapping and provides a neat appearance. There is no need for cleaning or polishing after welding. Full fastener strength is developed—the weld is as strong as the fastener and parent metal. The fasteners cannot vibrate loose or drop off. The studs can be precisely positioned at any desired location. Recommended practices for stud welding are presented in ANSI/AWS Standard C5.4.

Limitations: Studs, fasteners, or other similar parts must be of a size and shape that permit chucking. Areas to be welded must be clean and free from rust, grease, oil, dirt, or plated materials. Studs or fasteners to be joined must be made of a weldable material, and one end must be designed for welding.

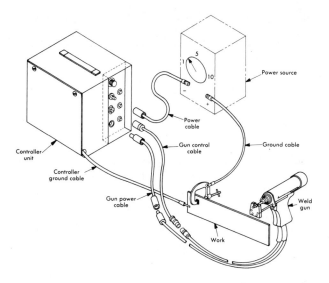

Figure 14-18 Electrical arrangement for arc stud welding *(Courtesy of KSM Fastening Systems)*

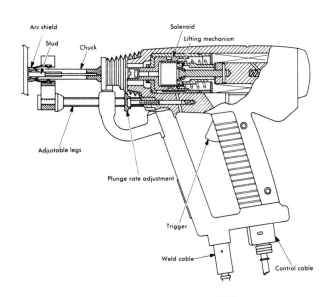

Figure 14-19 Typical arc stud welding gun *(Courtesy of KSM Fastening Systems)*

Plasma Arc Welding

Plasma arc welding (PAW) is an arc welding process that employs a high-temperature constricted or nonconstricted plasma column to obtain the melting and coalescence of most metals. The term *plasma* refers to a gas that has been sufficiently ionized to conduct an electrical current. The plasma is produced by forcing an inert gas and an electrical current from a tungsten electrode through a constricting orifice (nozzle). As a result, the plasma arc takes on a narrow columnar shape with properties that can enhance welding. See Fig. 14-20.

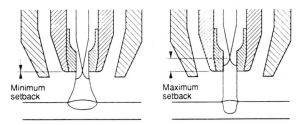

Figure 14-20 Electrode setback for plasma arc welding

Applications: Plasma welding is not a new process, but only in the past few years has it gained significant acceptance. It has now proven its value in the area of repetitious automated welds and is being used most frequently as an alternative to the gas tungsten arc welding (GTAW) process.

Plasma welding is being used extensively in the automotive industry for the production of various subassemblies, such as alternator, transmission, drivetrain, and engine components. Other applications include formed sheet metal boxes, filing cabinets, computer cabinets, door and window frames, battery and capacitor canisters, and home appliances. The process is also being used in the production of pipe and tubing and for joining coils and other cylindrical components made from flat plate stock.

Advantages: For most applications, the plasma arc process offers increased electrode life, reliable arc starting, improved arc stability, better penetration control, and reduced current levels. In some cases, it permits increased travel speeds and improved weld quality. Also, the plasma arc process is less sensitive to operating variables.

Electrode protection. In the plasma arc process, the tungsten electrode, which is secured inside the plasma torch and behind the orifice, is protected from outside impurities that would normally attack a hot surface. With this protection, the electrode is not exposed to base material contaminants such as forming and stamping oils, degreasers, and surface oxides. These contaminants, under intense arc temperatures, can constantly attack a tungsten electrode, causing contamination and erosion. The tungsten electrode in plasma welding can operate many hours before requiring a change.

Reliable arc starting. Arc initiation for the plasma arc process is provided by a pilot arc that resides in the orifice area of the torch. The pilot arc is an arc that exists between the tungsten electrode and the orifice. It is started by imposing high frequency (from a small high-frequency generator inside the control console) on a low direct current for a short duration of time to start the ionization of the gas. Once the pilot arc has been established, the requirements for high frequency are no longer needed. The pilot arc now remains on to assist the starting of the main transferred welding arc.

Limitations: Possible limitations of the plasma welding process inlcude the high initial cost of the equipment, size of the torches, and the reduced accessibility to certain weld joint configurations. Plasma welding is also limited to metal thicknesses of approximately ⅜″ (9.5 mm) on stainless steel and ½″ (12.7 mm) on titanium. The process is generaly limited to flat, horizontal, or vertical-up welding when performing single-pass welds in the keyhole mode.

Other Arc Welding Processes

In addition to the methods already discussed, there are other arc welding processes, but most are obsolete or seldom used. The methods include carbon arc welding, bare metal arc welding, and atomic hydrogren welding.

Carbon Arc Welding: Carbon arc welding (CAW) is an arc welding process that produces coalescence (joining) of metals by heating them with an arc between a carbon (graphite) electrode and the work. No shielding is used, and pressure and filler metal may or may not be used. The process is the oldest form of arc welding and is seldom used now for joining because carbon can be introduced into the weld metal and make the joints brittle. When used, the process is normally performed manually with electrode-negative polarity d-c and is capable of welding thin metals.

Carbon arc welding is also used for cutting and gouging metals, as discussed subsequently in this section.

Gas carbon arc welding (CAW-G). This method is a variation of carbon arc welding in which shielding is obtained from a gas or gas mixture, resulting in higher quality welds. The process, however, has little or no commercial application.

Shielded carbon arc welding (CAW-S). This variation of carbon arc welding provides shielding from the combustion of a solid material fed into the arc or from a blanket of flux on the work, or both. Pressure and filler metal may or may not be used. This process is seldom used.

Twin carbon arc welding (CAW-T). In this variation of carbon arc welding, coalescence of metals is produced by heating them with an electric arc between two carbon electrodes. The work is not part of the electrical circuit. No shielding is used, and pressure and filler metal may or may not be used. This process is used primarily for maintenance operations, with small a-c arc welding machines generally employed as the power source. Copper-coated carbon electrodes are common.

Bare Metal Arc Welding:
Bare metal arc welding (BMAW) is an arc welding process that produces coalescence (joining) of metals by heating them with an electric arc between a bare or lightly coated metal electrode and the work. Neither shielding nor pressure is used, and filler metal is obtained from the electrode.

A major disadvantage of welding with a bare electrode is that the molten weld metal and filler metal (if used) are exposed to the atmosphere. This can result in oxidation, improper fusion, porosity, high hardness, and poor ductility. Covered electrodes are now generally used for this process instead of bare or lightly covered electrodes.

Atomic Hydrogen Welding:
Atomic hydrogen welding (AHW) is an arc welding process that produces coalescence (joining) of metals by heating them with an electric arc maintained between two metal electrodes in an atmosphere of hydrogen. The arc is maintained entirely independent of the parts being welded. Shielding is provided by the hydrogen. Pressure and filler metal may or may not be used, depending on the application.

Plasma Arc Cutting

Plasma arc cutting (PAC) is an arc cutting process that severs metal by melting a localized area with the heat of a constricted arc. Molten metal is removed with a high-velocity jet of hot, ionized gas issuing from the orifice. The arc penetrates the workpiece as in keyhole welding with a plasma arc, previously discussed in this section. The voltage used for plasma arc cutting, however, is much higher, and the nozzle is designed to create a higher velocity arc to blow away the molten metal (see Fig. 14-21).

Applications:
While originally developed for severing nonferrous metals, such as aluminum, and stainless steels, modifications of the plasma arc process and equipment now make it possible to cut any metal that conducts electricity. The method is being used extensively to cut carbon steel, generally from about 0.038 to 1½″ (0.95 to 38 mm) thick.

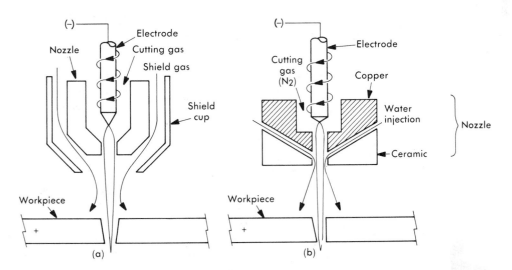

Figure 14-21 Plasma arc cutting: a) gas shielded; b) water-injected *(Courtesy of Hypertherm, Inc.)*

Operations performed include stack cutting, plate and pipe edge beveling, shape cutting, and piercing. Plasma cutting torches are being mounted integrally on CNC punch presses for making contours, slots, and large cutouts in sheet metal.

Advantages: A major advantage of the plasma arc process is the fast cutting speeds possible. Low-carbon steel, ½″ (12.7 mm) thick, can be cut at 100 ipm (2540 mm/min). Speed and cost advantages compared to oxyfuel cutting decrease, however, with increasing workpiece thicknesses.

The fast speeds possible with plasma arc cutting minimize thermal distortion and result in a narrow heat-affected zone. No preheating is required, and parts cut in this way can be handled immediately after the operation. More precise cuts can generally be made at lower costs than with air-carbon arc cutting.

Limitations: A possible limitation to the use of plasma arc cutting is that the top edges of the cuts are generally rounded, and the cuts are beveled (wider at the top than the bottom). Smoothness of the cut surfaces is generally satisfactory for most applications.

Another possible limitation is that capital equipment costs for plasma arc cutting are higher than for oxyfuel cutting. Also, power demands are high. Depending on the material and thickness to be cut, the power supply may have to provide up to 250 V at 1000 A.

Other Arc Cutting Processes

In addition to air-carbon arc cutting and plasma arc cutting, discussed previously, there are several other arc cutting processes, but they are not used extensively or only for special applications. These include oxygen arc cutting, gas metal arc cutting, gas tungsten arc cutting, shielded metal arc cutting, and carbon arc cutting.

Oxygen Arc Cutting: In oxygen arc cutting, oxygen passes through a tubular electrode made from a ferrous metal and covered with a flux. An electric arc between the electrode and the workpiece

provides the heat required for an oxidation reaction. Cuts produced in this way are not of high quality, but are satisfactory for some applications. The method is used primarily for underwater applications.

Gas Metal Arc Cutting: In gas metal arc cutting, an electric arc between a continuously fed wire electrode and the workpiece, with inert gas shielding, produces the required heat. Force from a pressure gradient in the gas ejects molten metal to form the kerf.

Gas Tungsten Arc Cutting: Gas tungsten arc cutting is similar to gas tungsten arc welding (GTAW) except that higher currents and shielding gas flows are used. Molten metal is blown away by the gas jet to form the kerf.

Shielded Metal Arc Cutting: In shielded metal arc cutting, standard covered electrodes are used without any compressed gas. Molten metal is removed by gravity.

Carbon Arc Cutting: In carbon arc cutting, heat is provided by an electric arc between a carbon electrode and the workpiece. Molten metal is removed by forces from the arc and by gravity.

Safety in Arc Welding and Cutting

Detailed recommendations with respect to safety in welding and cutting are presented in ANSI/AWS Standard Z49.1. Fire prevention in the use of these processes is the subject of NFPA Standard 51B.

General Requirements: Good housekeeping is essential for safety in arc welding and cutting. All equipment should be kept in good, clean, and dry condition, with frequent inspections and maintenance. Welding areas should also be kept neat, clean, dry, and free of hazards. Flammable materials, liquids, or gases should be removed or stored in tightly sealed metal containers. Hot electrode stubs should be placed in metal containers.

Properly trained operators with skilled supervisors are critical to safety. Nonreflecting curtains or screens are advisable to protect others near the welding area. Warning signs should be posted to identify welding and cutting areas and the need for protective devices.

Eye Protection: Arc welding and cutting result in infrared radiation from the molten metal and ultraviolet radiation from the electric arc. Eye exposure to ultraviolet radiation causes irritation and repeated exposure may result in permanent eye injury. As a result, handheld shields, face shields, helmets, or goggles equipped with filter lenses are necessary.

Specifications for eye protection equipment are contained in ANSI Standard Z87.1, "Practice for Occupational and Educational Eye and Face Protection." Recommendations for filter lenses are presented in ANSI/AWS Standard Z49.1. Safety goggles should also be worn when chipping or grinding slag from welds.

Skin Protection: Burns can occur from contact with hot metal or sparks during arc welding or cutting. Overexposure to ultraviolet and infrared radiation from the electric arc can also cause severe skin burns. To prevent this, nonflammable protective clothing, including aprons and gloves, is generally required.

Respiratory Protection: Fumes, gases, and particulate matter in the air can cause respiratory problems. The hazard potential depends on the chemical composition of the materials used, the concentration of the chemicals in the breathing zone, and the duration of exposure. Air contaminants result from components of the electrodes, filler rods, and metals being joined, as well as shielding gases, when used. Ozone and oxides of nitrogen are the principal toxic gases produced by arc welding.

The best protection against respiratory problems is to provide adequate and effective, positive ventilation by means of exhaust systems. Supplied-air respirators may be required for welding in confined spaces. Regulations issued by OSHA, as well as local codes, specify requirements with respect to ventilation. Recommended practices for respiratory protection are contained in ANSI Standard Z88.1. Methods for sampling airborne particulates generated by welding and allied processes are presented in ANSI/AWS Standard F1.1.

Hearing Protection: Properly fitted ear plugs or other ear protection to prevent noise exposure may be needed, especially when cutting with the air-carbon arc and plasma arc processes, to meet OSHA regulations.

Electrical Shock: Electrical shocks experienced at welding voltages do not generally cause severe injury, but under certain conditions, they can be lethal. Even mild shocks can produce involuntary muscle contractions that may cause injuries. Wearing damp clothing or working in wet conditions reduces skin contact resistance and increases the risk of shock.

To minimize the possibility of electrical shocks, all machines used should meet national standards, such as those issued by NEMA, and the machines and equipment should be inspected and maintained on a regular schedule. All electrical equipment and the workpieces should be grounded, and cables of the correct size should be used. Electrode holders and connections should be fully insulated, and welding cables should be free of worn or frayed insulation. All connections should be kept tight, clean, dry, and in good condition. Operators and maintenance personnel should wear insulated gloves when making adjustments.

Safety with Various Processes: Shielded metal arc welding. Major requirements for this process are eye protection and protective clothing because of exposure to the electric arc and molten metal or slag spatter.

Gas tungsten arc welding. Safety precautions for this process are the same as for shielded metal arc welding except that a darker shade of lens is generally required for eye protection because the gas tungsten arc is more intensive.

Gas metal arc welding. Potential hazards with this process include fumes and gases, high-voltage electricity, ultraviolet radiation from the arc, and noise.

Flux-cored arc welding. Depending on the shielding used with this process (self- or gas-shielded), safety precautions are similar to shielded metal arc welding or gas metal arc welding.

Electrogas welding. Safety considerations required for this process are much the same as for the other continuous-wire arc welding processes. Eye protection is required because the arc is continuous from start to finish of the operation. A consideration intrinsic to the process is the presence of larger than normal amounts of molten weld metal. If this metal escapes, it creates both a safety and a fire hazard. Workpieces to be welded must be securely braced to eliminate the possibility of their falling. Also, because heights are involved, precautions should be taken to prevent personnel from falling.

Submerged arc welding. There are few health and safety problems associated with this process. Fume and gas levels are generally negligible, radiation is usually nonexistent, and noise and heat levels are low. No eye protection is needed, but safety glasses and gloves are generally used. The safety glasses are often tinted to protect in case the arc is inadvertently exposed.

Plasma arc welding and cutting. With these processes, protection is required from the intense glare of the arc, spatter, fumes, and noise.

Electroslag Welding

Electroslag welding (ESW) is a process in which coalescence of metals is produced by molten slag that melts the filler metal and the surfaces of the work to be welded. The molten weld pool is shielded by this slag, which moves along the full cross section of the joint as welding progresses.

Electroslag welding is not an arc welding process, but it is initiated by an arc that heats the slag. Also, it uses the same basic equipment as the other consumable-electrode arc welding processes and is most similar to electrogas welding, previously discussed in this chapter. When the arc is extinguished, the conductive slag is maintained molten by its resistance to electric current passing between the electrode and the work. In consumable-guide electro-

slag welding, the most commonly used variation of electroslag welding, filler metal is supplied by an electrode and its guiding member (see Fig. 14-22). Consumables used for electroslag welding of carbon and high-strength, low-alloy steels are specified in ANSI/AWS Standard A5.25.

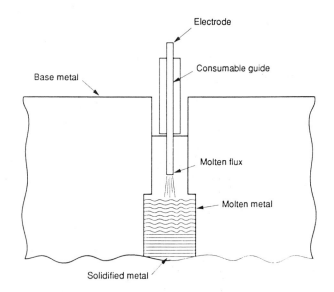

Figure 14-22 Consumable-guide electroslag welding

Applications

The major user of electroslag welding has been the heavy-plate fabrication industry, which includes manufacturers of frames, bases, and metalworking machinery. A frequent use of the process is the splicing of rolled steel plates to obtain a larger piece for a specific application.

Another major user of electroslag welding is the structural steel industry, for making subassemblies for steel buildings. It has also been used for field erection at building sites. A common application is the welding of continuity plates inside box columns. The continuity plate carries the load from one side of the column to the other side at the point of beam-to-column connections. Continuity plates must be welded with complete-penetration welds to the two sides of the box column. The electrical machinery industry also utilizes electroslag welding for producing electric motor housings.

Process Advantages

The electroslag welding process is one of the most productive welding processes when it can be applied. Some of its advantages are:

1. Extremely high metal deposition rates. Electroslag has a deposition rate of 35-45 lb/hr (15.9-20.4 kg/hr) per electrode.
2. Ability to weld thick materials in one pass. Because there is only one pass, only one setup is required, and interpass cleaning is not necessary.
3. High-quality weld deposits. Weld metal stays molten longer, allowing gases to escape.
4. Minimized joint preparation and fitup requirements. Mill edges and square flame-cut edges are normally employed.
5. It is a mechanized process: once started, it continues to completion. There is little operator fatigue because manipulative skill is not involved.
6. Minimized material handling. The equipment may be moved to the work, rather than the work moved to the equipment.
7. High filler-metal utilization. All of the welding electrode is melted into the joint. In addition, the amount of flux consumed is small.
8. Minimum distortion. There is no angular distortion in the horizontal plane. There is minimum distortion (shrinkage) in the vertical plane.
9. Minimal time. It is the fastest welding process for large, thick materials.
10. There is no weld spatter, and finishing of the weld is minimal.
11. There is no arc flash, so a welding helmet is not required.

Limitations

The major limitation of electroslag welding is that of welding position. The process can be used only when the axis of the weld is vertical. A tilt of up to 15° is permitted, but beyond this the process may not function correctly. A second limitation is that the process can be used only for welding steels. Also, the long thermal cycle of the process may result in low toughness of the weld metal and the heat-affected zone. High heat input and slow cooling can also produce coarse grain size.

A possible problem is lack of fusion at the sidewall on one surface if the electrode is incorrectly placed. Also, there may be lack of fusion if the weld stops and has to be restarted. These problems are rarely encountered, however, with the use of good welding practices.

Resistance Welding

Resistance welding (RW) is a group of welding processes that produce coalescence of metals with the heat obtained from the resistance of the work to electric current flowing in a circuit of which the work is a part, and by the application of pressure. There is no external heat source, and pressure is applied by the welding machine through electrodes. No flux, filler metal, or shielding is used, but in welding reactive metals, the process is sometimes performed in a vacuum or inert-gas environment.

The major types of resistance welding, all discussed in this section, are spot, seam, projection, flash, upset, percussion, and induction. Some of these processes are illustrated schematically in Fig. 14-23. Essential elements for resistance welding include a low-voltage, high-current welding transformer; electrodes for contacting the work; conductors connecting the electrodes with the welding transformer; means for exerting the electrode force (pressure) on the work; means to regulate current by changing the

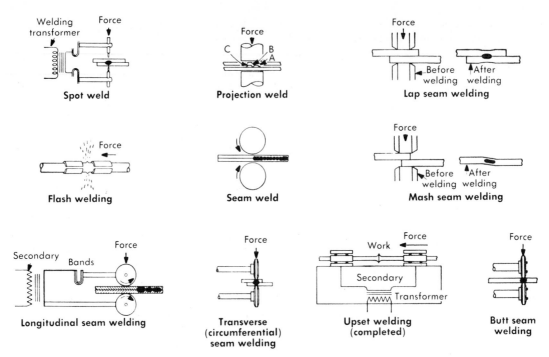

Figure 14-23 Basic methods of resistance welding

transformer turns ratio or by electronic phase-shift heat-control unit; a power contactor to open and close the circuit to the welding transformer; and a welding timer to control energization and deenergization of the power contactor (see Fig. 14-24).

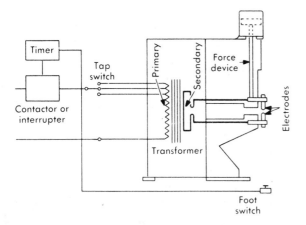

Figure 14-24 Essential elements for resistance welding

Resistance Spot Welding

Resistance spot welding (RSW) produces coalescence at the faying surfaces in one spot. The size and shape of the individually formed welds (nuggets) are influenced primarily by the size and contour of the electrodes. Most spot welding is done by clamping the workpieces between a pair of electrodes and passing a low-voltage, high-amperage current through the electrodes and workpieces for a short cycle. Resistance heating at the joint contacting surfaces forms a fused nugget of weld material. The heat developed in spot welding depends on several variables, including the magnitude of the current, electrical resistance of the workpieces, time of current flow, conduction losses, and electrode force.

Applications: Spot-welded lap joints are used extensively to join sheet steels up to about ⅛″ (3.2 mm) thick when gas- or liquid-tight joints are not required. Sometimes, steel thicknesses to ¼″ (6.4 mm) are joined. With special equipment, 1″ (25.4 mm) thicknesses or more can be welded, although these thicknesses are more suited for other joining processes.

Applications include the fabrication of containers and the attachment of braces, brackets, and similar components. The process is commonly used by mass production industries such as automotive, appliance, and furniture. The ease and speed of the welding operation also make the process suitable for the assembly of components that are to be subsequently brazed or bonded.

Advantages:
A major advantage of resistance welding is its high speed. Also, the process is adaptable to mass production requirements, and equipment can be made an integral part of production lines. However, the process is also used for many job shop operations because it is faster than arc welding and can be performed with less skilled operators.

Because no flux, filler metal, or shielding gas are used with resistance welding, the composition of the base metal is not altered. Also, the application of electrode force refines the grain structure and makes it more uniform. With proper controls, the process produces consistently sound, high-quality welds at high production rates and with low labor costs.

Other advantages include no limitations with respect to welding position; localized heating, which minimizes the possibility of distortion; and applicability to practically all steels and aluminum and copper alloys. The process is often more economical than using mechanical fasteners for assemblies that do not require gas- or liquid-tight joints and where disassembly is not required.

Limitations:
Equipment costs for resistance welding are generally higher than for arc welding, and the spot welds have lower strength. Because workpiece clamping is required, access to both sides of the joint is necessary. Special fixtures and material handling equipment are required for mass production applications. Another possible limitation is the high power demands of resistance welding, even though the duration of current flow per weld is short.

Process Variations:
Spot welding is done by either the direct or indirect method. Parallel and series variations are used for multiple spot welding. Other variations include roll spot welding and weldbonding.

Direct welding. In this method, both the welding current and the pressure are applied by the electrodes. All of the secondary current passes through the weld nugget(s). This results in indentations in both components of the assembly unless special provisions are made in electrode design.

Indirect welding. In this method, the welding current is applied to one of the workpieces through a contact located next to the electrode that applies pressure. Indirect welding with two transformers, sometimes called push-pull welding, produces a higher voltage for welding metals having high electrical resistance.

Parallel welding. In this method, two or more spot welds are made simultaneously with current flowing parallel from a single transformer.

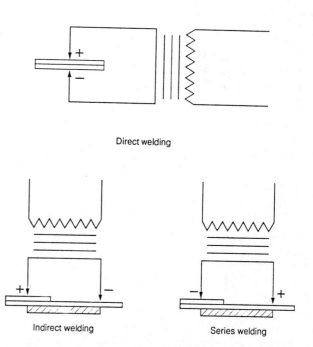

Direct welding

Indirect welding　　　　Series welding

Figure 14-25　Spot welding variations

Series welding. In this method, current flows from one electrode into a third electrode or mandrel and then to the second electrode, producing two spot welds.

Roll spot welding. In this method, a row of separate and spaced spot welds are made with a seam welding machine (discussed later in this section). The rotating electrode wheel is not retracted, and electrode force is continued between welds.

Weldbonding. This method is a combination of resistance spot or seam welding and adhesive bonding. The procedure used most commonly is to apply a structural adhesive to the area to be joined, followed by spot welding through the adhesive. Another method consists of applying tape or film adhesive, with holes cut in the adhesive where welds are required.

Advantages of weldbonding over spot welding or adhesive bonding alone include improved fatigue life and durability, and better resistance to peel forces. Also, the adhesive acts as a seal in the joints to provide better corrosion protection and a generally tighter construction.

Resistance Seam Welding

Resistance seam welding (RSEW) produces coalescence at the faying surfaces by a series of overlapping spot welds made progressively along a joint by rotating wheel-like or roller electrodes. Seam welding has much in common with spot welding, discussed in the preceding section. Welds produced may be direct or indirect, similar to spot welding. The major difference is that seam welding uses rotating electrode wheels that maintain contact force during a succession of welds along a seam (see Fig. 14-23).

Applications: Seam welding is used for a variety of workpiece shapes. Applications include longitudinal welds and encircling welds on round, square, or rectangular parts. A major application is producing gas- or liquid-tight joints on sheet metal tanks. Other applications include the welding of mufflers, cans, and other containers.

Advantages: Seam welding offers similar advantages to spot welding, previously discussed, with the additional benefit of being capable of producing continuous, leaktight welds. Also, overlaps can be less than for spot or projection welding, and seam widths can be less than the diameters of spot welds. Seam welding is generally practical for metal thicknesses ranging from 0.001 to 0.187" (0.03 to 4.75 mm).

Limitations: In addition to the same limitations discussed previously for spot welding, an additional limitation is that seam welds generally have to be in a straight or uniformly curved line, with no obstructions or sharp corners. The lengths of longitudinal seam joints are limited by the throat depths of the welding machines available.

Warpage of workpieces is a factor that must be considered in seam welding, but several techniques are used to minimize distortion. Metal thicknesses more than about 1/8" (3.2 mm) are more difficult to weld than with the spot or projection methods. Seam welding is not ordinarily used for joining large sheets because of the high amounts of electrical energy that are required.

Resistance Projection Welding

Projection welding is a resistance welding process wherein coalescence is produced by the heat obtained from the resistance to the flow of current through the work parts held together under pressure by electrodes. The resulting welds are localized at predetermined points by the design of the parts to be welded. Localization is accomplished by projections, embossments, or intersections that direct the flow of current from one workpiece to the other. The projected metal embossment is heated to a temperature sufficient to fuse the parts together. Force is always applied before, during, and after the application of current.

Applications: Projection welding is used principally to assemble blanked, stamped, formed, and machined parts. The process is especially useful for producing several welds simultaneously between two parts. Mechanical fasteners, brackets, pins, handles, clips, and similar components are attached to many products in this way. Cross-wire welding, discussed subsequently in this section, is used extensively for producing stove and refrigerator parts, fence wire, electronic connections, and grills. The process is generally used to join metal thicknesses ranging from 0.020 to 0.125″ (0.51 to 3.18 mm).

Advantages: An important advantage of projection welding is that a number of welds can be made in a single cycle. Also, the welds require less overlap, can be spaced closer, and can be produced with narrower flanges than spot welds. Weld locations are more accurate, and nugget diameters and thicknesses are generally more consistent than those produced in spot welding.

Another advantage of projection welding is that thicker materials can be joined than with spot welding, including thickness ratios of six or more to one.

Flash, Upset, and Percussion Welding

Flash welding (FW), upset welding (UW), and percussion welding (PEW) are related resistance welding processes. All three processes produce coalescence of metals by the application of electrical heating and pressure. They differ in the method of heating and the timing of the pressure application.

In flash welding, which is limited to the production of butt and miter welds, the abutting surfaces of the workpieces are heated prior to the application of pressure to forge the surfaces together. In upset welding, pressure is applied before the application of current and is maintained throughout the heating period to produce butt or seam welds. In percussion welding, coalescence of abutting surfaces is produced by heat from an arc established by the rapid discharge of electrical energy and pressure applied percussively during or immediately following the electrical discharge.

Similar equipment is used for flash and for upset welding. Flash welding is preferred in many indus-

tries because the resulting weld exhibits greater weld strength and a smaller upset. Power demand is less, more heat is evident at the welded surface and less in the body of the work, and less preparation of weld surface by machining is required. Dissimilar metals of widely varying fusion temperatures may be flash welded together because flashing (arcing) may be continued until the fusion temperature of each metal is reached. Successful flash welding of workpieces formed from relatively light gages of sheet aluminum is accomplished on a production basis (see Fig. 14-26).

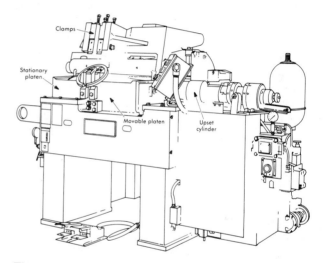

Figure 14-26   Flash welding machine *(Courtesy of Taylor-Winfield Corporation)*

Flash Welding: In flash welding, the parts are loaded in the machine in very light contact with each other or slightly separated. After clamping by the electrodes (dies), current is applied and movement of the traveling platen is initiated practically simultaneously. Heating results from resistance of the workpiece contact surfaces to the flow of electric current and by arcs between the faying surfaces. Force applied by the platen expels molten metal from the joint and upets the base metal. The flow of current is usually stopped during upsetting.

Applications. Flash welds are most commonly employed in joining two pieces of metal end to end or in welding one piece of metal to a projecting part of another piece. Some examples are the welding of strips end to end in steelmaking and processing to form a continuous strip; the welding of circled strips or bars to form rings for automobile wheel rims and ring gears; the welding of tubular sections end to end; the production of electrical motor and generator frames; and joining airframe and jet engine structural members.

Advantages. Flash welding is a fast and economical process for producing uniform, high-quality welds in many ferrous and nonferrous metals. A variety of shapes, including sheet, plate, rings, pipe, tubes, wire, and extrusions, can be joined. Little or no joint preparation is necessary and ejection of metal during upsetting helps remove impurities from the interface of the joint.

Limitations. Safety precautions are necessary when using flash welding because of the hot, molten metal particles ejected. Another possible limitation is that the parts to be joined must have cross sections that are practically identical. Also, for some applications, the upset material must be removed, thus adding to production costs.

Upset Welding:
Upset welding is a resistance welding process that produces coalescence simultaneously over the entire areas of abutting surfaces or progressively along a joint. Heating to welding temperature results from the resistance to electric current through the area where the surfaces are in contact. Pressure is applied before heating starts, is maintained throughout heating, and increases to upset the workpieces when the welding temperature is reached. Upset welding differs from flash welding, discussed previously, in that the heating results entirely from the resistance to current at the contact surfaces, and there is no flashing or arcing.

Applications. Upset welding is used extensively in the manufacture of continuously welded pipe and tubing and to join wire coils for continuous operations. The process is also employed to make many different products from wire, bar, strip, and tubing.

Advantages and limitations. Upset welding has advantages and limitations similar to flash welding except that safety precautions for flashing and arcing are not required. Upset welds are generally characterized by large symmetrical upsets. Capabilities of the process include joining wire and rod ranging from 0.05 to 1.25″ (1.3 to 31.8 mm) diam.

Percussion Welding:
Percussion welding is a resistance welding process that produces coalescence over the entire areas of abutting surfaces. Heat is supplied by a high-current arc produced by the rapid discharge of electrical energy between the two workpieces to be joined. Force is applied percussively during or immediately following the short pulse of electrical energy. The impact of one workpiece against the other extinguishes the arc, expels molten metal, and completes the weld. There are two major variations of the process: capacitor-discharge and magnetic-force percussion welding.

Applications. The use of percussion welding for butt joints (joining wires, rods, or tubes of equal cross section end to end) is generally limited to dissimilar metals and/or where minimum upsetting is required. This is because similar metals can be butt welded more economically by other processes. Major applications include the production of electrical and electronic connections and contact devices, and joining small components to other or larger parts.

Advantages. An important advantage of percussion welding is that the short time the arc exists limits melting of the base metal to a thin surface layer. This results in a shallow heat-affected zone and minimum upsetting, oxidation of the abutting surfaces, and alloying of dissimilar metals. Heat-treated and cold-worked metals can generally be welded without any softening, and prefinished metals are usually unaffected. Wires as small as 0.005″ (0.13 mm) diam can be joined with the capacitor-discharge process. The magnetic-force method can join flat workpieces with weld areas from 0.04 to 0.70 in.^{2} (25.8 to 452 mm^2).

Limitations. Flat parts have to be joined to flat surfaces and butt joints require parts of similar sections. As previously mentioned, butt welds of similar metals can be made more economically by other processes. Percussion welding requires two pieces to be joined; the ends of a single workpiece cannot be joined to produce a ring.

High-Frequency Welding

With the high-frequency welding processes, the coalescence of metals is produced with the heat generated from the resistance of the workpieces to a high-frequency alternating current. In high-frequency resistance welding (HFRW), called the contact method, current is introduced to the workpieces by actual physical contact (see Fig. 14-27). An upsetting force is rapidly applied after heating is substantially completed.

In high-frequency induction welding (HFIW), called the induction method, current is induced in the workpieces by an external induction coil (see Fig. 14-28). There is no contact between the workpieces and the current.

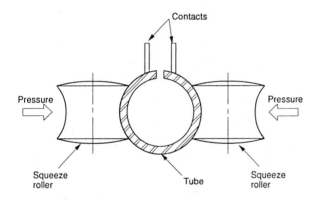

Figure 14-27   High-frequency resistance welding

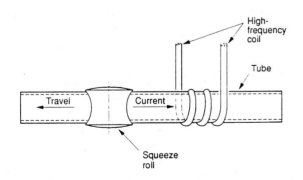

Figure 14-28   High-frequency induction welding

Applications: The most common application for the high-frequency welding processes is the continuous seam welding of the edges of a single piece of metal in the production of metal pipe and tubing. Another application is the welding of butt joints between two parts, such as joining coil ends or sections and producing large strip and sheet blanks for forming. The processes are also used to produce structural shapes, spiral pipe and tubing, and helically and longitudinally finned tubing.

Satisfactory welds are normally produced in air, and the welds can be made with water or soluble-oil cutting fluids present. For some applications, such as the welding of titanium alloys, inert gas shielding is used. Flux is not generally required, but is helpful in welding some copper alloys.

Advantages: An important advantage of high-frequency welding is the narrow heat-affected zone produced. This limits oxidation and distortion and generally results in stronger joints. Concentration of the heating current at the work surfaces (shallow heating) permits welding temperatures to be reached with less power consumption than other resistance welding processes. High speeds make the processes suitable for high-production applications. Some pipes and tubes can be welded at rates to 1000 fpm (305 m/min).

Limitations: High-frequency induction welding requires a closed-loop path or a complete circuit for the flow of current entirely within the workpieces. This limits applications to flat, coiled, or tubular stock having a constant joint symmetry throughout the workpiece lengths. Equipment required is generally built into fully automated mills or production lines, necessitating a high capital investment.

Special precautions are necessary to protect personnel from the hazards of high-frequency current. Also, because the equipment operates near the radio-frequency range, care is necessary to avoid radiation interference and to meet regulations of the Federal Communications Commission.

Safety in Resistance Welding

Major hazards with resistance welding processes include the possibilities of electric shock, moving machine parts, and, in the case of flash, upset, and percussion welding, the ejection of molten metal particles. Because of the many variations in resistance welding processes, individual evaluations are required with respect to safety considerations. Recommendations for safety in welding are presented in ANSI/AWS Standard Z49.1.

General Requirements: Good housekeeping is essential for safety in resistance welding. Equipment and welding areas should be kept in good, clean, and dry condition, with frequent inspections and maintenance. Properly trained operators with skilled supervisors are also important for safety.

Machines and Mechanical Equipment: Machines for resistance welding should be equipped with guards and safety devices to prevent injury to operators. Initiating devices should be arranged or guarded to prevent inadvertent operation, with one or more emergency stop buttons provided. On press-type flash and upset welding machines, safety blocks or other means must be provided to prevent movement of the platen during maintenance or setup, and a fire-resistant shielding is required to protect the operator and other personnel from the expulsion of molten metal particles.

Eye Protection: Eye or face shields or hardened lens goggles are recommended for most resistance welding processes. For flash, upset, and percussion welding, shaded lenses are required.

Skin Protection: Because burns can occur from contact with hot metal in some resistance welding processes, it is recommended that personnel wear nonflammable protective clothing, including aprons and gloves.

Electrical Shock: All electrical equipment, including controls, must be manufactured and in-stalled in accordance with safety requirements of local, state, and national standards and codes, such as those issued by NEMA. The equipment must be grounded and high-voltage parts insulated and protected by enclosures with access doors that are electrically interlocked.

With resistance welding equipment that uses capacitors, the capacitors should be enclosed and insulated, and interlocks should interrupt the power and short-circuit the capacitors through a resistive load when the access door is opened. With high-frequency welding processes, precautions are necessary to prevent injuries from the power sources.

Electron Beam Welding and Cutting

Electron beam welding (EBW) is a fusion joining process accomplished by impinging a high intensity beam of electrons on the joint to be welded. This results in precise melting and coalescence of the joint interface surfaces. This accurately controllable process provides a direct means of delivering high-energy densities (see Fig. 14-29).

Applications

Electron beam welding is employed in a variety of precision and production applications. In the automotive industry, semiautomated and fully automated partial vacuum and non-vacuum EBW systems are being used to hermetically assemble die cast aluminum manifolds, steel torque converters, and catalytic converters, and for the fabrication welding of a large number of transmission components of varying materials. Other products joined by electron beam welding include solenoid valves, transducers, sealed bearings, diesel engine valves and injectors, and medical implants.

In the aerospace and nuclear industries, high-vacuum and partial-vacuum manual, semiautomated, and fully automated systems are used to perform

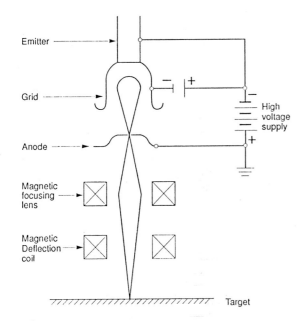

Figure 14-29   Optics system for electron beam welding

a broad range of production assembly and repair procedure tasks on a wide variety of materials. In the saw blade industry, air-to-air mode, high-vacuum semiautomated and fully automated systems are used to produce the bimetallic (dissimilar metal) strip employed in making improved hack and bandsaw blades. Fast production of thin-walled tubing is another major application.

The various applications of electron beam welding cover a wide range of production rates, ranging from tens to hundreds of parts per hour. They involve making weld penetrations ranging from less than 0.050″ (1.27 mm) to greater than 6″ (150 mm) deep in a single weld pass.

With regard to the cost of employing the EBW process in production, figures given by various present users show a "total operating cost" experience that ranges from $0.05 to $0.95 per kilowatt of applied beam power per hour. This wide range in operating cost experience results from differences in the operating mode employed, the degree of vacuum and wire-feed assistance used, the level of preventive maintenance provided, and other factors.

Advantages

An important advantage of the EBW process is its capability for making high-quality welds that are deeper and narrower than arc welds and that are made with lower heat input. Very shallow welds with almost parallel sides can also be produced. Thick sections can be welded in a single pass, and the heat-affected zones (HAZs) are narrow, thus minimizing distortion. Welding speeds are fast, typically 30-100 ipm (762-2540 mm/min).

By projecting the electron beams, welds can be made in locations that are normally inaccessible. The beams can also be deflected to produce various shapes of welds and oscillated to improve quality and penetration. No filler metal, flux, or shielding gas are normally required, and welding can be done in any position. With the high-vacuum mode of operation, contamination of the metals being joined is minimized.

Limitations

Capital equipment costs for electron beam welding equipment are higher than for other welding processes, but operating costs are lower for many applications. Workpiece sizes that can be welded are limited by available vacuum chamber capacities. Many applications require precise edge preparation and alignment, and good fitup, which adds to costs.

When using the vacuum mode of EBW, production rates are limited by the time required to pump down the work chamber. With nonvacuum EBW, the distance that workpieces can be placed from the electron gun is limited. Electron beam welding also requires safety precautions for protection from X-ray and visible radiation.

Electron Beam Cutting

In electron beam cutting (EBC), an electron beam is focused to a beam spot intensity of approximately 10^{10} W/in² (1.55 x 10^{13} W/m²). This intensity is several orders of magnitude greater than that employed for electron beam welding. When impinged on a workpiece, the electrons produce complete vaporization of material in the beam spot's path. The EBC process provides an effective method for severing (cutting or slitting) refractory-type materials with accurate control.

The EBC process is normally accomplished under fairly high-vacuum conditions. This mode of operation requires an optimum degree of beam focusing capability and beam control versatility to be achieved. Precisely contoured slitting or cutting of thin materials can be performed with minimal kerf and maximum processing speed. The beam is usually operated in a relatively high-frequency pulsed mode for this type of operation.

Electron beam cutting, however, is used to only a limited extent. More recently, laser beam cutting (LBC), discussed next in this chapter, has become a major competitor of EBC. This is primarily because LBC can be accomplished in the atmosphere and therefore can be used with or without a supplementary cutting gas. For applications requiring an extremely fast beam motion or a totally inert ambient atmosphere, however, the low-inertia, high-vacuum EBC process is still an ideal method. Another advantage of EBC over LBC is the ability to drill trepan, or cut slots to more controllable and precise depths.

Safety in Electron Beam Welding and Cutting

In addition to the safety precautions required against the common welding hazards, discussed previously in this chapter, protection must be provided for the special dangers of high energy used in electron beam welding and cutting. These include radiation and possible electric shock from the high voltages used. Details with respect to safety precautions are presented in AWS Publication F2.1, "Recommended Safe Practice for Electron Beam Welding and Cutting," and ANSI Standard Z49.1,

"Safety in Welding and Cutting." Regularly scheduled inspection and maintenance are important.

Radiation: Radiation hazards include both visible radiation and the radiation from X rays. Visible radiation from the molten metal requires eye protection. Specifications for eye protection equipment are contained in ANSI Standard Z87.1, "Practice for Occupational and Educational Eye and Face Protection." Recommendations for filter lenses are presented in ANSI/AWS Standard Z49.1

Steel walls of the work chambers generally provide protection from X rays in low-voltage machines. Lead coverings are provided on high-voltage machines. Leaded glass windows are used for both low- and high-voltage systems. For nonvacuum systems, radiation-tight enclosures are also provided.

Electrical Shock: To minimize the possibility of electrical shocks from the high voltages used, the machines should be manufactured and installed in accordance with national standards, such as those issued by NEMA.

Respiratory Protection: There is little danger from toxic gases or contaminants when using high-vacuum electron beam processes because of the small amount of air left in the chambers. With medium-vacuum and nonvacuum systems, however, this can be a problem. The best protection against possible respiratory problems is to provide adequate and effective, positive ventilation by means of exhaust systems. Regulations issued by OSHA, as well as local codes, specify requirements with respect to ventilation.

In specialized applications such as welding toxic materials, such as beryllium or uranium, some danger exists that finely divided particles of vaporized, deposited materials may be agitated into suspension by the inrushing air when the chamber is vented to the atmosphere. Upon opening the chamber door, these particles can be released to areas adjacent to the machine. Care must be taken to confine such contamination or to render the machine functions harmless.

Laser Beam Welding and Cutting

Laser beam welding and laser beam cutting are both being used extensively for industrial applications. The word laser is an acronym for "light amplification by stimulated emission of radiation."

Laser Beam Welding

Laser beam welding (LBW) is a fusion joining process that produces coalescence of metals with the heat generated by the absorption of a concentrated, coherent light beam impinging on the components to be joined. In the LBW process, the laser beam is focused to a small spot for high power density and directed by optical elements such as mirrors or lenses. It is a noncontact process, with no pressure being applied. Inert gas shielding is generally employed to reduce oxidation, but filler metal is rarely used.

While laser beam welding is similar to electron beam welding, discussed in the preceding section, there are important differences. Unlike electron beam welding, which often requires a vacuum, laser beam welding can be performed in air or in a controlled atmosphere. Laser beams do not penetrate sections much thicker than 3/4" (19 mm); electron beams can penetrate metal thicknesses of 2" (51 mm) or more in a single pass.

Applications: Most applications of laser beam welding can be grouped into one of four major categories: structural, assembly, sealing, and conduction welds. Structural welds are generally butt and fillet welds with metal thicknesses ranging from about 1/32 to 1/2" (0.8 to 12.7 mm) where maximum load-carrying efficiency is required per unit of joint length.

Assembly welds are usually lap, spot, or seam welds in thin metals, to about 1/8" (3.2 mm) thick, where strength is not a major consideration. Partial-penetration assembly welds, however, are made in thicker metals. Sealing welds are a special class of assembly welds for joining two parts (usually a cover to a container) and providing the joint with a specified level of hermeticity. Sealing welds are often made in a chamber filled with a special atmosphere that is contained in the product after sealing to improve component life or to permit detection of leaks in service.

Conduction welds are another special class of assembly welds for joining electrical wires or connectors. The main requirement is the establishment of sufficient joint area to pass the required amount of electricity with minimum disturbance to current flow.

Laser beam welding is being used for an extensive variety of applications. A number of welds are being made in the production of automotive transmissions and air-conditioner clutch assemblies. In the latter application, laser welding permits the use of a design that could not otherwise be manufactured. The process is also being used in the production of relays and relay containers and for sealing electronic devices and heart pacemaker cases. Other applications include the continuous welding of aluminum tubing for thermal windows and for refrigerator doors.

Advantages: Major advantages of laser beam welding include the following:

1. Heat input is close to the minimum required to fuse the weld metal; thus, metallurgical effects in adjacent material (heat-affected zones) are reduced, and heat-induced workpiece distortion is minimized. Materials that would be damaged by heat can be assembled close to laser welds.

2. Single-pass laser welding procedures have been qualified in materials more than 1/2" (12.7 mm) thick, reducing the time required to weld thick sections and reducing or eliminating the need for filler wire and elaborate joint preparation.

3. No electrodes are required; welding is performed with freedom from electrode contamination, indentation, or damage from high-resistance welding currents. Because LBW is a noncontact process, distortion is minimized and tool wear eliminated.

4. The laser can be located a convenient distance from the workpiece and redirected around tooling

and obstacles in the workpiece, permitting welding in areas not otherwise accessible. Laser beams are readily focused, aligned, and redirected by optical elements.

5. The workpiece can be located and hermetically welded in an enclosure that is evacuated or that contains a controlled atmosphere.

6. The laser beam can be focused on a small area, permitting the joining of small, closely spaced components with tiny welds.

7. A wide variety of materials can be welded, including some combinations formerly considered "unweldable."

8. The laser can be readily mechanized for highly automated, high-speed welding techniques, including numerical and computer control.

9. Surface contaminants such as oxides, organic materials, and dirt from handling are evaporated when the beam is used at maximum intensity and thus may not cause unacceptable defects in some noncritical welds.

10. Welds in thin material and small diameter wires are less susceptible to burn-back than is the case with arc welding.

11. Laser welds are not influenced by the presence of magnetic fields, as are arc and electron beam welds.

12. Laser welds are somewhat more tolerant of poor joint fitup than are electron beam welds, but fitup should be as tight as possible.

13. The laser beam tends to follow the weld joint through to the root of the workpiece, even when not exactly aligned with it. Electron beams tend to penetrate straight through a part, regardless of alignment.

14. Although lasers generate a beam at low efficiency (about 10%), narrow, deep welds can usually be produced at an energy saving when compared to arc welds.

15. Metals with dissimilar physical properties, such as resistance, can be welded.

16. No vacuum or X-ray shielding are required.

17. Aspect (depth-to-width) ratios—up to 5:1—are attainable when the weld is made by forming a cavity in the metal.

Some advantages are more important to one major application category than another.

Assembly welds exhibit the advantages of low heat input, minimum distortion, elimination of electrodes, and high speed offered by laser beam welding. Laser sealing welds take advantage of the fact that welding can be accomplished under conditions where the interior of the container is filled with a special atmosphere at or near ambient pressure. Advantages of laser beam welding for conductors include the ability to weld in crowded areas where electrodes would not fit, avoidance of marking or deformation of delicate conductors, and reliability for high-volume production.

Limitations:
Laser beam welding has several limitations when compared to electron beam and conventional arc welding methods. These limitations include the following:

1. Joints must be accurately positioned laterally under the beam and at a controlled position with respect to the focal point of the beam. With short focal length lenses, the focus limits can be more critical than for electron beams; for long focal length lenses, the focus lengths can be comparable to limitations for electron beams.

2. If surfaces to be welded must be forced together mechanically, the clamping mechanisms must ensure that the final position of the joint is correct with respect to limitation 1, compared to resistance welding, which can clamp and weld in one action.

3. Laser weld depth is generally less than that produced by electron beam welders. Laser beam welding is also limited with respect to the maximum metal thicknesses that can be joined.

4. Laser welds have lower depth-to-width ratios than electron beam welders operating above 100 kV.

5. Materials such as magnesium tend to evaporate, producing voids. Rimmed steels, when welded at high speeds, also exhibit voids. Killed or semikilled steels may have to be substituted when high-speed welding is required. The reflectivity and high heat conductivity of some materials, such as aluminum and copper alloys, reduces weldability.

Laser Beam Cutting

Laser beam cutting (LBC), like laser beam welding just discussed, uses a concentrated, coherent light beam impinging on the workpieces. The heat produced generally results in melting and vaporization of the material to be cut. However, with some materials, such as carbon, material removal is entirely by vaporization. For most applications, an externally supplied, pressurized gas is used.

Applications: Laser beam cutting is being used for both straight and contour cutting of sheet and plate stock, as well as formed components, in a wide variety of materials. Complex contour cutting of cylindrical surfaces is being done by a combination of laser beam movement and workpiece rotation, using NC or CNC for control. Many lasers are being used as an integral part of or as attachments for CNC punch presses.

Advantages: Important advantages of laser beam cutting are that it produces a narrower kerf and a smaller heat-affected zone than other thermal cutting processes. This permits cutting fragile and intricate parts with minimum distortion and provides material savings. Other major advantages include fast speeds, the ability to cut a wide range of materials, and the capability of cutting in locations having limited accessibility. Being a noncontact process, there are no mechanical forces applied to the workpieces and no wear, as with mechanical cutting tools.

Generally, no special surface preparation is required for laser beam cutting, but heavily scaled or rusted metals may prevent cutting. Subsequent finishing of the cut surfaces is generally not required. The process is easily automated, and the use of CNC provides low tooling costs and flexibility in workpiece design.

Limitations: Equipment costs for laser beam cutting are high compared to oxyfuel gas and plasma arc cutting. However, the process is cost effective for many applications, especially if the same equipment can also be used for welding requirements. The process is also limited with respect to material thicknesses that can be cut. While 2″ (51 mm) thick steel has been cut in this way, most metal applications are for thicknesses of ½″ (13 mm) or less. Thickness capability depends on speed requirements and the quality of cut desired.

Most applications of laser cutting require the use of a high-velocity gas jet. Cutting speeds possible vary with the power density of the laser, the thickness of the cut, and the thermal properties of the workpiece material. Partial-depth operations, such as countersinking and pocketing, cannot be performed because the process cuts through the entire material thickness.

Safety in Laser Welding and Cutting

In addition to the safety precautions required against the hazards common to other welding and cutting processes, discussed previously in this chapter, protection must be provided against the specific hazards inherent with the use of lasers. These include eye damage, skin damage, respiratory problems, and electric shock. Details with respect to safety precautions are presented in ANSI Standard Z136.1, "Safe Use of Lasers."

Eye and Skin Protection: Safety glasses appropriate for the specific laser system used must be worn. Specifications for eye protection are contained in ANSI Standard Z87.1, "Practice for Occupational and Educational Eye and Face Protection." Recommendations for filter lenses are presented in ANSI/AWS Standard Z49.1 and the laser eyewear guide published by the Laser Institute of America. Protection against skin burns can be provided by proper enclosure of the laser beam.

Respiratory Protection: The best protection against possible respiratory problems is to provide adequate ventilation by means of an exhaust system. Regulations issued by OSHA, as well as local codes, specify requirements with respect to ventilation.

Electrical Shock: To minimize the possibility of electrical shocks from the high voltages, laser equipment should be constructed in conformance with national standards, such as those from NEMA.

Thermit Welding

Thermit, a term commonly used to identify aluminothermic welding processes, is a registered trademark of Th. Goldschmidt AG, Essen, West Germany. In Thermit welding, coalescence (joining) of metals is produced by heating them with superheated molten metal from a reaction between a metal oxide and aluminum. Although termed a welding process, Thermit welding by definition actually more closely resembles metal casting.

The process offers advantages for certain specialized applications, especially for joining heavy and/or complex cross sections that very often are not weldable with conventional gas or electric arc processes. The most common application is welding rail sections into continuous lengths. Other applications include welding and splicing concrete-reinforcing steel bars together, welding electrical connections, and repairing large components.

Process Principles

When finely divided aluminum and iron oxide are blended and fired by means of a special ignition device, the aluminothermic reaction is as follows:

$$Fe_2O_3 + 2Al \rightarrow \quad Al_2O_3 + 2Fe + heat$$

It is the affinity of aluminum for the oxygen of the iron oxide compounds that sustains the aluminothermic reaction until completion.

Because no external heat source is required, but heat is generated during the chemical reaction between aluminum and iron oxide, the reaction is exothermic in nature. Because of the difference in density of the final components, Al_2O_3 (slag) and Fe (thermite iron), both components will automatically separate within seconds (see Fig. 14-30), and the liquid iron can be used for various welding applications.

For technical purposes, alloying elements in granular form can be added to match the chemistry, as well as the physical properties, of the parts to be Thermit welded. The amount of heat generated by the aluminothermic reaction results in a superheated metal that fuses with the parent metal of the parts to be welded, resulting in a metallurgically pure bond after solidification. Besides iron oxide, there are various modifications of copper oxides commonly used for technical applications described later in this section.

Depending on the application, elements such as magnesium, silicon, or calcium can be substituted for aluminum. However, characteristics such as the low boiling point of magnesium and calcium, the hygroscopy of calcium, and the high melting points of calcium oxide and magnesium oxide severely restrict the technical use of these metals.

Depending on the size of the granules used, aluminothermic reactions can become violent. This requires the addition of nonreacting constituents. The maximum temperature should not exceed 4500°F (2480°C) to avoid losses due to vaporization of the individual components. Lower temperatures will lead to incomplete separation of metal and slag, with slag inclusions entrapped in the metal matrix.

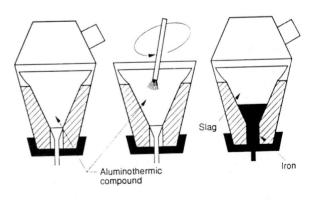

Slag

Iron

Aluminothermic compound

Figure 14-30 Principles of aluminothermic welding

In general, aluminothermic mixtures in granular form are not explosive and are nonhazardous. Depending on the grain size of the constituents, as well as the quantity of nonreacting components, the ignition temperature is in the area of 2700°F (1480°C). The mixture is ignited by an external heat source.

Repair Welding

Thermit welding is being used extensively for specialty repair operations, especially those involving the joining of heavy cross sections. Parts repaired in this way include large diameter rolls and shafts; ingot molds; machine and mill frames and housings; and rudder and stern frames for ships. Because each of these applications is different, the molds and boxes, contrary to rail welding, are prepared at the job site to fit the individual joint.

Mold Preparation: With the parts to be welded properly aligned and having the correct gap, a wax collar is built around the gap, between the two weld faces. Once the wax collar is completed—its shape being identical to the final weld collar—a mold is rammed. The mold provides for the location of vents, risers, and running gates, identical to standardized foundry practices. Care must be taken that the wax collar will not be damaged during the preparation of the mold.

Molding Sand: The quality of the molding sand requires special attention. It must have high refractory characteristics, adequate permeability, and good shear strength. It also must be free of clay components having low melting points.

Wax Removal: Once the mold is completed (see Fig. 14-31), the inside of the mold and weld faces are preheated. The heat is slowly initiated to melt the wax first. The wax then drains through a special spout. Afterward, the spout is plugged with sand to prevent runout of liquid Thermit during the pour. After complete removal of the wax, the heat is gradually increased to preheat the faces until they reach a temperature range between 1500 and 1800°F (815 and 980°C).

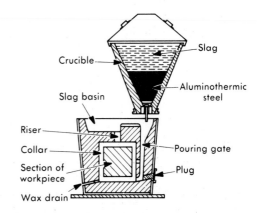

Figure 14-31   Repair arrangement for Thermit welding *(Courtesy of Orgo-Thermit, Inc.)*

Reinforcement Bar Welding

Continuous-welded reinforcement bars permit the design of complicated concrete structures smaller in diameter or thickness than those where unwelded bars would have been applied. Thermit full-fusion welding without preheat is one way of welding and/or splicing concrete-reinforcing steel bars together. Another means of utilizing the aluminothermic process for butt splicing that is finding widespread application consists of filling a metal sleeve with liquid Thermit steel. With this process, a mechanical rather than a welded splice is obtained.

The full-fusion method uses two mold halves, manufactured by either the CO_2 or shell mold process, that are positioned at the joint of the aligned bars and sealed to the bars to avoid the loss of molten metal. The aluminothermic welding mixture is placed in the crucible part of the mold, the mixture being separated from the interior cavity of the mold section by a set of tapping discs. After completion of the aluminothermic reaction, the liquid metal melts the tapping discs and flows into the mold cavity to fill the gap between the bar ends. Arrangements for horizontal and vertical welding are shown in Fig. 14-32. For the mechanical-sleeve bar splice, a graphite mold is substituted for most of the sand mold.

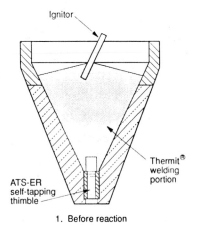

1. Before reaction

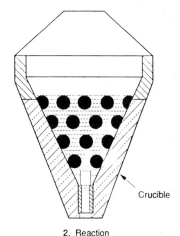

2. Reaction

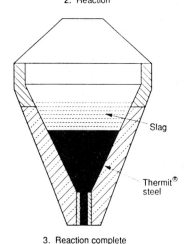

3. Reaction complete

Figure 14-32   Full-fusion Thermit welding of reinforcement bars *(Courtesy of Orgo-Thermit, Inc.)*

Welding Electrical Connections

For welding of electricity-conducting joints, the iron in the aluminothermic mixture is fully or partially replaced by copper, resulting in the following reaction:

$$3\,Cu_2O + 2\,Al \rightarrow \quad Al_2O_3 + 6\,Cu + heat$$

This process is preferably used for welding cables and wires, as well as solid copper or steel conductors, against construction parts, such as steel rails that serve as grounding devices (see Fig. 14-33). Graphite is the most suitable material to use for the one-part crucible mold setup.

Safety Considerations

Any moisture present in the Thermit mix or crucible, or on the workpieces, can cause the formation of steam during the reaction. This can cause ejection of molten metal from the crucible. To prevent this, the mix, crucible, and workpieces should be kept dry.

The area in which Thermit welding is performed should be kept free of combustible materials and should be well ventilated. Operators and any other personnel in the area should wear protective clothing such as face shields with filter lenses and safety shoes. When preheating is used, the safety precautions discussed for oxyfuel gas equipment should be followed.

Diffusion Welding

Diffusion welding (DFW) is one of several solid-state welding processes. As mentioned in the introduction to this chapter, with solid-state welding, workpieces are joined by the application of heat and usually pressure, or by the application of pressure only.

Temperatures produced in the solid-state welding processes are generally below the melting points of the materials being joined. As a result, there is usually no melting, and any liquid metal present is squeezed from the joint by the pressure exerted.

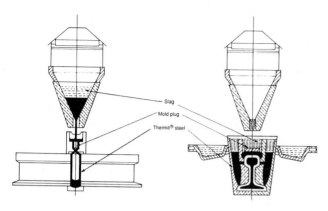

Figure 14-33 Thermit welding of rails *(Courtesy of Orgo-Thermit, Inc.)*

In diffusion welding, the surfaces to be joined are brought together under moderate pressure at an elevated temperature, generally in a controlled atmosphere. There is no melting of the materials being joined, and there is only mimimum deformation of the workpieces. The primary mechanism for joint formation is solid-state diffusion.

Applications

Diffusion welding is being used in the aircraft, aerospace, and nuclear industries to join high-strength materials. Applications include joining similar and dissimilar metals, often with a thin layer of a different metal (a diffusion aid) between them. In some applications, diffusion welding is being combined with superplastic forming to produce complex components, thus reducing the number of parts required and assembly costs. The process is generally most economical when close dimensional tolerances or special material properties are required.

Advantages

Advantages of diffusion welding include the following:

1. High-quality welds can be produced that have essentially the same physical, chemical, and mechanical properties as the base metal, with no impairment of the base material's properties.
2. Welds can be produced below the recrystallization temperature of nearly all metals, thus minimizing distortion and metallurgical damage and often requiring no subsequent operations.
3. Weldability is largely independent of material thickness.
4. Many dissimilar metals, not weldable by fusion processes, can be joined.
5. Continuous, leaktight welds can be produced.
6. Numerous welds in an assembly can be made simultaneously.
7. Joints with limited access can be welded.

Limitations

Diffusion welding is only capable of low production rates because weld cycles are longer than other processes. Equipment costs are high, and consumable material costs are also high if precious-metal fillers and/or inert gases are used. If the diffusion rate of one metal is considerably higher than the other metal, there is a possibility of porosity in the weld. Also, if the metals being joined have a large difference in thermal expansion, failure may occur during cooling of the weldment.

Friction Welding

Friction welding (FRW) is a solid-state joining process that produces coalescence in metals or nonmetals using the heat developed between two surfaces by a combination of mechanically induced rubbing motion and applied load. Mechanical energy is directly converted to thermal energy at the joint interface. Under normal conditions, the faying surfaces do not melt. Filler metal, flux, and shielding gas are not required with this process, but shielding gas is sometimes used for welding reactive metals, Fig. 14-34.

Applications

Friction welding has been established in all areas of metalworking. Typical applications include the following:

- Automotive industry:
  Engine valves, driveshafts, steering shafts, transmission shafts, gears, clutch components, turbochargers, fan-clutch shafts, air conditioning clutch housings, and struts.

- Truck and agricultural industries:
  Track rollers, hydraulic piston rods, pin assemblies, cluster gears, axle housings, and power takeoff shafts.

- Aerospace and aircraft industries:
  Compressor rotors, fan shafts, cluster gears, rivets, driveshafts, propeller hub extensions, drag braces for landing gears, rocket-engine injector posts, helicopter main-rotor shafts, and fuel cell ports.

- Oil and gas industries:
  Drill pipe-to-tool joints, sucker rods, pump shafts, manifold or surface pipe to connections, and high-pressure valve flanges.

- Miscellaneous:
  Copper-aluminum electrical connectors, bi-metallic electric motor shafts, bimetallic outboard motor shafts, drills, reamers, hubs to pulleys, socket wrenches, bomb fuse housings, hydraulic pump

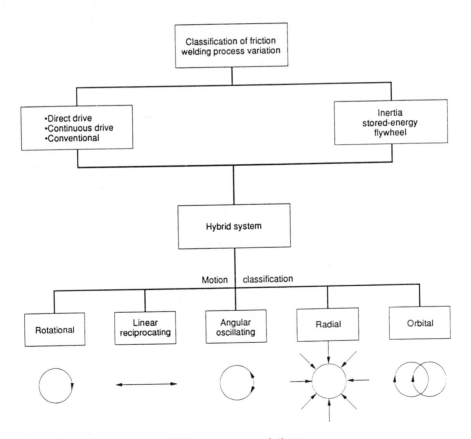

Figure 14-34   Classification of friction welding process variations

pistons, bicycle forks, aluminum-steel anodes, steel-steel anodes, and printing press rollers.

Advantages

Important advantages of friction welding include the suitability of the process for joining a wide variety of dissimilar metal combinations, short cycle times, and adaptability to automation for mass production applications. Joints produced are generally as strong as the base metals, and, because the heat is localized at the interface, only a narrow heat-affected zone results. Surface preparation and cleanliness are less critical than for other solid-state welding processes, and power requirements are less than for flash welding.

Friction welding can sometimes be performed on finish machined parts, maintaining common manufacturing tolerances. The process is being used to replace large, long, costly forgings with bar stock welded to smaller forgings, thus reducing costs.

Limitations

A possible limitation to the use of rotational friction welding is that one of the components must be capable of being rotated about its axis, and the weld interface should generally be axially symmetric (circular). It is not necessary that both pieces be of the same cross-sectional shape throughout; for example, small diameter shafts can be welded to large square or rectangular plates or irregular-shaped forgings. Initial equipment costs for friction welders are generally higher than for flash or upset welders, but return on investment can be rapid. Also, alignment of workpieces after welding (axial displacement) can cause a problem if finished parts are to be welded.

Safety Considerations

Most friction welding machines are similar to lathes and presses and should be equipped with guards, shields, and safety devices. Recommended safety practices for lathes and presses should be followed. Operators should wear protective clothing and eyeshields.

Ultrasonic Welding

Ultrasonic welding (USW) is the joining of materials induced by clamping the components together under a modest static force normal to their interface and applying oscillating shear stresses of ultrasonic frequencies approximately parallel to the plane of the interface. The combined static and vibratory forces cause oscillating, interfacial shear stresses between the workpieces, dispersing surface films and other foreign matter so that intimate contact and bonding of the component surfaces occurs. The solid-state ultrasonic welding process does not involve melting of metals nor does it involve the high pressures and large deformations characteristic of deformation welding; the process is accomplished in much shorter times and at lower pressures than those that are required for diffusion bonding. See Fig. 14-35.

Applications

With increased understanding of the bonding phenomenon, with development of more efficient and powerful equipment, and with continued experience in solving diversified joining problems, the uses of ultrasonic welding have been expanded to encompass the joining of a broad range of similar and dissimilar materials in a variety of conventional and unusual geometric forms, including spot welds, line welds, ring welds, and continuous-seam welds. This versatility of ultrasonic welding makes the process valuable for joining applications that cannot be satisfactorily accomplished by other metallurgical joining techniques. Thus the process has been introduced into an increasing number of production operations in the electronics and electrical switchgear

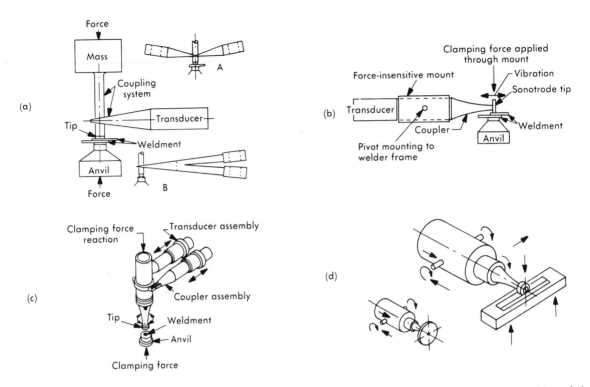

Figure 14-35 Ultrasonic welding machines: a) wedge reed spot welder; b) lateral-drive spot welder; c) ring welder; and d) continuous-seam welder.

fields, in the fabrication of nuclear reactor components, in packaging, in wire and foil splicing, and in other areas.

Although many metals can be ultrasonically bonded, the easiest to weld are aluminum and copper alloys. Typical applications include foil welding in aluminum and copper mills, wire-to-wire wire terminations, tube-to-sheet welding for solar panels, power transformer wire terminations, field coils, motor armatures, and brush-wire terminal attachments.

Limitations

One possible limitation to the use of ultrasonic welding is that the workpiece next to the tip must be relatively thin. A thickness of ⅛″ (3.2 mm) or less is generally preferred, depending on the material and application. However, there is no thickness limitation on the other workpiece being joined. Another limitation is that the process is restricted to lap joints. Butt welds are not possible because there are no means of applying clamping forces and supporting the workpieces.

High capital equipment costs is another possible limitation to the use of ultrasonic welding, but the negligible cost of consumables and welding cycles that are faster than brazing or soldering often offset the initial costs. Ultrasonic welding is generally limited to soft metals; with ultrasonic welding of hard metals, tip wear is faster.

Safety Considerations

There are no unusual hazards to personnel in the operation of ultrasonic equipment for welding either metals or plastics. The high voltages involved, however, require proper machine design, installation, and operation, with adequate interlocks, insulation, and other safety precautions. Guards and/or other devices must also be provided to protect operators from clamping forces.

Explosive Welding and Cladding

Explosive welding (EXW) is a joining process in which the controlled energy of a detonating explosive is used to create a metallurgical bond between two or more similar or dissimilar metals. No diffusion occurs during bonding, no intermediate filler metal is needed to promote bonding, and no external heat is applied. The solid-state process is also commonly termed explosion or explosive cladding and explosive bonding.

Applications

Explosive welding is being used for a wide variety of industrial applications. These include the production of chemical process vessels, conversion rolled billets, and transition joints. Other uses include electrical, marine, tube and pipe, and specialty applications, as well as buildup and repair operations. See Fig. 14-36.

Advantages

In addition to the advantages of combining the desirable properties of dissimilar metals, reduced costs, weight savings, reduced corrosion of joint interfaces, improved electrical conductivity, increased reliability, and reduced maintenance, there are additional benefits that can be derived from explosive welding and cladding. Of major importance are the versatility of the process and the size capabilities.

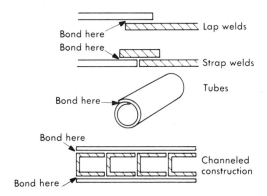

Figure 14-36   Explosive welding applications.

Limitations

Possible limitations with respect to the use of explosive welding and cladding include the following:

- Problems with explosive welding and cladding include the inherent hazards of storing and handling explosives; the ability to obtain explosives with the proper energy, form, and detonation velocity; and the undesirable noise and blast effects.
- Metals to be explosively bonded must possess some ductility and resistance to impact. Brittle metals and metal alloys cannot be used because they fracture during bonding.
- In certain metal systems in which one or more metals to be explosion-clad have a high initial yield strength or a high strain-hardening rate, a high-quality bond may be difficult to achieve. This phenomenon is magnified when there is also a large density difference between the metals. Such combinations are often improved by using a thin, low-yield-strength interlayer between the metals.
- In general, the process is best suited to the bonding of flat and cylindrical surfaces that allow straight-line egression of the high-velocity jet emanating from between the metals during bonding.
- Backer thinness rather than thickness is a limiting factor. Thin backers must be supported, thus adding to manufacturing cost.

- The preparation and assembly of clads are not amenable to automated production techniques. Each assembly requires considerable manual labor.

Safety Considerations

Explosive welding and cladding should only be done by trained, experienced personnel because of the inherent dangers of handling and using explosives. Procedures must comply with applicable federal, state, and local regulations. Ear protection for all personnel is required.

Other Solid-State Welding Processes

In addition to the solid-state welding processes discussed previously—diffusion, friction, ultrasonic, and explosive welding—there are several others of industrial significance that are mentioned briefly in the remainder of this section.

Cold Welding

Cold welding (CW) is defined as a solid-state welding process in which coalescence is produced by the external application of mechanical force alone. A characteristic of the process is minimum heat. No heat is applied externally, and little is generated by the welding process itself. With extensive plastic deformation, however, some heat is generated, but this heat is not required to complete the weld and is not generally sufficient to cause any problems.

The welding operation is done at or near room temperature, and there is substantial deformation. A fundamental requirement for satisfactory cold welding is that at least one and preferably both of the metals to be joined be highly ductile and not exhibit extreme work hardening. As a result, the process is generally used for nonferrous materials.

Forge Welding

Forge welding (FOW) is one of the earliest solid-state welding processes and was used extensively by blacksmiths to mount rims on wagon wheels. In this process, the components to be joined are heated to high temperatures below their melting points and are then forged together by dies, hammers, or rollers to cause permanent deformation at the interface. These processes are limited to special uses and have been largely replaced by the other welding processes described in this chapter.

Related processes similar to forge welding include the following:

- *Roll welding (ROW).* In this process, two or more heated sheets or plates are stacked together and passed through rolls until deformation produces a solid-state weld.
- *Hammer welding.* Forge welding is the preferred term for this process, which is performed with hammer blows.
- *Die welding.* Forge welding is the preferred term for this process, which is performed between dies, generally in a hydraulic press.
- *Thermocompression (hot pressure) welding.* This specialized deformation method is used for joining connections of ductile metals in electronic circuits. Resistance heating is generally used, with the heat being transmitted through an indentor tool.

Coextrusion Welding

In this solid-state welding process, two or more metal parts are coextruded by heating and forcing the metals through an extrusion die. Some cold coextrusion welding has been done, but the metal parts are generally heated to reduce pressure requirements and improve the welding process.

Workpieces to be welded are generally placed in a tapered retort to facilitate extrusion. For reactive metals, the retort is usually evacuated. Coextrusion welding is used to join a variety of metals, including low-carbon steels, aluminum and copper alloys, nickel-based alloys, and reactive metals, such as titanium and zirconium.

Pulsed Magnetic Welding

Pulsed magnetic welding is a solid-state process similar in concept to explosive welding, previously discussed, but without the hazards of using explosives. Metallurgical bonding is produced by impacting metal parts against each other at high velocities using high-frequency, high-intensity pulsed magnetic fields. The process is used to join stainless steels, Inconel, and other metals. Dissimilar and crack-susceptible metals can be joined. Bond lengths of five to ten times the cladding thickness can be produced. See Fig. 14-37.

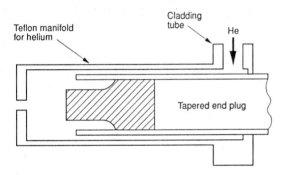

Figure 14-37 Tubing and end plug used in making an end closure with magnetic pulse welding

Vibration Welding

Vibration welding differs from ultrasonic welding, discussed previously, in that frictional heat from a small reciprocating linear motion is used to join thermoplastic and rubber parts. Frictional heat is generated by clamping two workpieces together under pressure and vibrating one workpiece at a preset amplitude and frequency (see Fig. 14-38). A continuous weld line is produced along the entire contact surface.

Frequencies commonly used for vibration welding are 120 and 240 Hz. Vibration amplitudes vary

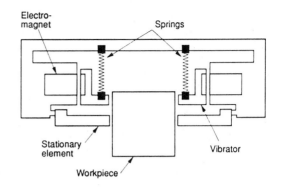

Figure 14-38 Components of a typical vibratory welding machine

between 0.030 and 0.140″ (0.76 and 3.56 mm). The heat generated by the friction melts material at the interface. When the vibration stops, the workpieces are held under pressure until the melted material solidifies and the parts are bonded.

Bonds produced by vibration welding are strong and structurally sound, and operating costs are low. The process is being used to produce pressuretight joints in both small and large parts of circular, rectangular, or irregular shape. Total cycle times, including loading and unloading, average six to fifteen seconds, and multicavity fixtures can be used.

Welding Plastics and Nonmetals

The welding processes described so far are used primarily with metals. Certain welding processes can also be used with plastics and other nonmetals. The most widely used of these are: ultrasonic welding, ultrasonic staking, ultrasonic inserting, vibration welding, spinomatic headforming, fusion bonding, induction welding, hot gas welding, and spin welding.

Ultrasonic Welding of Plastics: Ultrasonic welding makes use of mechanical energy broadcast at frequencies higher than the range of human hearing. The high-frequency electrodynamic field causes heat to be generated in the plastic so that plastic surfaces fuse together, forming a bond. Ultrasonic welding is the fastest means for welding plastics. A wide variety of thermoplastic materials can be ultrasonically welded and ultrasonically staked. Some of these are acrylic multipolymer cellulosics, phenylene-oxide based resins, rigid PVC, acetal, fluoropolymers, nylon, polyester, polyethylene, polymethylpentene, polyphenylene, and polyphenylene sulphide.

Ultrasonic Staking of Plastics:
Ultrasonic staking involves joining plastic parts by inserting a plastic stud or protrusion and mushrooming the stud using an ultrasonic staking horn. The staking horn uses ultrasonic energy to mushroom the stud.

Ultrasonic Inserting of Plastics:
Ultrasonic inserting involves putting metal inserts in thermo parts using the concept of electrosonic heating. This is done by creating a hole in the part that is slightly undersized. The material around the hole is heated ultrasonically as the metal insert is placed into it. This causes the surrounding plastic to flow into the knurls on the insert, thus locking the insert in place.

Vibration Welding of Plastics:
Vibration welding involves pressing one part against another and vibrating it to create heat. The vibration is so rapid and over so small a deplacement area that it creates heat, causing the two parts to fuse.

Spinomatic Headforming of Plastics:
This is a method of joining two parts by inserting a stud or rivet through matching holes and using a special spinomatic headforming tool to upset the inserted material, forming a head.

Fusion Bonding of Plastics:
Fusion bonding sometimes refers to heat welding, or hot plate welding. It is a particularly effective process in assembling thermoplastic materials. It involves holding the two surfaces against a heated metal surface until there is a sufficient flow of molten material and then quickly pressing the two parts together under a small amount of pressure. The flow of the molten material causes the two parts to fuse.

Induction Welding of Plastics:
This process is also known as magnetic heat bonding. It involves placing a special thermoplastic electromagnetic compound on the bonding surfaces of the two plastic parts. The joint is then subjected to high-frequency alternating current, which brings the two surfaces to the fusion temperature. Enough pressure is applied to ensure that the two surfaces properly bond.

Hot Gas Welding of Plastics:
This is basically the same process used for metals except that an open flame is not used. Instead, heated gas is directed at the joint while a filler rod made of the same thermoplastic material that is being welded is applied to the joint. This is a relatively slow process that requires a great deal of skill on the part of the operator.

Spin Welding of Plastics:
This process involves creating heat by friction when one part is rotated rapidly while in contact with the mating part. The frictional heat produces surface melting. Once surface melting has been accomplished, the rotating is stopped to allow the two parts to bond.

MECHANICAL FASTENING

Assembly in manufacturing often involves some type of mechanical fastening of a part to itself, or two or more parts or subassemblies together, to form a functional product or a higher level subassembly. Mechanical fasteners are available in a wide variety of types and sizes to suit the individual requirements for different joint and assembly designs. Types discussed in this chapter include integral, threaded, nonthreaded, and special-purpose fasteners. Other methods of mechanical fastening also discussed in this chapter are stitching and stapling, shrink and expansion fitting, and injected metal assembly.

The numerous mechanical fasteners available have resulted in inconsistent nomenclature and made identification difficult. While it would be desirable to have all fastener names based on their shapes and/or features, many are named for their application or the product on which they are used, the materials from which they are made, or their size.

While standard mechanical fasteners are available in many types and sizes, there are numerous requirements and an increasing demand for special fasteners. For some applications, fastener manufacturers can meet special requirements with only slight alterations to existing fasteners, thus reducing costs compared to designing an entirely new special fastener.

Metrication of mechanical fasteners has progressed further than for most other products, particularly in the automotive industry. General Motors Corp. started metrication for its 1977 line of large cars, and today about 95% of the attachments on all its cars are made with metric fasteners. One major advantage of metrication has been the reduced number of standard thread diameter-pitch combinations. Metric and inch standards are discussed in subsequent sections devoted to individual types of fasteners.

Selection of a specific mechanical fastener or fastening method depends primarily on the materials to be joined, the function of the joint strength and reliability requirements, weight limitations, dimensions of the components, and environmental conditions. Other important factors that must be carefully considered include costs, available installation equipment, appearance, and whether the assembly has to be dismantled. Value analysis in the product design stage can often make assembly easier and more economical by reducing the number of components in the assembly or by modifying the design or processing to facilitate assembly.

When dismantling of assemblies is required, threaded or other types of fasteners that can be removed quickly and easily should generally be used. However, such fasteners should not have a tendency to loosen after installation. When disassembly is not necessary, permanent fasteners such as rivets or threaded fasteners locked with adhesives are often used. Permanent joints are also often made by other processes, such as welding, brazing and soldering, and adhesive bonding.

Mechanical Fastening of Metals

Mechanical fastening is an assembly process which involves joining parts using any of a variety of mechanical fasteners. These include such families of fasteners as integral fasteners, threaded fasteners, and special-purpose fasteners.

Integral Fasteners: Integral fasteners are formed areas of the component part or parts that function by interfering or interlocking with other areas of the assembly. This type of fastening is most commonly applied to formed sheet metal products and is generally performed by lanced or shear-formed tabs, extruded hole flanges, embossed protrusions, edge seams, and crimps (see Fig. 14-39). In all these methods, the joint is made by some method of metal shearing and/or forming.

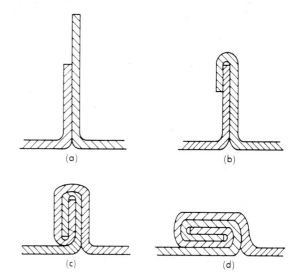

Figure 14-39 Steps in forming a double-lock seam

Threaded Fasteners: Threaded fasteners are separate components having internal or external threads for mechanically joining parts. The most common types of threaded fasteners are bolts, studs, nuts, and screws. Figure 14-40 illustrates some of the more widely used threaded fasteners. Figure 14-41 shows terms used to designate dimensions of threaded fasteners.

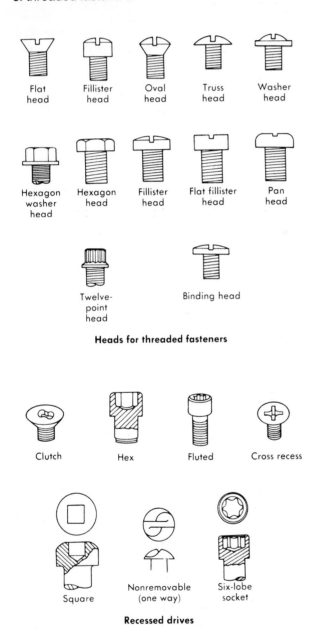

Heads for threaded fasteners

Figure 14-40 Various types of head styles and recessed drives for threaded fasteners

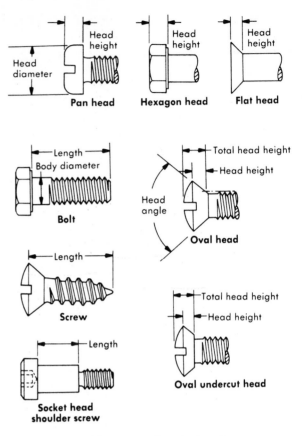

Figure 14-41 Terms used to designate dimensions of threaded fasteners

Special-Purpose Fasteners: Despite the many types and sizes of standard mechanical fasteners available, there is an increasing demand for special fasteners to meet specific requirements. Special fasteners include modified standard fasteners and fasteners designated to perform one or more special functions for specific applications.

Special fasteners, including threaded and non-threaded types, sometimes perform several functions and often reduce assembly costs or the number of parts required for an assembly. In some cases, they permit the use of thinner and less expensive panel materials by using the strength of the fasteners to meet requirements. Some special fasteners may cost more than standard fasteners, and their use should therefore be based on reduced assembly costs and/ or improved product quality.

It is beyond the scope of this section to cover the many different types of special-purpose fasteners available, and only some of the more commonly used fasteners will be discussed.

Widely used special-purpose fasteners include: quick-operating fasteners, spring clips, tamper-resistant fasteners, expanding fasteners, self-sealing fasteners, and fasteners made of plastic.

Other Mechanical Fasteners: In addition to integral, threaded, and special-purpose fasteners, there are a variety of other mechanical fasteners used in assembling metal parts. The most widely used of these are rivets, eyelets, pins, washers, stitching/stapling, shrink-expansion fits, and injected metal assembly. Figures 14-42, 14-43, and 14-44 are examples of other mechanical fastening devices/methods.

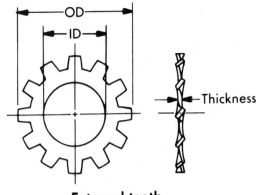

External teeth

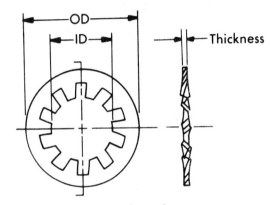

Internal teeth

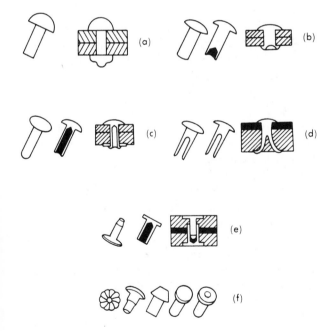

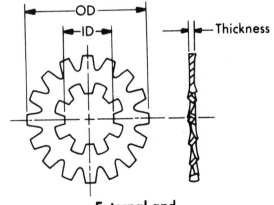

External and internal teeth

Figure 14-42 Types of small rivets: a) solid; b) semitubular; c) tubular; d) bifurcated; e) compression; and f) special rivets

Figure 14-43 Types of toothed lockwashers

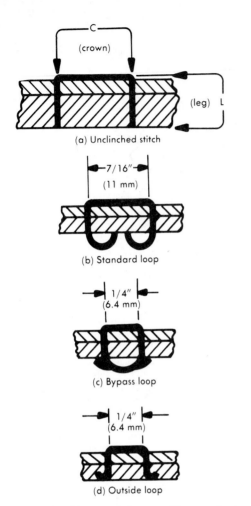

Figure 14-44 Nomenclature and types of wire stitches

Mechanical Fastening of Nonmetals

Plastics and composite materials can also be assembled using mechanical fasteners. The sections which follow explain some of the more widely used methods/devices.

Mechanical Fastening of Plastics: The more extensive use of plastics in various products and the many types of plastics available have increased the demand for special fasteners. Advantages of such fasteners over standard types often include lower torque requirements for driving the fasteners into assemblies, higher shear strengths because of the special threads used, and the capability of withstanding higher torque loads before the fastener threads begin to strip the plastics. Screw thread inserts are used extensively to hold fasteners in plastics.

Many types of special fasteners are available because requirements vary with the plastics used in the assemblies. The plastics must be sufficiently strong to withstand the strain of fastener insertion, and the fasteners must distribute the loads and stresses properly. General requirements for special fasteners used in plastics include large flank areas on their threads, wide thread spacing, and sharp threads.

Special fasteners of the thread-forming type, which eliminate the need for tapping and inserts, thus resulting in lower costs, are used most extensively for softer plastics. Thread-cutting fasteners are more common for harder plastics. Metal inserts are sometimes provided in the plastics components, especially if the fasteners must be removed periodically. Most fasteners are available with a variety of head and point styles.

Thread-forming types of special fasteners for plastics are generally made of low-carbon steels (SAE 1018 to 1022), and are case hardened to about Rc45. The fasteners are commonly zinc plated, but other finishes are also available. One fastener design has a single-lead, coarse thread with a one- to two-thread tapered point. It roll forms threads in plastics without cutting and minimizes radial stresses. A fastener developed specifically for use with heat-sensitive thermoplastics has a twin-lead thread. The number of threads is the same as a single-lead fastener, but each of the two leads has only half as many threads. This design permits faster insertion with less frictional heat generated.

Another special fastener for plastics has a double-lead thread of dual-height design. The lower thread on this fastener varies in height from one-third to one-half that of the higher thread. This design provides high strength and resistance to pullout forces.

Push-in or push-on fasteners that require no rotation during assembly are also available. These fasteners have flexible barbs, rings, ribs, or threads on their shanks and are pressed into thermoplastic assemblies. The pressure flanks of the barbs, rings, ribs, or threads grip the material.

Mechanical Fastening of Composites:

The advent of advanced composite materials, which are finding increased use in the aircraft and aerospace industries because of their strength and light weight, has posed some fastening problems. Many metallic fasteners are fairly incompatible with composite materials because of corrosion. Stainless steel and titanium fasteners work relatively well for composites, but stainless steel introduces some weight penalties, and titanium results in increased costs.

The Vought Corporation through both in-house funding and an Air Force Materials Laboratory contract, has been working on the development of composite fasteners. Fasteners made of glass or graphite-reinforced plastics do not corrode galvanically, are lightweight, and reduce costs because corrosion-resistant coatings and sealants are not required.

KEY TERMS AND PHRASES

Air-acetylene welding
Atomic hydrogen welding
Bare metal arc welding
Carbon arc welding
Coextrusion welding
Cold welding
Diffusion welding
Electrogas welding
Electron beam welding
Electroslag welding
Expansion fit
Explosion welding
Flash welding
Flux-cored arc welding
Forge welding
Friction welding

Gas metal arc welding
Gas tungsten arc welding
High-frequency resistance welding
Hot pressure welding
Injected metal assembly
Integral fastener
Laser beam welding
Oxyacetylene welding
Oxyhydrogen welding
Percussion welding
Plasma arc welding
Pressure gas welding
Resistance spot welding
Resistance projection welding
Resistance seam welding
Shielded carbon arc welding
Shielded metal arc welding
Shrink fit
Stitching
Stud arc welding
Submerged arc welding
Thermit welding
Threaded fastener
Ultrasonic welding
Upset welding

QUESTIONS FOR ADDITIONAL STUDY AND REVIEW

1. Describe the following arc welding processes and the most common applications of each:

   - Submerged arc welding
   - Gas tungsten arc welding
   - Bare metal arc welding
   - Shielded carbon arc welding

2. Describe the following oxyfuel gas welding processes and the most common applications of each:

   - Oxyacetylene welding
   - Oxyhydrogen welding
   - Pressure gas welding

3. Describe the following resistance welding processes and the most common applications of each:

   - Resistance spot welding
   - Upset welding
   - Percussion welding
   - Electroslag welding
   - Thermit welding

4. Describe the following solid-state welding processes and the most common applications of each:

   - Diffusion welding
   - Ultrasonic welding
   - Cold welding
   - Hot pressure welding

5. List five different types of integral fasteners.

6. List the most widely used types of threaded fasteners. *p406*

7. Describe the most widely used methods for mechanically joining plastics. *(7)*

8. Describe the most widely used methods for mechanically joining composites. *(7)*

9. Describe the following processes used for welding plastics:

   - Ultrasonic welding
   - Ultrasonic inserting
   - Vibration welding   *Names on Test*
   - Gas welding

CHAPTER 15

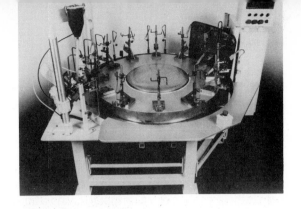

Brazing, Soldering, and Adhesive Joining

MAJOR TOPICS COVERED

BRAZING AND SOLDERING

Brazing and soldering are joining processes that use heat and filler metals to produce metallurgical bonds. Unlike most of the fusion welding processes discussed earlier, brazing and soldering do not involve any melting of the base metals being joined. As a result, the mechanical and physical properties of the base metals are not generally duplicated at the joints. However, diffusion brazing can produce a strength equal to the base metal.

While both brazing and soldering use filler metals, the processes differ with respect to temperature and bonding action. In brazing, the filler metals have liquidus temperatures *above* 840°F (450°C), but below those of the base metals, and the filler metals are distributed between the mating surfaces of the joints by capillary action. In soldering, the filler metals have liquidus temperatures *below* 840°F. Filler metals are distributed by both capillary action and wetting between the surfaces of the components that are being soldered, using the surface energies of the materials that are being joined.

Brazing

Brazing is defined by the American Welding Society (AWS) as: "A group of welding processes which produces coalescence of materials by heating them in the presence of a filler metal having a liquidus above 840°F (450°C) and below the solidus of the base metal. The filler metal is distributed between the closely fitted faying surfaces of the joint by capillary action." Braze welding differs from brazing in that the filler metal is not distributed in the joint by capillary action.

Applications

Applications for brazing are widely varied, and the process is used in practically every industry, from jewelry to aerospace. High-vacuum, refrigeration, and air-conditioning equipment manufacturers use the process extensively in making leaktight joints. Applications in the automotive industry include the production of accessories and steering wheels and in joining tubing. Aircraft and aerospace uses include making honeycomb structures, engine nozzles, tubing joints, and many other brazements.

Heating and plumbing manufacturers and contractors use brazing for joining pipe, tubing, and headers. Seams and spud connections for water heaters and tanks are made by brazing. Pasteurizers, separators, and tanks for dairy equipment are also brazed. Electrical wires, cables, and bus bars are joined by brazing, and the chemical industry uses the process for producing tanks, vats, and piping.

The selection of brazing versus welding or other joining processes depends primarily on the sizes of the components and the materials to be joined, configurations of the joints, thicknesses of the sections, the number of joints to be made, and service requirements. Brazing is generally more suitable for joining smaller parts because of the difficulty in applying the required heat to larger components. However, parts as large as 70″ (1780 mm) diam and 15′ (4.6 m) long are brazed. The process is also usually preferred for joining thin sections to thick sections because reduced heat requirements minimize distortion.

Brazing is used extensively for joining many dissimilar material combinations and is often better for joints having interfaces with complex contours. When designed properly, applications satisfy requirements for permanent, strong joints. The process is generally not used for nonpermanent joints that require disassembly or for permanent, low-strength joints where other joining processes are generally more economical.

Advantages

Brazing is selected as a fastening process over other joining methods, such as welding, mechanical fastening, soldering, or adhesive bonding, because of the following characteristics:

1. Inaccessible joint areas that could not be made by gas metal arc, gas tungsten arc, and spot or seam welding can be joined by brazing.
2. Thin-walled tubes and light-gage sheet metal assemblies not joinable by welding can be joined by brazing.
3. Brazing can join dissimilar materials such as copper to stainless steels, brass to carbon steel, and ceramics to nickel alloys.
4. Leaktight joints for pressurized and vacuum systems are readily joined by brazing.
5. The joining of materials with filler metals at temperatures below 1300°F (705°C) can be performed.
6. The nickel-brazed joints in steel and the nickel alloy brazed joints in stainless steels are made for high-temperature service.
7. Multiple joints can be made at one time, as in furnace brazing, with potentially high production rates. Brazements produced in furnaces with protective atmospheres do not require cleaning or stress relieving after brazing.
8. Corrosion resistance can be provided for food-service equipment that employs silver or nickel filler metals for joining stainless steels. The chemi-

cal industry uses nickel filler metals for brazing stainless steels subject to corrosive service.

9. Less-skilled operators are required for high-production brazing.
10. Diffusion brazing can be used to join heat-resistant base metals for service temperatures far above the solidus temperature of the nickel filler metal.
11. Braze joints are ductile.
12. Brazing is readily automated, and high production rates are possible.

Limitations

Size limitation of the parts to be brazed is of major importance. Extremely large assemblies, although brazable, may often be made economically by welding, particularly if the linear distances to be joined are small, because of the cost and availability of large equipment such as brazing furnaces. By definition, brazing requires closely mating parts to ensure capillary flow of the filler metal. The cost of machining to attain the desired fit may rule out brazing as a joining process.

The general availability of equipment for either torch, induction, or furnace brazing in a plant or by a vendor may be a determining factor in selecting the process. The true worth of the process and determining factor in its use must be decided from its cost and desired joint characteristics on any particular joining operation. In such a case, a value analysis must be made to compare brazing accurately with any other joining process under consideration.

Brazing Processes

There are many brazing processes currently being used. They are generally classified by the method used to heat the assembly. In some applications, however, several methods of heating are used to produce brazed joints. Selection of a process depends primarily on the parts to be brazed, equipment available, and costs. Some brazing filler metals and base metals can be brazed by only one of the heating methods.

The most common brazing processes are torch, induction, dip, infrared, and furnace brazing. Other processes used less commonly include arc, diffusion, electron beam, exothermic, laser beam, resistance, block, blanket, and flow brazing.

Torch Brazing: A torch is the most common process of heating for brazing. Heat for the torch brazing operation is supplied by burning gas combinations such as air and natural gas, oxygen and acetylene, air and propane, and other mixtures, depending on heat requirements.

Handheld torch. By far the most easily used process is handheld torch brazing. The operator plays the torch flame on the parts, being careful to apply more heat to the heavier and more conductive sections first. A brazing flux applied to the joint area prior to heating prevents oxidation of the parts during heating. As the flux becomes molten, it protects the joint area from oxidizing and removes any residual oxides, thus preparing the surfaces for wetting by the filler metal. Parts should be clean and free of oxides and other foreign material before brazing. The brazing filler metal is usually hand-fed to the joint area as soon as the joint is up to temperature, but can also be preplaced in the form of rings, shims, and other shapes. In the case of paste alloys, both flux and filler metals are applied in a single step prior to heating. Figure 15-1 illustrates torch brazing with a handheld torch.

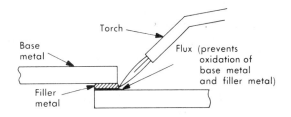

Figure 15-1   Torch brazing

Prepositioned torch. By means of prepositioned torches and simple movement of the workpieces, it is often advantageous to preheat the entire assembly by one set of torches and make the final braze with a second set or, in some cases, a handheld torch, at which time the filler metal is hand- or face-fed to the joint area. By using prepositioned torches, it is possible to preplace the filler metal in the form of paste alloy deposits or preformed rings or washers so that the operation proceeds fairly automatically. Shuttle machines are available to perform this type of brazing.

Semiautomatic brazing. Prepositioned torches for preheating and brazing can be arranged to heat large volumes of smaller parts passed through the heating stations in an in-line conveyor or rotary table machine. The last station or position in this case may be a cooling station to allow the filler metal to solidify completely and the part to cool. In the brazing of brass and steel parts by semiautomatic brazing, for example, the flux is sprayed on automatically, filler metal is preplaced, and then the joint is brazed. The final operation may consist of rinsing the still-warm part on the rotary table with water, which will in most cases remove the bulk of the brazing flux residue rapidly and economically and cool the part for operator removal.

High-production brazing of small assemblies by torch-heated, in-line, or rotary indexing machines has been designed to accomplish the following operations on an automatic basis:

1. *Assembly of details.* In many cases, small details can be fed from rotary or vibratory hoppers to fixtures that hold the parts during brazing.
2. *Slurry fluxing.* Slurry fluxes can be metered and deposited at the joint area after assembly.
3. *Preplacement of filler.* Rings or other preforms can be considered another detail in the prebraze assembly and included in or near the joint area.
4. *Paste brazing filler metal addition.* In many cases, brazing paste, consisting of a binder, powdered braze filler, metal, and flux, can be applied directly to the joint area by automatic applicators.
5. *Gaseous-flux additions.* The addition of gaseous organic borate flux to the fuel gas in torch brazing

will aid greatly in spreading the filler metal and reducing the requirements for paste brazing flux. In some cases, the gas flux by itself may be sufficient.
6. *Automated wire feeders.* Automated wire feeders apply the proper amount of the brazing filler metal to the heated joint.

Induction Brazing: Induction heating, applied widely in other operations such as heat treating, is ideally suited as a heat source for brazing, especially where rapid heating is required. In contrast to torch brazing, the immediate limitations are the necessity of locating the inductor precisely close to the workpiece and the selection of fixture materials for holding parts during brazing. The fixtures should be kept out of the induction field as much as possible to avoid excessive heating of fixtures or should be constructed of nonmagnetic materials such as ceramics.

Induction heating has a distinct advantage in that once properly set up, a very closely controlled heating area (generally smaller than that possible with torch brazing) can be obtained. In this manner, brazing can often be accomplished close to previously heat-treated areas without seriously lowering their hardness. Typical joint and coil designs used in induction brazing are shown in Fig. 15-2.

Generators. Induction brazing generators are of the following three principal types:

- Motor generators that have outputs from 3 to 10 kHz.
- Solid-state power supplies that produce output frequencies to 50 kHz.
- Vacuum-tube type units with output frequencies from 100 to 450 kHz. These generators are often referred to as RF or radio-frequency units.

For steel and ferrous alloys, the motor generator type is quite adequate because of the good magnetic coupling between the alternating field and the work. The heating pattern tends to be deeper, and this type is best if thorough heating of the parts to be brazed is indicated. Solid-state power supplies can be substituted for the motor generator units and have similar frequency and power applications for brazing. Radio-

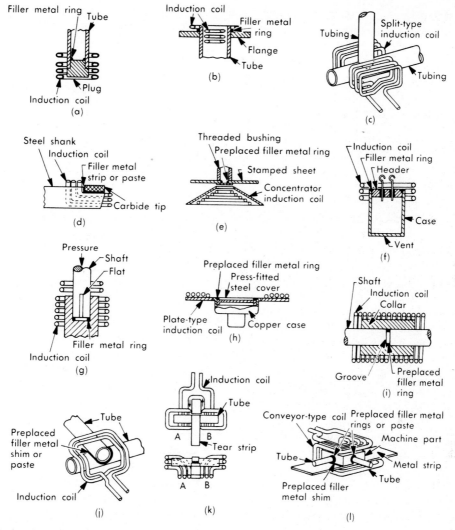

Figure 15-2   Induction brazing coil and joint design

frequency generators operate at higher frequencies and tend to heat a shallower band of material close to the surface of the parts. They will, in addition, be more effective in heating copper, brass, and aluminum alloys. Power sources are available in output ranges from 1 to 50 kW.

Because power output and time at heat can both be precisely controlled in induction heating, the process has the distinct advantage of allowing setup for use by less-skilled operators. The filler metal is generally preplaced in the joint area. Induction heating is being used for semiautomatic and automatic brazing. Most or all of the features covered in the previous section on semiautomatic torch brazing will apply to induction brazing.

Dip Brazing: In dip brazing, the heat required is furnished by a molten chemical or metal bath. When a molten chemical bath is used, the bath may act as a flux. When a molten metal bath is used, the bath provides the filler metal. A cover of flux is provided over molten (filler) metal baths.

The principal use of dip brazing is in joining aluminum and its alloys using a molten bath of fluoride and chloride salts with melting points in the range of 660 to 950°F (350 to 510°C). Essential features of the process include the following:

1. Precleaning is performed prior to brazing, usually in a chemical bath, to reduce aluminum oxide and prepare the surfaces.
2. Components are assembled, and the filler metal is placed in the joint area, often in the form of a paste or wire preform. Many assemblies incorporate sheet aluminum clad with the braze filler metal, a design used especially for dip brazing.
3. Because brazing operation takes place at temperatures in the range of 1040 to 1160°F (560 to 625°C), very close to the melting point of the parent metals, a means must be provided for supporting the assembly at these temperatures to prevent sagging or collapse of components. As far as possible, attempts should be made to make assemblies self-fixturing by such means as twist-tab crimping of sheet metal, swaging of tube connections, or spinning of one component to form the primary closure. When self-fixturing is not possible, lightweight nickel alloy fixtures can be used to restrain the parts. Springs and clips of Inconel X750 are frequently used, which maintain their usefulness over long exposure at temperatures in the 1000°F (540°C) area.
4. Any convenient means of preheating parts can be employed, but an air furnace is best suited. The assemblies or fixtured parts are preheated to about 1000°F and then transferred to the molten-salt bath for brazing. Preheating is required to:
   a. Avoid carryover of moisture into the molten salt that might result in steam generation and accidental explosion. Many aluminum dip brazing operations utilize a mixture of powdered braze filler metal and flux. This mixture is mixed with water to facilitate its application to the joint. The water, however, must be dried thoroughly before placing the assembly into the bath.
   b. Prevent localized freezing of the salt on the part.
   c. Minimize distortion in heating and prevent thermal shock.
   d. Promote uniform heating and better flow of the filler metal.
5. The preheated parts rapidly attain the temperature of the salt bath. It is seldom necessary to have the parts in the molten salt more than one to six minutes, depending on the size of the work. The filler metal melts and rapidly fills the joint areas. After brazing, the load is raised from the bath, and the excess flux is drained back into the bath. Joints should be designed properly to facilitate drainage of the flux.
6. As soon as the filler metal has solidified and while the parts are still hot—500°F (260°C)—the parts are immediately lowered into a hot water rinse. This rinse cracks and loosens the bulk of the flux residues. Subsequent warm and cold rinses remove the remaining flux and salt.

Infrared Brazing: Infrared brazing primarily uses quartz-iodine incandescent lamps as a source of heat energy. The special lamps are tubular and can easily be focused to concentrate the heat at the area to be brazed. With this technique, it is not uncommon to obtain heat from ten 1000 W lamps (10 kW) concentrated at a joint area of less than 10 in.^{2} (64.5 cm^2) or wattage density of about 1000 W/in.^{2} (155 W/cm^2).

The United States Navy pioneered the use of equipment in making tubular brazed connections in shipboard piping. In this application, the heat source is a ring of high-powered lamps, and its holder or mounting is split in the middle and hinged. Its primary use was for high-pressure, copper alloy, silver-brazed pipe connections. Tests indicate it is one of the most reliable methods of silver brazing these connections, particularly in hidden or in inaccessible joint areas. The unit can be easily controlled through a silicon-controlled rectifier (SCR) master control that receives its primary signal from a thermocouple in the joint area. Timing and temperature are exactly reproducible in this manner, thus lowering the training requirements for operators performing the brazing.

Gas infrared heat sources are used to preheat assemblies for brazing to a temperature somewhat below the actual flow point of the filler metal, as in silver brazing. The final braze then can be performed easily and rapidly with torch heating. The preheating part of the cycle is particularly effective when large sections must be heated to brazing temperature.

Furnace Brazing:
Furnace brazing is the process most suited to mass-production brazing and for critical applications. This is particularly true in brazing small- to medium-sized components of up to 3-4 lb (1.4-1.8 kg) each. This process probably accounts for the largest share of brazed hardware in the United States today. The following features distinguish furnace brazing:

1. The filler metal must be preplaced so that it will flow into the joints with no operator assistance after the parts have reached brazing temperature.
2. Fixturing of the parts must be kept at a minimum and best design makes the brazement self-fixturing. Large quantities of fixtures increase process cost and lower furnace productivity by adding deadweight.

3. An atmosphere protects the parts from oxidation at brazing temperatures, reduces trace oxides, and aids in the wetting of the filler metal on the parent metal.

Furnace types. Furnace brazing may be performed as either a batch or a continuous operation. Batch operations use retorts or cold-wall vacuum furnaces in which the load is stacked in rows on trays of nickel-chromium alloy. The entire load is then brought to brazing temperature, and all the parts braze at the same time. Vacuum furnaces are hermetically sealed, and the air is pumped out to produce a protective atmosphere. Semicontinuous vacuum furnaces are used for brazing aluminum automotive components such as radiators and air-conditioner heat exchangers. Continuous furnace brazing uses a conveyor mechanism that carries the parts through the heat zone and into a cooling zone on a mesh belt or on rolls driven by a chain and sprocket arrangement. The latter design is known as a roller-hearth furnace.

Figures 15-3 and 15-4 schematically illustrate the

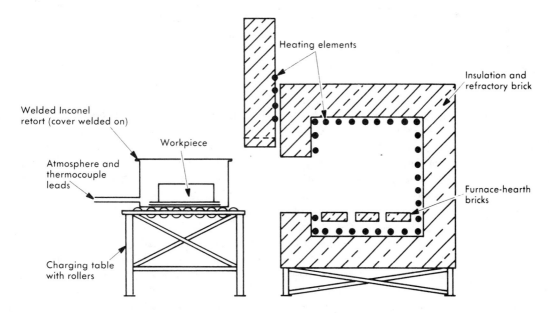

Figure 15-3 Electric-fired box furnace for brazing

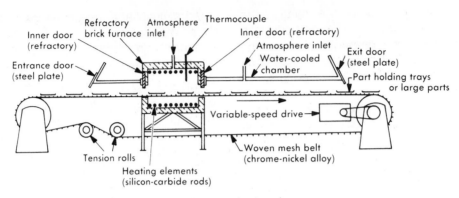

Figure 15-4 Continuous mesh-belt conveyor furnace for brazing

general arrangement of two types of furnaces used for furnace brazing. Figure 15-4 illustrates the principle of continuous furnace brazing on a mesh belt in which an exothermic or nitrogen-based atmosphere is used for copper brazing steel parts. If hydrogen were to be used as the atmosphere, the heating chamber would be raised above the entrance and exit level to contain the light gas, and the furnace would be known as a hump furnace.

Resistance Brazing: Resistance brazing involves the use of low-voltage, high alternating-current power applied between two electrodes. The workpiece to be brazed is held between the electrodes under light pressure, and the heat developed in the workpiece from the resistance to the flow of electric current causes the filler metal to melt and flow into the joint. Two typical examples are brazing of electrical contacts and copper transformer leads. In the first case, the contact is clad on the back face with the filler metal, usually one of the BAg silver brazing filler metals. Heat is usually applied through the power supply of a resistance spot welder, with pressure adjusted carefully so that only enough pressure is applied to secure the position of the contact at brazing heat. The tips of the welder are generally shaped to the contour of the electrode. In some cases, it is advisable to use one of the lower conductivity electrode materials and let the electrode act as a heat source as it heats itself. Flux is employed and heating time is generally short.

In the joining of copper leads to large transformers, the ends of the power leads are equipped with carbon electrodes or faces that heat to a red heat. This additional heat source is required because of the high thermal conductivity of the metal. Filler metal is usually one of the BCuP series. No flux is required.

Laser Brazing: The use of lasers as a source of heat for brazing and soldering is a relatively recent development. A major advantage of using lasers is the capability of selectively applying heating energy to small areas without heating the entire component. Another advantage is close control of heat input and the ability to locate or position the heat accurately. The use of lasers also controls grain structure and intermetallic formations.

Because of their advantages, lasers are being used for the production of miniature and thin precision parts, to make joints near thermally sensitive connections, and for connections inside evacuated or pressurized vessels or containers. However, because of the high costs of laser equipment, the method is generally only being used when other brazing methods are not found to be adequate.

Diffusion Brazing: Diffusion brazing differs from other brazing methods in that a distinct layer of brazing filler metal is diffused into and with the base metal to change the physical properties of the joint. During diffusion brazing, the filler metal melts or a eutectic liquid forms from alloying between the two higher melting metals or alloys such as copper and silver-plated copper. Diffusion at the interface continues, and a layer of a new alloy may remain or the filler metal may disappear. As a result, the joint properties are nearly the same as those of the base metal. A limitation is that the cycles for diffusion brazing are longer than for other brazing processes. Depending on the variables of temperature, quantity of filler metal, and mutual solubility, the time at the brazing temperature can range from ten minutes to many hours.

An example of diffusion brazing is high-temperature, nickel-based metal brazed with BNi-1a filler metal at 2150°F (1175°C) for 30 minutes at heat, with a joint clearance of 0.002″ (0.05 mm). The filler metal has a solidus temperature of 1700°F (925°C). However, after the diffusion cycle, the remelt temperature is above 2500°F (1370°C). Thus, the brazement can operate in a 1900°F (1040°C) temperature for the life of the base metal and designed service.

Electron Beam Brazing:
Electron beam welding equipment is only being used to a limited extent for brazing. Applications are generally restricted to small assemblies or the encapsulating of packaged devices. High vacuums in the work chambers permit the brazing of clean joints without the need for a flux or an atmosphere. The electron beams are defocused to reduce the power density and heating effect.

Exothermic Brazing:
In exothermic brazing, the heat required is generated by the reaction of several chemical compounds. Solid-state or nearly solid-state metal-metal oxide reactions are used. Ignition of the exothermic mixture is by a flame, a hot spark, or a resistance heater. The preparation of the brazement, filler metal, flux, or atmosphere is similar to other brazing processes.

Other Brazing Processes:
There are several other brazing processes, generally less commonly used than the methods that have been described.

Arc brazing. In this process, the heat required for brazing is obtained from an electric arc. In twin carbon arc brazing, the electric arc is established between two carbon electrodes.

Block brazing. In this process, the heat required for brazing is obtained from heated blocks applied to the parts to be joined.

Flow brazing. In this process, a molten nonferrous metal is poured over the joint until brazing temperature is attained.

Blanket brazing. In this process, a resistance-heated blanket is placed over the parts to be joined, generally using ceramic dies. Heat is transferred to the parts by conduction and radiation. This process is used frequently for brazed honeycomb fabrication.

Step brazing. In this method, which can be used with many of the brazing processes discussed, brazing of successive joints on an assembly is done with filler metals of successively lower melting temperatures. In this way, joining is accomplished without disturbing the joints previously brazed.

Fluxes

Fluxes are an important element of the brazing process. They facilitate the flow of molten metal into the joint and eliminate oxides that could have a harmful effect on the integrity of the joint. In order to form a strong bond, a brazed joint must be clean. For this reason it is important to include cleaning in the joint preparation process.

One of the most widely used flux materials is fused borax. There are also a variety of other fluxes available. Fluxes come in both powder and paste form. The type used depends on the application.

Brazing of aluminum requires a special flux. These special fluxes for aluminum contain metallic halide salts, sodium chlorides, and potassium chlorides. Fluoride and lithium compounds are sometimes added as activators.

It is important to thoroughly clean a brazed joint of all residual flux after the brazing process has been completed. The materials used as fluxes are generally very corrosive.

Because aluminum is particularly susceptible to flux-related corrosion, brazing procedures that do not use flux have been developed.

Removing residual flux from a brazed joint normally requires nothing more than immersion in hot water, particularly if the immersion takes place while the flux is still hot.

Joint Design

The design of a joint is a key factor in the strength of the joint. Butt, scarf, and lap joints are the most effective, Fig. 15-5. Of these, lap joints are used when maximum strength is needed. To increase the strength of the joint even more, pressure can be applied to the parts during the brazing process and during the cooling period.

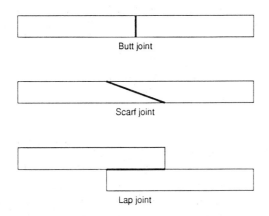

Butt joint

Scarf joint

Lap joint

Figure 15-5 Most effective joint designs for brazing

Safety in Brazing

Brazing may produce fumes that are hazardous to health. Brazing fluxes may evolve gases containing fluorides and chlorides. Certain silver brazing filler metals containing cadmium or zinc will give off vapors. Adequate ventilation with a positive change of air is necessary under these conditions, and respiratory protection equipment may be needed. For specific details, the reader is referred to ANSI Standard Z49.1 for safety measures to be taken in the performance of brazing. Because cadmium is considered poisonous when vaporized from a cadmium-containing filler metal, many users are changing to filler metals not containing cadmium. Fluxes that give off fluorides also require adequate ventilation to prevent hazardous health conditions.

Soldering

Soldering is defined by the American Welding Society (AWS) as:

"A group of welding processes which produce coalescence of materials by heating them to a suitable temperature and by using a filler metal having a liquidus not exceeding 840°F (450°C) and below the solidus of the base material. The filler metal is distributed between the closely fitted surfaces by capillary attraction."

Soldering is one of the oldest methods of joining metals and still finds varied and extensive use in industry. Most soldering operations produce a metallurgical intermetallic-type bond between the filler metal and the base material. Joints can be made to surfaces without this bond as in glass-to-metal joining, where surface activity and adhesion are the main mechanisms of joining.

Selection of soldering as a joining method over mechanical fastening, welding, brazing, or adhesive bonding depends primarily on end-use requirements with respect to joint strength, application, and operating temperature and environment, as well as production costs.

Applications

Application areas of soldering vary widely. They include copper plumbing systems, automotive copper and brass radiators, aluminum refrigeration components, and electrical and electronic connections. The most sophisticated computers contain many thousands of soldered joints.

The methods of producing the soldered joints and the availability of a wide range of soldering alloys facilitate these uses. The technology is still changing, and new joining materials in the soldering group continue to appear and find application.

Electrical and electronic applications, including printed circuit boards, represent the major use for soldering. Common products produced by soldering include television and radio sets, car radiators, light bulbs, telephones, typewriters, and automotive fuel and ignition systems.

Advantages

Soldering offers many advantages for joining operations, including the following:

1. *Versatility.* The wide variety of solders, fluxes, and heating methods available make the process suitable for numerous applications. Multiple joints can be soldered simultaneously or sequentially.
2. *Reliability.* Reliable joints, impermeable to gases and liquids, can be produced consistently. The quality of most soldered joints can be evaluated by visual inspection, and unsatisfactory joints can be easily repaired and reworked. Low temperatures employed for soldering minimize distortion and heat damage to components being joined.
3. *Precise control.* The amount of solder and flux used, as well as the amount of heat applied, can be controlled accurately, thus ensuring consistent quality.
4. *Fast production.* The process is easily automated to attain high production rates.
5. *Low cost.* Soldering is generally an economical joining process, with minimal energy requirements.

Limitations

A possible drawback to the use of soldering is the limited mechanical strengths attained. However, joints strong enough for many applications can be made with proper joint designs, filler metals, and soldering procedures.

Soldering Methods

Soldering methods are generally classified by the method of heat application. Typical methods are con-

duction, convection, radiation, resistance, and induction. Ultrasonic energy may also be used as an aid to soldering. Selection of a heating method depends primarily on the cost and efficiency of the method, production requirements, and the sensitivity of the assembly to heat.

Conduction Heating: Conduction is the transmission of heat through, or by means of, a thermal conductor that is in physical contact with a body without appreciable displacement of the molecules of the material. In this type of heating, a soldering tip is heated, and the heat is transferred to the area to be soldered by direct contact. For example, a simple handheld soldering iron is a type of conduction heater. Consequently, it is of primary importance that the heat transmission area be kept clean and free from any insulating layers such as oxides that may be formed at elevated temperatures.

Soldering irons and guns. Heating of soldered joints with conventional soldering irons is the oldest soldering method. Soldering guns are electrical soldering irons with pistol grips and quick-heating, relatively small bits. A bit is that part of the iron or gun, usually made of plated copper, that transfers heat (and sometimes solder) to the joint. The most common electrical irons are heated by internal elements. Irons are also heated by direct flame or in ovens. Handheld irons are generally used when joints are few in number, when they can be made one at a time, or when they are so varied that another method is not sufficiently versatile.

Component and wiring layout for the irons must provide for easy soldering without damage to adjacent parts—either by conduction or by radiation. Heat sinks can be used to conduct heat away from sensitive parts. If wiring is complex or many closely spaced components are involved, the order in which joints are soldered can also be important. Temperature-controlled irons are available.

Large soldering irons with heating elements of several hundred watts can produce tremendous amounts of heat for soldering such items as large cans and similar assemblies. Soldering irons are not limited to electrical soldering.

Hot plates. Hot plates and similar surfaces are also used to conduct heat to the work. These heaters are simple and relatively low in cost, but usually require a certain amount of special fixturing. It is essential that all heat-transferring surfaces be kept absolutely clean; otherwise the temperature will vary as the surface oxidizes.

Oxidation is difficult to control at elevated temperatures. The hot plate heating method is quite suitable for automation, and the temperature of the hot plate itself can be used as a safeguard for the maximum temperature permissible for the total assembly operation.

The hot plate surface can be heated by flames or electric current. In some cases, the heating elements are built right into the fixture when the assemblies are prestacked and ready for soldering. The disadvantage of this method lies in the cooling time required for the solder joint. During this cooling time, if the fixtures are not adequate, microcracks can develop.

Dip soldering. In dip soldering, the solder and heat are applied simultaneously to the work by a molten metal bath. All prefluxed metallic surfaces coming into contact with the molten solder are rapidly wetted. This method allows high production volume at minimum cost of equipment and joint and permits soldering entire assemblies with any number of joints. Drawbacks of dip soldering include dross formation, the need for skimming, and requirements for jigs or fixtures.

Wave soldering. Wave soldering was developed to eliminate some of the drawbacks of dip soldering and to shorten soldering time by increasing the dynamic movement of the solder over the surface (a 75-80% reduction). This shorter time reduces warpage; air, flux, and vapor entrapments; and other disadvantages. With wave soldering, numerous connections on printed circuit boards are being simultaneously soldered in seconds. Automatic systems use a conveyor to transport the boards through fluxing, preheating, and wave soldering operations.

In wave soldering, solder is lifted to the connections by one or more standing waves of molten solder. All joints are formed during the passage of an assembly over the waves. The operation is continuous and limited in speed only by time and heat requirements. Because the wave is formed by continuously circulated, fresh, hot solder raised to the surface from the depths of the heater reservoir, drossing and local chilling are eliminated. At any given time, only a small band of the assembly is immersed in the wave, and excess heat exposure is therefore eliminated. Narrow, modular wave soldering stations can be inserted where they are needed in the production line.

Jet soldering. Wave soldering is not limited to the use of wide wave orifices. By restricting the flow of the solder from the nozzle, jets of special configuration can be aimed at various areas in the assembly, giving rise to the newer technique of jet soldering. This method is applicable to such items as the terminals of transformers and the lips of cans.

Solder waves and jets can be used with or without the addition of oil to change the surface tension of the solder and to alter soldering parameters by lowering soldering temperatures and allowing a fine, thin coating of solder. However, the use of oil always requires a postcleaning operation to remove any oil that may be left on the surfaces.

Convection Heating: Convection is the transfer of heat by moving masses of fluids or gases. With convection equipment, heat can be applied to the work by a stream of hot gases that may be either reducing or inert in nature. The heat-transfer medium is not limited to gases. Many liquids, such as oils, may be used to raise the work to the soldering temperature.

Torches. Soldering torches are used for solder preforms and paste alloys, and for line soldering of enclosures for hermetic sealing. Clearance must be allowed for the entire flame, and materials directly behind the joint must be able to withstand the temperature. Various fuel gases are burned with oxygen to provide the desired flame temperature.

Ovens (furnaces). Ovens or furnaces as sources of heat for soldering are another form of convection heating equipment that is well established in industry. Continuous ovens, with some sort of conveyor arrangement to carry the part through the heat zone, are used for production soldering. Various atmospheres can also be introduced into the oven to eliminate oxidation and the need for corrosive fluxes.

Vapor-phase soldering. In this process, a high-temperature vapor generated by boiling fluorinated hydrocarbons is used as the heat-transfer medium. The process is being used for reflow soldering with solder preforms in place and for joining small parts having unusual configurations. Soldering times generally range from ten to 45 seconds, depending on the size of the assemblies.

Hot gas blankets. For small assemblies, especially in electronics, the use of large ovens or other equipment maintaining specific atmospheres is not always economical. The size of the assemblies and the varieties of operations to be carried out during soldering may make the use of hot gas blanket heaters attractive. Hot gas blanket soldering employs rather common equipment and concepts.

The atmosphere used is generally contained in a cylinder or other industrial container and is passed through a normal arrangement of regulators and flowmeters into an air heater, where the atmosphere is equal to the required soldering temperature plus the necessary increment of temperature for proper wetting. The assembly to be soldered is then passed under the hot-stream blanket of atmosphere, where it is heated and the solder connection is made.

Radiation Heating:
Radiation is the total effect of emittance, transmittance, and absorptance of energy. Thermal radiation is electromagnetic energy in transport. Soldering is concerned mainly with the radiation of heat. In practice, the three methods of heat transfer—convection, conduction, and radiation—are difficult to separate into the various types of equipment.

Unfocused radiation. The most common sources of radiant heat are light waves covering the spectrum from white light to the infrared range. The use of ordinary heat lamps is recommended for simple types of heating arrangements. The distance from the lamps and the speed with which the work passes through the lighted area will determine the temperature the assembly will reach. This is a clean form of heat

application, because no physical contact with the work is required.

Focused radiation. Focused infrared light is often used for miniature soldering. The energy radiated by a source may be focused at a desired location by an optical system. A light beam concentrated on a spot is a particularly suitable high-temperature soldering method in a difficult-to-reach location or even behind a glass cover. Laser soldering is a type in this category.

Laser soldering. Lasers are being used for brazing and soldering. An advantage is the capability of delivering the output light energy from a laser to a small spot, 0.002″ (0.05 mm) or less in diameter, resulting in the precise, selective application of heat. This makes the process desirable for microelectronic manufacturing and joining products having temperature-sensitive components. Other advantages include the reduced formation of intermetallic compounds and fine grain size because of rapid processing and fast solidification.

Possible limitations to the use of lasers include the high inital cost of equipment required, special fixturing needed for some applications, and necessary safety precautions. Also, when improperly performed, laser soldering can result in reflected energy damage to components and charring of any flux residue.

Neodymium-doped, yttrium aluminum garnet (Nd:YAG) lasers provide a wavelength readily absorbed by conductive materials such as tin-lead, copper, beryllium copper, nickel, and other metals. Carbon dioxide (CO_2) lasers provide a wavelength more easily absorbed by insulative materials such as plastics, ceramics, and fiberglass.

Resistance Soldering:
An electric current generates heat as it flows through a circuit. Contact soldering uses resistance heating elements to apply a preset amount of pressure to the feet of surface-mounted components. The current is programmed through the elements to reflow solder the components to printed circuit boards.

Electrodes vary from 0.078″ (1.98 mm) diam metal probes to large carbon blocks. Resistance soldering has the advantage of high joint production, no warmup requirements, and instant, controlled heat. Joints can be made in from 0.5 to 2 seconds, depending on wire size and materials involved. Another advantage is the degree of miniaturization possible; tiny electrodes can be used to connect modular circuitry components or other closely spaced components.

Induction Soldering: Electromagnetic induction soldering uses the part to be soldered as the heating element. Current induced in the part by an induction coil heats the joint to a depth that depends on current frequency. Because of skin effects, the higher the frequency, the more heat will be confined to the material surfaces—an extremely useful phenomenon in soldering because it minimizes distortion and oxidation of the base metal. Flux and solder are applied to the joints prior to joining, and preformed solder shapes can be used. A requirement for induction soldering is that the base metal be electrically conductive.

Ultrasonic Soldering: Cavitation induced by ultrasonic excitation of molten solder removes oxides from submerged metal surfaces to allow alloying of the molten solder with the base metal. Implosion of the cavitation bubbles creates a scrubbing action that fractures and dislodges oxides from the metal surfaces, and the oxides float to the surface of the molten solder.

This method eliminates the need for flux in many soldering operations and is used to join hard-to-solder metals such as aluminum. However, the ultrasonic action does not enhance wetting of the metal surfaces, as do fluxing agents, and there is no capillary flow of the molten solder. As a result, it is sometimes necessary to pretin one or both surfaces to be joined or place preformed or solid wire solder directly into the joint before or during ultrasonic excitation. However, it is not necessary nor desirable to pretin aluminum surfaces to be joined by ultrasonic soldering because this requires an extra operation and accelerates the rate of aluminum dissolution into the solder bath.

Two modifications of this process are used to produce aluminum tubular joints in air-conditioner coils. In the first technique, the joint components are

solder coated in an ultrasonic solder bath. They they are simultaneously heated to soldering temperature and pressed together to produce interference fits. The second technique involves immersing an assembled, air-conditioner coil having special joints into a molten solder bath excited by ultrasonic vibration energy.

Other Soldering Processes: There are several soldering processes in addition to those already discussed, most of which are used for specific applications.

Abrasion soldering. In this variation of soldering, sometimes called friction soldering, the faying surfaces of the base metals are mechanically abraded with the solder or other instrument during soldering.

Screen printing. Solder plates (blends of powdered filler metals, fluxes, and paste binders) are being used with automatic applicators and screens, generally 60-80 mesh, to provide precise placement of solder dots, each containing a premeasured amount. The pastes provide tack retention for several hours, acting as temporary adhesives to hold components in place until they are reflow soldered. Heat for melting the solder is applied by electric hot plates, convection ovens, infrared, lasers, or vapor-phase systems.

Spray gun soldering. Gas-fired and electrically heated guns are being used to spray molten or semi-molten solder from a continuously fed wire onto joints.

Step soldering. This process consists of soldering successive joints on an assembly with solders of successively lower melting temperatures to obtain joining without disturbing the joints previously soldered.

Sweat soldering. A process in which two or more parts that have been precoated with solder are reheated and assembled into a joint without the use of additional solder.

Fluxes in soldering

It is particularly important to have a clean joint when soldering. Unlike the fluxes used in brazing, soldering fluxes will not eliminate surface dirt. Soldering fluxes fall into two categories: corrosive and noncorrosive. The most widely used noncorrosive soldering flux is rosin. The most widely used corrosive fluxes are muriatic acid and zinc/ammonium chlorides.

Noncorrosive soldering fluxes are typically used with copper, brass, tin, cadmium, and silver-plated parts. Corrosive soldering fluxes are typically used on bronze, steel, and nickel. They can also be used on other materials as long as the joint is cleaned immediately after the soldering process.

Safety in Soldering

Potential hazards with respect to soldering include heat, fumes, chemicals, and electricity. Details of safety precautions that are common to welding, brazing, and soldering are discussed in ANSI Standard Z49.1. The use of adequately trained personnel and competent supervision will minimize possible danger from the hazards. National safety standards shall be observed and kept in force.

Heat Hazards: In soldering, precautions are necessary to prevent burns from handling or contact with hot parts or equipment. Electric-heated soldering irons should be grounded and, when not in use, be kept in fireproof holders. Water should be kept away from molten solder to prevent expulsion of the solder.

Fumes: Solder, fluxes, and foreign materials on the surfaces of parts to be joined often produce fumes or smoke when heated that may be irritating or toxic. Fumes can be minimized by keeping soldering temperatures as low as possible. Adequate ventilation is essential to avoid any hazards from fumes. Eating and smoking in the work area should be discouraged.

Chemicals: The chemicals present in fluxes require careful handling and use to avoid contact with the skin and eyes, and they shold not be ingested. Metals should be handled with care, and exposure should be kept to a minimum, below hazard levels.

Electrical Hazards: All electrical equipment used for heating in soldering should conform with NEMA standards. Contact must be prevented with current-carrying elements in soldering irons, ovens, resistance units, and induction equipment.

ADHESIVE JOINING

While no universal theory of adhesion exists, the following definition explains the bonding or joining process: "The molecular force exerted across a surface of contact between unlike liquids or solids that resists interfacial separation. One surface is the adhesive while the other is the adherend." The adhesive is a substance capable of holding materials together by surface attachment. The adherend is a body that is held to another body by an adhesive. Structural (engineering) adhesives are bonding agents used for transferring required loads between adherends exposed to service environments. Additional definitions are presented in ASTM D 907, "Standard Definitions of Terms Relating to Adhesives."

Curing is the changing of the physical properties of an adhesive by chemical reaction, which may be condensation, polymerization, or vulcanization. It is often accomplished by the action of heat and/or a catalyst and with or without pressure. Setting is the conversion of an adhesive into a fixed or hardened state by chemical or physical action.

Advantages and Limitations

Advantages of Adhesive Joining

Advantages with respect to the use of adhesive joining include the following:

1. Stresses are distributed uniformly over a large area, significantly reducing stress concentrations that cause fatigue and failure.

2. A wide variety of similar and dissimilar materials, as well as combinations of materials, can be joined, including those with vastly different thermal coefficients of expansion.
3. Very thin and fragile materials not suitable for mechanical fasteners or welding, as well as thick parts, can be fastened.
4. Components of all sizes and shapes can be joined.
5. Joints with smooth surfaces and contours can be produced.
6. Joints can be sealed against a variety of environments, heat transfer may be slowed, and electrolytic corrosion may be reduced.
7. Fatigue life is improved, vibration is damped, and thermal shock and impact are resisted.
8. Cures are effected at relatively low temperatures, avoiding the need for the high temperatures required for some other joining processes.
9. Costs are frequently less than for other fastening methods.
10. The weight of assemblies can be significantly reduced.
11. Joint design is simplified.
12. Some adhesives form flexible bonds that are tolerant of repeated cycling, resulting in improved fatigue life.
13. Special properties can be produced. Adhesive formulations are available to provide electrical insulation, conduction, or semiconduction between members.

Process Limitations

Possible limitations with respect to the use of adhesive joining include the following:

1. Careful adhesive selection is required to resist a specific environment. This may necessitate carefully planned testing with respect to the anticipated service of the assembly.
2. Rigid attention is demanded with respect to surface preparation and cleanliness prior to adhesive joining.
3. Heat and pressure or a relatively long cure period are sometimes required.

4. Jigs and fixtures are often necessary for good location of the parts to be assembled.
5. Maximum service temperatures of organic adhesives are low compared to the temperatures that can be withstood by many metals.
6. Nondestructive inspection of adhesive-bonded joints is difficult but desirable.
7. Many adhesive-bonded joints are not readily able to be disassembled.
8. Rigid process control is sometimes necessary.

Typical Applications

Adhesives have been used for thousands of years to join various materials. Their use for bonding metals in structural (load-bearing) applications, however, did not begin until World War II. Structural adhesives were first used in the aircraft industry, but are now being applied in a variety of industries.

Now, the major users of adhesive bonding are the automotive, aircraft, building products, and packaging industries. These four groups consume a major portion of the adhesive raw materials sold today. Other industries using adhesives include the shoe, apparel, furniture, bookbinding, electrical, railroad, shipbuilding, and medical industries. The following few specific examples serve to illustrate the importance of the adhesive joining process as an assembly technique.

Automotive Uses

Beginning in 1960, automobile companies began to use heat-curing plastisol mastic adhesive to bond the inner and outer panels of hood and trunk compartment lids. This system eliminated the flutter and rattle of hood and trunk lid components over rough roads or at high speeds and reduced the weight of the lid assemblies. The adhesive is oil tolerant and can be dispensed from automated applicators in an assembly line operation. Because the adhesive may be applied in conjunction with spot welding on the same part, it can be applied in a parts stamping operation and then heat cured later in the paint ovens. The joining method combining structural adhesives and resistance spot welding, called weldbonding, is discussed later in this section.

Mastic adhesive is also used for bonding interior reinforcements to door panels and framing members to the inside of van-type vehicles. The automotive industry also uses adhesives for joining metal to fabric for interior trim, vinyl-to-metal exterior trim, improved performance of tire cords, adhering brake linings, and general fastening. For adhering the textured vinyl coverings to metal roof surfaces, the contact neoprenephenolic cements have shown excellent resistance to exterior weathering conditions. Hot-melt adhesives are used to bond various carpet materials for floor mats and interior kick panels.

Food Packaging

In the food packaging industry, hot-melt adhesives are used for a large number of applications such as carton, can, and bag sealing, and the lamination of films, papers, and foils. The advantages of hot melts for such applications include rapid setup on cooling, which permits the use of high-speed fabrication machinery, and no volatile byproducts during the joining process, which permits their use on nonporous materials such as plastic film and metal foil. As a result, a number of rapid coating techniques have become feasible for manufacturing. In the heat sealing of plastic bags and containers, the plastic itself acts as the adhesive by sticking to itself in the melted state.

Structural Applications

Other major uses for adhesives include veneer and plywood laminated structures. In making wood particle boards, the adhesive is mixed uniformly with the particulate wood so it becomes the matrix holding the whole structure together. Similarly, epoxy adhesive is used as the binder material holding fiberglass, carbon, or boron fiber in composite structures. In the building construction industry, contact adhesives often replace nails and screws for attachment of paneling to studs.

The sidewall construction for over-the-road trailers and motor homes is often a sandwich panel construction in which the exterior metal and interior metal, wood, or plastic facings are adhesively bonded directly to insulating plastic foam slabs. Similarly, the wall panels for commercial buildings and schools may consist of metal, wood, or plastic facings adhered directly to a wide variety of insulating foam core materials.

Weldbonding

Weldbonding is a joining method that combines structural adhesives and resistance spot welding. Advantages over spot welding alone include improved fatigue life and durability and better resistance to peel forces. Also, the adhesive can act as a sealant to provide better corrosion resistance. Possible problems include making good welds through an adhesive and preventing contamination of visible metal surfaces and the electrodes by the adhesive. Applications include aircraft construction, aluminum truck cabs and van body sidewalls, and aluminum body sheets for automobiles.

The predominant weldbonding method consists of applying a paste adhesive to the area to be joined, followed by spot welding through the adhesive. In another method, a tape or film adhesive is applied to the area to be joined, holes are cut in the adhesive where the spot welds are required, and then conventional spot welding is performed. Yet another method consists of spot welding the parts together, applying adhesive to the edges of the joint, and then heating to cause the adhesive to flow between the joined surfaces by capillary action.

Bonded Sandwich Construction

One of the lightest and strongest constructions is the laminated or bonded sandwich consisting of thin, high-density facing members adhesively joined to a relatively thick, lightweight core. Both the facing and core materials can vary from metals like aluminum and steel to nonmetals such as wood, paper, and plastics. The basic elements of a bonded sandwich are shown in Fig. 15-6. Many structural honeycomb panels are made with reticulating adhesive where surface tension causes the adhesive to move up or down the walls of the honeycomb and form a fillet of adhesive. Applications of adhesively bonded sandwich structures are ever increasing in number; some examples are listed in Fig. 15-7.

Use in Aircraft: The honeycomb sandwich structure used on a large military transport plane, the Lockheed C-5A, is shown in Fig. 15-8. It illustrates the strength-weight effectiveness of honeycomb by the large area in this one craft of 24,000 ft² (more than half an acre), which equals 2230 m². A complete and comprehensive investigation of adhesive bonding in aircraft has been conducted by Douglas Aircraft Co. under an Air Force contract. In this investigation, a full-sized main fuselage of a large transport aircraft was entirely joined with adhesive and instrumented for every kind of test applicable to the service life of such an aircraft. The study is known today as the PABST program, which stands for Primary Adhesive Bonding Structural Technology.

Advantages: Advantages of sandwich structures include the following:

- High strength-to-weight ratios.
- High stiffness-to-weight ratios.

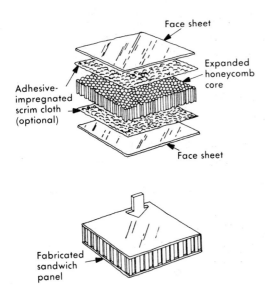

Figure 15-6   Elements of a bonded sandwich

Aircraft:	
Control surfaces	Doors (structural access, and entry)
Control tabs	Engine cowling
Bulkheads	Wing panels
Helicopter blades	Fairings
Flooring (cargo and passenger compartment)	Fan air ducts
Missile and spacecraft electronics and communications:	
Fins and control surfaces	Radomes
Structural shells	Shipping containers
Antenna reflectors	Intertank structures
Tankage	Electronic packaging
Heat shields	
Buildings:	
Prefab shelters	Partitions and doors
Curtain walls	
Miscellaneous:	House-trailer flooring
Desk tops	Boats
Scaffolding	Cargo containers

Figure 15-7   Applications of bonded sandwich construction

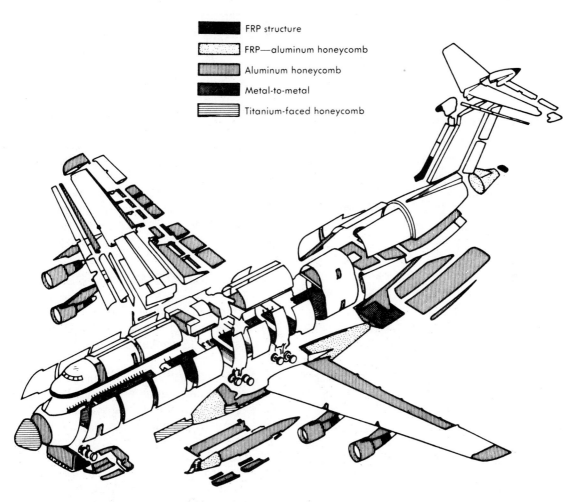

FRP structure

FRP—aluminum honeycomb

Aluminum honeycomb

Metal-to-metal

Titanium-faced honeycomb

Figure 15-8   Honeycomb sandwich structures used on a modern aircraft

- Compound-contoured fabrications.
- High fatigue resistance as a result of the even distribution of stresses.
- Smooth exterior surfaces.

It should be of particular interest to manufacturing engineers to note an example of the ability of structurally bonded metal joints for resisting fatigue-type failures. For example, the PABST program showed that a deliberately machined crack in the adhesively bonded area did not propagate into catastrophic failure after all the fatigue testing was concluded. In contrast, it is common to find riveted aircraft construction in which catastrophic failures are induced by fatigue stresses radiating out from the drilled rivet hole.

Limitations: Possible limitations with respect to the use of sandwich structures include the following:

- Cost is usually higher than for conventional structures.
- Making attachments requires special attention.
- The thin skin provides poor resistance to punctures and dents.

Design Requirements: Before adhesive-bonded sandwiches are applied, design data, inspection data, and producibility data should be obtained. The following basic requirements must be considered in sandwich design:

1. The facings must have sufficient thickness and strength to withstand the tensile, compressive, and shear stresses induced by the design load.

2. The core must have sufficient strength to withstand the shear stresses induced by the service loading.

3. The core must be thick enough and have sufficient shear modulus to prevent overall buckling under the design load.

4. The stiffness of the core and the compressive strength of the facings must be sufficient to prevent wrinkling of the face sheets under the service requirements.

5. The core cells must be of proper dimension to prevent intracell buckling under the design load.

6. The core must have sufficient compressive strength to resist crushing by design loads acting normal to the panel facings or by compressive stresses induced through flexure.

7. The structure must have adequate strength in the flexural and shear modes to prevent permanent deflections under design load.

8. Ease of carving, forming, and tooling must be considered.

9. The type and weight of the adhesive must be considered. In extremely lightweight structures, face sheets 0.010″ (0.25 mm) or less in thickness, the weight of the adhesive becomes an important factor.

10. The operating environment must be considered, including temperature, moisture, vibration (fatigue), and expected length of service. The operating temperature of the assembly is important because adhesives degrade and creep at temperatures lower than metals.

The basic fabrication process for bonded sandwich construction is like that for any structural adhesive-bonded part.

Types of Adhesives

Just as a variety of materials can be bonded with adhesives, there are thousands of adhesive formulations available for bonding these materials. Adhesives are available as liquids (pastes, solutions, and emulsions) and solids (films, tapes, rods, pellets, and powders). Formulations are often identified by brand name, but it is important to the user to be able to identify the chemical type as well. Suppliers are usually willing to provide such information, as well as pertinent data on the properties of the adhesive and test results on its performance in joints.

Adhesive Material Categories

The three main adhesive material categories are: (1) natural product raw materials, (2) inorganic raw materials, and (3) synthetic organic materials.

Natural Adhesives: Examples of natural product materials are gums and resins, starch, dextrin, casein, soya flour, and animal products such as blood and collagen. Adhesives made from these natural materials are most applicable to products where lower stresses are permissible. They are usually too weak for metal joints that may need to resist intermittent or steady stressing conditions. In many product applications, however, relatively large areas can be used so that the unit load is small. The number of such applications is large enough that natural-product-based adhesives still constitute the major poundage of adhesives used.

Inorganic Adhesives: The principal inorganic adhesives are sodium silicate and magnesium oxychloride. They have the advantage of low cost, but have serious shortcomings in their low strength, negligible flexibility, and, in some cases, sensitivity to moisture.

Synthetic Adhesives: The synthetic organic adhesives are of primary interest to the manufacturing engineer. These adhesives have been developed in the laboratory to give high-strength bonds to wood, glass, plastics, and metals. Technical assistance is usually available from the adhesive manufacturers to fit one of these adhesives to a given assembly process. The synthetic organic adhesives fall into the raw material classes of elastomers and resins.

Resins may be further subdivided into thermoplastic and thermoset types. The most common individual members of these classes are styrene block copolymers; acrylic, polyolefin, nylon, and vinyl thermoplastic resins; and acrylic (anaerobics), epoxy, phenolic, polyurethane, and silicone thermosets. New technology also includes many hybrid types, which are alloys of the older classic types.

A polymer will serve as an adhesive if: (1) it adheres sufficiently to a particular adherend to give a useful bond and (2) it converts from a liquid to soild state during the actual bonding step. The latter requirement is not necessary for pressure-sensitive adhesives. Using these criteria, it is logical to classify adhesives by the manner in which they convert from the liquid state to the solid state during bonding.

Chemically Reactive Adhesives (Class I)

The chemically reactive adhesives all undergo a curing or crosslinking reaction within the adhesive. Most reactive adhesives provide high lap-shear strengths, to 7000 psi (48.3 MPa) or more, at room temperature. When crosslinked (thermoset), these adhesives retain proerties well. Because many of these thermoset resins are relatively brittle, the peel strengths are frequently low. To improve the peel strengths, polymer alloys are commonly prepared from chemically reactive adhesives and various flexible thermoplastics and elastomers.

Plural Components (Class IA): In this type of adhesive, the chemical reaction is initiated by mixing a reactive component or catalyst with the adhesive before application. The reaction then proceeds at some rate, depending on the particular curing agent or catalyst, until an inert-thermoset,

chemically resistant resin develops. Heating will usually accelerate the cure rate as well as improve initial fluidity for better substrate wetting, resulting in improved bond durability. Epoxies are probably the most common resin bases for this class of adhesives, although polyester, polysulfide, polyurethane, and silicone resins are available in two-part mix formulations.

Soaring energy and labor costs and the need to improve productivity have made it increasingly advantageous in recent years to use adhesives that can cure rapidly at room temperature, adhere to a wide variety of adherends, and need no mixing or metering prior to application. In these respects, some modified structural acrylic adhesives can be mentioned as having such characterisitcs. While a curing catalyst or accelerator does not have to be premixed with resins in such adhesives, a separate component must be applied to one or both adherend surfaces before the joint is closed. Such adhesives are characterized as being two-step types, as opposed to two-part adhesives, where the ratio of parts and their mixing are important to their properties. The curing can be effected in a matter of minutes, and strong joints can be made with little or no surface preparation and, in some instances, on oily parts.

Current commercial products are described as second- or third-generation acrylics. The catalyst need only be applied to one adherend, while the resin is applied to the second adherend. Mating the surface automatically mixes the resin and catalyst, producing a thermoset bondline in a few minutes. As originally introduced in the marketplace, these adhesives lacked toughness and flexibility and required good surface preparation on metal adherends. The incorporation of polymeric elastomers and new acrylic resins have favorably altered these properties and made the adhesives highly tolerant of oil contamination.

Epoxy resin formulations that cure at room temperature have been a mainstay of structural bonding in general manufacturing for many years. Details of many structural bonding applications with these adhesives are discussed in several of the publications listed in the bibliography at the end of this text. The most convenient commercial form of such epoxy adhesives has been the equal parts of A and B mix types; the ratio is not highly critical to achieving adequate curing, and the use of automated mixing and application equipment is easy. A variety of inorganic fillers can be used to control the viscosity to fit a particular application. The rigidity and sensitivity of the bondline to crack propagation in earlier formulations has been eliminated by blending elastomeric rubber with the epoxy.

Microencapsulated two-part epoxy adhesives, which are coated onto threaded fasteners to replace lock washers, remain dormant until the shearing action of engaging threads causes some of the capsules to break, thus allowing the adhesive to cure. The capsules that do not break on initial assembly allow the removal and reuse of the fastener several times with only a slight loss in break-loose, break-away, and prevailing torque.

Heat-Activated Adhesives (Class IB) — Epoxies, Urethanes and Phenolics:
This class of adhesives is often referred to as the one-part heat-curing type. All of the necessary ingredients have been premixed by the adhesive supplier, but heating is required to initiate the chemical reaction. Because they are premixed, shelf life, even at room temperature, may be limited to a few months. Such adhesives can be stored at subambient temperatures to improve their shelf life. Every manufacturer of this type of adhesive tries to optimize shelf life, yet permit as rapid a cure as possible in the 180-350°F (82-177°C) temperature range.

While some industries will always prefer a room temperature curing system, certain major industrial markets, such as light fixtures, appliances, motors, speakers, metal furniture, hydraulic oil filters, and other high-volume consumer products will traditionally use a heat-cured adhesive. Material economics and durability of product are two of the most important reasons for using these products.

The phenolic resin materials are generally used as a modifying agent for imparting strength and water resistance to other resins. For example, blending a phenolic resin with a vinyl thermoplastic resin has produced a class of adhesives known as vinyl-phenolics, which have had one of the best histories of durable bonding of metals in aircraft. Similarly, the addition of phenolic to epoxy resin has produced a class of aircraft bonding adhesives known as epoxy-phenolics with high service temperature capability.

One of the first phenolic-modified adhesives for bonding aircraft was made by blending nitrile elastomer rubber with phenolic resin. Their resistance to high-humidity service environments when bonding metals is seldom equaled by any of the most modern adhesives in the marketplace.

One-Part Specially Catalyzed Adhesives (Class IC)—Cyanoacrylates and Anaerobics:
There are several types of adhesives that need neither on-site mixing nor heat to cure, including cyanoacrylates, anaerobics, and acrylics with surface activators.

Cyanoacrylates. One of these types of adhesives that has attracted considerable attention because of ease of use is a cyanoacrylate. The picture of an elephant being supported by the strength developed by one drop of adhesive is familiar. It seems incredible that a tensile strength of 5000 psi (34.5 MPa) is developed without the benefit of adding a separate catalyst or heat. This high strength is developed within a minute after the bondline is closed. Polymerization of the cyanoacrylate only occurs rapidly in the presence of a weakly basic compound, such as an amine, an alcohol, or trace amounts of water on the surface. For this latter reason, some describe the cure as moisture induced.

Advantages of cyanoacrylates include: (1) ease of use, (2) rapid formation of bonds, (3) small quantity required, (4) adherence to dissimilar materials, (5) colorless bondlines, and (6) good resistance to many solvents.

General limitations exist and include the following: (1) poor gap-filling characteristics; (2) bonds have low shock resistance and low peel strength; (3) with some adherends, like glass and metals, the bonds have poor moisture resistance; (4) bonds lose strength after exposure to temperatures higher than 160°F (71°C);

and (5) curing is sometimes accompanied by a white haze or halo adjacent to the bondline.

As with many adhesive evolutions, the manufacturers have developed systems or alloys that have overcome many of the limitations without losing the basic advantages of speed and strength. Cyanoacrylate alloys are available having temperature capabilities to 250°F (120°C), having high impact and peel strength, or existing in a gel form for gap-filling capability. Unfortunately, all these characteristics are not as yet available in one formulation, but may soon be with continuing development.

Anaerobics. Also prominent in this one-part class are the anaerobic adhesives that achieve cure at room temperature only in the absence of oxygen. As long as oxygen is available, the curing mechanism cannot proceed, which is why these adhesives are stored in oxygen-permeable containers. When oxygen is excluded, such as by confinement between surfaces to be joined, polymerization can start, and the adhesive becomes a thermoset plastic. These adhesives have important properties, including rapid cure at ambient temperature, no need for metering and mixing prior to application, and resistance to a wide variety of solvents and industrial fluids. From a purely chemical point of view, these properties are not always achieved optimally and simultaneously. Ingenuity in chemistry, however, has permitted remarkable tradeoff compromises in such properties.

Present-day anaerobic structural adhesives are the culmination of an evolution that began with the anaerobic machinery adhesives used for sealing and bonding of rigid parts. While ideally suited to do the job of improving the strength and reliability of threaded fasteners and sealing leakage in connected parts, they lacked the flexibility and toughness of true structural adhesives. Sophisticated combinations of the former methacrylate chemistry with urethane chemistry has produced desirable structural characteristics, while retaining the property of curing in the absence of oxygen. Unlike the second-generation acrylic adhesives mentioned earlier, the anaeorobic-type acrylics should only be used to bond clean or specially surface-treated metal, glass, or ceramic surfaces. Some typical application areas for these

improved anaerobics are the assembly of firearms and fuel pumps, electronic components for high-temperature service, bonding metal to glass, glass stemware, and honing stones.

Radiation-Curing Adhesives (Class ID):
Radiation curing of adhesives permits rapid curing, conserves energy, allows easy automation, and avoids air pollution by eliminating volatile products. Energy sources used for radiation curing are ultraviolet (UV) light, visible light, electron beam (EB), and gamma radiation. Gamma radiation has limited application, being restricted to a few specialized and electronic uses.

Ultraviolet light curing adhesives. Modified acrylics, anaerobics, and epoxies can be cured with UV light at 365 nm (3650 angstrom units) wavelength and 10000 to 100000 $\mu W/cm^2$ (64500 to 645000 $\mu W/in.^2$) intensity. They are prepared with photoinitiator chemicals that become active in the presence of the light. At the higher light intensities, cure takes place in three to 15 seconds, and air-exposed anaerobic material can be cured dry to touch. Obviously, the bondline must be visible to the light from at least one substrate to have direct activation. This would seem to limit their usefulness to glass and UV-clear plastics. However, in some cases, the formulations are made with dual or triple activation. As long as a fillet is visible, parts can be fixtured in seconds and strength developed anaerobically by surface activation or with heat at a more leisurely pace of minutes or hours.

The convenience and speed of UV curing has allowed many batch operations to be replaced by line curing. Mercury arc lamps are most widely used as the source of light. Because these light sources can be ten times as strong as the UV intensity of sunlight, operator protection is essential. In the production of transformers, UV-cured adhesive coats and penetrates the laminations, reducing hum and insulating the components. Fast curing with this method eliminated the batch drying formerly required.

Electron beam curing. Electron beam (EB) curing adhesives are being used with flocking, metallized paper, plastics, and foil laminates. Applications include the manufacture of magnetic discs and tapes with thermoplastic hot-melt or polyurethane adhesives.

Moisture-Curing Adhesives (Class IE) — Polysulfides, Polyurethanes, and Polysiloxanes (Silicones):

These are liquid or paste adhesives that react on exposure to atmospheric moisture. Moisture-curing polysulfides are primarily used as adhesive/sealants, but polyurethanes can be applicable for either true structural bonding or as adhesive/sealants. The silicones are also available in moisture-curing room-temperature-vulcanizing (RTV) formulations that are structural or adhesive/sealant in nature.

True structural-strength silicone bonds are more frequently two-part catalyzed-type formulations that fall in the Class IA group previously discussed. The urethane adhesives in structural applications are also generally two-part catalyzed systems. Such adhesives have been used extensively for many years to bond polyester-fiberglass to itself or polyester-fiberglass to metals in automotive manufacturing. It is usually only necessary to remove a mold release agent from polyester-fiberglass surfaces to secure strong, durable bonds, but, on metal adherend surfaces, a special epoxy primer is often required to achieve water-durable bonds with polyurethane adhesives.

Evaporative Adhesives (Class II)

With evaporative adhesives, curing or setting occurs through the loss of solvent or water. Therefore, at least one of the adherends must be porous enough to absorb the solvent or water, or sufficient drying time must be allowed before assembly. Both thermoplastic and thermoset systems can be applied by this method. Soluble, nonreactive materials include rubber, vinyl resins, thermoplastic urethanes, acrylics, phenoxy resin, and natural materials such as cellulose esters, asphalt, starch, and casein. Many reactive resins, such as phenolics and urethanes, are also used in solvents. Some of these adhesives are flexible and have good peel strengths, some up

to 100 lb/in. (17.5 N/mm) of width. Adhesion in shear or tension will generally be low and susceptible to more creep than the chemically reactive types. Latex (emulsion) adhesives are being used to bond impermeable surfaces when the required longer drying time can be tolerated or if forced drying is used.

There have been continuing environmental and economic pressures on organic solvent-based adhesive users in recent years, thereby increasing the market potential for water-based adhesives. Some of the current uses of water-based adhesives are for labels, packaging, wood bonding, fabric bonding, panel lamination, high-pressure laminate bonding, construction mastics, bonding of floor and wall tile, and tapes.

If water-based adhesives are to be considered for any application, it is important to secure as much information as possible about their application, drying, and bonding capabilities. The difficulty of rapidly removing water from bondlines as compared with organic solvents has always favored the use of the organic solvent types. This has activated extensive research by adhesive suppliers to study water removal methods, with only modest results. It is still difficult to achieve production speeds equal to those with organic solvents.

Hot-Melt Adhesives (Class III)

Hot-melt adhesives must be formulated with thermoplastic resins because by definition a thermoset resin will not form a melt condition upon reheating. Synthetic polymers used in hot-melt adhesives include ethylene vinyl acetate (EVA), polyethylene, styrene block copolymer, butyl rubber, polyamide, polyurethane, and polyester. Hot-melt adhesives must be applied in the molten state and depend on a rapid solidification for the development of bondline strength. Thus, polymer properties such as melting point, hot tack, melt viscosity, and heat stability are most important in determining the usefulness of resins in hot melts. The apparent simplistic manner of applying and developing fast bond strength using hot melts would lead to the conclusion that they might be the perfect adhesive product, but there are both advantages and disadvantages that should also be recognized. Hot-melt adhesives are used extensively in the packaging industry and for product assembly applications to bond a variety of substrates, including metals, plastics, glass, fabrics, wood, and paper-related products.

Advantages: Advantages of hot-melt adhesives include the following:

1. Bonds form rapidly, resulting in high-speed assembly and short clamp time.
2. Variable gaps can be filled in joints.
3. Most materials can be bonded.
4. Clean, easy handling.
5. Cost is less per unit assembly than for many mechanical fasteners.
6. Easy recovery and repair of substandard assemblies.
7. No problems with solvent or fume flammability.
8. Simple materials inventory and storage.
9. Precise bond control through variations of the temperature and the quantity of adhesive.
10. Equipment available for hand or automated assembly.
11. Easily maintained equipment.
12. Minimal production-line space requirements.

Limitations: Because of their thermoplastic nature, there are several characteristics of hot-melt adhesives that may limit their use, including the following:

1. Bonds lose strength at elevated temperatures.
2. Some bonds may creep and fail with time (delamination).
3. Hot melts may be sensitive to some chemicals and solvents.
4. Some adherends may be sensitive to the hot-melt application temperature.
5. Sophisticated application equipment may be required for high-performance hot melts, which can be highly viscous.
6. Some hot melts have a tendency to degrade at application temperature unless protected from the air.
7. Some hot melts become brittle at low temperatures.

8. Controlled wettability on adherends that have high heat-conductivity properties (for example, metals) must be designed into the manufacturing operation.

Delayed-Tack Adhesives (Class IV)

Delayed-tack adhesives are nontacky solids that are heat-activated to produce a state of tackiness that is retained upon cooling for periods of up to several days. Blends of a resin such as polyvinyl acetate, polystyrene, or polyamide, with a solid plasticizer give this characteristic.

Film Adhesives (Class V)

Film adhesives are related to the one-part heat-activated, chemically reactive adhesives (Class IB) discussed previously in that similar adhesives are used and similar bond properties are obtained. They may also be similar to Class III or Class VI adhesives. The advantages of film adhesives include: (1) controlled glue-line thickness, (2) ease of application, (3) freedom from solvents, and (4) the opportunity to prepare two-sided films, each side with different adhesive properties to bond dissimilar surfaces. Also, film adhesives may be supplied on a flexible carrier, such as cloth or paper, in sheet or tape form. The most serious disadvantage for the curing type is the requirement for precise heating of the parts for an extended length of time. The difficulty of automating the tape feeding and cutting limits the application of these adhesives to hand operations.

The most common use for structural film adhesives is in metal laminations where the film can be crosslinked and cured after assembly. For this reason, tape and film adhesives have dominated the airframe market for many years. The usage has increased from several hundred pounds of tape adhesive on early commercial jets such as the Boeing 707 to several thousand pounds on jumbo jets as the Boeing 747. (Note: 1 lb = 0.4536 kg.)

In aerospace and aircraft applications, much of the adhesive is used in honeycomb construction, producing very lightweight assemblies with high peel strength, high impact strength, and cleavage and fatigue strength hitherto impossible. The interlayer in automotive safety glass is also based on a film adhesive made from polyvinyl butyral resin. Many other laminated structures are made with thermoplastic film adhesives. Thermoplastic films based on polyolefins are heat-laminated; films having pressure-sensitive adhesive on both sides are used to assemble without heat.

Pressure-Sensitive Adhesives (Class VI)

A pressure-sensitive adhesive may be defined as a material capable of bond formation by the brief application of pressure on a coated adherend at room temperature. The adhesive is applied to one surface from solution, emulsion, or hot melt, and then the adhesive is dried to a permanently tacky state. The coated surface is then brought into contact with a second adherend, and light pressure is applied to flow the adhesive on to the surface.

Masking tape, surgical tape, and labels are the major uses for pressure-sensitive adhesives, which are collectively called PSAs in the trade. A variety of other products using PSAs include wall and shelf coverings, imitation wood grain coverings, ceiling and floor tile, disposable diaper tabs, medical and sanitary products, graphic artwork, and protective maskings.

PSAs consist of a combination of elastomers, tackifying resins, plasticizers, and fillers. Pressure-sensitive adhesives are usually identified by the chemical nature of the elastomer used, such as natural rubber, styrene-butadiene rubber (SBR), acrylic, and others. While most PSAs are still applied from organic solvent solutions, the industry is developing alternatives because of rising solvent prices and legislation aimed at reducing environmental pollution. This has led to the development of aqueous emulsion systems and hot-melt pressure-sensitive adhesives (HMPSAs). Pressure-sensitive

adhesives are also available in 100% solids formulation, where curing of block copolymer thermoplastic rubber has been effected by electron beam (EB) or ultraviolet (UV) light radiation. Both cohesive strength and solvent resistance properties can be measurably improved by such a technique. Those grades of PSAs with high cohesive strength are now being used for assembly applications. Automotive applications include sound and vibration damping, roof tops, side moldings, emblems, and brake quadrant assemblies.

Primers for Structural Adhesives

Primers used for structural bonding function as adhesion promoters or surface protectors. Adhesion promoters are generally silane materials and provide little surface protection. Primers used for surface protection, which also generally promote adhesion, are comprised of a resin, a crosslinking agent, film formers, a corrosion inhibitor, and a solvent carrier.

Application Methods

Before choosing a method of applying the adhesive, the user should consider the following:

1. Various methods for the best filling of the bondline and wetting of the adherends.
2. Economy of the application.
3. Production rate for the piece being fabricated.
4. Method of application from the viewpoint of simplicity.

The testing of the adherend should be initiated at the beginning of the investigation. The tests will likely reveal several suitable ways to apply the adhesive. Adhesives may be applied manually by roller, brush, extrusion and flow, and trowel. They can be applied semiautomatically with spray guns or high-pressure extrusion guns, or they can be applied automatically by machine methods that are usually geared for mass production of a particular part.

Industrial robots are also being used for the application of adhesives and sealants.

Manual Roller Application

Rollers for manual application can be constructed from wood, paper, cork, metal mesh, rubber, or synthetic fibers. The length of nap on a roller determines the amount of material left on the coated surface.

Screen or Stencil Printing

Anaerobics are uniquely suited for screen or stencil application because of their stable nature in the presence of air. Accurate control of quantity is possible, and intricate patterns are applied in a second or two.

Brushing

Brush bristles for applying adhesives are made of various types of hair, synthetic fibers, wood, and metal. Compatibility with the adhesive may be important. The anaerobics, in particular, may require the use of all synthetic fibers so that the material does not cure in the bristles. Brushing is usually a manual operation, although sometimes the adhesive is fed to the brushes under pressure.

Extrusion and Flow

Extrusion and flow are general methods of applications used by operators equipped with caulking guns. Extrusion application is also used in curtain coaters, flow coaters, and high-pressure air-powered extrusion units. Rotary extrusion is a method similar to screen printing for applying precise patterns of hot-melt adhesive to continuous webs of various substrates. A rotating print cylinder and doctor-blade assembly forces adhesive from heated supply units through the patterned mesh opening of the cylinder onto the substrate. Hot-melt adhesives are also being applied with extruders having capillary rheometers that permit rapid measurement of melt viscosity.

Troweling

A toothed trowel normally leaves a fairly constant amount of adhesive on the work surface. Small cutouts or teeth along one margin of the trowel allow a predictable amount of material to pass through and remain on the surface.

Spraying

The selection of spray equipment over other methods of application is usually predicated by economic considerations. This is particularly true when the products are large or of a complex shape. Spraying is fast and provides a means of reaching inaccessible areas easily. Furthermore, the drying time of the coating usually is reduced when it is sprayed because of the fine distribution of solvent into the airspace above the workpiece. When automated spray equipment is employed, particularly for long runs of identical objects, the optimum advantages of spray equipment are realized. Spray equipment can be classified by method: air spray or airless spray, depending on the technique used to project the liquid.

Air Spray: With this adhesive application method, low fluid pressure moves the material to the spray-tip area, where air is introduced to atomize the adhesive into an acceptable spray pattern. Figure 15-9 illustrates an equipment layout for air-spray applications.

Airless Spray: Pressurized adhesive passing through a small opening atomizes. Once the liquid has left the nozzle, momentum is the only force that carries it forward because the only material emerging from the gun is the adhesive itself. The air between the nozzle and the target resists the motion of the particles, slowing them down appreciably, which reduces overspray. Figure 15-10 illustrates an equipment layout for airless-spray application.

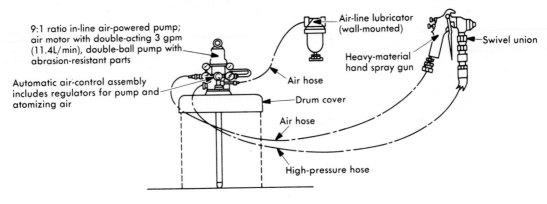

9:1 ratio in-line air-powered pump; air motor with double-acting 3 gpm (11.4L/min), double-ball pump with abrasion-resistant parts

Automatic air-control assembly includes regulators for pump and atomizing air

Air-line lubricator (wall-mounted)

Swivel union

Heavy-material hand spray gun

Air hose

Drum cover

Air hose

High-pressure hose

Figure 15-9   Equipment layout for air-spray installation

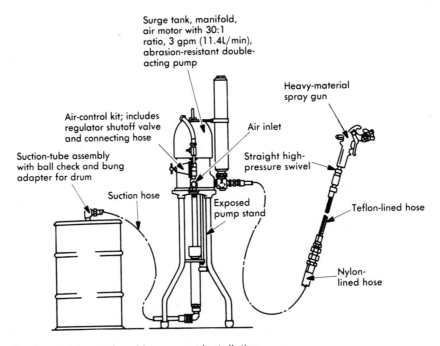

Surge tank, manifold, air motor with 30:1 ratio, 3 gpm (11.4L/min), abrasion-resistant double-acting pump

Heavy-material spray gun

Air-control kit; includes regulator shutoff valve and connecting hose

Air inlet

Suction-tube assembly with ball check and bung adapter for drum

Straight high-pressure swivel

Suction hose

Exposed pump stand

Teflon-lined hose

Nylon-lined hose

Figure 15-10   Equipment layout for airless-spray installation

Use of Heat: With either method of spray application, the adhesive can be heated prior to atomization to lower the viscosity and decrease the atomization energy required. This makes it possible to apply heavier films and reduce overspray losses. In addition, the use of the proper amount of heat can eliminate the effects of ambient humidity or temperature on the coating. Either can adversely affect the coating by the precipitation of water vapor or postthinning of the material on a relatively warm surface. Figure 15-11 compares spray patterns and energy requirements for hot and cold air and hot and cold airless sprays.

Roll Coaters

More adhesives are applied with roll coaters than by any other single method. Roll coaters are very efficient, with waste as low as 2%. They may be used to coat webs or individual flat sheets or panels of materials such as paper, paperboard, plastics, synthetic rubbers, cloth, wood composition materials, and metals. Bench-type roll coaters are available in widths from four to 26″ (102 to 660 mm). Some models have open-end rollers that permit material larger than the rollers to be fed through the machine. Floor-mounted roll coaters are available in various types, including kiss-roll, pressure-roll, and reverse-roll coaters. Figures 15-12 through 15-16 illustrate some of the common types of roll coaters available.

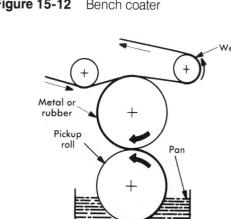

Figure 15-12 Bench coater

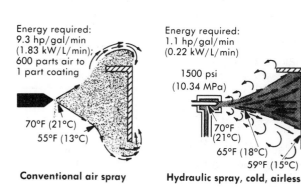

Figure 15-11 Comparison of spray methods

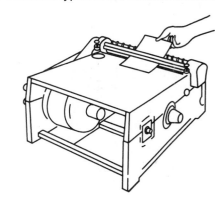

Figure 15-13 Kiss-type roll coater

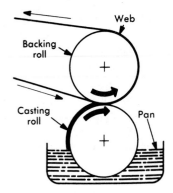

Figure 15-14   Pressure roll coater

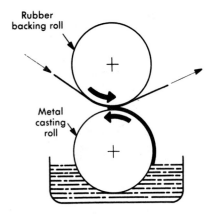

Figure 15-15   Reverse roll coater

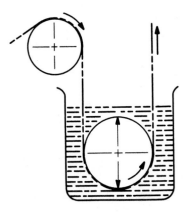

Figure 15-16   Dip roll coater

Vacuum Impregnation

Vacuum impregnation is commonly used, especially in applying anaerobic adhesives to powder metal, laminated, and die cast parts. Adhesive is pushed into microscopic pores after air has been excluded by a vacuum cycle. This is done in a large mesh basket in a vacuum vat with the parts immersed. Excess adhesive is spun off, leaving a relatively clean surface.

Manual Applicators

Adhesive applicators can be handheld or machine (or fixture) mounted. Handheld applicators include heavy-duty diaphragm-valve handguns and light-duty pinch-tube pencil applicators with fingertip lever actuators. With the actuator depressed, adhesive flows out of the nozzle; when released, flow stops. Pencil applicators are also available with poppet valves in the nozzles—when the nozzle is pushed against a surface, the valve opens and adhesive flows; when lifted, flow stops.

Automatic Applicators

Machine or fixture-mounted adhesive applicators are available in a number of different designs.

Stationary Applicators: Stationary nozzle applicators are generally operated by depressing a foot switch. An operator or machine positions a part under the nozzle, and adhesive is dispensed onto the part.

Touch Applicators: Touch applicators are operated by a switch located behind the nozzle. The operator places the part onto a custom-made dispensing nozzle, and the adhesive is deposited at a specific location on the part.

Advancing Nozzle Applicators: Advancing nozzle applicators are used where there must be a clearance between the moving parts and the nozzle, as on assembly machines. The applicator is operated by a foot switch or a machine-generated signal. When energized, the nozzle advances to the point of application, dispenses, and retracts. These applicators can dispense a drop, strip, or circulator bead of adhesive.

Rotospray Applicators:
Rotospray applicators are used where a 360 bead of adhesive is required inside a hole. These applicators consist of an adhesive valve, an air motor, and a revolving disc. They are usually mounted on a slide, and the disc is advanced into the hole. Adhesive is dispensed onto the revolving disc, where centrifugal force spins the adhesive from the disc and applies a bead at the selected location. If the rotospray is advanced while dispensing, a film of adhesive can be applied to the length of the hole.

Pressure-Time Vacuum Dispensing System:
A pressure-time vacuum dispensing system consists of a disposable plastic syringe barrel that is filled with adhesive, an air regulator and gage to control the pressure, and an electrical timing circuit to control the dispense-cycle. When the system is energized, a timed pulse of air is transmitted to the top of the syringe barrel and pushes a metered amount of adhesive out a nozzle attached to the bottom of the barrel. When the timer times out, the pressurized air in the barrel is exhausted, and an amount of vacuum is drawn on the adhesive to hold it suspended in the barrel and nozzle.

The amount of adhesive dispensed is controlled by the pressure and timer settings. Higher pressure and longer time will cause more product to be dispensed; lower pressure and shorter time will cause less product to be dispensed. With this type system, a dispense accuracy of 15% can be expected unless adjustments are made to either the timer or pressure settings to compensate for the adhesive volume change within the barrel as adhesive is used up.

Positive-Displacement Dispensing System:
Another common system for dispensing anaerobic and modified-acrylic adhesives uses a ram-piston positive-displacement pump with a gravity-fed adhesive reservoir and an actuating device. Custom nozzles can be attached directly to the discharge outlet of the pump or an adhesive feedline connected to a remote applicator. Positive-displacement pump systems are capable of dispensing high-viscosity adhesives. They are unaffected by ambient temperature changes and viscosity and pressure fluctuations normally associated with pressure-time systems.

Adhesive is gravity-fed directly from a container, bottle, or tube into the inlet port of the pump to fill the metering chamber. When the pump is energized by the actuator, the pump piston, driven by an air cylinder, extends forward into the metering chamber to displace a predetermined amount of adhesive through a nonreturn check valve and out the dispensing nozzle. When the actuator is de-energized, the air cylinder and pump piston retract, ready for another cycle. As the piston is retracting, the check valve closes, and a slight vacuum develops between the valve and the end of the piston so that the chamber refills with adhesive. The amount of adhesive dispensed is determined by the piston stroke length within the metering chamber, and this is controlled by a stroke adjuster, ususally attached to the back of the air cylinder. Increasing piston diameter and lengthening stroke will allow larger amounts to be dispensed per cycle. Decreasing piston diameter allows small quantities to be displaced. Dispense accuracy of 2% is common with ram-piston pump applicators.

Robotic Applicators

Industrial robots are being used for the application of adhesives and sealants. The robots are generally used to manipulate the dispensing gun, but occasionally the parts to be joined are manipulated by the robots. Advantages of using robots for such applications include reduced labor requirements and costs, faster production, consistently high quality, and reduced adhesive usage. Adhesives can be applied to a number of parts simultaneously by using multiple guns on a single robot. A possible limitation is that high volumes are generally necessary for cost-effectiveness. However, the flexibility of robots permits handling a variety of different parts in small batches.

Robots Used: Selection of a robot for adhesive or sealant application depends on the specific application. For light-duty applications with small parts having flat or slightly contoured surfaces, robots having low payload, reach, and positioning capacity are often satisfactory. Speeds below 600 ipm (15 240 mm/min) are common for such applications. However, variable speed capability with fast, smooth acceleration and deceleration is generally desirable for most applications to increase flexibility. For heavy-duty applications and faster production, robots with increased capacity, often specially engineered for the specific application, are usually necessary.

Five-axis robots are generally adequate for most applications, but a sixth axis may be necessary for nonsymmetrical nozzles. Electric servocontrolled robots having a high degree of accuracy and repeatability are usually preferable to hydraulic units because of smoother motions and better repeatability. Dispensing speeds to 3000 ipm (76 200 mm/min) have been used for straight-line applications, but 1200 to 1800 ipm (30 480 to 45 720 mm/min) are more typical speeds, depending on bead-path complexity. Programming can be accomplished with a teach pendant, a programmable controller, or off-line CNC.

Automotive Application: One robot dispensing system being used by automotive manufacturers is of gantry design to allow the system to straddle production lines. Figure 15-17 illustrates a car-door assembly system. A programmable interface integrates the unit with the parts handling system.

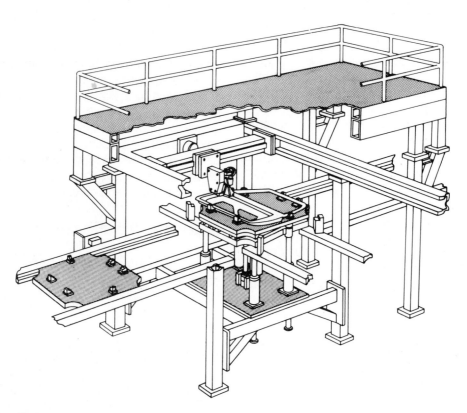

Figure 15-17   Robotic door assembly system

Applying Various Adhesives: Hot melts, urethanes, and two-part epoxies are adhesives being applied extensively by robots. The hot-melt application equipment consists essentially of a melting and pumping unit, flexible hose or a pipe-hose system, and a heated gun and nozzle. An electronic control system is provided to vary the output of either the pump or the gun, or both, while the robot performs its program. Internal flow and bubble detection devices and external bead sensing units are also generally provided to ensure proper operation.

Selection of Equipment

The selection of equipment for dispensing of adhesives is the basis for the selection of a whole system to apply adhesives. If your adhesive supplier cannot address the whole system, then another may be chosen. The application equipment may dictate the type or at least the characteristics of the adhesive. It is imperative that a systems approach be taken right at the beginning, with the adhesive, process, and equipment all considered together. Broadly, the considerations include the following:

1. What adhesives can give satisfactory bond strength and life on the substrates?
2. Can these adhesives be handled and fed in the proper quantity and at the required speed to meet production requirements?
3. Can the equipment prevent operator exposure to improve safety?
4. Can the equipment provide automatic inspection of the quantity dispensed and inspection of the cured bond?
5. Will parts handling by machine ensure cleaner assemblies or perhaps perform cleaning as part of the assembly?
6. Will the conditions of cure be closely controlled by machine cycles of temperature, time, and humidity?

Once an adhesive and a method of application have been selected, the features of the equipment are still to be decided. Before buying any particular equipment, ask if the following considerations can be met:

1. Cleanup should be easy and any equipment parts with cured material easy and inexpensive to replace.
2. Control of adhesive quantity per part should be within the requirements of the specific application. If proportioning and mixing are required, how accurately is it done? Are there easy ways to check?
3. The life expectancy of the equipment and components should be known; replacement and overhaul are necessarily part of the future cost of manufacturing. Trouble-shooting charts for the equipment are helpful because they aid early detection and quick repair.
4. Production rates for the equipment should be known, as well as whether these rates are for continuous or intermittent production. Do not be trapped by average numbers; the machine rates and quantities must span all conditions and tolerances.
5. Does the machine have provisions for shutdown or power failure?
6. The control of adhesive temperature and the use of temperature indicators may be necessary for some adhesives.
7. Manual and setup operation should be possible.
8. Equipment operation should be as simple as possible. Simplicity makes training fast and avoids mistakes that hinder reliability.
9. When equipment breaks down, service backup will be necessary. Availability of a manufacturer's field service personnel, spare parts, schematic drawings, and parts lists all help shorten the amount of time the equipment is down.
10. Warranty coverage is important to anyone thinking of buying equipment. Are either or both the adhesive and equipment warranted to perform? Installation service should be available, as well as manuals for installation, repair, and operation.
11. Extreme care should be taken to make sure that the adhesive is fully compatible with all parts of the equipment. Adhesives can cause corrosion, swelling, and failure of certain types of metals, elastomers, and plastic parts. Anaerobic-radical curing adhesives can be destabilized by metals

and impurities in plastics, which cause curing in lines and valves. Equipment for these materials should always be coordinated with the manufacturers.

Joint Design and Surface Preparation

Joint design is an important factor in ensuring a strong bonded joint. There are two basic types of joints used with adhesive bonding: continuous-surface bonds and core-to-face bonds. With the former, both surfaces are the same size and shape. Also they are large surfaces in relation to the size of the parts. With the latter, one of the surfaces is significiantly smaller than the other. To increase the strength of adhesively bonded joints, it is important to design joints so that they are subjected primarily to shear or tension. Adhesively bonded joints do not perform well when subjected to peel or cleavage.

It is also important to properly prepare joints that are to be adhesively bonded. Proper surface preparation of a joint involves cleaning, etching, rinsing, and drying.

KEY TERMS AND PHRASES

Abrasion soldering
Adhesion
Arc brazing
Blanket brazing
Block brazing
Bonded sandwich construction
Conduction heating
Convection heating
Delayed-tack adhesives
Diffusion brazing
Dip brazing
Dip soldering
Electron beam brazing
Evaporative adhesives
Exothermic brazing
Expanded honeycomb core
Fabricated sandwich panel
Film adhesives
Focused radiation
Furnace brazing
Heat activated adhesives
Hot-melt adhesives
Hot plates
Induction brazing
Induction soldering
Infrared brazing
Inorganic adhesives
Jet soldering
Laser brazing
Laser soldering
Moisture-curing adhesives
Natural adhesives
Plural components
Pressure-sensitive adhesives
Radiation-curing adhesives
Radiation heating
Resistance brazing
Resistance soldering
Screen printing
Specially catalyzed adhesives
Spray gun soldering
Step brazing
Step soldering
Sweat soldering
Synthetic adhesives
Torch brazing
Ultrasonic soldering
Unfocused radiation
Vacuum impregnation
Wave soldering
Weldbonding

QUESTIONS FOR ADDITIONAL STUDY AND REVIEW

1. What are the most common applications of brazing?

2. List five advantages of brazing.

3. What are the limitations of brazing?

4. Describe the following brazing processes:

   - Torch brazing
   - Induction brazing
   - Dip brazing
   - Resistance brazing
   - Blanket brazing
   - Step brazing

5. Explain the major safety considerations to be observed when brazing.

6. What are the most common applications of soldering?

7. List four advantages of soldering.

8. What are the limitations of soldering?

9. Describe the following soldering processes:

   - Conduction soldering
   - Wave soldering
   - Vapor-phase soldering
   - Resistance soldering

10. What are the major safety considerations to be observed when soldering?

11. List four advantages of adhesive joining.

12. List three process limitations of adhesive joining.

13. Explain how adhesive joining is used in the following application areas:

    - Automotive
    - Food packaging
    - Structural
    - Aircraft

14. What are the three main categories of adhesive material?

15. Explain the advantages and limitations of hot-melt adhesives.

16. Explain the following applications methods:

    - Manual roller
    - Screen printing
    - Brushing
    - Troweling
    - Spraying
    - Vacuum impregnation

16

Automated Assembly

MAJOR TOPICS COVERED

- Overview of Automated Assembly
- Considerations for Automated Assembly
- Product Design for Automated Assembly
- Assembly Machines and Systems
- Parts Feeding, Orienting, and Positioning
- Joining and Fastening in Automated Assembly
- Inspection and Testing in Automated Assembly
- Safety in Automated Assembly

AUTOMATED ASSEMBLY

Assembly in the manufacturing process consists of putting together all the component parts and sub-assemblies of a given product, fastening, performing inspections and functional tests, labeling, separating good assemblies from bad, and packaging and/or preparing them for final use. Assembly is unique compared to the methods of manufacturing such as machining, grinding, and welding in that most of these processes involve only a few disciplines and possibly only one. Most of these nonassembly operations cannot be performed without the aid of equipment; thus the development of automatic methods has been

necessary rather than optional. Assembly, on the other hand, may involve in one machine many of the fastening methods, such as riveting, welding, screwdriving, and adhesive application, as well as automatic parts selection, probing, gaging, functional testing, labeling, and packaging. The state of the art in assembly operations has not reached the level of standardization; much manual work is still being performed in this area.

Assembly has traditionally been one of the highest areas of direct labor costs. In some cases, assembly accounts for 50% or more of manufacturing costs and typically 20-50%. However, closer cooperation between design and manufacturing engineers has resulted in reducing and in a few cases eliminating altogether the need for assembly. When assembly is required, improved design or redesign of products has simplified automated (semiautomatic or automatic) assembly.

Considerations for Automated Assembly

Before automated assembly is adopted, several factors should be considered. These include practicality of the process for automation, simulation for economic considerations and justification, management involvement, and labor relations.

Practicality of Automation

Determining the practicality of automated assembly requires careful evaluation of the following:

- The number of parts in assembly.
- Design of the parts with respect to producibility, assemblability, automatic handling, and testability (materials, forms, sizes, dimensional tolerances, and weights).
- Quality of parts to be assembled. Out-of-tolerance or defective parts can cause production losses and increased costs because of stoppages.
- Availability of qualified, technically competent personnel to be responsible for equipment operation.
- Total production and production-rate requirements.
- Product variations and frequency of design changes.
- Joining methods required.
- Assembly times and costs.
- Assembly line or system configuration, using simulation, including material handling.

The best candidates for successful and economical automated assembly are generally simple, small products having a fairly stable design life. Such products are usually required in relatively large volumes and have a high labor content and/or a high reject rate because of their manual assembly. However, the development of flexible, programmable, and robotic assembly systems (discussed subsequently in this chapter) can decrease production and product-life requirements.

Potential Advantages: Potential advantages resulting from assembly automation include the following:

1. Improved product quality, consistent product repeatability with fewer rejects, and a high degree of production reliability as a result of reducing or eliminating human errors. Component inspection and part testing during assembly prevents defective parts from being used. The consistently high-quality products obtained reduce liability and warranty costs.
2. Reduced manufacturing costs resulting from decreased labor requirements and increased productivity. Savings result from reductions in both direct and indirect labor.
3. Improved safety and better working conditions by removing operators from hazardous operations.
4. More efficient production scheduling (such as just-in-time techniques) and reduced inventory requirements because of the ability of automated assembly systems to respond immediately to production demands.
5. Reduced floor space requirements.

Product Design for Automated Assembly

Optimum design or redesign of a product and its components is essential for successful, efficient, and economical automatic assembly. Considerable amounts of money are often spent to automate the assembly of existing product designs when it would be much more economical to redesign the products to facilitate automatic assembly. Design for assembly (DFA) is being increasingly practiced because of the realization of potential production savings and better quality and improved reliability in the product.

Close cooperation is required between design and manufacturing engineers in evaluating a product design for improved assembly. The inherent capabilities and limitations of assembly operations should be considered during the early design or redesign stages. At the earliest possible design stages, it is also best to assess the parts for the ease with which they can be supplied and oriented. Assembly of various designs should be evaluated and compared.

Design for Simplification

The optimum product design is one that eliminates the need for assembly or reduces the number of parts to be assembled to a minimum. One simple example is illustrated in Fig. 16-1, which shows a single stamping that replaces a two-part assembly. Such designs usually reduce total product and assembly costs.

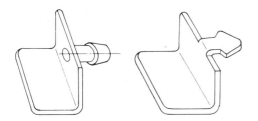

Figure 16-1   Two-part assembly (left) replaced by a simple stamping

When single-component products are impossible or uneconomical, the number of parts required should generally be kept as low as possible, and their complexity should be minimized. There are rare occasions, however, where it may be more economical to manufacture two or more pieces to replace one. The reason for minimizing the number of parts is to improve the remaining, more functional parts and to eliminate nonfunctional ones. To determine if a part can be eliminated, the following three questions should be answered:

1. Does the part move with respect to other parts?
2. Is the part made from a different material than the other parts?
3. Will the part require removal for product servicing?

An affirmative answer to any of these questions generally indicates that the part is required. Negative answers to all three questions indicate that the part may not be necessary and any function it performs may be able to be transferred to a more essential component.

Design for Ease of Automatic Assembly

Parts to be assembled automatically should be designed for ease of handling, feeding, orienting, positioning, and joining. A design checklist to facilitate automatic assembly is presented in Fig. 16-2.

Part configurations that can be easily oriented include the following:

1. Completely symmetrical parts such as spheres, cylinders, pins, and rods. Figure 16-3 illustrates some examples of how parts can be made symmetrical. In general, the lengths of cylindrical parts should be at least 25% longer or shorter than their diameters to facilitate feeding.
2. Substantially disproportionate parts, either with respect to weight or with respect to dimensions, such as headed screws, bolts, and rivets. The center of gravity should be near one end of each part to produce a tendency to naturally feed in one specific orientation. If this natural orientation is not the desired position, it is relatively easy to rotate the parts to the proper position.

Assembly Machines and Systems

A broad variety of machines and systems is available for automated assembly. A general outline of some of the concepts is shown in Fig. 16-4. In addition, combinations of these basic systems and flexible, robotic, and electronic assembly systems are discussed subsequently in this section.

Single-Station Assembly

Machines having a single workstation are used most extensively when a specific operation has to be performed many times on one or a few parts. Assembling many parts into a single unit, like

Keep number of parts to be assembled to a minimum

Make product and component designs as simple as possible

Provide a base or main body on which other parts can be assembled or, if possible, that can serve as its own fixture or work carrier

Provide locating surfaces or holes, orientation characteristics, and accessibility to all assembly areas when fixtures or work carriers are required

Design for optimum sequencing, with each part added from above if possible

Avoid need for expensive and time-consuming joining operations

Design components for easy handling, feeding, orienting, positioning, and joining:

    Keep center of gravity low

    Minimize number of orientations required

    Avoid designs that cause nesting, tangling, shingling, jamming, or wedging

    Design parts to be stiff and rigid, but not brittle or fragile

    Avoid designs that are subject to variations in humidity, temperature, pressure, magnetism, and static electricity

    Eliminate burrs and flash or design into areas that do not interfere with assembly

    Provide adequate strength and rigidity to withstand forces of assembly without bending or distortion

    Provide chamfers, tapers, radii, or other guiding surfaces and locating surfaces for loading and positioning

    Minimize the number of smooth finished surfaces that cannot be scratched or damaged

    Provide clearances for assembly tooling

Figure 16-2   Design checklist for automatic assembly

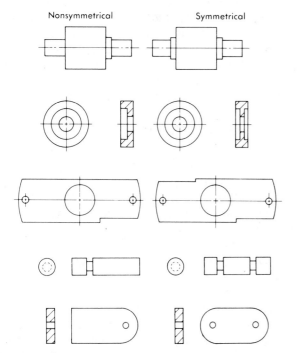

Figure 16-3   Parts made symmetrical for easier orientation

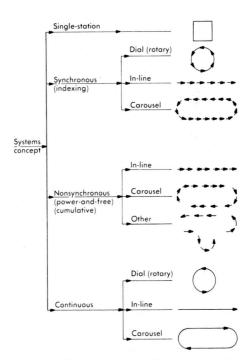

Figure 16-4   Basic concepts for automated assembly systems

inserting blades or buckets into turbine or compressor wheels, is a common application. These machines may also be used when a number of different operations have to be performed, if the required tooling is not too complicated. These machines are also incorporated into multistation assembly systems.

Synchronous Assembly Systems

Synchronous (indexing) assembly systems are available in dial (rotary), in-line, and carousel varieties. With these systems, all pallets or workpieces are moved at the same time and for the same distance. Because indexing intervals are determined by the slowest operation to be performed at any of the stations, operation time is the determining factor affecting production rate. Operators cannot vary the production rate, and a breakdown at any station causes the whole line to stop. By proper consideration to line balancing and parallel assembly operations, such downtime problems can be minimized.

Nonsynchronous Assembly Systems

Nonsynchronous transfer (accumultive or power-and-free type) assembly systems, with free or floating pallets or workpieces and independently operated individual stations, are being widely used where the times required to perform different operations vary greatly and for larger products having many components. Such machines have slower cycle rates than synchronous machines, but slower stations can be double or triple tooled to boost production. One major advantage of these so-called power-and-free systems is increased versatility. The individually actuated, independent stations operate only when a pallet, supplied on demand, is present and when manual and automatic operations can easily be combined. Different methods can be used to meet line balancing needs. For example, multiple loading, joining, or testing stations can be banked or sent down multiple tracks for longer operations, while shorter operations are done on a one-at-a-time basis. Nonsynchronous machines often have a lower initial cost, but require more controls (a set at each station) and generally require more space.

Continuous-Motion Systems

With continuous-motion systems, assembly operations are performed while the workpieces or pallets move at a constant speed and the workheads reciprocate. High production rates are possible because indexing time is eliminated. However, the cost and complexity of these systems are high because the workheads have to synchronize and move with the product being assembled. Applications for continuous-motion automated assembly are limited except for high-production uses in the packaging and bottling industries. The systems are, however, used for the manual assembly of large and heavy products, such as automobiles and refrigerators, with the operators moving with the products while performing their functions.

Dial (Rotary) Assembly

Dial or rotary index machines of synchronous design, one of the first types used for assembly, are still used for many applications. Workstations and tooling can be mounted on a central column or around the periphery of the indexing table. These machines are generally limited to small- and medium-sized lightweight assemblies requiring a relatively low number of operations that are not too complex; as the table diameter increases, its mass and complexity can become impractical. Another possible disadvantage is limited accessibility to the workheads and tooling. Also, servicing the indexing table and mechanism, as well as the controls, is difficult with center-column designs (see Fig. 16-5).

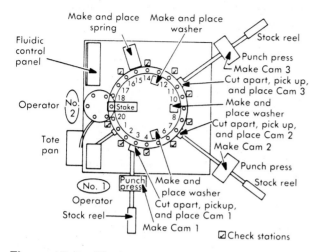

Figure 16-5 Block diagram of a 20-station dial index machine

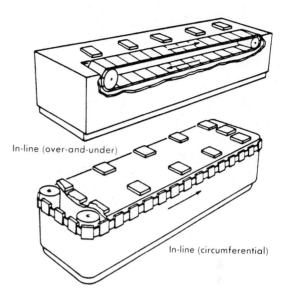

Figure 16-6 In-line indexing assembly machine

In-Line Systems

In-line assembly machines are used in synchronous (indexing), nonsynchronous (accumulative or power-and-free), and continuous designs. In-line indexing assembly machines can be of the wraparound (circumferential) or over-and-under type (see Fig. 16-6) or of the conventional transfer-machine type. In the over-and-under type, workholding pallets or platens move horizontally in a straight path and when empty return to the loading station on a conveyor under the machine. In the wraparound type, the work moves around the periphery of the machine in an oval, rectangular, or square path.

Carousel Machines

Similar to the synchronous in-line assembly systems just discussed, carousel machines consist of a series of fixtures or holding devices attached to a roller chain, precision chain, or steel belts or moved by fingers from one workstation to another. However, the carousel machine moves the work in a horizontal plane through a rectangular path, or some

variation of the same, returning the pallets to their starting point. All parts are indexed at the same time for the same distance on either a timed or an on-demand basis.

Advantages of the carousel include utilization of all the fixtures in the system because none are returned below, possibility of more operations in the same space, operations can be performed on all sides of the machine, and workpieces are returned to the starting point.

Flexible Assembly Systems

Greater flexibility from automated assembly systems is essential because of continuing increases in product differences resulting from market demands and reductions in product life-cycles. Requirements for high-volume, long-running production are decreasing.

Considerable development work has been done and is continuing with respect to more flexible assembly systems for handling smaller lot sizes and a wider variety of products. The objectives of such systems include increased cost-effectiveness and reduced obsolescence of capital equipment expenditures.

One developing concept is the use of automatic guided vehicles (AGVs), which are currently being applied to low-volume large assemblies such as automotive and appliance products. The vehicles are usually self-powered electrically or by compressed air. They electrically follow cables buried in the floor and are computer controlled for any required paths to various assembly stations. The cost of AGVs and their control systems limit their application to large assemblies required in low volumes. Combining AGVs with programmable workstations offers considerable flexibility.

Two major classifications of flexible assembly systems are programmable and adaptable. Programmable and adaptable systems include those using industrial robots, which are discussed next in this section.

Dedicated, Flexible, and Adaptable Systems:

Dedicated, special-purpose assembly systems are designed to assemble specific products with few or no modifications. They generally require high-volume production for economic justification. Flexible assembly systems are capable of assembling more than one product model or models. Truly flexible systems can assemble on demand from an ensemble of different but similar products without tooling changeovers. Other systems may require only extra fixtures or different pallets, changes in tooling, and, for some applications, extra stations. These systems can be economically justified with lower production requirements.

Adaptable systems that are totally automated and capable of assembling any variety of products are difficult to implement and are rare today, but they are expected to become more common in the future. They require both passive controls for programming and active controls (sensors) capable of decision and control tasks. A mixture of manual, dedicated, and flexible methods seems to be one promising solution for adaptable assembly systems.

Degrees of Flexibility:

There are many ways of obtaining various degrees of flexibility in assembly, including the following:

- Increased use of manual operations.
- Design or redesign of products and components for commonality to facilitate flexible assembly.
- Use of standard components and subassemblies whenever possible.
- Use of modular systems for fast changeover and conversion to future requirements.
- Use of programmable workheads that can perform a number of operations, with different programs for each product to be assembled.
- Provision of redundant modules, with different combinations of modules activated to assemble various products.
- Provision of additional space and/or idle stations for possible future design changes and production requirements.
- Use of universal or adjustable workholders (pallets) to simplify changeover.
- Use of coded pallets with programmable controller or computer control.
- Provision of buffer storage and repair loops.
- Use of automatic guided vehicles (AGVs) for material handling because they are easier to reprogram than changing conveyors.
- Use of versatile feeding and orienting devices (discussed later in this chapter) that can be readjusted to handle different sizes and shapes of parts.
- Provision of interchangeable feeders; multiple feeders at required stations, with provisions for selecting the one needed; or interchangeable feeders that can be plugged into the assembly system.
- Use of more magazines, containing preoriented parts, that can be interchanged on assembly systems.
- Use of advanced controls, such as microprocessor-based programmable controllers or computer systems, instead of hard-wired inflexible controls.

Robotic Assembly Systems

Industrial robots are programmable manipulators that perform a variety of tasks. An effective robotic assembly system requires careful consideration of the delivery of components to the workstations, component feeding and orienting, robot end effectors, sensing requirements, and system controls.

Robot characteristics that are especially suited for assembly applications include the following:

- High accuracy and repeatability in both point-to-point and path conformance.
- Reliability, flexibility, and dexterity.
- Capability for a large number of inputs and outputs.
- Sensory communications and system communications capability.
- Off-line programmability with adaptability to a high-level language.
- Memory capacity for program storage.

Accuracy is the precision with which the robot moves from its home position to a designated coordinate location. It is often expressed as a distance differential between the point where the robot manipulator actually is and the point that the controller indicates. Robot accuracy is affected not only by resolution of the controller and inherent mechanical inaccuracy of the robot, but also by speed, payload, and direction of approach and by position within the work volume. A claimed accuracy of ± 0.004″ (0.10 mm) is common and ± 0.002″ (0.05 mm) is becoming available.

Repeatability is a measure of the precision of the robot to return to a predefined, programmed point on demand, cycle after cycle. It is expressed as a distance differential when the robot arm returns to a taught point within a certain range of speeds and payloads. A repeatability of ± 0.002″ (0.05 mm) is common and ± 0.001″ (0.03 mm) is becoming available. Figure 16-7 is an example of a robotic assembly system.

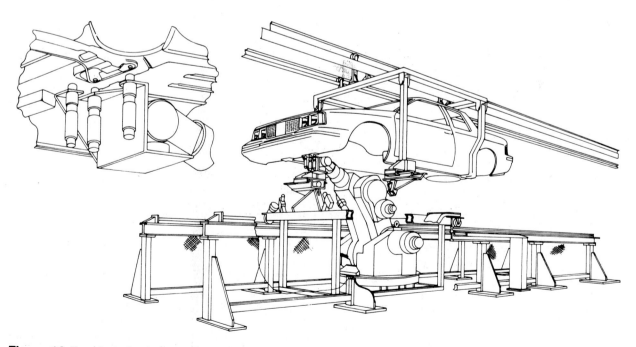

Figure 16-7   Underbody bolt securing using a vision-guided robot

Automated Electronic Assembly

Most electronic assemblies consist of inserting components into or placing them onto printed circuit boards (PCBs) or substrates. Components assembled include the following:

- Axial lead components that have a wire lead extending out from the end(s) along its axis. These include resistors, capacitors, diodes, inductors, and other electronic devices normally supplied on lead tape.
- Integrated circuits (ICs) contained in dual in-line packages (DIPs). They have circuit leads or pins extending symmetrically downward from their bodies and are normally supplied in plastic stick magazines.
- Radial lead components that have their leads coming off the peripheries. These include transistors, disc capacitors, ICs, potentiometers, and light-emitting diodes (LEDs).
- Small outline transistors (SOTs) that have their three leads bent outward, the two outer leads bent in one direction and the center lead bent in the opposite direction.
- Odd-shaped electronic or electromechanical components such as connectors, transformers, relays, and switches.
- Surface-mounted devices (SMDs) are leaded or leadless electronic devices that are soldered directly to pads on the surfaces of PCBs, as opposed to through-hole insertion mounting.

Transistors that incorporate metal-oxide-silicon semiconductor layers are referred to as MOS devices. A microelectronic circuit fabricated from a single semiconductor IC having the equivalent of more than 10,000 individual gates or active circuit functions is called a medium-scale integration (MSI) chip. Arrays of ICs on a single substrate that comprise 100,000 or more individual active circuit functions or gates are referred to as large-scale integration (LSI) packages.

Automation of printed circuit board assemblies has progressed from manually formed component leads, with blueprint-guided insertion, to fully automatic insertion machines and robotic systems. All types of components are now being sequentially inserted through a continuous array of in-line machines or through groups of machines bridged by material handling equipment. Today's electronic manufacturing facility is also equipped with a wide range of automated test equipment, controlled by computers. See Fig. 16-8.

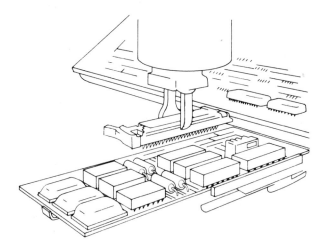

Figure 16-8   Connectors and odd-shaped components can be placed by robots

Parts Feeding, Orienting, and Positioning

The importance of automatic feeding, orienting, and positioning of parts to be assembled cannot be overemphasized. Without automation equipment to perform these functions, a large percentage of automated assembly would be economically impractical. Even when assembly systems are economically feasible, a major cost of tooling is for orienting, feeding, and placing components from a bulk condition.

Bulk-Storage Feeders: Bulk-storage feeders provide storage and maintain a supply of parts for orienting and feeding. Major types include overhead gravity-feed storage hoppers and elevating-belt bulk feeders. Selection of a specific type requires consideration of part size(s), production requirements, the method to be used for loading the bulk storage unit, floor space and height limitations, frequency of changeover if more than one part is involved, and the condition of the parts—dry or wet, clean or dirty, soft or hard, and the presence of burrs, flash, or chips.

After considering all pertinent factors, the minimum bulk-load capacity is recommended because excessive storage in hoppers or bins can make maintenance and changeover cumbersome. Level sensors with warning signals or lights are available to detect a low quantity of parts in the hoppers or bins. Means for washing, cooling, or lubricating parts in the hoppers or bins are also available.

Vibratory Bowl Feeders: Vibratory bowl feeders are one of the most common types of devices for feeding and orienting small cylindrical, flat, or other shaped components. By the use of directional vibration, randomly oriented parts loaded in bulk into bowls are caused to climb gently ramped tracks attached to and encircling the inner walls of the bowls. The bowls are mounted on vibratory drive units that cause the bowls to reciprocate vertically while oscillating horizontally. The bottoms of the bowls are generally made slightly convex or conical to assist the outward movement of the components as they rotate around the bowl under the influence of the vibration.

Parts in the vibrating bowls move uniformly, largely independent of adjacent parts. The fact that the parts are conveyed in a controlled manner, rather than by rolling or sliding, makes these feeders one of the most versatile types for orienting parts having relatively complex geometric shapes. The gentle feeding action permits many fragile parts to be fed and enhances separation of nested and tangled parts. See Fig. 16-9 and 16-10.

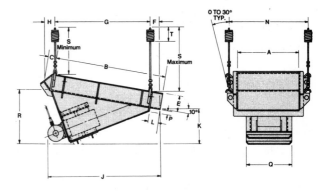

Figure 16-9   Parts feeder *(Courtesy of FMC Corporation, Material Handling Equipment Division)*

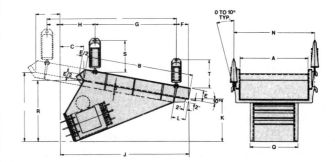

Figure 16-10   Parts Feeder *(Courtesy of FMC Corporation, Material Handling Equipment Division)*

Nonvibratory Hopper Feeders: A wide variety of nonvibratory hopper feeders are used for supplying parts to assembly operations. Some of the more common types are discussed in this section.

Centrifugal feeders. In this type of feeder, the centrifugal and gravity forces resulting from the rotation of a slightly conical disc in the bottom of a stationary hopper (bowl) causes the parts to slide to the periphery of the hopper. They are then carried by the disc to an escapement gate or profile where they are discharged in a single line. Smaller diameter centrifugal feeders now available are replacing some vibratory feeders.

Centerboard hopper feeders. With these feeders (see Fig. 16-11), a centerboard is arranged to be

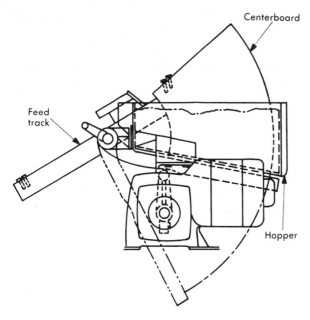

Figure 16-11   Centerboard hopper feeder

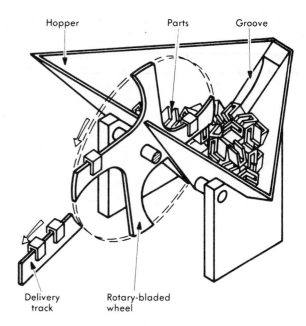

Figure 16-12   Rotary-bladed wheel lifts parts from fixed hopper and drops them on track

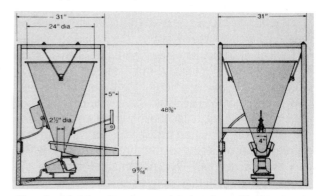

Figure 16-13   Reciprocating feeders *(Courtesy of FMC Corporation, Material Handling Equipment Division)*

alternately raised and lowered through a fixed hopper, usually having its base sloping toward the centerboard. Some of the parts in the hopper, properly oriented to fit the shaped upper edge of the centerboard, will stay on and at the top position, slide or roll off into a feed track. With a deeply slotted centerboard or two adjacent centerboards (spaced apart to receive the bodies of the parts), these feeders can handle long-headed pieces satisfactorily.

Bladed or hooked wheels. With these feeders, a rotary wheel with blades or hooks is used to feed parts from a fixed hopper. In the design shown in Fig. 16-12, a rotating bladed wheel (paddle wheel) causes some parts to fall into a shaped groove in the bottom of the hopper. These oriented parts are raised by the blades and slide onto a feed track. In some designs, the parts slide into tracks from the hoppers without being lifted. Other feeder designs have hooks projecting from the rotating wheel to enter the open ends of cup-shaped parts, lift the parts from the hopper, and drop them into delivery chutes.

Reciprocating feeders. These feeders (see Fig. 16-13) are used primarily for handling balls or

symmetrical cylinders of small size, although end-for-end orienting is sometimes performed outside the hopper. Commonly, a tube exit chute is reciprocated through parts held in a funnel-shaped receptacle. Often the tube is stationary and the parts holder is reciprocated. Bearing balls and rolls are fed through multiple tubes for assembly. Reciprocating blade-type hoppers pick up headed parts on the upper end of a reciprocating blade and elevate them to a stationary gravity track. As the blade stops at the top of its upward travel, the parts slide off onto the external chute where orienting is performed.

Rotary disc hoppers. These feeders usually have one feature in common. A rotating disc or sleeve carrying peripheral exit gates allows parts properly oriented to pass the gates to a chute section. The simplest of these is the pin gate—so called because the gates are pins, shaped or straight. Pin gates are used for fast feeding or simple parts having diameters greater than their length. Rotary hoppers can be designed in endless variety. They may operate vertically, inclined, or horizontally; may have single or multiple rows of exit gates; and may be driven steadily or intermittently.

Pocket hoppers. Pocket hoppers (see Fig. 16-14) are frequently used to count batches of balls or small rollers and may be arranged with a rotating or indexing plate for automatic feeding. Pockets arranged on the periphery of a drum are used to feed multiple chutes with a time succession of simple parts. Mold cavities on a moving belt are loaded with pop sticks. Rotating discs with shaped pockets are often mounted at an angle so the pocket is moved through a pile of parts

and then discharged at or near the high point of the revolution, either through an opening of the chute into which it falls or by being wiped off and guided into a side chute. Fast-feeding hoppers of the latter type are used in large quantities for feeding buttons.

Tumbling barrels and drums. These feeders are often used for parts susceptible to tangling or nesting and dirty parts, but they are not suitable for fragile parts or those that have been hardened and finish ground. The feeders carry parts in a rotating barrel or drum so arranged with vanes or buckets as to lift the parts and drop them on or into various orienting or chute arrangements. Basically, a drum feeder is a means to recirculate parts, but it is very versatile because special orienting means to suit most parts can be used. Parts are subject to a tumbling action and by use of a gap between drum and pan or by screen sections in the drum much debris such as dirt or chips can be eliminated in the hopper.

Drum hoppers have large capacity for their size and can be lined with plastic, fiberglass, or bonded neoprene. Although they can easily be baffled to reduce the dropping distance of parts, they are not advisable for fragile parts. Drum hoppers do not always provide uniformly high feed rates and tend to be noisy. They are recommended for tangling parts and for applications requiring multiple chutes, high delivery rates, complicated or positive orienting, and large capacity.

Feed Tracks: Feed tracks are used to deliver properly oriented parts into the proper positions to be assembled. They can also serve as a buffer storage of oriented parts to allow production to continue when a feeder jam or parts shortage exists. It is generally preferable to have straight feed tracks, and with proper machine planning, curved tracks can usually be avoided. The tracks are arranged to support and guide parts and to maintain their orientation. Some parts cannot be confined and fed by simple feed tracks because of thin edges wedging or overlapping tendencies, some parts can be moved only in a straight line and require transfer or other means to change direction or position, and some parts will not retain a preferred orientation while

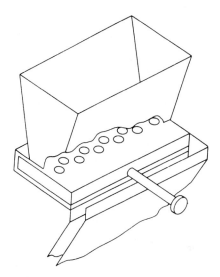

Figure 16-14   Simple form of pocket hopper

moving along feeder tracks. Parts transfer means are too often considered minor and unimportant segments of automated assembly systems; however, improperly designed tracks can make an otherwise efficient system a total failure. Before specifying feeder requirements, a comprehensive study should be made of part characteristics.

Positioning (Placing) and Inserting Devices:

Most automated assembly operations require that one properly oriented part, or possibly several parts, be transferred from a magazine, feed track, or conveyor to a predetermined point (nest, pallet, or previously assembled parts) where it is assembled. The placement mechanism may vary in complexity from a simple mechanical transfer device to a programmable industrial robot. Inserting can vary from simply dropping parts into place by gravity

(generally unreliable) to the use of powered workheads. The type of placement device selected will depend on the size and shape of the parts, the distance the parts have to be transferred, the placement accuracy required, the complexity of the transfer motion, and production rate requirements (see Fig. 16-15).

Basic rules for efficient parts positioning include the following:

- Accurate and positive parts placement is preferable to gravity fall.
- Actuation means should be consistent and controllable.
- Checks for parts presence and completion of strokes are desirable to prevent jams and to minimize the production of improper assemblies.
- Synchronization with travel of nest, pallet, or assembly and the assembly operation.

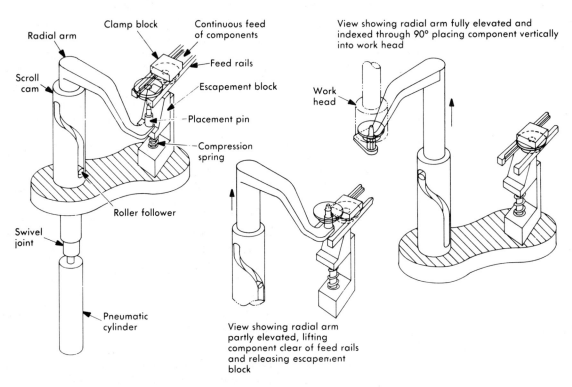

Figure 16-15   Unit designed for placing flanged bushings with lift-swing-lift motions

Parts Detectors: To prevent jamming and provide optimum efficiency in automated assembly, the presence of components must be verified at the point of assembly. Various methods used for parts detection include electric, electromechanical, air or vacuum, optical, and other devices or sensors of both the contact and noncontact types. Various sensors are discussed in the preceding section on automated robotic assembly.

In-Process Storage: Many different devices are used for temporary in-process storage of parts. Elevating storage feeders commonly serve the storage function and also provide elevation to the parts for passing on to the next assembly operation in oriented condition. Spiral-type conveyors and vibrating banking towers are also popular because they retain orientation of the parts while providing a substantial float between operations and because they release parts to subsequent operations on demand. Stacker cranes, which can be made high to utilize overhead space and completely automatic to store or supply parts on demand, are also used.

Joining and Fastening in Automated Assembly

It is desirable to design or redesign products to facilitate automated assembly, reduce the number of components to be assembled, and, when possible, eliminate or minimize the need for joining and fastening operations. Although snap and press fits can often be made as part of the normal machine functions, many assemblies require the use of joining and fastening processes. When required, joining and fastening operations should generally be performed at separate stations, preceded by devices that automatically check the presence and position of the components.

Practically every known method of joining and fastening is being performed on assembly machines.

Selection of a particular joining or fastening method for a specific application depends on several factors, including the following:

- The materials to be joined.
- Size, weight, and geometry of the components to be assembled.
- Joint designs and accessibility.
- Functional requirements of the assembled product, including strength, reliability, environment, appearance, and whether it has to be dismantled for maintenance or repair.
- Production requirements (rate and total).
- Edge and surface preparations necessary.
- Adaptability and compatibility of the joining method to automation, and effects on joint properties.
- Available equipment.
- Tooling requirements.
- Costs.
- Safety considerations.

Shrink and Expansion Fits: High joint strength and holding power are attained with shrink and expansion fits without the need for separate fasteners. Such fits are obtained by eliminating interference between two parts during assembly by heating or cooling the parts to change their dimensions.

Induction heating units are commonly used to expand holes and arbors as pressure units or workhead mechanisms push mating components into the holes. Electrical resistance units are being used to heat and hot upset anchor pins to mating components. Magnetic pulse forming is being used to automatically shrink copper rings for retaining rubber seals on ball-joint housings for automotive suspension systems.

Integral Fasteners: Integral fasteners are formed in areas of components that interfere or interlock with other areas of assemblies, thus eliminating the need for separate fasteners. These fasteners are commonly used for assembling sheet metal products with lanced or formed tabs, extruded holes, embossed flanges and protrusions, seams, crimps, beads, and dimples.

Injected Metal Assembly: In injected metal assembly, pressure die casting is used to inject molten metal for the permanent assembly of components.

As cooling and solidification occur, shrinkage locks the injected metal into undercuts, ridges, grooves, knurls, or keys in the parts being joined.

In a related process, thermoplastic resin (nylon mixed with chopped glass fibers) is being automatically injection molded on assembly machines to form bearing retaining rings on automotive propeller shafts. Vibratory bowls feed a predetermined amount of plastic pellets into the injection heads.

Threaded Fasteners:

Threaded fasteners include screws, bolts, studs, nuts, and similar components having external or internal threads. They are available in a wide variety of types, sizes, and strengths to suit individual requirements for different joints and assembly designs. The required functions for threaded fasteners should be carefully evaluated in automated assembly. They are commonly used for load-carrying requirements and especially when disassembly and reassembly are necessary.

Selection of the proper type of threaded fastener can facilitate automated assembly. For example, cone and oval-point screws with symmetrical driving heads are easier to insert because they tend to centralize themselves in holes. With self-tapping screws, thread-forming types are generally better than thread-cutting types for automated assembly because they do not produce chips that could interfere with feeding and orienting.

Assembly of threaded fasteners requires the application of torque and rotation. Proper tightening (tensioning) and control of torque is done in several ways. Both hand- and power-operated wrenches, nutrunners, and screwdrivers are used, the choice between hand and power depending primarily on production requirements. Multispindle nutrunners are used extensively for high-production applications. Industrial robots are also being used for the assembly of some threaded fasteners.

Riveting:

Rivets are unthreaded, permanent fasteners available in solid, semitubular, tubular, compression, split, and special types. They are used for fastening two or more pieces together by passing their bodies through holes in the pieces and then clinching or forming a second head on the body end. Riveting is easily adapted to automated assembly, and the rivets can be installed economically and rapidly.

Clinching, setting, or driving of rivets is commonly done by impact peening with a succession of blows, compression squeezing, or a combination of compression and rolling or spinning. On automatic riveting machines, rivets are fed from hoppers and clinched between a driver and a die. Automatic drilling and riveting machines are being used by the aircraft industry, and industrial robots are employed for some riveting applications. Orbital, radial, and electromagnetic riveting are other riveting methods.

Eyeleting:

Eyelets are thin-walled, unthreaded, tubular fasteners having a flange or formed head on one end. They differ from rivets in that their bores extend completely through the fasteners. Eyelets are used to assemble light-gage parts and often serve the dual function of feeding wires through an assembly and holding the assembly together. They can be easily applied in automated assembly with low costs and high production rates.

Eyelets are set (clinched) by forcing their small diameter ends against dies that curl or funnel the edges and clinch the eyelets against the workpieces. Eyeleting machines are similar in operation to riveting machines. Semiautomatic and automatic machines are available with special positioning and feeding devices for single or multiple settings.

Stitching and Stapling:

Stitching and stapling are used for many automated assemblies. Applications are broad with respect to the thickness and materials that can be joined. Wood, paper, fiberglass, plastics, cloth, and even thin metals can be joined by stapling. Stitches are formed on the machines that apply them, while staples are preformed and applied from strips, generally with pneumatic tools. Wire stitching machines feed accurate lengths of wire from a coil, cut and form the wire into U-shaped stitches, and drive them through the materials to be joined.

Other Mechanical Fasteners: Other mechanical fasteners often used in automated assembly include retaining (snap) rings, pins of various shapes and types, and washers—flat (plain), spring, and special-purpose.

Welding: Many of the numerous welding methods are used for automated assembly. These include both fusion and solid-state processes.

Arc welding. Arc welding processes commonly used for automated assembly include gas tungsten arc (GTAW or TIG), gas metal arc (GMAW or MIG), flux-cored arc (FCAW), submerged arc (SAW), stud (SW), and plasma arc welding (PAW). Possible problems include proper venting and removal of gases and fluxes and selection of proper heat-resistant materials for fixtures. Shields are generally required for protection from flash and spatter. Gas metal arc welding is the predominant process used for robotic assembly.

Resistance welding. Resistance welding is often desirable for automated assembly because it eliminates the need for filler metals, inert gases, and other materials. Possible problems include electrode and fixture wear and the need for good controls and monitoring. Demagnetizing may be necessary for some assemblies and workholding pallets. For electronic applications, surface cleanliness prior to welding is critical.

Resistance spot welding is especially adaptable to high-speed automated assembly. Fully automatic, multigun spot welders are used extensively for high-production applications. Industrial robots are being used to position and manipulate spot welding guns automatically. Projection welding is also very adaptable to automation and is used extensively to attach mechanical fasteners and when multiple welds must be made simultaneously.

Electron beam welding. Electron beam welding is adaptable to automated assembly, and both semiautomated and fully automated partial vacuum and nonvacuum systems are being used. Advantages include fast speeds, high-quality welds, and the capability of welding prefinished components with minimum distortion.

Laser beam welding. The laser beam welding process is easily integrated into automated assembly systems. Advantages include the ability to generate localized, high-power densities without mechanical contact, thus eliminating contamination and tool wear. Robots equipped with lasers are being used to reach into difficult areas and to provide multiaxis capabilities. Possible limitations include space requirements and the need for properly guarding the laser path for operator protection.

Ultrasonic welding. In ultrasonic welding, vibration transmitted to the interface of parts to be joined causes friction and forms a bond. The process is easily automated and is being used to join similar and dissimilar metals, primarily aluminum and copper alloys, and thermoplastics. Other applications of ultrasonics include the following:

- Insertion—encapsulating metal components such as threaded inserts or studs into thermoplastics.
- Staking or heading—forming plastics over and/or around other components.
- Activating, reactivating, or curing adhesives.
- Cutting and/or sealing synthetic materials.
- Crimping or piercing two pieces to hold them together.

Figures 16-16, 16-17, 16-18, and 16-19 are examples of modern welding equipment.

Figure 16-16   Robotic welding *(Courtesy of Cincinnati Milacron Marketing Corp.)*

Figure 16-17   Laser and electron beam welding machine *(Courtesy of EBTEC EAST)*

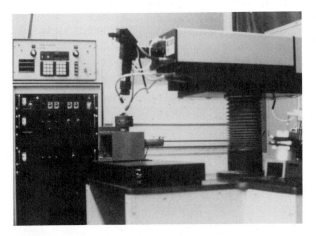

Figure 16-18   Laser and electron beam welding machine *(Courtesy of EBTEC EAST)*

Figure 16-19   Laser and electron beam welding machine *(Courtesy of EBTEC EAST)*

applications. Various methods of heating are described in Chapter 15. In the production of printed circuit boards, automated systems are equipped with conveyors to transport the boards through fluxing, preheating, and wave soldering operations. Robotic versions of these processes provide additional flexibility.

Soldering and Brazing: The soldering and brazing processes can be readily automated. Advantages include the capability of producing leaktight joints and joints in inaccessible areas. Possible limitations include the need for closely fitting joints with clean surfaces and close control of temperatures and time cycles. The use of preformed fillers and the automatic application of pastes and fluxes are common in automated assembly. Rotary index tables and in-line systems are used for such

Adhesive Joining: Advantages of adhesive joining include the uniform distribution of stresses over large areas, the ability to join both thin and thick parts, and reduced assembly weights. Possible limitations include the need for carefully selecting an adhesive to suit the specific application, rigid process control, and safety precautions. Also, surface preparation and cleaning are generally required, and precautions must be taken to prevent contamination of fixtures, feed tracks, and placement units.

Heat, pressure, or long cure times are required with some adhesives, but most can be cured rapidly. Some adhesives cure at room temperature and others can be heat cured after assembly. Solvent and catalyst accelerators are also used to speed curing. The advent of radiation curing with ultraviolet (UV) light, electron beam (EB), or gamma radiation has reduced curing time, facilitated automation, and avoided air pollution.

Although adhesives and sealants are still being applied manually for many applications, semiautomatic and automatic machines are also being used. The development of improved dispensers has facilitated the use of adhesive bonding in automated assembly. Optical sensors are employed for some applications to detect the presence of adhesives or sealants. Industrial robot applicators are being used to manipulate dispensing guns and sometimes to move the workpieces. Multiple guns can be used on a single robot.

Auxiliary Operations: Secondary operations sometimes performed on automated assembly machines or systems include counting, lubricating, marking, and, in some cases, packaging. Marking is done by roll or magnetic means, stamping, the application of paint or ink, with lasers, or the application of labels. Packaging, often done separately, may consist of closing, sealing, vacuum packing, and wrapping operations. Unloading of automated assembly machines and systems commonly consists of ejection to bulk storage.

Inspection and Testing in Automated Assembly

Inspection for automated assembly equipment is a critical and integral function that fills multiple roles. In addition to satisfying product assurance needs through dedicated inspection tests, an additional benefit from inspection is the monitoring of each function of the automated equipment. Every feeding operation and many of the work operations in automated assembly equipment must be tested immediately after the task is performed to ensure the effective operation of the assembly process. Furthermore, each machine motion that is not a mechanical link to the central driveshaft of the base machine

should be considered as a candidate for a probable functional test point.

A wide variety of equipment is used for inspecting and testing assembly machine operations. This category of equipment includes probes, mechanical and electromechanical switches, proximity and magnetic devices, capacitance and inductance units, and pressure and vacuum devices. More recently, optical and photoelectric gaging, eddy-current devices, lasers, robots, and machine vision have been increasingly applied for inspection.

Inspection for selective assembly is performed in some applications, with the gaging equipment used to select parts for assembly on the basis of fit rather than absolute size. In one application, the depths of pockets in pump bodies and the thickness of gears are automatically inspected, and the parts then segregated into one of six classes. Next, pivoting arms automatically transfer external gears of the proper thickness into position, where they are pressed into mesh with internal gears.

With quality control programs, there is a need for documentation of product parameters. This generally involves serialization or date coding to provide proof that the products meet specifications. The procedure reduces the possibility of product recalls and product liability lawsuits. Most modern inspection equipment provides an electrical signal for recording the appropriate parameters.

Controls for Automated Assembly

A variety of control products are being used for the automation of assembly operations. Primary objectives of the controls include maintaining or improving product quality, increasing output, reducing inventories and scrap, and creating and processing production information (database). Specific requirements of the controls for integrated automation include the following:

- Determine where (and what) each part to be assembled is, track the part from station to station, and know the specific operation to be performed at each station.

- Evaluate the overall quality of the parts, subassemblies, or assembled products at each station, with provisions for rejecting them if necessary.
- Verify the operations performed and product quality attained at each station.
- Prepare for and accommodate operational and/or product changes on-line.

Hierarchical Control Systems:
Depending on the degree of sophistication needed or desired, automated control systems can be provided in a hierarchy of interactive levels. Cam-actuated assembly machines generally require a minimum of control sophistication. Power-and-free machines having independent stations need more extensive control systems. Flexible assembly systems require programmable controls. Integrated automation systems involve the coordinated operation of multiple microprocessor-based controls and rely on computer-based production scheduling and data management linked by interactive communication networks.

Modern hierarchical control systems, exclusive of the actual mechanical elements, can include the following:

1. *Programmable logic controllers.*
2. *Motion or robot controls.*
3. *Computers.*
4. *Communication systems.*

Machine Controls:
Essential to any automated assembly machine and forming the base for hierarchical control systems are real-time control devices that interface to programmable controllers and other control devices. These devices are generally connected via input/output (I/O) modules that interface limit switches, pushbuttons, proximity switches, solenoids, motor starters, pilot lights, and other sensing and drive devices. The devices typically involve digital I/O points or on/off controls.

A more sophisticated category of I/O modules offers not only interface to real-time devices but also some conversion and communication capabilities. An analog input module in which a varying voltage or current is converted to a digital number is an example. New developments in analog I/O devices include modules that read, convert, and forward signals dealing with level, temperature, speed, light intensity, position, and wire faults and offer high levels of common-mode isolation. With the use of a concept called Block Transfer and a minimum of programming, large amounts of information can be quickly and efficiently transferred between I/O modules and the processors of programmable controllers.

Station Controls:
Also essential to any automated assembly machine and forming a next higher level for hierarchical control systems are devices for real-time control at the station level. This is a more complex level and generally involves the use of intelligent I/O modules, real-time, logic-solving programmable controllers, and various motion control systems.

Intelligent I/O modules. These modules are called intelligent because they preprocess information—looking at input status, providing control algorithms and solutions, and directly controlling outputs, all as an integral part of a programmable controller system. Developments have increased the capabilities of intelligent I/O modules. These capabilities include the following:

- Motion control offering closed-loop servocontrol, open-loop stepper-motor positioning, and even specialized control of clutches and brakes for mechanical presses.
- Proportional, integral, derivative (PID) control implementation. Closed-loop controls can be executed independently of the programmable controller scans.
- High-speed logic control, providing high-speed through put, reading inputs, making decisions, and controlling outputs independent of the scan.
- Direct communication capability. An intelligent I/O module can divide control among one or a number of processors on small programmable controllers that report to a larger (supervisory) controller.
- User-written BASIC programs can be run on specially designed intelligent I/O modules and implemented independent of processor memory.

Programmable logic controllers. Operation at the station level involves single or multiple programmable controllers performing real-time decision making based on input from I/O modules. These devices are available in small, medium, and large sizes.

Even the smallest programmable controllers are now considered cost-effective replacements for many electromechanical relays, timers, hard-wired logic, and drum controllers. Advantages include the superiority of solid-state configuration, reduced wiring and panel space requirements, and increased flexibility and cost savings. In addition to ladder logic for machine control, they offer additional capabilities such as floating-point mathematics, interactive report generation, data manipulation instructions, and other features for performing computation and data acquisition functions. The devices also have peripheral interfaces such as CRTs and color graphics systems that allow interaction with the machine or process under the control of the programmable controller.

Motion controls. Numerous developments in microprocessor-based motion controls allow many improvements in productivity, including reduced inventories, smaller lot sizes, and higher product quality. Some of the motion control systems used primarily for assembly stations include the following:

1. *One- to three-axis motion controllers for velocity and position control.* These devices can be operated in a nonintegrated environment and are usually matched to stand-alone machines. Programming of these devices is typically done through keyboards integral with the units.
2. *Stepper or servopositioning modules.* These devices are integral parts of many programmable controller-based systems. They provide distributed control for point-to-point positioning applications. The units are typically located in the remote I/O racks of systems for distribution of a wide range of motion control functionality within the system.
3. *Synchronized axis controllers.* This classification covers a large group of sophisticated velocity/position controllers with synchronized axis and multiaxis capabilities, often controlling several axes simultaneously. They include devices that can follow complex paths generated by either a host computer or taught to them by teach pendants; examples include CNCs and robot controls. They offer from 2 to 17 axes of control and generally feature color graphics displays of motion paths and a variety of operator interface functions. In addition to interfacing with power amplifiers and feedback devices, they communicate with programmable controllers, other control devices, and/or host computers via local area networks such as the Data Highway.
4. *Power amplifiers.* These controllers provide the power to drive servomotors for actual process motions. They are available in a wide range based on modularity, power conversion types, and ratings.
5. *Integrated controllers.* Integrated velocity/position controllers with power amplifiers are a combination of technologies for use on motors integrated into a system. These systems tend to be more application specific; a typical example is a single-axis slide position controller used for transfer functions.

Cell Controls: At the cell level, control emphasis shifts to the coordination of multiple stations, with the level of control moving upward from real-time operations to supervisory tasks. High-capability supervisory programmable controllers or computers use either Data Highway or peer-to-peer communications to direct the operations of station-level programmable controllers or computers. This is the basis for the concept of distributed control and computer-integrated manufacturing (CIM).

Distributed control. With distributed control, supervisory programmable controllers or computers oversee networks of smaller controllers located close to the actual operation over which they are exerting real-time control. Such a system reduces the severity of a particular station becoming inoperative and increases both system flexibility and fault-isolation time.

Beginning with the supervisory functions of the cell level, greater importance becomes placed on information generation and operator interface. Documentation of the program and I/O wiring, for example, is extremely critical. At the top of the cell level, the focus turns toward linking the databases that support plant management with the real-time activities that occur on the plant floor. This task represents the foundation of the concept called area management.

Area management. Area controllers are the tools through which the database-to-real-time link can be implemented. Cell-level industrial management systems are interfaced with station-level controllers. Designed to operate in industrial environments, area controllers gather data for transmission over local area networks (LANs) such as a Data Highway. They then interpret the collected data and communicate it, both horizontally to other area controllers and upward to assembly center and plant computers over a broad-band communications network. Information requirements and production directions are then sent back down from these computers to the appropriate controllers on the plant floor.

Assembly Center and Plant Levels: Above the cell level, computers at the assembly center and plant levels coordinate large areas of intraplant activity. Planning and management functions are usually implemented at the assembly center level, while strategies and direction of the complete overall functions are generally done at the plant level.

At these upper levels of control, a prominent issue centers around high-level broad-band communications between diverse automated devices from various manufacturers. The issue is protocol standardization of the variety of schemes available for intraplant (multilevel) communications.

The Manufacturing Automation Protocol (MAP) standardization program is an international effort geared toward dealing with this issue. The MAP program is a multivendor communications standard that can reduce communication costs and increase the uptime of the application by effectively utilizing VLSI (very large scale integration) technology and communication standards. In a basic MAP scheme, communication between vendor's equipment is not routed through the central-level computer. Instead, the equipment is supported by the vendor's own gateway or a direct MAP interface module. The communication network between the plant computer and the gateway or MAP module is a multivendor open network.

Communications: A final requirement for a hierarchy of automation control (MAP) is a system of integrated communications. The basis for a system of communication networks is the integration of control automation functions both horizontally and vertically. Horizontal integration covers single-level communications between like and unlike devices such as programmable controllers, CNCs, robots, and computers. Vertical integration, using one or more networks, ties together the various levels of control. An integrated system of communication networks provides the link to and from the real-time, plant-floor level through multiple-station (supervisory) control and up to database management, scheduling, and administration.

At lower control levels, proprietary master-slave systems of local and remote I/O communications are most effective. Such a system can transfer information between a central processor and an I/O subsystem. For the next level of control, low-cost, general-purpose networks, often referred to as Data Highways, communicate through the station and cell levels. This is the ideal communications medium for moving blocks of data between stations (production profiles).

The next higher level of communications is a flexible, service-oriented system called mini-MAP. This network differs from the Data Highway in that it is more optimized for cell subnetwork applications. Demands placed on this network include fast, predictable response times and current or eventual compatibility with the industry's evolving communications standards. For the highest control level, the cell-level controllers communicate with the computers through a broad-band system. A broad-band system carries communications capability from the cell level to the top of the automation control hierarchy.

Safety in Automated Assembly

The advent of automated assembly machines and systems in the workplace has reduced the number of human operators active in industrial assembly tasks and in many cases reduced the potential for human operator injury. The presence of automated systems in the factory, however, poses several safety issues that have not been present with older industrial machinery. In many cases, operators interface with an assembly machine for tasks that previously mandated contact with several human operators. In assembly systems, the operator may work with several cooperating machines, including robots. These machine motions, which are dictated by a computer, may at times appear unpredictable to the observer.

Generally, the safety rules that apply to any industrial machine also hold true for assembly machines. In addition, characteristics unique to automated assembly systems and assembly machine interfaces demand special safety considerations. Safety issues must be given close attention when planning for automation, and accident prevention measures must be initiated. Manufacturing engineers must use their best judgment and experience to attain a proper balance between safety systems and the access required to maintain good machine productivity.

Designing and Planning Stages: An

assembly machine, robot, or series of machines and robots should not be installed without giving early consideration to how the arrangement will be inherently safe to operators and maintenance personnel. Designing and laying out automated assembly systems that provide for operator safety must be planned for in the earliest stages of design.

Designers and manufacturers of automation machinery are legally responsible for anyone who is injured by the equipment as long as the equipment is operational and regardless of how ill conceived the intentions of any injured party. It is in the best interest of everyone to give the automation equipment built-in features that prevent exposure to irregular hazards and that cannot be circumvented by inappropriate personnel.

Identifying hazards. The planner of an automated assembly installation must identify all of the major hazards that apply to the specific application and to the assembly equipment under consideration. This is the first step toward formulating a defense against personnel injury. Figure 16-20 contains a list of hazards most often responsible for injury.

The planner should complete the hazards analysis by attempting to anticipate what can go wrong in the automated assembly application. Then the arrangement should be modified to prevent the unwanted events or to minimize their consequences. This can be accomplished by:

1. Specifying the basic elements of the assembly application.
2. Searching for hazards associated with these elements.

Hazard	Potential Causes
Tripping	Objects in operator's path
Slipping	Highly polished surfaces, oil drippings
Bumping of head	Low overheads, equipment protrusions
Electricity	Uncovered electrical leads
Burns	Uninsulated hot surfaces, hot process materials
Pinching	Catch points
Impact shock	Uncontrolled acceleration or oscillation of machine members
Noise	Rapid release of compressed gas, metallic impacts
Toxic substances	Degreasing solvents, process decomposition products
Pressure	Escaping gases, hydraulic forces
Radiation	Electromagnetic UV ionizing energy sources
Explosion or fire	Unmonitored flammable liquid and vapor sources

Figure 16-20   Hazards typical of assembly machinery

3. Specifying how the hazards have the potential for causing injury.
4. Determining how the arrangement for the application can be modified to eliminate or guard against the unwanted event.

This technique, sometimes known as idiot-proofing, is essential during the mockup phase of an auto-mated assembly project. The most effective and inexpensive remedies to unsafe equipment situations are developed at this time. In the case of a straightforward purchase of an assembly machine, hazards can be eliminated in much the same way by a design review and a preacceptance inspection by the purchaser.

Figure 16-21 contains a list of some specific safety-related design tasks.

- There should be automatic overload and shutoff devices built into the machine
- The assembly machine should automatically shut down in the event of failure
- Mechanical devices should be used for directly feeding and rejecting parts on an assembly machine
- Motor drift and run-on times should be short
- Energy sources should diminish safely to zero energy state when machine goes down
- Access platforms or ladders should be provided for inspection and maintenance access in higher machine locations
- All standing, walking, and climbing surfaces around the equipment should be of good traction material
- Precautions and warnings should be clearly displayed
- Machine system emergency procedures should be clearly displayed
- Machine chassis and subsystems should be electrically grounded
- Controls should be located so that the operator will not be too close to the operation whenever activation is required
- Controls should be placed so that the operator will not have to reach excessively or be off balance
- Fail-safe interlocks should be present on automated assembly machinery to prevent production operation during operator or maintenance access. Key-accessed operation, which can defeat the interlocks, should only be possible for maintenance personnel
- The machine controls should be interlocked to ensure that the machine can only be operated in the sequence desired
- All control knobs and buttons should be clearly distinguishable
- Controls should be positioned or guarded so that they cannot be accidentally activated
- An emergency stop or panic button for operator shutdown of the automated assembly system should be present in an easily accessible location
- All possible sources of objectionable noise should be minimized
- Operator training and retraining is essential
- Periodic audit of conformance to safety is necessary
- Safety measures should give preference to the following procedural order: the operator, assembly machines, peripheral machinery, assembly robots, and then workpieces and tooling
- Machine and assembly system should be designed so that it is impossible to gain access to a hazard point during operation
- All moving machine parts that could engage the operator should be covered
- Accidental unclamping of work (by operator or machine) should not propel the workpiece toward the operator. If this is possible, then shielding should be in place
- Operator should be shielded from any type of spray, chip, or broken tool ejection
- Operator should have safe, easy access to the workstations that must be interfaced with as part of the job
- Operators involved in a symbiotic relationship with an assembly machine should not be made to maintain an unrealistic workpace
- Moving parts should be designed to be fail-safe or to prevent operator injury should they fail
- Safety features should be designed so that they cannot be easily removed or circumvented
- Explosion-proof motors or fluid power should be used in explosive environments
- Power transmission and fluid drive mechanisms should preferably be an integral part of the machine or machine system

Figure 16-21 Automation planning safety checklist

KEY TERMS AND PHRASES

Automated assembly
Automated electronic assembly
Bulk storage feeders
Carousel assembly system
Cell controls
Continuous assembly systems
Design for automated assembly
Feed track
Flexible assembly system
Hierarchical control systems
In-line assembly system
Machine controls
Part detector
Parts feeding
Parts orienting
Parts positioning
Robotic assembly system
Single-station assembly system
Station controls
Synchronous assembly system
Vibratory bowl feeders

QUESTIONS FOR ADDITIONAL STUDY AND REVIEW

1. Define the term *automated assembly* 446

2. What are the factors that should be considered before adopting automated assembly?

3. List three potential advantages of automated assembly.

4. Explain the concept of *design for simplification.* 448

5. Name some part configurations that can be easily oriented.

6. Explain the following types of automated assembly systems:
   - Single-station
   - Synchronous
   - Nonsynchronous
   - Continuous

7. What is a *flexible assembly system?*. 452

8. List five robot characteristics that are especially suited for assembly applications.

9. Name five types of components that are assembled in an automated electronic assembly setting.

10. What are three major types of parts feeders?

11. What is a *pocket hopper?*

12. What is a *tumbling barrel?*

13. What is a *feed track?*

14. List three basic rules for efficient positioning of parts.

15. What is a *parts detector?*

16. List five factors to consider when selecting a joining/fastening method in automated assembly. 459

17. Name four different inspection methods used with 463 automated assembly.

18. List four specific requirements of the controls for integrated automation.

19. List three capabilities of intelligent I/O modules.

20. Describe the three steps in a hazards analysis for an automated assembly system.

CHAPTER 17

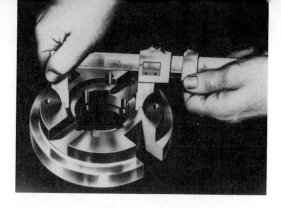

Metrology and Assurance of Quality

MAJOR TOPICS COVERED

- Definition of Quality
- Quality Considerations
- Quality Improvement
- Inspection Equipment and Techniques
- Nondestructive Testing
- Mechanical Testing
- Statistical Process Control (SPC)
- Just-in-Time Manufacturing (JIT)
- Total Quality Control

Definition of Quality

Vital to the understanding of the implications of quality in a manufacturing enterprise is a perception of the meaning of quality. According to the American Society for Quality Control (ASQC), quality is the totality of features and characteristics of a product, or service that bear on its ability to satisfy given needs. The definition implies that the needs of the customer must be identified first because satisfaction of those needs is the "bottom line" of achieving quality. Customer needs should then be transformed into product features and characteristics so that a design and the controlling product specifications can be prepared. It should be carefully noted that it is really a composite

of product features and characteristics taken as a whole that must satisfy the needs of a broad range of customers.

In addition to a proper understanding of the term quality, it is important to understand the meaning of the terms quality management, quality system, quality assurance, and quality control. In the past, there has been a considerable variation in the use of these terms. Some of this variation is due to the inconsistent use of the terms in job titles. Figure 17-1 illustrates the use of these terms by the quality profession.

Quality management is that aspect of the overall management function that determines and implements the quality policy. The responsibility for quality management belongs to senior management. This activity includes strategic planning, allocation of resources, and related quality program activities.

A *quality system* is the collective plans, activities, and events that are provided to ensure that a product, process, or service will satisfy given needs. The elements that comprise a quality system are discussed later in this chapter. It should be noted that a quality system should be as comprehensive as required to meet the objectives of the company and company contract requirements.

Quality assurance includes all the planned or systematic actions necessary to provide adequate confidence that a product or service will satisfy given needs. These actions are aimed at providing confidence that the quality system is working properly

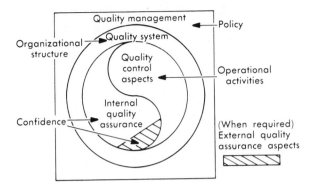

Figure 17-1   Relationship among quality management, quality system, quality assurance, and quality control

and include evaluating the adequacy of the designs and specifications or auditing the production operations for capability. Internal quality assurance aims at providing confidence to the management of a company, while external quality assurance provides assurance of product quality to those who buy from that company.

Quality control comprises the operational techniques and activities that sustain a quality of product or service so that the product will satisfy given needs. It is also the use of such techniques and activities. The quality control function is closest to the product in that various techniques and activities are used to monitor the process and to pursue the elimination of unsatisfactory sources of quality performance.

Quality Considerations

Many factors must be taken into consideration when developing a quality system. Some of the most important factors are the following:

- Prevention of defects.
- Customer focus.
- Standards.
- Legal liability.
- Total involvement.
- Selection and training.

Prevention of Defects

Many of the quality systems of the past were designed with the objective of sorting good products from bad products during the various processing steps. Those products judged to be bad had to be reworked to meet specifications. If they could not be reworked, they were scrapped. This type of system is known as a "detection/correction" system. With this system, problems were not found until the products were inspected or when they were used by the customer. Because of the inherent nature of human inspectors, the effectiveness of the sorting operations was often less than 90%. The old cliche "You can't inspect quality into your product..." was proven over and over. Quality systems that are preventive in nature are being widely implemented. These systems prevent problems from occurring in the first place by placing emphasis on proper planning and problem prevention in all phases of the product cycle. The various elements of this type of system are described later in this chapter.

Customer Focus

The final word on how well a product fulfills needs and expectations is given by the customers and users of that product and is influenced by the offerings of competitors that may also be available to those customers and users. It is important to recognize that this final word is formed over the entire life of the product, not just when it was purchased.

Being aware of customers' needs and expectations is very important, as was previously discussed. In addition, focusing the attention of all employees in an enterprise on the customers and users and their needs will result in a more effective quality system. For example, group discussions on product designs and specifications should include specific discussion of the needs to be satisfied. In this way, the risk that the product is viewed by employees as only an inanimate object is minimized.

Standards

The ramifications of not being aware of and hence not complying with applicable industry standards can be very significant to a manufacturing enterprise. Standards exist for many industrial and business areas such as design, procurement, manufacturing, quality control, marketing and distribution, and use of product, its service and ease of repair.

The subject matter or coverage of industrial standards is also very broad. Standards can cover size and strength characteristics; performance in terms of quality, reliability, and safety; assembly methods; inspection, testing, and other control procedures; packing and packaging; distribution; and documentation and identification. They can also cover safe use, which would include warnings, labels, and instructions.

Quality Improvement

A basic commitment of management should be that quality improvement must be relentlessly pursued. Actions should be ingrained in the day-to-day workings of the company that recognize that quality is a moving target in today's marketplace driven by constantly rising customer expectations. Traditional efforts that set a quality level perceived to be right for a product and direct all efforts to only maintain that level will not be successful in the long haul. Rather, management must orient the organization so that once the so-called right quality level for a product has been attained, improvement efforts continue to achieve progressively higher quality levels.

To achieve the most effective improvement efforts, management should ensure that the organization also has ingrained in its operating principles the understanding that quality and cost are complementary and not conflicting objectives. Traditionally, recommendations were made to management that a choice had to be made between quality and cost—the so-

called tradeoff decision—because better quality inevitably would somehow cost more and make production difficult. Experience throughout the world has shown that this is not true. Good quality fundamentally leads to good resource utilization and consequently means good productivity and low quality costs. Also significant is that higher sales and market penetration result from products that are perceived by customers to have high quality and performance reliability during use.

Quality Cost

One way of looking at quality costs is to view them as the costs that are associated with the activities and events taking place in the quality system. Four basic categories that quality costs can be placed in are the following (see Fig. 17-2):

- Prevention—costs incurred in planning, implementing, and maintaining a quality system that will ensure conformance to quality requirements at economical levels. An example of prevention cost is training in the use of statistical process control.
- Appraisal—costs incurred in determining the degree of conformance to quality requirements. An example of appraisal cost is inspection.

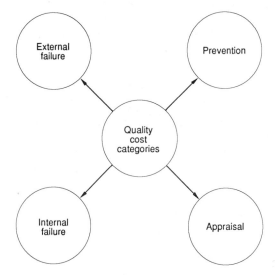

Figure 17-2   Quality control categories

- Internal failure—costs arising when products, components, and materials fail to meet quality requirements prior to transfer of ownership to the customer. An example of internal failure cost is scrap.
- External failure—costs incurred when products fail to meet quality requirements after transfer of ownership to the customer. An example of external failure cost is warranty claims.

Corrective Action

A problem-solving approach should be followed in seeking quality improvement. The results of any improvement effort will not be permanent unless the root causes of the problems have been found so appropriate (irreversible) corrective action can be implemented.

The root cause can be defined as the real cause of a problem. This is often quite different from the apparent cause, which appears after a superficial investigation. A frequently asked question is how to know when the root cause is found and when the investigator is not still being deceived by the apparent cause. A meaningful answer is that if the root cause has been found, the problem is able to be turned on and off by adding or removing the cause.

Once the root cause has been found, an irreversible corrective action must be implemented so there is no foreseeable situation by which the root cause can return and so permanent improvement results.

INSPECTION EQUIPMENT AND TECHNIQUES

Although the level of quality control is determined in large part by probability theory and statistical calculations, it is very important that the data collection processes on which these procedures depend be appropriate and accurate. The best statistical procedure is worthless if fed faulty data, and like machine processes, inspection data collection is itself a process with practical limits of accuracy, precision, resolution, and repeatability.

All inspection and/or measurement processes can be defined in terms of their accuracy and repeatability, just as a manufacturing process is evaluated for accuracy and repeatability. Controlled experiments can be performed, and statistical measures of the results can be made to determine the performance of a method of inspection relative to the parts to be inspected. Suitability of one or another method can be judged on the basis of standard deviations and confidence levels that apply to each approach as used in a given inspection situation.

The necessity of performing an experiment to validate the inspection approach will probably depend on the specifics of the situation. Choice of the inspection method can then be made based on the required sensitivity and chances of error as well on tooling cost and skill level availability.

Other criteria may also enter into the choice of inspection method. The nature and quantity of inspection called for by a project are overriding considerations as is the availability of existing inspection tooling. General-purpose measuring gaging may be necessary only for the first piece produced because there may be high confidence in the integrity of the molds, dies, or other fabrication tools. In other cases gaging may be on a sampling basis or a 100% inspection basis. This could lead to a significantly increased load on the inspection resources and a search for more efficient measuring methods.

Fundamental Units and Standards

Measurement is the means whereby data or information is collected about an item or event. The first basic requirement of measurement is that the measuring units be consistent. In other words, each unit should have one universal value.

Two major systems of units are in use throughout the world today, the English or Imperial system and the metric system. English units are now defined in terms of the metric units, making the latter the primary system of units; in this way, consistency of units is assured. It should be noted that the metric system, by virtue of its greater simplicity, is supplanting the English system in many countries, even in England where the system originated. At present, more than 90% of the people in the world use the metric system, and it is probable that within the next 50 years the metric system will be used universally in certain fields of measurement. Figure 17-3 is a Metric/English conversion chart.

Conversion Table

1 meter = 39.37 inches = 3.28083 feet = 1.0936 yards
1 centimeter = 0.3937 inch
1 millimeter = 0.03937 inch = $\frac{1}{25}$ inch, approximately
1 kilometer = 0.62137 mile
1 foot = 0.3048 meter
1 inch = 2.54 centimeters = 25.4 millimeters

Table for Converting Millimeters to Inches and Decimals

mm in.	mm in.	mm in.	mm in.
1 = 0.03937	26 = 1.02362	51 = 2.00787	76 = 2.99212
2 = 0.07874	27 = 1.06299	52 = 2.04724	77 = 3.03149
3 = 0.11811	28 = 1.10236	53 = 2.08661	78 = 3.07086
4 = 0.15748	29 = 1.14173	54 = 2.12598	79 = 3.11023
5 = 0.19685	30 = 1.18110	55 = 2.16535	80 = 3.14960
6 = 0.23622	31 = 1.22047	56 = 2.20472	81 = 3.18897
7 = 0.27559	32 = 1.25984	57 = 2.24409	82 = 3.22834
8 = 0.31496	33 = 1.29921	58 = 2.28346	83 = 3.26771
9 = 0.35433	34 = 1.33858	59 = 2.32283	84 = 3.30708
10 = 0.39370	35 = 1.37795	60 = 2.36220	85 = 3.34645
11 = 0.43307	36 = 1.41732	61 = 2.40157	86 = 3.38582
12 = 0.47244	37 = 1.45669	62 = 2.44094	87 = 3.42519
13 = 0.51181	38 = 1.49606	63 = 2.48031	88 = 3.46456
14 = 0.55118	39 = 1.53543	64 = 2.51968	89 = 3.50393
15 = 0.59055	40 = 1.57480	65 = 2.55905	90 = 3.54330
16 = 0.62992	41 = 1.61417	66 = 2.59842	91 = 3.58267
17 = 0.66929	42 = 1.65354	67 = 2.63779	92 = 3.62204
18 = 0.70866	43 = 1.69291	68 = 2.66716	93 = 3.66141
19 = 0.74803	44 = 1.73228	69 = 2.71653	94 = 3.70078
20 = 0.78740	45 = 1.77165	70 = 2.75590	95 = 3.74015
21 = 0.82677	46 = 1.81102	71 = 2.79527	96 = 3.77952
22 = 0.86614	47 = 1.85039	72 = 2.83464	97 = 3.81889
23 = 0.90551	48 = 1.88976	73 = 2.87401	98 = 3.85826
24 = 0.94488	49 = 1.92913	74 = 2.91338	99 = 3.89763
25 = 0.98425	50 = 1.96850	75 = 2.95275	100 = 3.93700

Figure 17-3 Metric/English conversion chart

A second requirement of units is that they be of convenient and practical size. It is cumbersome, for instance, to express all length measurements in miles or even in meters. The English system employs an assortment of units such as the inch, the foot, and so on up to the mile to cover the wide range of length measurement. In the metric system there is one primary unit for each parameter. For dimensional measurement, it is the meter. Larger and smaller quantities are expressed as multiples and submultiples of the meter; the various multiples and submultiples are related by factors of 10. This decimal logic is one of the attractive features of the metric system. No such logic exists in the English system, in which a foot is 12 inches, a yard is 3 feet, a rod is 5.5 yards, a furlong is 40 rods, and so on.

Units are defined and embodied in standards. Units are the language of measurement, and standards are the hardware. For example, the meter was originally defined as the distance between two lines on a specific bar maintained at the International Bureau of Weights and Measures in Paris; that bar was the standard for the meter.

One of the primary requirements of a basic standard is that it be unchangeable. To satisfy this condition, the standard must be indestructible (or if destroyed it should be capable of exact reproduction) and it must be stable. It was this consideration of immutability that led to the adoption of the new basic standard of length, the wavelength of a certain radiation of light. The radiation is produced by a krypton lamp; the wavelength of light produced by the lamp is an atomic constant and thus never changes. The meter bar, on the other hand, is a specific bar that if destroyed could not be reproduced exactly; moreover, it is dimensionally unstable.

A second requirement for a basic standard is that it be reproducible and not singular, as is the case of the meter bar or the kilogram. Any laboratory with adequate facilities can maintain a krypton lamp, and many do. No longer are they dependent on the meter bar at Paris to define their unit of length.

Yet another requirement of standards is that of practicality. This requirement is particularly dominant in working standards used throughout industry. The popularity of gage blocks as standards of length is in no small measure due to their simplicity and practicality. It is also important that standards be as insensitive as possible to outside influences such as temperature and pressure. This requirement is particularly difficult to satisfy and has led to the adoption of standard measuring conditions.

General-Purpose Measuring Devices

Long the mainstay of the inspector, general-purpose measuring devices are still used in toolrooms, receiving inspection areas, and calibration labs for taking many precision measurements. They are often used in conjunction with a surface plate and are capable of measurements with accuracies of 0.001″ (0.02 mm). Instruments with high resolution permit measurements of 0.0001″ (0.002 mm) to be determined. General-purpose measuring devices are usually fabricated of hardened tool steel and are subject to error because of mishandling and the introduction of dirt or cutting chips. It is therefore necessary to calibrate these devices periodically to ensure their integrity. When tolerances of 0.005″ (0.12 mm) are required, these devices can be relied on to give accurate results. Instruments with high repeatability may be used to calibrate the tooling on which the parts are produced because tooling tolerances are typically 10% of product tolerances.

Skill requirements for the use of these general-purpose precision measuring instruments is relatively high. Inspectors and/or toolmakers performing measurements of this type must know how to read drawings, how to use and read the instruments themselves, and how to perform basic trigonometric calculations to relate the physical measurements to the manufacturing requirements. Tooling costs for this type of inspection are relatively low because most instrumentation is general purpose and can be used on a wide variety of projects.

Use of these tools implies that inspection is to be done by measuring the part rather than determining if it is within specified limits. Of the two approaches, measuring is the more costly and slower because specific readings have to be taken. Determining if the part is within specified limits on a "GO/NOT-GO" basis can take much less time, but the setup of the inspection process usually requires some additional planning and tooling in the form of preset gages or visual references.

Nongraduated Tools or Instruments

As their name implies, nongraduated measuring tools do not have linear or angular graduations incorporated in the tool. These tools are generally used when comparing measurements, and their size must be verified by a graduated measuring device.

Surface Plates: A surface plate is a flat plane that is used as a reference surface from which final dimensions are taken. They should be inspected periodically with an autocollimator to ensure flatness. When an overall unilateral flatness of 0.00005″ (0.0013 mm) or finer is required, toolmakers' flats or optical flats are used as a reference surface.

Originally, surface plates were made from cast iron and had cross-ribbed bases to reduce weight and increase resistance to warpage. Currently, however, they are made from different types of hard and homogeneous granite. The most important advantages of granite surface plates are closer tolerances and lower prices. The next most important feature is their noncorroding and nonrusting property. They are also not subject to contact interference. In addition, granite surface plates are nonmagnetic, hard, stable, long wearing, easy on the eyes, easy to clean, and have exceptional thermal stability.

Sine Bars and Plates: The sine bar is a hardened, stabilized, precision ground and lapped tool for accurate angle setting or measuring. It consists of a bar to which two cylinders are attached. When the cylinders are brought in contact with a flat surface, the top of the bar is parallel to that surface.

Sine bars are used in conjunction with gage blocks and a surface plate. The operation of the sine bar is based on known trigonometric relationships between the sides and angles of a right-angled triangle.

Sine blocks and plates are similar in design to sine bars. The primary difference is the width of the instrument and whether it has an attached base or not. Sine blocks are generally wider than 1″ (25 mm) and have tapped holes in the bar for attaching parts as well as a stop to keep the parts from sliding off. Sine plates have a hardened base attached to them. Sine bars and blocks are usually manufactured in lengths of 5 or 10″ (125 or 250 mm). This length is the distance between the axes of the two supporting rolls (see Fig. 17-4).

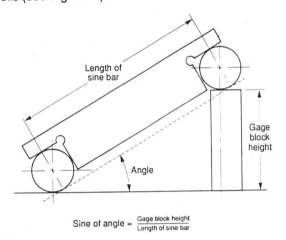

$$\text{Sine of angle} = \frac{\text{Gage block height}}{\text{Length of sine bar}}$$

Figure 17-4   Sine bar

Graduated Tools or Instruments

Graduated measuring tools have either linear or angular graduations incorporated into the measuring system of the tool. These tools are applied directly to the part being measured, and the dimension is read by the user.

Rules: The rule is a basic measuring tool from which many other tools have been developed.

Because rules are so frequently used on a variety of work, a wide selection exists to suit the needs of the precision worker. They range in size from as small as ¼″ (6 mm) in length for measuring in grooves, recesses, and keyways to as large as 12′ (3.5 m) in length for large work.

Rules are made from carbon steel or stainless steel, and many have a satin-chrome finish and enameled graduations for ease of reading. They are graduated in the English or metric system units and sometimes scales for both systems are provided on a single rule. The graduations can be on each edge of both sides and even on the ends. English graduations are commonly as fine as 0.01″ in decimals or 1/64″ in fractions. Metric graduations are usually as fine as 0.5 mm.

Calipers: Slide calipers. Slide calipers are a refinement of the steel rule and are capable of more accurate measurements. With these tools, a head or pair of jaws is added to the rule; one jaw is fixed at the end and the other movable along the scale. Provision is made for clamping the movable jaw to lock the setting. The slide is graduated to read inside or outside measurements. The scale is graduated in increments of either 1/32 or 1/64″ for the English system and in increments of 0.5 mm for the metric system.

Vernier calipers. A typical vernier caliper consists of a stationary bar and a movable vernier slide assembly. The stationary rule is a hardened, graduated bar with a fixed measuring jaw. Vernier calipers are available in sizes ranging from 4 to 80″ (100 to 1500 mm). The size of the caliper indicates the maximum dimension that can be measured. The stationary rule frequently is graduated in increments of 0.050″ for the English system and 0.5 mm for the metric system.

The vernier slide assembly combines a movable jaw, vernier plate, clamp screws, and adjusting nut. It moves as a unit along the graduations of the bar to bring both jaws in contact with the work. The vernier plate is graduated in increments of 0.001″ for the English system and 0.02 mm for the metric system.

Caliper height gages. Like the vernier caliper, the caliper height gage consists of a stationary bar or beam and a movable slide. The graduated, hardened, and ground beam is combined with a hardened, ground, and lapped base. The vernier slide assembly can be raised or lowered to any position along the bar. It can be adjusted in thousandths (English system) or hundredths (metric system) by means of the vernier slide fine-adjusting knob. Caliper height gages are available in sizes ranging from 8 to 72" (200 to 900 mm).

The primary use of caliper height gages is in the field of surface plate work as a layout tool. It is commonly used for marking off vertical distances and for measuring height differences between steps at various levels. When marking off distances, scribers are attached to the contact jaw.

Vernier depth gage. The vernier depth gage differs slightly from the vernier caliper and the caliper height gage in that the vernier slide assembly remains fixed while the steel rule is moved to obtain the desired measurements. The vernier slide also forms the base that is held on the work by one hand while the blade is operated with the other. Vernier depth gages are available in sizes ranging from 6 to 12" (150 to 300 mm).

Obtaining a measurement is accomplished in the same manner as with a vernier caliper gage. After the blade is brought into contact with the bottom of a slot or recess, the clamp screw adjacent to the fine-adjusting nut is tightened. Then the fine-adjusting nut is turned to obtain an exact measurement. Once the final measurement is obtained, the clamp screw next to the vernier plate is tightened.

Gear tooth vernier caliper. The gear tooth vernier caliper measures chordal thickness or thickness at the datum circle of a gear tooth to an accuracy of 0.001" or 0.01 mm, depending on the units. It can also measure hobs and form and thread tools. Its construction combines in one tool the function of both the vernier depth gage and vernier caliper.

In use, the vertical slide is set to depth by means of its vernier plate fine-adjusting nut so that when it rests on top of the gear tooth, the caliper jaws will be correctly positioned to measure across the datum circle of the gear tooth. The horizontal slide is then used to obtain the chordal thickness of the gear tooth by means of its vernier slide fine-adjusting nut.

Dial calipers. Similar to vernier calipers, dial calipers have a stationary bar and a movable slide assembly. The bar is graduated in increments of 0.1" or 2 mm and is available in sizes ranging from 4 to 12" (100 to 300 mm).

The vernier plate is replaced by a caliper dial graduated in increments of 0.001" or 0.02 mm. A pinion gear actuates the dial hand as it moves along a rack located in the stationary bar.

Because the dial caliper is direct reading, there is no need to determine the coincident line on a vernier scale. This feature facilitates the reading of these instruments. Dial heads are also incorporated on caliper height gages and depth gages.

Digital calipers. Because gaging is a vital part of SPC, a new generation of electronic instruments has been produced. These instruments incorporate liquid crystal displays (LCD) and are capable of interfacing with a data collection device. Both inch and metric units are incorporated in one tool. The electronic feature is available on calipers, height gages, and depth gages.

Micrometers: A variety of micrometers exists for different applications. The three major types of micrometers are outside, inside, and depth. All micrometers operate based on the principle that an accurately made screw will advance a specified distance with each complete turn. Micrometers graduated in the inch system advance 0.025" for each turn; those graduated in the metric system advance 0.5 mm for each turn.

Micrometers have both a linear and circumferential scale. The linear scale measures the axial advance of the spindle. It is generally graduated in increments identical to the pitch of the micrometer screw. The circumferential scale indicates the amount of partial rotation that has occurred since the last complete revolution. For inch-based micrometers, this scale is divided into 25 equal parts, with each division representing 0.001". For metric-based micrometers, the circumferential scale is divided into 50 equal parts, with each division representing 0.01 mm. Some micrometers also have a third scale that permits the evaluation of fractions of circumferential graduations.

Depending on the units, each division on this scale represents either 0.0001″ or 0.002 mm.

Outside micrometers. An outside micrometer consists of a C-shaped frame with an anvil and a threaded spindle. The thread is precision ground to ensure uniform movement of the spindle toward or away from the anvil. The spindle moves as it is rotated in the stationary spindle nut. A graduated stationary sleeve and a graduated rotating thimble are the bases for determining measurement. A locking mechanism can be provided for holding an established reading. A friction thimble or ratchet stop is also available to establish a uniform feel among individual users.

Outside micrometers generally are available in a variety of sizes. Size refers to the limits of its measuring range. The most common size is 1″ (25 mm), which permits measurements over a range from 0 to 1″ (25 mm). Larger outside micrometers are also available in sizes up to 60″ or 600 mm.

In addition to the standard outside micrometers, micrometers also exist with different anvil and spindle shapes for specialized applications. Blade micrometers are used for measuring narrow slots and grooves. The disc micrometer is used for measuring thin materials such as paper as well as for measuring the distance from a slot to an edge. Hub micrometers can be put through a hole or bore to permit the measurement of the hub thickness of a gear or sprocket. Screw thread micrometers measure the pitch diameter of screw threads.

Like calipers, outside micrometers are also available with the capability to interface with data collection devices. These micrometers have an LCD that replaces the graduations on the sleeve and thimble.

Inside micrometers. An inside micrometer consists of a micrometer head with one permanent contact. The other contact consists of accurate rods in various increments that are seated snugly in the opposite end of the head against a shoulder and securely locked in place. Inside micrometers are available with solid or tubular rods. Handles can be attached to the micrometer head for measuring into deep holes.

The smallest bore that can be measured with this type of micrometer is 2″ (50 mm), and the maximum upper limit depends on the rods available. Inside micrometers with solid rods are capable of measuring bores of up to 32″ (800 mm); with tubular rods, the largest bore size is 107″ (2700 mm).

Another type of internal micrometer consists of a specially designed micrometer head and three self-aligning measuring points on the other end. The self-aligning property of this instrument is particularly useful when measuring deep bores.

Three-point internal micrometers are available in sizes from 0.275 to 12″ (6 to 300 mm). The individual instrument has a measuring capacity varying from 0.075″ (2 mm) for the smallest size to 1.0″ (25 mm) for the largest size. Three-point internal micrometers are also available with digital readouts, both mechanical and electronic.

Depth gages. Depth gages consist of a hardened, ground, and lapped base with a micrometer head. Measuring rods are inserted through a hole in the micrometer screw and brought to a positive seat by a knurled nut. The screw is precision ground and has either a 1″ or a 25 mm movement. The rods are furnished to measure in increments of 1″ (25 mm); rods are available to measure to a depth of 9″ (225 mm). Each rod protrudes through the base and moves as the thimble is rotated.

Depth gages measure the depth of holes, slots, recesses, and keyways from a flat reference point. They are available with standard or digital readout.

Bench micrometer. The bench micrometer is a precision instrument ideal for bench use either in the shop or inspection laboratory. It can be used as a comparator measuring to 50μin. (1μm) or for direct measuring to 0.0001″ (0.001 mm). It can also be adapted for electronic readout.

The anvil actuates the indicator through a motion transfer mechanism and can be retracted by a lever for repeated measurements. A heavy-duty micrometer head mounted at the right of the base reads directly in 0.0001″ (0.001 mm) and has a range from 0 to 2″ (50 mm). Some bench micrometers have an adjustable base permitting measurements up to 4″ (100 mm).

An adjustable worktable is centered beneath the anvil and the spindle. Work can be accurately aligned between anvil and spindle by adjusting the table to the proper height and then locking it in position by a lockscrew.

Protractors:
Protractors are used to directly measure angular surfaces. The tools most commonly used are the simple protractor, the protractor head, and the universal bevel protractor.

Simple protractor. A simple protractor consists of a rectangular head graduated in degrees along a semicircle with a blade pivoted on the center pin. By rotating the blade on the center pin, any angle from 0 to 180° can be set.

Protractor head. The protractor head is one of several tools on the combination square. It has revolving turrets with direct-reading double graduations a full 0-180° in opposite directions. This permits direct reading of angles above or below the blade.

Universal bevel protractor. The universal bevel protractor consists of a round body with a fixed blade on which a graduated protractor dial rotates. The turret is slotted to accommodate a 7 or 12″ (180 or 300 mm) nongraduated blade. The blade and dial may be rotated as a unit to any desired position and locked in place by means of the dial clamp nut. The blade may also be independently extended in either direction from the protractor dial.

The protractor dial is graduated 360° reading 0-90°, 90-0°, 0-90°, and 90-0°. Each 10° increment is numbered, and each 5° increment is indicated by a line longer than those on either side of it. The vernier is graduated in 12 spaces, with each increment representing 5 minutes. Figures 17-5 through 17-9 are examples of graduated tools and instruments.

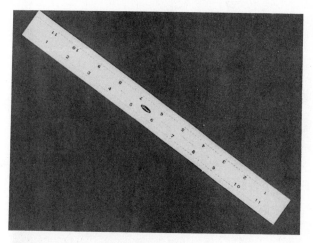

Figure 17-6   Graduated rule

Figure 17-7   Dial indicator

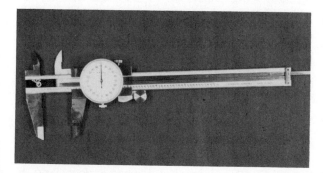

Figure 17-5   Dial caliper

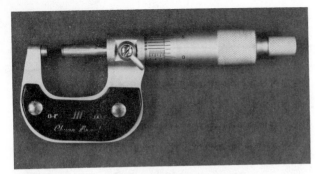

Figure 17-8   Typical measurement tool

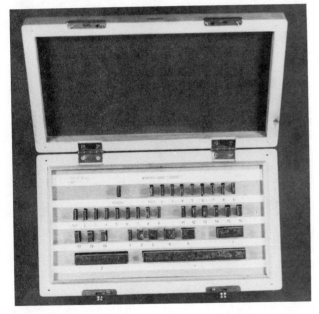

Figure 17-9   Gage blocks

Comparative Instruments

Comparative instruments compare the workpiece being measured against a master that was used to calibrate the instrument. Because these instruments are compared against a master, they are generally only capable of measuring the amount of deviation as well as the direction of deviation from the calibrated size. The range of the deviation that can be measured

depends on the type of comparative gage used. The three most commonly used comparative or indicating gages are mechanical, pneumatic, and electronic.

Mechanical Indicating Gages: Mechanical indicating gages mechanically amplify or magnify variations or displacements in dimensions for the purpose of making precise observations. This magnification may be accomplished by gear trains, levers, cams, torsion strips, reeds, or a combination of these. The direction of the original displacement that can be sensed by an indicator may be in line with the instrument spindle axis or normal to the contact lever swinging over a small angle. For some applications, attachments can be also used to redirect the original displacement to the contact element of the indicator instrument.

Mechanical amplifying devices must be used in conjunction with a reference point, line, or surface to produce either a direct or comparative measurement. The combination of the mechanical amplifier or indicator and the reference comprises a gage.

Dial indicators. The magnification of a dial-type indicator is obtained by means of a gear train. This type of indicator is most commonly used because its magnification accuracy meets the large majority of requirements. A typical dial indicator is shown in Fig. 17-10.

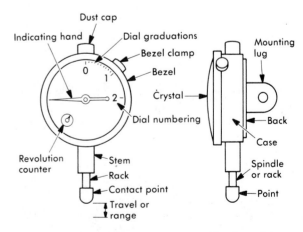

Figure 17-10   Nomenclature used in describing dial indicator components

In operation, a sensitive contact or point is attached to a rack that transfers the motion to the rack gear. A train of three to five gears, depending on the magnification desired, magnifies and transmits the movement of the contact to the pinion gear on which the indicator hand is mounted with a hairspring and takeup gear to eliminate backlash. Some indicators are designed with a spring-loaded link at some part of the gear train to absorb the impact of a sudden shock and protect the indicator against damage.

Test indicators. Test indicators sense and measure displacements that occur in a direction perpendicular to the shaft of the contact point (see Fig. 17-11). Magnification is obtained by gears and levers. Because they are small, test indicators are particularly useful in setup inspection and toolroom work.

Reed-type indicators. In this type of indicator, the reed magnifying mechanism uses various combinations of flat steel reeds to obtain mechanical amplification (see Fig. 17-12). The sensitive spindle is mounted on a block that floats on reeds connected to a fixed block that is attached to the mounting. Extending from the top of the two blocks is a vertical member consisting of a pair of reeds, one of which is attached to each of the fixed and the floating blocks; a hand or pointer is mounted on this member. Slight motion of the sensitive contact flexes the reeds and moves the hand along a vertical arc.

Pneumatic Indicating Gages:
Pneumatic or air gaging uses the restriction of airflow between a nozzle tip and the part being tested to determine part size. Although a variety of instrument designs and modes of operation exist, a pneumatic gage cannot operate without a regulated air supply, a flow metering device, and one or more nozzles. A typical pneumatic circuit is shown in Fig. 17-13.

In operation, the air from the regulated supply flows through the restriction and then through the nozzle. When the nozzle is free and open to the atmosphere, there will be a maximum flow of air through the nozzle. In addition, there will be a minimum of pressure in the system downstream of the restriction. If a plate is moved in front of the nozzle and slowly brought toward it, the airflow will gradually be restricted until the nozzle is shut off. At this point,

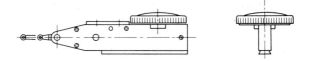

Figure 17-11   Typical test indicator

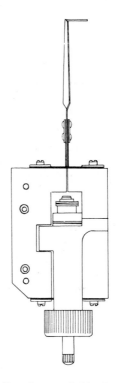

Figure 17-12   Reed-type dial indicator

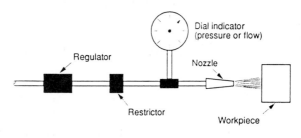

Figure 17-13   Air gage components

the airflow would be 0. When the nozzle has been completely closed off, the pressure downstream of the restriction will build up until it becomes the same as the regulated supply.

Electronic Indicating Gages:
The three characteristics most responsible for the ever-widening use of electronic gaging equipment are its ability to sense size differences as small as 1μin. (0.025 μm), its ability to amplify these small measurements as much as 100,000 times, and its ability to generate an electronic signal that can be computer processed. Systems measuring dimensions having very tight tolerances [10μin. (0.25μm)] are best put to use in laboratory measuring instruments such as gage block comparators and in comparators and height gages for shop applications. Electronic gages also find their way into automatic sizing and automatic gaging and sorting systems. These applications will be discussed subsequently in the section on automatic gaging and process control.

When using an electronic comparator, the gage is first calibrated by a master to the master dimension. The workpieces are then compared with this dimension, and the variation is displayed on an indicator (see Fig. 17-14).

Most electronic gages of the comparator type are used in a manner similar to dial indicators. The major difference is that the electronic gage can read much smaller deviations because the signal is digitized.

Because electronic instruments are highly stable, they can be used as absolute measuring devices. Thin parts, up to the maximum range of the instrument, can be measured directly without the use of a master. The accuracy depends on the type of probe and gaging system. For the best accuracy, one master is always required.

Differential measurements are also commonly made with electronic gages. Two gages are connected to one amplifier, and the difference or sum of the gage head outputs is measured. This technique can be used for checking roundness, thickness, parallelism, and taper. Because two gaging operations are combined in one, time savings are considerable.

Squareness, or lack of it, can be detected to 10μin. (0.25μm) through use of electronic gage heads and simple fixtures. Electronic gaging is also used in ultraprecision laboratory instruments such as gage block and ring and disc comparators, roundness checkers, and other master-checking devices. Such units are seldom, if ever, found in a shop; they are operated within special controlled-environment rooms or modules.

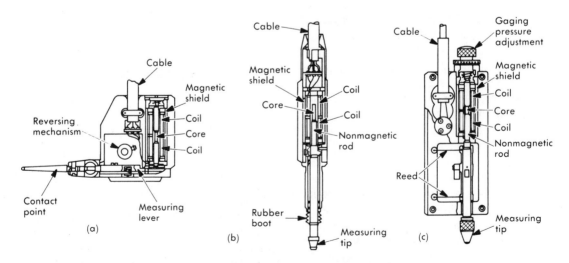

Figure 17-14   Common gage heads: a) lever-type; b) cartridge type; and c) frictionless type

Gage Blocks

Linear measurement and size agreement of parts, tools, and gages manufactured by various companies in different locations is essential to interchangeability. Gage blocks are the master gages providing the reference standard for comparison in linear measurement. They are made of steel, carbide, or chromium plated steel that has been stabilized for dimensional stability. The measuring surfaces of these blocks are plane, parallel, and at a specified distance apart. Common shapes for the gaging surfaces of these blocks are rectangular and square; most square blocks have a hole in the center.

Gage blocks are available individually or in sets. In the English system of units, sets contain from 5 to 88 blocks and permit a systematic progression of measurements. Attachments are available to use a combination of gage blocks for height gage measurements, length, and internal and outside diameter checking. Combinations of gage blocks can be formed in increments as small as 25μin. ($1\,\mu$m).

When using gage blocks, it is extremely important that the individual blocks and any associated tooling be free of dirt, grease, and foreign matter. The block faces should, however, have a light film of oil on them. The complete set of blocks should be taken to the location where the inspection will be performed to minimize the potential of scratching or nicking the individual blocks. The blocks selected for a specific application should be removed from the box and placed on clean paper, cloth, or chamois (see Fig. 17-15).

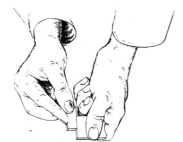

Figure 17-15   Wringing gage blocks together

Fixed Functional Gages

Unlike the general measuring devices, which can be used for a variety of applications, fixed gages are designed for a specific application. The value of these gages is in their ability to check parts much faster than an inspector can measure parts using the general-purpose measuring devices. If the gage is properly designed, good parts are ensured by the interaction of the gage points and the part being inspected. However, little is known about the exact measurements of the part. The nature of the part to be inspected, its material composition, the precision desired, the number of pieces to be checked per hour or day, and the skill of the inspector all enter into the choice of this type of gage.

Fixed functional gages are the direct or reverse physical replica of the workpiece dimension being measured. They are usually designed to measure a single dimension. The gage may represent the part in its nominal condition or in one of its limit conditions.

Gages manufactured to the nominal size are referred to as master gages. They are primarily used for setting up comparator-type measuring instruments. Another application of master gages is calibrating measuring tools.

Cylindrical Plug Gages

A cylindrical plug gage is a hardened and accurately ground steel pin. A typical plug gage consists of a handle and two gage members; one is the GO gage member and the other the NOT-GO. Plug gages larger than 2 1/2″ (64 mm) usually only have one gage member attached to the handle. Another style of plug gage combines both gage members into one and is referred to as a progressive plug gage. The front two thirds of the gage is ground to the GO size, and the remaining portion is ground to the NOT-GO size (see Fig. 17-16).

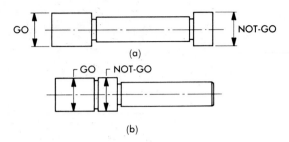

Figure 17-16   Typical plug gage

Cylindrical Ring Gages

Cylindrical ring gages are used for checking the limit sizes of a round shaft. They are generally used in pairs—one gage checks the upper limit of the part tolerance (GO gage) while the other checks the lower limit (NOT-GO). The NOT-GO ring is distinguished from the GO ring by a groove in the outside diameter of the gage (see Fig. 17-17).

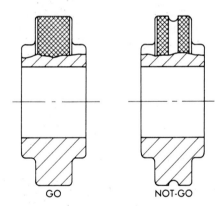

Figure 17-17   Ring gage set

Snap Gages

A snap gage is a fixed gage that has the gaging members arranged for measuring diameters, lengths, thicknesses, or widths. An external-measuring snap gage consists of a C-frame with gaging members in the jaw of the frame (see Fig. 17-18). The form of the gaging members may be selected to fit the particular part configuration. These members can usually be adjusted within a specific range to provide two gage sizes corresponding to the dimensions being measured. The outer gaging button, where the workpiece enters the gage, is set at the GO dimension. Snap gages are generally not recommended for inspecting part dimensions if the tolerance is smaller than 0.002″ (0.05 mm).

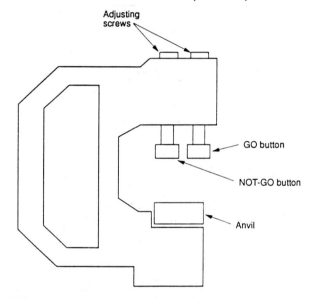

Figure 17-18   Typical snap gage

Taper Gages

Taper body forms are commonly used to achieve a precise alignment yet detachable connection between mechanical members. The critical dimensions of machine tapers are the included angle and the diameter at a specific reference level.

Taper gages are made for both internal and external tapers in the form of plug and ring gages, respectively. They are also made to inspect machine tapers with or without tangs.

Thread Gages

Fixed-limit thread gages are single-purpose gages in that they are made for a specific thread system, form, size, and class. Each designation is stamped or marked on the gage. These gages incorporate the essential functional dimensions of the thread and are used primarily to ensure the ability to assemble the product thread with its mating part.

Fixed-limit gages are generally made from tool steel that has been treated for wear resistance and dimensional stability. For extreme part tolerances or abrasive work conditions, other gage materials, such as carbides and chrome plate, are used. Because solid thread gages are subject to wear, a periodic inspection of these gages should be made; worn gages should be discarded.

The accuracy to which these gages are manufactured is determined by their intended use. Gages that directly check the product thread are made to X tolerances. Gages that are used as reference or master gages are made to W tolerances. The X tolerances are three times larger than W tolerances for most common sizes. The designated tolerances for unified inch screw threads and metric screw threads are given in ANSI B1.2 and ANSI B1.16M, respectively (see Fig. 17-19).

Spline Gages

A common way of inspecting splined workpieces prior to assembly is with fixed-limit gages. External splines are checked with internal-toothed rings, whereas internal splines are checked with external-toothed plugs.

Basically there are only two types of fixed-limit spline gages, composite and sector. Composite gages have the same number of teeth as that of the part. Sector gages have only two sectors of teeth 180° apart. These gages are further subdivided into GO and NOT-GO gages.

The GO gages are used to inspect maximum material conditions (maximum external or minimum internal dimensions). They may be used to inspect an individual dimension or the relationship between two or more functional dimensions. In addition, they control the minimum looseness or maximum interference.

The NOT-GO gages are used to inspect minimum material conditions (minimum external, maximum internal dimensions), thereby controlling the maximum looseness or minimum interference. Unless otherwise agreed on, a part is only acceptable if the NOT-GO gage does not enter or go on the part. A NOT-GO gage can only check one dimension. See Fig. 17-20.

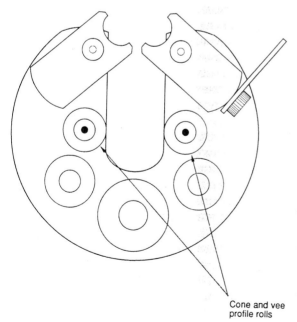

Cone and vee
profile rolls

Figure 17-19   Thread snap gage

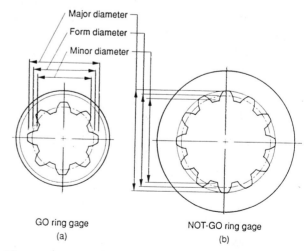

GO ring gage
(a)

NOT-GO ring gage
(b)

Figure 17-20   GO and NOT-GO ring gage

Visual Reference Gaging

Visual references are used in a number of gaging procedures to check parts. When part features are easy to see and feature tolerances allow wide enough latitude, overlay visual templates may be used directly with the part to gage shape without magnification. When tolerances are too tight to judge by eye alone, optical comparators or toolmakers' microscopes may be used, employing magnifications ranging from 5 to 200X. Between these extremes, overlay templates are sometimes used with supplementary magnification supplied by inspection loupes or bench magnifiers of various types.

Visual references consist of transparent materials that are dimensionally stable and can be either engraved or marked with reference lines to accurately show feature sizes and/or position; typical materials are glass and plastic. Examples of visual references are optical comparator charts, microscope reticles, and engraved plastic overlay templates. These gages can be made to show a large number of features on the same piece of glass or plastic, and even parts that are oversized for the available visual field can be "stepped" into view using precisely controlled positioning stages or fixtures.

The advantages of visual reference gaging, together with some examples, include the following:

- Many dimensions can be checked simultaneously because they can appear together on the gage. (The inspection of gaskets, stampings, and die-cut parts benefit from this.)
- Complete contours, including irregular or mathematically defined shapes, may be checked for total form instead of probed at specific points. (Cam surfaces and form-ground parts are examples.)
- Unskilled personnel may be used as inspectors, or process operators may quickly and simply verify their own work because the part outline and associated tolerances are usually obvious on the gage. Written instructions can appear on the gage when necessary.

- Gage setup and calibration are facilitated because instructions may be incorporated into the gage, and calibration measurements may be directly verified with an optical comparator or coordinate measuring machine having a video pickup or microscope viewing head.
- Zero gaging pressure is required because contact probes are not used. (The inspection of soft and/or delicate parts such as foamed plastic, small springs, rubber, foil, or paper parts benefits because of this feature.)
- Duplicate gages are easily fabricated for use by machine operators, quality control personnel, vendors, or customer receiving personnel.
- Changes are easily incorporated as designs are revised. (The photoengraving masters or scribing-control NC tapes or files can usually be altered or reworked and new gages issued quickly.)
- Families of similar parts may often be incorporated onto one gage, depending on part geometry. (Fasteners, spacers, washers, and brackets are examples.)

In addition to these generic advantages of visual reference gaging, specific other advantages that result from the use of overlay templates, microscopes, and optical comparator charts are discussed in the appropriate subsections that follow.

Overlay Templates

Overlay templates are transparent plates that are often used in the inspection of flat parts made of paper, rubber, plastic, fabric, and metal as well as other materials. They are also used to check out processes such as the registration of printing on paper and plastic, the legibility and quality of text coming off of computer printout devices, and the size and positioning of test images in photographic processes.

Overlay templates are made of a transparent material onto which is engraved or scribed the min-max profile of the part or feature to be inspected. Incorporated into the overlay may be fixturing devices such as stops, dowel pins, or other machined features to promote precise positioning of the overlay and the part being inspected. See Fig. 17-21.

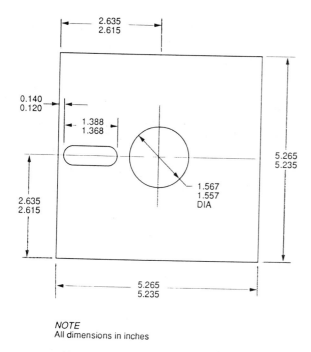

NOTE
All dimensions in inches

Figure 17-21   Sight gaging for a floppy disk envelope

Toolmakers' Microscopes

The toolmakers' microscope consists of a microscope mounted to a base that carries an adjustable stage, a stage transport mechanism, and optionally supplementary lighting for the objects mounted on the stage. Micrometer barrels are often incorporated into the stage transport mechanism to permit precisely controlled movements, and digital readouts of stage positioning are becomimg increasingly available. Various objective lenses provide magnifications ranging from 10 to 200X.

Engraved glass reticles, mounted in a reticle holder in the eyepiece of the microscope, can be used to measure parts or to inspect parts on a GO/NOT-GO basis just as overlay templates are used. In some microscope setups, other types of reticles can more easily be introduced into the optical path of the microscope by a light-splitting arrangement that lets the reticle be mounted outside the microscope barrel.

Here, film or engraved plastic reticles may also be used to check parts.

Optical Comparators and Comparator Charts

An optical comparator (sometimes also called an optical or profile projector) is basically a small parts-measuring microscope, similar in many functions to a toolmakers' microscope, but using a large projection screen instead of eyepieces. It has a stage for mounting parts to be measured and/or inspected, stage transport mechanisms, stage lighting, an optical path that is usually folded by means of mirrors within the machine itself, and a viewing and control area where the operator/inspector works. The image appears on the screen as either an inverted (reversed) or erect image where the part is seen exactly as it is staged. The comparator bounces the image off of one or more mirrors to reverse the inverted image. See Fig. 17-22.

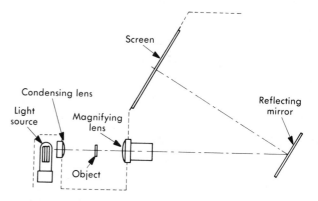

Figure 17-22   Horizontal shadow lighted optical comparator

Optical Comparator Charts: The comparator chart for inspecting a specific workpiece is a very accurately scribed, magnified outline drawing of the workpiece to be gaged containing all the contours, dimensions, and tolerance limits necessary for the purpose and mounted in an appropriate way on the viewing screen. Chart gages may be made on glass, certain types of plastics, paper, or vellum and laid out by hand drafting methods, special scribing, or chart layout devices. The material and method of layout are such that the chart gage will not significantly add to or detract from manufacturing tolerances. Glass offers the greatest dimensional stability; paper or vellum is suitable only for temporary use. See Fig. 17-23.

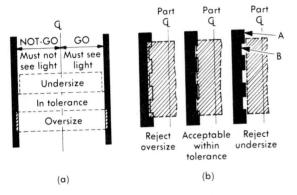

<table>
<tr><td></td><td>Part</td><td>Part</td><td>Part</td></tr>
</table>

(a)   (b)

Figure 17-23   Optical gaging for tolerances

Laser Inspection Devices

The word "laser" is an acronym that stands for "Light Amplification by Stimulated Emission of Radiation." Laser light differs from ordinary light by being extremely intense, highly directional, strongly monochromatic, and coherent to a high degree. Unlike light emitted from an ordinary source, the waves of laser light are coordinated in time and space (they are coherent) and have essentially the same wavelength (they are monochromatic). Directionality results largely from the geometry of the device and the coherence of light. The intensity of the laser beam is the result of the light energy at a single wavelength in a particular direction.

There are a number of different types of lasers available. The type of laser used depends on the specific application. Manufacturing operations such as welding metals or drilling and cutting tough steels,

ceramics, and diamonds employ high-energy, solid-state lasers such as pulsating ruby lasers or high-power molecular carbon dioxide lasers. For metrology, low-power lasers, usually of a continuous-wave output type, are employed; these are generally gas lasers.

The uses of the laser in metrology arise from the characteristics of laser light that differentiate it from ordinary light. Those characteristics are the extreme intensity, the highly directional, small, collimated beam, the monochromaticity, and the coherent nature of the light.

Laser Scanning Instruments

For the accurate measurement of the diameter of soft, delicate, hot, or moving objects, noncontacting sensors must be used. Devices of this character include capacitive gages, eddy-current gages, air gages, and optical sensors.

Optical sensors have advantages over these other gages because of the nature of light itself. The principal advantages are the following:

1. They do not require direct mechanical contact between the sensor and the object to be measured.
2. The distance from the sensor to the object to be measured can be large.
3. The response time is limited only to that of the photodetector and its electronics.
4. Light variations or interruptions are directly converted to electrical signals.

Optical sensors used for the dimensional gaging of part profiles employ various techniques, such as shadow projection, diffraction phenomena, diode arrays, and scanning light beams. If the object to be measured is small or does not move about more than a small fraction of an inch, a dimensional gage based on diffraction phenomena or diode arrays can be used. However, if the object to be measured has a dimension of more than a small fraction of an inch, diffraction techniques and diode arrays become impractical.

System Components and Operation:

A typical laser scanning instrument consists of a transmitter module, a receiver module, and processor electronics (see Fig. 17-24). The transmitter contains a low-power HeNe gas laser, a power supply, a collimating lens, a multifaceted reflector prism, a synchronizing pulse photodetector, and a protective window. In operation, the transmitter module produces a collimated, parallel, scanning laser beam moving at a high, constant, linear speed. The scanning beam appears as a line of red light and sweeps across its measurement field. When a part is placed in the field, it interrupts the beam. The receiver module collects and photoelectrically senses the laser light transmitted past the part being measured. The processor electronics process the receiver signals, converting them to a convenient form and then displaying the dimension being measured.

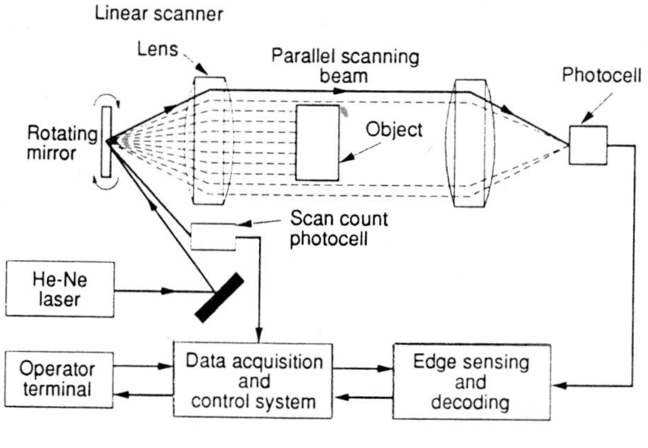

spot sizes or footprints on the part being measured. The large spot size is a disadvantage when the part to be measured is small or of a nonflat geometry. Laser radar devices tend to be only moderately precise and relatively expensive.

Of the many optical techniques, several procedures have been utilized. These include measurement of the width of a spot with a conical or tapered beam, measurement of spacing between two projected spots with the input angles being selected for sensitivity, and single-spot laser triangulation. Of these three, laser triangulation is the preferred method for high-accuracy measurements. The simplicity of this method allows the development of a highly rugged, reliable, and for the most part accurate device as part of the mechanical and optical hardware design, Fig. 17-25.

Figure 17-24   Laser scanning instrument

Laser Triangulation

A variety of noncontact techniques can be used for proximity or range-type measurements. These include time-of-flight techniques such as laser radars, ultrasonic and acoustic radar ranging, and a variety of optical techniques. Ultrasonic and acoustic systems have the advantage of large range, but in general are only capable of providing medium resolutions of proximity. Also, they use relatively large

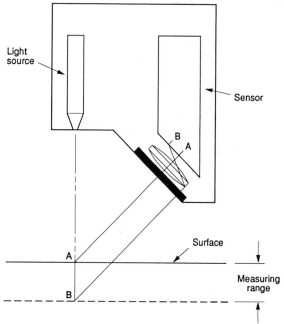

Figure 17-25   Laser triangulation

It is important to note that there are a number of techniques that fit under the general title of laser triangulation. These include structured light, light stripe, and single-spot techniques. This discussion is limited to single-spot laser triangulation techniques.

Safety: Laser triangulation sensors typically use a low-powered laser (solid-state or helium-neon) as their light source. As such, they must be certified to the appropriate class under current governmental regulations. These include mandatory warning labels and indications of the power level from such lasers. Laser power levels are typically a few thousandths of a watt. Because solid-state lasers operate in the infrared region of the electromagnetic spectrum (the beam is invisible), additional care must be exercised during their use.

Autocollimators

The popularity of autocollimators rests on their ability to sense remotely, with high accuracy, the angular rotation of a flat mirror around axes that are in the plane of the mirror. With sensitivities approaching 1/10 arc second, or even less under special conditions, it has become common practice to use autocollimators not only to monitor angular tilts as such, but to convert linear displacements into angular ones so that they can be monitored with this versatile instrument.

Optically, an autocollimator is simply a special form of a telescope. It consists basically of an illuminated target pattern or reticle located in the focal plane of the telescope objective. A plane mirror perpendicular to the optical axis in front of this telescope will reflect an image of the pattern back on itself in the same plane and in focus. A rotation of the mirror by an angle about its perpendicular position causes the return image to be displaced by a specific amount. The amount of displacement can be calculated using the equation:

$$d = 2f\theta$$

where:
  d = displacement, in. (mm)
  f = focal length of the autocollimator objective, in. (mm)
  θ = angular rotation of the mirror

A viewing system is required to observe the relative position of the image, which can be in the form of an illuminated slit or cross line or cross hair in an illuminated field. A simple eyepiece may serve or a compound microscope can be used as shown in Fig. 17-26. The fiducial index should be designed for maximum precision in zeroing the image; for example, a double line to frame a single line. Measurement is made by moving either the image or the index under micrometer control. Although most autocollimators measure around one axis only, a suitable target pattern and a two-axial index micrometer system are all that is required to make readings about two axes.

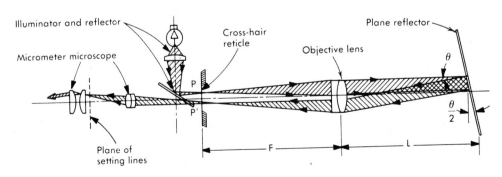

Figure 17-26 Principle of autocollimation

Photoelectric Autocollimators: Autocollimators that replace the judgment of the human eye with appropriate photoelectric systems have some important advantages that can outweigh their increased cost and complexity. Setting accuracy is improved and no longer differs between observers. Readings can be made remotely and monitored continuously when required. Such autocollimators come in sizes from 1″ (25 mm) (with null-setting sensitivity better than 0.1 arc second) to very large instruments with 10″ (250 mm) objectives. Some provide merely a photoelectric null setting without measuring capability, while others have analog or digital readout with ranges from 10 seconds to a full degree or more.

In the system shown in Fig. 17-27, the illuminated target reticle slit is imaged back in its own plane through the autocollimator objective and reflecting mirror, but displaced radially for convenience. It is then reimaged onto a vibrating slit by means of a relay lens. Behind the slit is a photocell whose output is now modulated by the vibrating slit, which makes possible the phase discrimination required to make the amplified output sensitive to the direction as well as the amount of mirror rotation from a central null

position. Such a system can be used to read mirror tilt in analog fashion on the meter. If the vibrating slit assembly is moved with a precision micrometer, a reading is obtained with the meter acting merely as a null indicator. In the latter case, the electronics need no longer behave linearly and may be simplified. A sensitivity of 0.1 arc second is reading obtainable.

Interferometers

Interferometric testing has long been used in optical metrology. The advent of the laser has not only made interferometry more convenient to use, but has also extended its range of application. Interferometry is used as a tool in optical fabrication, precision metal finishing, microlithography, and optical and electro-optical systems alignment.

For most interferometry, the output of the test is an interference fringe pattern that can be observed in real time and photographed to produce an interferogram. The type of pattern is determined by the particular measurement configuration and by the errors in the part under test. The quantitative reduction of an interference fringe pattern is usually based on

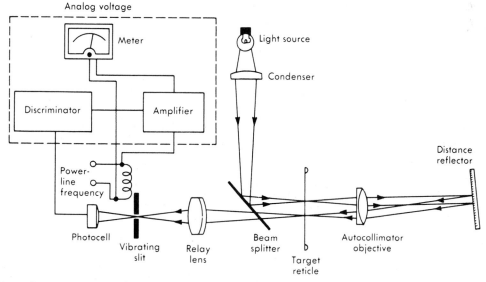

Figure 17-27 Schematic of photoelectric autocollimator

ascertaining the fractional deviation of the interference fringe pattern from some ideal, best-fitting pattern. The denominator of the fractional deviation is the measured spacing between a pair of fringes in the ideal pattern.

The quantitative usefulness of an interference pattern is dependent on having a method of data extraction and reduction. Interference pattern reduction can range in complexity from a simple visual evaluation to an elaborate reduction of the data extracted by an automatic microdensitometer with a large computer. Between these extremes there are a great variety of means for hand reduction and a number of microprocessor-based interferometer and data reduction systems. Figures 17-28 and 17-29 are two types of interferometers.

Automatic Gaging and Process Control

Automatic control over forming, machining, inspection, and assembly ensures greater productivity and lower costs, higher quality, and maximum use of machine capability. Control units must be accurate, have high-speed response, and be unaffected by vibration, oil, dirt, and coolant.

Practically all dimensions, conditions, or spatial relationships can be automatically inspected, including internal and external diameters, length, depth, taper, out of round, and geometrical conditions

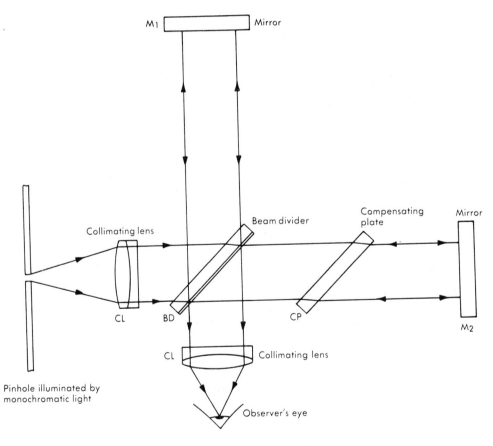

Figure 17-28 Twyman-Green specialization of Michelson interferometer

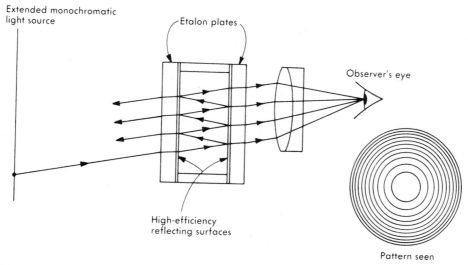

Figure 17-29   Fabry-Perot etalon

such as squareness, parallelism, concentricity, and center distance. Advances in electronic circuitry permit almost all configurations of workpieces to be inspected during all stages of the manufacturing process. Parts with large interruptions can be moved or rotated through gage fingers and measured to an accuracy of 20μin. (0.5μm) by damping, filtering, or by electronically detecting the interruptions and disregarding the resulting size change.

Automatic gage systems often include statistical process control features to ensure that corrections are made to the process only when the corrections are warranted. For example, if one workpiece in 100 measures oversize because of some periodic malfunction in the process, statistical controls will cause the system to disregard the measurement and not provide a correction to the workpiece.

Types of Systems

Automatic gaging devices are usually referred to by function or position in the manufacturing process: as preprocess gages (inspection before machining), in-process gages (inspection during machining), postprocess gages (inspection after machining), final inspection gages, and assembly gages. Combina-

tions of various types of gaging can provide fully automatic control over dimensional size from the moment the part enters the manufacturing process through assembly.

Preprocess Gaging: In preprocess gaging, the part is inspected before being loaded in the machine tool to ensure proper conditions of stock and location of machining area. Preprocess gaging helps to avoid damage to the machine and/or tooling, eliminates the expense of machining parts with insufficient stock, and extends tool life by ensuring that only correct parts are fed to the manufacturing process.

In-Process Gaging: With in-process gaging, the gage measures the part during metal removal and stops the process when the correct size is reached. With the advent of the flexible machining system concept there is more demand for in-process gaging to control the indexing and/or changing of the tooling.

Part shape and tolerances, type of machining, method of chucking, and the ability of the machine to utilize the gaging signal determine the type of in-process gaging employed. Earlier applications tended to be air or air-electric gaging. More recently, the flexibility of electronic gaging has led to its being the most commonly used system. The noncontact capabilities of electro-optical gaging and the ease with which it may be interfaced to computers and control systems have sparked interest in that approach.

Postprocess Gaging:
Postprocess gaging has been the most common type of automatic gaging, with the part being gaged after the manufacturing operation is completed. Feedback signals can be sent to the producing machine to warn, adjust, or shut down the machine if faulty parts are being produced. Frequently, automatic classification and segregation of parts by dimensional size is performed by postprocess gages. The postprocess gage may also function as the preprocess gage for a subsequent operation.

Many earlier postprocess automatic gages employed air gaging or air-electric gaging; some even used fluidic logic systems. Air-electronic systems are used primarily when there are internal dimensions to be checked and high speed is required. The dominant system used today is the solid-state electronic gage, which is fast in operation, highly accurate, and readily interfaced with microprocessors and computers.

Final Inspection Gages:
Final inspection gages are usually high-speed gages that inspect 100% of the output of a line of manufacturing machines. They may inspect as many as 25,000 parts per hour, but more commonly will inspect at a rate of several thousand parts per hour. Frequently they may categorize the parts by size and segregate salvageable parts from the rejects. Data may be kept relating to total throughput and individual categories.

Assembly Gaging:
An automatic assembly gage may be used for preassembly gaging, selective fit assembly, or postassembly inspection. Electronic gaging circuits are normally used in automatic assembly for both pre- and postassembly inspection. Parts are inspected for dimensional correctness and selective assembly.

The automatic assembly of a taper-rolling bearing illustrates how this system works. In operation, a preassembly gage checks the diameter and flange thickness of the inner race to determine the correct roller size to be assembled within a given ring. Then the gage feeds a signal to one of six preselected-size storage hoppers to release 18 rollers to the assembly station where race, rollers, and cage are assembled into a bearing of predetermined tolerance. The bearing is then inspected under a revolving-load condition for torque, noise level, and standout, the latter usually being checked with a linear displacement transducer of the LVDT type. Standout is the distance that the back face of the cone extends from the cup. Bearings are segregated as acceptable or into reject classes based on noise, torque, or standout.

Gage Transducers

The most common type of transducer used for automatic measurement and process control systems is the linear variable differential transformer (see Fig. 17-30). This device produces an electrical output proportional to the displacement of a separate movable core. Three coils are equally spaced on a cylindrical coil form. A rod-shaped magnetic core positioned axially inside this coil assembly provides a path for the magnetic flux linking the coils. When the primary or center coil is energized with alternating current, voltages are induced in the two outer coils.

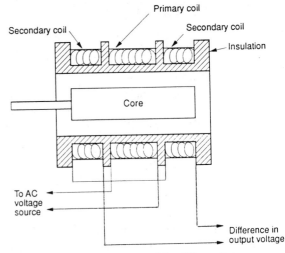

Figure 17-30 Linear variable differential transformer

Process Control

Gaging systems used for machine size control are most often used on external grinders, ID grinders, centerless grinders, and double disc grinders to precisely locate parts, indicate wheel infeed, measure wheel wear, and measure and control part size. They are also used extensively in automatic transfer lines to monitor each station and correct for size variations or to halt the process in the event that catastrophes caused by tool breakage occur.

There are two types of process control systems in use: in-process and postprocess. In-process gages are used to measure the workpiece during grinding and control the grinder wheel slide to produce workpieces within the desired tolerance limits. Postprocess gages measure the workpiece after it has been ground and provide a size offset that will apply a correction to the next workpiece to be ground.

Coordinate Measuring Machines

With the advent of numerically controlled machine tools, the demand has grown for a means to support this equipment with faster first-piece inspection and, in many cases, 100% dimensional inspection. To fill this need, coordinate measuring machines (CMM) were developed in the early 1960s. A few CMMs can even be used as layout machines before machining and for checking feature locations after machining. Thus the CMM plays a vital role in the mechanization of the inspection process because it is a universal measuring machine.

Since their development, CMMs have been increasingly used throughout industry; the automotive and aerospace industries are the primary sectors where CMMs are used. Although they were once considered an exotic tool for ensuring quality control, CMMs are now becoming a mandatory piece of equipment for both the large manufacturing plant and the small job shop. This is primarily due to the need for an accurate measuring instrument and detailed documentation of the components being produced.

Currently, coordinate measuring machines are being used in one of three ways in a manufacturing firm. The simplest approach is to place the CMM at the end of the production line or in an inspection area. With this approach, the CMM is used to inspect the first part of a production run to verify the machine setup. Once the setup is verified, it then measures parts on a random basis. For many applications, this permits the best approach to inspection.

Another approach is to incorporate the coordinate measuring machine between two workcenters and then measure 100% of the parts produced at the first center before any secondary operations are performed at the second workcenter. This approach is possible because CMMs are capable of measuring three-dimensional geometry and making many different measurements within a short period of time. When this approach is used, the CMM indirectly controls the production process. In this setting, however, the CMM must be "hardened" to perform in the shop environment or it must be completely enclosed to provide an optimum environment for part inspection.

A third approach integrates the CMM into the production line. This permits the CMM to directly control the production process. In operation, an integrated system would measure the workpiece, compare the measurements with required dimensions, and, if necessary, automatically adjust the machine controls so that the part is manufactured within the required specifications.

A basic coordinate measuring machine consists of four elements: (1) the machine structure, which basically is an X-Y-Z positioning device, (2) the probing system used to collect raw data on the part and provide input to the control system, (3) machine control and computer hardware, and (4) the software for three-dimensional geometry analysis. The measuring envelope is defined by the X, Y, and Z travel of the machine.

Although a variety of machine designs and configurations exist, all designs incorporate the same fundamental concept of three coordinate axes. Each axis is square in its own relationship to the reference plane created by the other two axes. Each axis is also fitted with a linear measurement transducer for positional feedback. This allows position displays within the envelope to be independent of any fixed reference point.

The most common reference systems in use are stainless steel and glass scales. Both systems utilize noncontact, electro-optical reader heads for determining the exact position of the machine. Stainless steel reference systems are widely used in shop environments because the difference in the coefficient of expansion between the stainless steel scale and workpiece is minimal. Glass scale reference systems are generally used in controlled environments because of the difference in the coefficient of expansion between glass and the metal workpiece. Although glass scales can be more accurate than stainless steel scales, the advent of computer compensation all but eliminates any performance differences.

The worktable of the machine generally contains tapped holes to facilitate the clamping and locating of parts. It may be made from granite because of its stability in various environments. Electronic or solid probes are inserted into the probe arm, which is supported by cantilever, bridge, gantry, or column members. Probe arm movement is guided by means of frictionless air bearings or mechanical bearings.

Coordinate measuring is a two- or three-dimensional process that determines the position of holes, surfaces, centerlines, and slopes. Up to six sides of a cube-shaped part may be inspected without repositioning.

In a typical operation, the part is placed on the table of the CMM at a random location; generally this is approximately central to the machine axes to access all the part surfaces to be inspected with the probe. Depending on the size of the part and the type of probes used, the part may need to be clamped to the machine table. If multiple inspections of similar parts are required, a reference location point may be established with a reference precision cube or sphere. The probe is then moved, manually or by machine control, until contact is made with desired part features. Reader heads, traveling on each axis along built-in axis measuring scales, transfer the

instantaneous machine position through the digital display to the computer interface. The dimensional and geometric elements may then be calculated, compared, and evaluated, or stored, or printed out as required.

Machine Configurations

A variety of machine configurations is available from the manufacturers of CMMs. Each configuration has advantages that make it suitable for particular applications. A total of 11 different machine configurations exist; however, some of these configurations are modifications of one of the five primary configurations: cantilever, bridge, column, gantry, and horizontal arm. See Figs. 17-31 through 17-35.

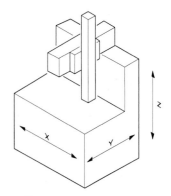

Figure 17-31   Cantilever-type coordinate measuring machine

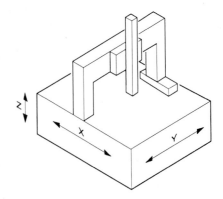

Figure 17-32   Bridge-type coordinate measuring machine

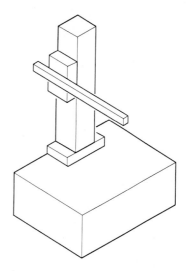

Figure 17-35   Horizontal-arm coordinate measuring machine

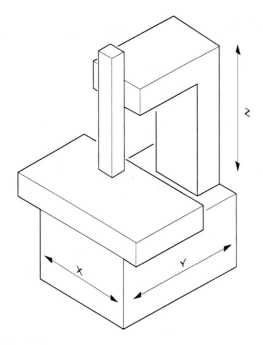

Figure 17-33   Column-type coordinate measuring machine

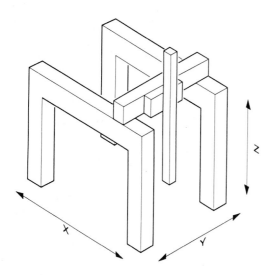

Figure 17-34   Gantry-type coordinate measuring machine

Probes

The utility of a coordinate measuring machine depends largely on the nature of the probing device. Three types of probes are commonly used: (1) hard, (2) electronic, and (3) noncontact. A probe is selected according to the dimensional and geometrical requirements of the inspection process.

Hard Probes: Hard probes consist of a shaft and a probe tip mounted in various ways to the probe arm. A variety of probe tip shapes and sizes are available; the shape of the probe determines its application. Conical probes are used for locating holes; ball probes for establishing surface locations; cylindrical probes for checking slots and holes in sheet metal parts; and edge-finder probes are used for part alignment and measurement of flat surfaces or edges of parts. Hard probes can only be used in small, manually operated CMMs when inspecting simple parts of a short production run.

Electronic Probes: Electronic probes are commonly classified into one of three categories: (1) switching, (2) proportional, and (3) nulling probes.

Switching probes are the most popular probes in use. This electronic probe, also called a touch probe, is an omnidirectional triggering device consisting of a probe body and a stylus; multiple stylus arrangements are also available. When the stylus is brought into contact with the workpiece, a signal is sent to the computer interface, indicating the instantaneous three-dimensional location of the stylus.

Noncontact Probes: Noncontact probes are used when fast, accurate measurements are required with no physical contact with the part. Several types of noncontact probes are used.

Optical probes are used when inspecting drawings, printed circuit boards, and small, fragile workpieces. When these probes are used, the basic measuring programs can still be used.

The two types of optical probes used on manual CMMs are a projection microscope and a centering microscope. On the projection microscope, the image under inspection is displayed on the screen. Part feature locations are obtained by moving the CMM to align the screen reticle to the feature. With the centering microscope, part feature locations are obtained in the same way as the projection microscope as the user looks through the eyepiece.

A third type of noncontact probe contains a laser light source that projects a small diameter spot on the part surface. A digital solid-state sensor detects the position of this spot and computes part surface location by optical triangulation. Because of the intrinsic nature of these probes, part inspection is generally limited to two dimensions.

Rotary Tables: Rotary tables are especially useful when inspecting complex, multifaced parts or workpieces with a rotation axis such as cams, gears, and rotors. A variety of sizes are available to accommodate different size workpieces. Rotary tables expand CMM measuring volume.

Rotary tables can be controlled manually or automatically. When automatically controlled tables are used, special software programs interact with the machine controls to control table movement and provide misalignment compensation.

Machine Vision Systems

Machine vision for industry has generated a great deal of interest in the technical community over the past several years. In a machine vision process, information is extracted from visual sensors to enable machines to make intelligent decisions. It has become practical with the advent of high-speed, low-cost computers, microprocessors, and advanced sensors. In addition, the availability of low-cost memory has led the way to cost-efficient machine vision systems.

The concept of machine vision goes back many years, paralleling the development of imaging sensors. In the mid-1960s, the growth of digital electronics led to experiments in electronic image processing techniques. These concepts began to capture the interest of a number of possible users for applications such as military reconnaissance, satellite image processing, medical testing, and optical character recognition. It was not until the late 1970s that shop floor applications of machine vision began to be a practical reality.

Many individuals within the industrial and research communities consider machine vision to be a subset of the larger field of artificial intelligence. Others view machine vision as a separate topic based on a number of other fields such as image processing, pattern recognition, and scene analysis. In either case, machine vision represents a relatively complex subject drawing on many technical disciplines.

To be classified as machine vision, the system must be capable of performing four primary functions. The first function is image formation. In image formation, incoming light is received from an object or scene and then converted into electrical signals. In the next step, the signals are organized in a form compatible with computer processing capabilities. The third function is to analyze and measure various features or characteristics of these signals that represent the image. Finally, a machine vision system interprets the data so that some useful decisions can be made about the object or scene being studied.

This description of machine vision makes a clear distinction between several broad categories of optical sensing equipment currently used in manufacturing applications. For example, optical comparators, which are used to project silhouettes of a workpiece on a viewing screen, would not fall under this classification because they do not possess the image analysis and interpretation capability normally associated with a machine vision system. Similarly excluded would be equipment such as photocells and other light-beam equipment for measuring presence or dimensions and closed-circuit television systems where the monitors are observed by human operators for off-line inspection applications.

Applications

Machine vision as applied to manufacturing extracts information from visual sensors to enable machines to make intelligent decisions. Such decisions are needed in quality control (detection of defects), process monitoring (prevention of defects), product routing (parts acquisition and sorting), and statistical reporting (performance evaluation).

The three main industrial application categories are inspection, identification, and machine guidance. Among the inspection tasks are the following:

- *Gaging.* Checking to make sure that dimensions fall within acceptable tolerance bands.
- *Verification.* Checking to make sure that a product is present, complete, or the right one in the proper orientation.
- *Flaw detection.* Checking for unwanted features of unknown shape anywhere on the observed portion of the product.

Among the identification tasks are the following:

- *Symbol recognition.* Deciding which one of many possible symbols is present in a given location. Examples of this application are reading serial numbers or bar codes.
- *Object recognition.* Deciding which of many possible objects is present by examining features of the object under test.

Among the guidance functions performed by machine vision are the following:

- *Object location.* Two- or three-dimensional determination of position and orientation for purposes of part acquisition, transfer, and assembly.
- *Tracking.* Continuously updating the position of a feature relative to a tool to control continuous processes such as gluing or welding.

The machine vision process consists of four basic steps. In the first step, an image of the scene is formed. The formed image is usually transformed into digital data that can be used by the computer. In the third step, the characteristics of the image are enhanced and analyzed. Finally, the image is interpreted, conclusions are drawn, and a decision is made so that some action can be taken, Fig. 17-36.

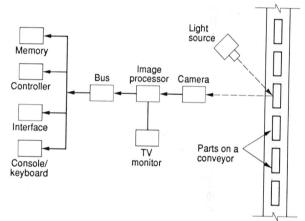

Figure 17-36   Machine vision schematic

Robotic Inspection Systems

Gaging systems can be broadly classified into fixed inspection and flexible inspection systems. Fixed inspection utilizes multiple contacting or noncontacting sensors mounted in a test fixture that holds the part to be inspected. This approach lends itself to the inspection of parts at high throughput rates. However, to switch from one part to another requires changing the test and inspection fixture. Flexible inspection utilizes sensors that are moved along a programmed path trajectory of the part being inspected. This approach lends itself to processing at moderate throughput rates. Changing from one part to another can be accomplished quickly by downloading to the machine controller a new path trajectory program. There are also systems available that move the part on an X-Y slide.

With the recent introduction of sophisticated machine vision systems into the workplace, it is now possible to expand the role of robots in flexible inspection. Recent advances in CAD/CAM technology now make possible the integration of CAD/CAM into robotic systems. This marriage of CAD/CAM with robotics significantly improves the productivity and economies of robot inspection systems.

The application areas for robotic inspection systems can be generalized as follows:

- Moderate throughput rates.
- Frequent part or model changes or model mix.
- Off-line part inspection requiring a large number of measurements.
- Large parts with complex geometry such as cavities.

The main components in a robotic inspection system are the robot, sensors, part presentation device, computer/control system, and software.

The Robot:
Robots are available in a variety of arm coordinate geometries. These designs fulfill a wide range of needs in material handling and assembly applications.

For inspection applications, the Cartesian-style robot appears most appropriate. Because of its geometric design, the Cartesian robot can provide higher repeatable positioning accuracy than other articulated arm robot styles. Experience has shown that a five-axis robot is adequate for most inspection work. This is because coordinate transformation algorithms can be used to correct sensor limitations imposed by a five-degree-of-freedom robot.

Vision Sensors:
There are three types of sensors typically used in gaging systems: (1) one-dimensional sensors, (2) contour sensors, and (3) array sensors. One-dimensional sensors give the range or distance from the sensor to a point on the object. These sensors use triangulation techniques, where the light source is usually a single-point laser diode set at a known angle from the pickup sensor. The pickup sensor is a one-dimensional linear device, either digital (solid-state line scan) or analog (lateral effect photodiode). The range can be calculated from the position of the reflected light on the linear sensor.

A contour sensor analyzes a line of light across an object; the light is usually from a laser. The laser in the visible range (red) is a gas tube device containing helium and neon. More recently these are being replaced by solid-state lasers that operate in the near-infrared range. The laser light source provides a point source of light that is converted to a line by using a cylindrical lens or by scanning the light with an oscillating or rotating mirror. It is placed at a known angle to the pickup sensor, which is usually a solid-state array camera. Subpixel techniques are used to obtain the X, Y, and Z values of the line of light across the part to better than one part in 1000 of the total field of view in the X and Z coordinates. The measurement resolution in the Y coordinate is the scanning resolution, which is typically 240 lines. Triangulation methods are used to locate and measure surfaces, contours, and edges.

An array sensor can be used to take area images of the part for locating features such as holes. This two-dimensional information can be further enhanced by adding a range sensor to obtain Z-axis information, effectively creating a simple but limited three-dimensional device.

Computer/Control Systems:
A robotic inspection system may be composed of two to four small computers that are required to perform different distributed processing functions. These computers are interconnected by a data communication and control network. This configuration allows a host computer to coordinate and control the robot and sensor(s). For example, a robot vision inspection system could be composed of a host computer or cell controller interconnected to a robot controller and a vision controller. Communications between the

vision controller and the robot controller can be direct or through the host computer, with the former most common and preferred.

The communication and control links can be either parallel or serial. Parallel links provide handshaking signals for synchronizing control activities and to handle high-speed transfer of measurement data. Serial data links provide two-way communications to allow the host computer to carry on a dialog with other processors in the system. This capability provides many advantages, and it makes possible many of the advanced control features discussed in the section on system software.

System Software:
The host computer required by the robotic inspection system can range from a small microcomputer or programmable controller to a powerful minicomputer, depending on the degree of flexibility desired and level of data processing and storage required. Consequently, the system software can range from a 64-byte package for a small microcomputer to several million bytes for a large minicomputer. Even the smallest software package should provide, as a minimum, the following functions:

- Initiate and coordinate the process inspection cycle.
- Read in and store sensor measurement data during inspection cycle execution.
- Transform measured data points into real-world coordinates and compare to desired measurement.
- Output process data results in some acceptable report format.
- Provide a limited operator interface to handle calibration and diagnostic requirements.
- Output warning and diagnosis messages to indicate system malfunction and type of error(s).

An example of the flexibility and increased system functions that can be provided by a large software package, running on a powerful minicomputer, is illustrated by the software functional diagram in Fig. 17-37. This configuration is used to operate a robot vision inspection system. In addition to the functions previously described, the software operating system provides the following functions:

- Uploading/downloading of robot path programs.

- Robot off-line programming.
- Vision off-line programming.
- Real-time robot program debugging through the computer terminal.
- Integration of the CAD/CAM database into the measuring system.
- Adaptive vision image processing.
- Adaptive real-time robot path trajectory control.
- Measurement of three-dimensional part features using a two-dimensional vision sensor.

The application-specific software can, depending on application requirements, be quite extensive. This software coordinates and controls the robot and sensor(s) to run reference point programs (required for setting up the CAD/CAM coordinate transformation system) and to run process inspection programs. Another function that it usually provides is acting as the database manager for storing processed inspection data. This manager can then retrieve selected portions of this data for outputting, in the proper report format, to a CRT terminal or hard-copy printer.

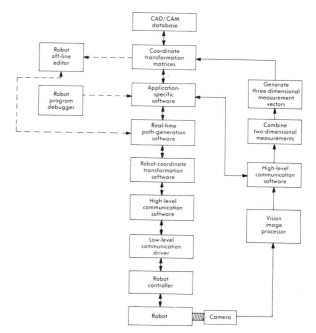

Figure 17-37 Software package needed to operate a robot inspection system using vision sensors

NONDESTRUCTIVE TESTING

Nondestructive testing is the examination of an object or material in a manner that will not impair its future usefulness. The purpose of the actual test may be to detect internal or surface flaws, measure thickness, determine material structure or composition, or measure or detect any of the object's or material's properties. Whatever the actual test may be used for, the three primary reasons for nondestructive testing are (1) to prevent accidents and save human lives, (2) to ensure product reliability, and (3) to make a profit for the user.

Nondestructive testing is also referred to as nondestructive evaluation (NDE), nondestructive inspection (NDI), and nondestructive testing and inspection (NDTI). In this chapter, the term *nondestructive testing* (NDT) will be used because it is generally the most commonly accepted term.

All nondestructive tests include the following five basic elements:

1. A source that supplies a suitable form and distribution of probing medium to appropriate regions of the test objects.
2. A modification of the probing medium or its distribution within test objects as a result of discontinuities or variations in material properties.
3. A sensitive detector responsive to changes in distribution or character of the probing medium.
4. A means of indicating or recording signals from the detector in forms useful for interpretation.
5. An observer or device capable of interpreting the indications or records in terms of test material properties or discontinuities.

Methods of Nondestructive Testing

There are a number of different methods used in nondestructive testing. Some have been in use for a long time, and others have come into play only in recent years. The more commonly used methods of nondestructive testing are as follows:

- Visual inspection
- Liquid penetrant
- Magnetic particle
- Ultrasonic
- Radiographic
- Eddy-current
- Leak testing
- Thermal
- Acoustic emission
- Neutron radiography
- Holographic

Visual Inspection

The principle of visual inspection is to illuminate the test specimen with light and then examine the specimen with the eye. Visual inspection often involves the use of optical aids. It can be used with almost any material. It is particularly effective for inspecting accessible surfaces. Internal surfaces may be inspected using a rigid or flexible borescope. Visual inspection has the advantage of being simple, easy to perform, and low in cost. However, it has the limitation of being dependent on the skills of the inspector and it can only be used to detect surface flaws. Figure 17-38 is an example of a rigid borescope with an incandescent illumination mechanism. Figure 17-39 is an example of a flexible borescope. Both are examples of tools used as optical aids in visual inspection.

Liquid Penetrant

In this method of nondestructive testing capillary action draws a liquid penetrant into surface flaws, which are then revealed by developer material to aid in visual inspection. It may be used for inspecting nonporous materials, metals, plastics, and glazed ceramics. It is particularly effective when used to detect surface flaws such as cracks, porosity, pits, seams, and laps. It has the advantages of being simple to perform and applicable to complex shapes; it can also be used to make inspections on site. This method also has limitations: It can detect only surface flaws; surface flaws must be clean in order for it to work; the penetrant washes out of large defects. Finally, standards are difficult to establish. Figure 17-40 illustrates how liquid penetrant inspection works.

Magnetic Particle

Magnetic particle nondestructive testing involves using magnetic particles to aid visual inspection. The magnetic particles are attracted by leakage flux at surface flaws on a magnetic object; these magnetic particles draw the eye of the visual inspector to

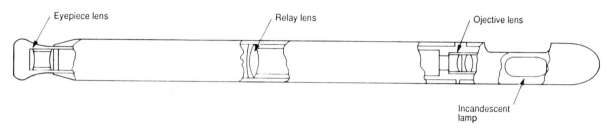

Figure 17-38   Typical rigid borescope

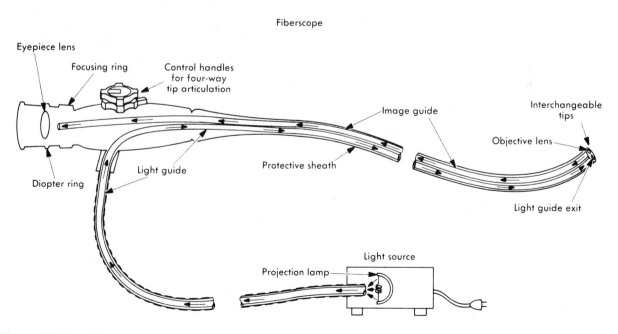

Figure 17-39   Flexible borescope

surface flaws. This process is particularly effective in detecting surface flaws such as cracks, laps, and seams. It is capable of detecting some subsurface flaws. It has the advantages of being fast, easy to interpret, and simple to perform. However, it also has limitations. Some of these are: It only works with ferromagnetic material; the parts inspected using this process must be clean and demagnetized; the process requires a high current source, and standards are difficult to establish. Figure 17-41 shows a cross section of a part undergoing magnetic particle testing. Figure 17-42 is an example of a wet horizontal magnetic particle test machine.

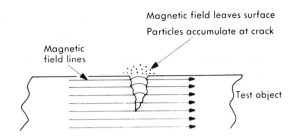

Figure 17-41   Cross section of a part undergoing magnetic particle testing

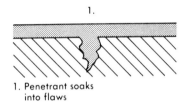

1. Penetrant soaks into flaws

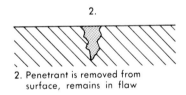

2. Penetrant is removed from surface, remains in flaw

Figure 17-42   Wet horizontal magnetic particle test equipment *(Courtesy of Ardrox, Inc.)*

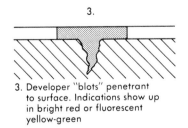

3. Developer "blots" penetrant to surface. Indications show up in bright red or fluorescent yellow-green

Figure 17-40   Diagram of liquid penetrant inspection

Ultrasonic

In this type of nondestructive testing, sound vibration waves are introduced into a test object. This energy is reflected and scattered by inhomogeneities or it becomes resonant. The behavior of the energy is interpreted from the cathode ray tube or read from a meter. This method can be used in metals, plastic, ceramics, glass, rubber, graphite, and concrete. Its applications include detection of inclusions, cracks, porosity, bursts, laminations, structure, lack of bond, thickness measurement, and weld defects. It has several advantages. These include: selective high sensitivity due to the wide variety of inspection elements in circuitry; high-speed testing; the ability to penetrate up to 60 feet of steel; and the ability to indicate flaw location. The process can be automated and recorded; and access to only one surface is usually needed. Its limitations include difficulty with complex shapes, the fact that either the surface of the test object or the defect orientation can affect the test, and that the only types of standards that can be used are comparative. Figure 17-43 illustrates immersion testing, which is one type of ultrasonic nondestructive testing; Figure 17-44 is a schematic which illustrates a computerized ultrasonic testing system.

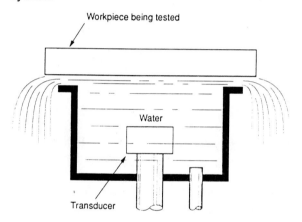

Figure 17-43   Immersion testing

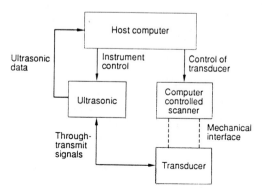

Figure 17-44   Computer-controlled ultrasonic testing system

Radiographic

The principle behind this method of nondestructive testing is penetrating radiation. Penetrating radiation is differentially absorbed by different materials, depending on the thickness and type of material. This fact allows the radiation to be used to detect a variety of different types of defects. It can be used with most materials. It is particularly effective for detecting internal defects such as inclusions, porosity, shrink, hot tears, cracks, cold shuts, and coarse structure in cast metals. It can also detect a lack of fusion and penetration in welds and missing parts in an assembly. Its advantages include the ability to detect internal defects, make a permanent film record of defects, and do automatic thickness gaging, and the fact that more standards have been established for this method than for most other methods. This method does have limitations, however. It can be dangerous; therefore, health precautions are necessary when using radiographic testing. Also, defects must be at least 2% of the total section thickness. It takes time, facilities, skill, and great care to properly process the film. This method is difficult to use on complex shapes and it is very expensive. Figure 17-45 illustrates the basic radiographic process; Figure 17-46

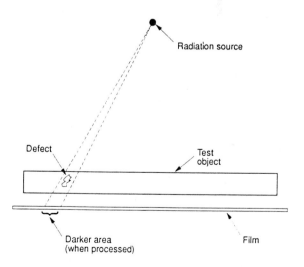

Figure 17-45   Basic radiographic process

is an example of a basic X ray tube; and Figure 17-47 illustrates the radiation symbol, with which all manufacturing personnel should be familiar.

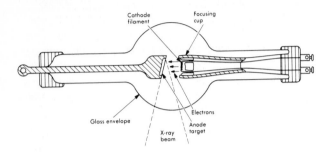

Figure 17-46　Basic X ray tube

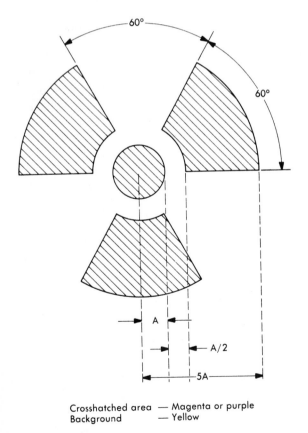

Crosshatched area — Magenta or purple
Background　　 — Yellow

Figure 17-47　Radiation symbol

Eddy-Current

This method of nondestructive testing uses alternating-current coil to induce eddy currents in the test object. Flaws and material properties affect the flow of the current in known ways. Information derived from the flow of current can be read on a meter or a cathode ray tube. Eddy-current testing is used exclusively with metals. It is particularly effective for uses such as material composition, structure, hardness changes, cracks, case depth, voids, large inclusions, tubing weld defects, laminations, coding thickness, and porosity. Eddy-current testing has several advantages: Intimate contact between coil and the materials tested is not required; it is a versatile process, and special coils can be easily made for odd-shaped test specimens; the operation can be automated; variations in the design of the electric circuit permit selective sensitivity and function; and finally, the current is sensitive to surface and near-surface inhomogeneities. Limitations include the fact that the current is sensitive to many variables. Sensitivity can vary with depth and reference standards are not well established. Figure 17-48 illustrates the basic eddy-current test system; Figure 17-49 illustrates the basic test coil types for eddy-current testing; Figure 17-50 is an example of double coil differential arrangements; and Figure 17-51 illustrates through-transmission eddy-current coil arrangement.

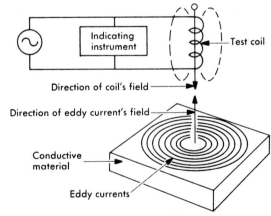

Figure 17-48　Basic eddy-current test system

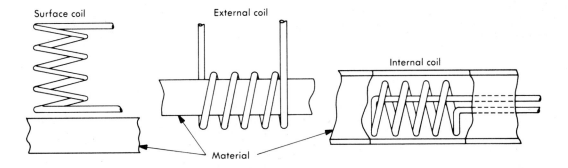

Figure 17-49   Basic test coil types for eddy-current testing

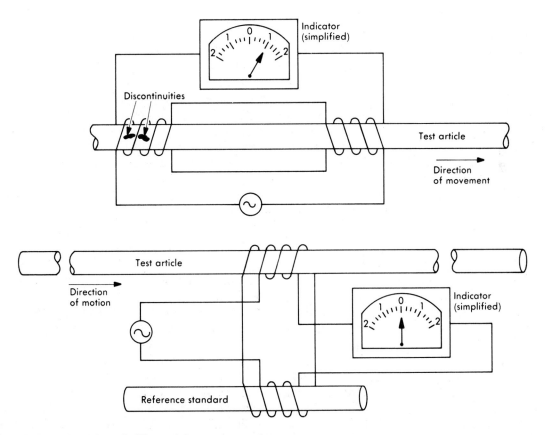

Figure 17-50   Double coil differential arrangements

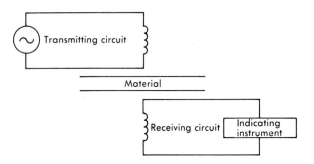

Figure 17-51 Through-transmission eddy-current coil arrangement

Leak Testing

In this type of nondestructive testing, material flows across an interface at a leak site. The rate of flow of material is dependent on pressure, time, and leak size. There are a variety of techniques used to detect the trans-interface migration. This method will work with metals, plastics, ceramics, glass, rubber, graphite, and any other type of material. It is particularly effective for testing any vessel containing a product at a pressure different from ambient or a vessel in which a pressure different from ambient can be created for evaluation. This method provides assurance that the vessel will contain its contents as defined. Figure 17-52 is a chart of the various sensitivities of leak testing methods; Figure 17-53 is a flowchart of leak testing methods and how they should be selected.

Thermal

This method of nondestructive testing uses electromagnetic radiation emitting from the test object above a temperature of absolute zero to detect flaws in the test specimen. Information gained during the test is displayed by a meter, recorder, photograph, or on a cathode ray tube. This method can be used for most materials. It is particularly effective for detecting discontinuities such as flaws, voids, inclusions, lack of bond, and so on, that interrupt flow. It can also detect higher- or lower-than-normal

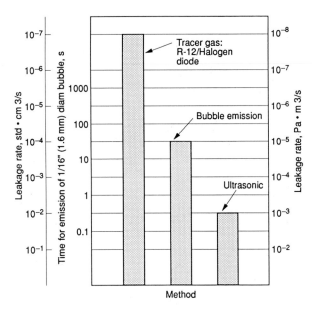

Figure 17-52 Sensitivities of leak testing methods

resistance in circuitry. It is a highly sensitive process that is applicable to complex shapes and assemblies of dissimilar components. It can be used with active or passive specimens. When using this method, however, emissivity variations in materials, codings, and colors must be considered; in multilayer assemblies, for instance, hot spots can be hidden behind cool surface components. In addition, this is a relatively slow testing process. Figure 17-54 shows the devices or materials used for thermal nondestructive testing.

Acoustic Emission

Acoustic emission is a transient elastic wave generated by the rapid release of energy from a localized source within a solid material. Rate and amplitude of high-frequency acoustic emissions are noted and correlated to structure or object characteristics. This is a very versatile nondestructive testing method that can be used with most solid materials, as well as with liquids and fluids. It is particularly effective for monitoring or determining the integrity of structures such as weldments and casting. With this method, remote and continuous real-time

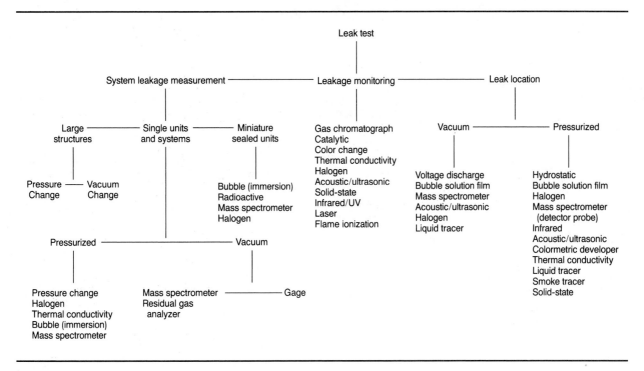

Figure 17-53 Leak testing method selection guide

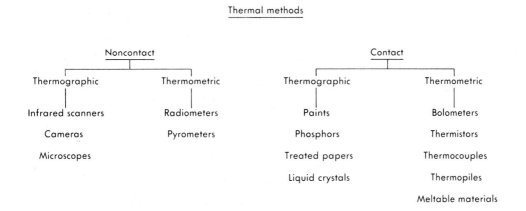

Figure 17-54 Devices or materials used for thermal nondestructive testing

surveillance of structures is possible; also, inaccessible flaws can be determined and permanent records can be made of them. However, with this method, nonpropagating flaws cannot be detected. Also, nonrelevant noise must be filtered out. Transducers must be placed on the object being tested. Figure 17-55 illustrates a typical acoustic emission detection system.

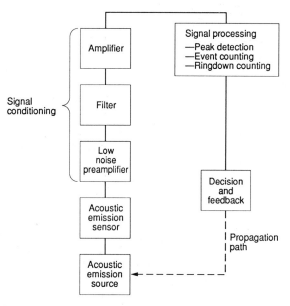

Figure 17-55 Typical acoustic emission detection system

Neutron Radiography

With this nondestructive testing method, a neutron beam is attenuated by the test object. The attenuation pattern of the test object is recorded at an image plane at conversion of the transmitted neutron beam and subsequent detection by film or some other imaging device. This testing method is particularly effective with hydrogenous material such as adhesives, explosives, and moisture. It can also be used with lithium, boron, cadmium, and several rare earth materials. This method detects cracks, voids, and density changes. It also detects the presence,

absence, or mislocation of internal components of a test specimen. This method makes a good penetration of most structural metals and has a high sensitivity to favorable metals. It also has the advantage of a permanent record of defects. However, it is a costly method that is not readily portable. In addition, it has the disadvantage of potential health hazards for operators. Figure 17-56 charts the relative attenuation characteristics of the elements for X-rayed and thermal neutrons; Figure 17-57 illustrates the two primary techniques used to expose film to the neutron beam.

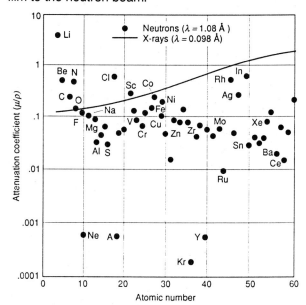

Figure 17-56 Attenuation characteristics of the elements for X rays (solid line) and thermal neutrons (dots)

Holographic

This nondestructive testing method is an optical means of capturing and recording the wavefronts resulting from a distorted object and then comparing them with the image of the true or undistorted object. It can be used with bonded and composite materials, synthetic rubber, and for three-dimensional imaging. It is particularly effective in detecting strain, plastic deformation, cracks, debonded areas, voids, and

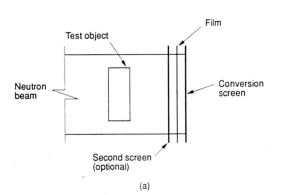

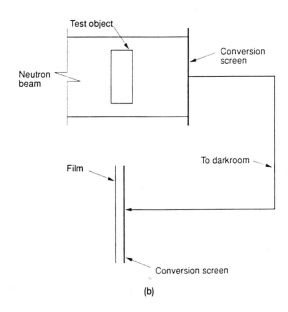

Figure 17-57 Direct exposure (a) and transfer exposure (b)

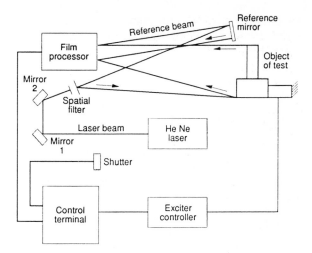

Figure 17-58 Diagram of a modular holographic camera system

MECHANICAL TESTING

Material testing is needed to learn about existing material properties and to develop new materials. Various tests are performed to explain why something works or does not work, or to meet a need not satisfied by existing materials. Material selection implies a choice to be made from several different materials. Testing is necessary to properly evaluate a material's potential for meeting the desired properties, as well as to identify any inherent shortcomings that may affect its performance. Quality control testing is done by the producer to control composition and uniformity of a specific material and by the manufacturer to confirm the specified properties and compare competing materials or sources of a given material.

Mechanical testing can benefit from automated data acquisition and analysis systems. Computer-aided systems have been developed and used for many types of tests, tension and fatigue tests in particular. A suitable computer-aided testing system can perform one or all of the following functions: (1) calibrate and control the equipment that excites the specimen or structure, (2) monitor and record the data generated during the test, and (3) manipulate

inclusions. It can also measure vibration. It requires no contact or special surface preparation. It can be used to test complex specimens. However, it must be used in a vibration-free environment. In addition, it is not particularly effective in identifying the type of flaw detected. Figure 17-58 is a diagram of a modular holographic camera system.

the data for analysis and automatically summarize the information in suitable tables, graphs, or frequency distributions.

Hardness Tests

Most hardness tests yield numerical values that are based on a material's resistance to indentation under the conditions imposed by the particular test. Resistance to scratching is another measure of hardness, as is the measurement of the energy absorbed by a material when struck by a falling object. Hardness numbers alone, because they indicate characteristics more than properties of materials, have practical significance only when correlated with service experience or a particular material property.

Perhaps the most common use of hardness tests is in quality control, where they are used to check material uniformity or processing treatment. Hardness numbers also provide a quick indication of the numerical value of a particular property of a material; before a hardness number can be used in this way, a relationship to the property must be established, and a comparison range must be defined. By correlating a series of hardness numbers with the corresponding service experience of a material in a particular use, it is possible to evaluate similar materials for use in the same application.

Brinell Hardness Test: In the Brinell hardness test, a known load is applied for a given length of time to the surface of the specimen through a hardened-steel or carbide ball of known diameter. The diameter of the resulting permanent indentation is measured and is usually converted to a Brinell hardness number by the use of standard tables. The Brinell hardness number may be calculated from the equation:

$$Bhn = \frac{P}{(\pi D/2)(D-\sqrt{D^2-d^2})}$$

where:

Bhn = Brinell hardness number
P = applied load, kg
D = diameter of steel ball, mm
d = diameter of impression, mm

There are two types of Brinell hardness testing machines in general use: hydraulic and deadweight lever-loading. Proving rings are generally used for calibrating the loads of the testers. Test blocks in any Brinell range also measure the load in an indirect manner.

Rockwell and Rockwell Superficial Hardness Tests: The Rockwell and the Rockwell superficial hardness tests are both based on the same principle. The tests yield an arbitrary number that is related to the difference in the depth of penetration of a penetrator subjected to a minor (initial) and a major (final) load under specified conditions. The Rockwell superficial hardness test is designed particularly for measuring the hardness of thin materials or case-hardened metals. The primary differences between the Rockwell and the Rockwell superficial hardness tests are lighter minor and major loads and a tester of higher sensitivity in the Rockwell superficial hardness test. The depth of penetration for the Rockwell superficial hardness test is approximately 0.00004″ (0.001 mm) for each scale division. For the Rockwell hardness test, the penetration is approximately 0.00008″ (0.002 mm) for each scale division. Figure 17-59 shows the Rockwell Hardness Scales.

Vickers Hardness Test: The Vickers hardness test consists of applying a known load for a specified time to the surface of a material through a square-base pyramid diamond having 136° between opposite faces. The Vickers hardness number, also known as the diamond pyramid hardness, is the applied load in kilograms divided by the area of the permanent indentation in square millimeters. The test is very similar to the Brinell test except for the indentor used.

Scale Symbol	Penetrator	Major Load, kg	Color of Dial Figures	Suggested Use
A	Brale	60	Black	For extremely hard material that might chip the diamond under higher load. For thin hard sheets where light loading is desirable.
B	1/16" ball	100	Red	For medium-hard metals such as low and medium-carbon steels in the annealed condition. Useful range B 0 to 100.
C	Brale	150	Black	Most commonly used for metals harder than B 100. Useful range C 20 upward. Should not be used below C 20.
D	Brale	100	Black	Used when a lighter load than the 150 kg load of the C scale is desirable.
E	1/8" ball	100	Red	For testing very soft metals.
F	1/16" ball	60	Red	Covers same range in hardness as E scale but uses 1/16" ball.
G	1/16" ball	150	Red	For metals a little too hard for the B scale.
L	1/4" ball	60	Red	Used when a lighter load than the 100 kg load of M scale is desirable for plastics and wood.
M	1/4" ball	100	Red	For testing plastics and wood.
R	1/2" ball	60	Red	Used for soft plastics.

Figure 17-59 Rockwell Hardness Scales

The two diagonals of the resulting square permanent indentation are measured with a micrometer microscope and then averaged. The average diagonal is usually converted to a Vickers hardness number by the use of tables supplied with the testing machine. The Vickers hardness number may be calculated by the use of the equation:

$$DPH = \frac{1.854L}{D^2}$$

where:

DPH = Vickers hardness number or diamond pyramid hardness
L = the applied load, kg
D = length of average diagonal, mm

The Vickers hardness number is, for all practical purposes, independent of the load used in making the test. The depth of the indentation is approximately one-seventh of the measured diagonal.

Scleroscope Hardness Tests: Scleroscope hardness is based on the height of rebound of a steel "hammer" falling on a specimen from a fixed height. The hammer is approximately ¼" (6 mm) in diameter and ¾" (19 mm) long with a rounded striking tip on its normally downward end. The hammer falls freely in a glass tube that has a scale graduated into 140 divisions. The height of the first rebound, which is the scleroscope hardness, is determined by visual observation or a dial indicating device. Repeat tests should not be made in the same location.

A scleroscope is a portable hardness tester. For this reason, it finds wide application in hardness measurements on large sections of metals, particularly when it is not convenient to take the piece into a testing laboratory. The approximate minimum thickness of metal that can be tested with a scleroscope is 0.01" (0.3 mm). Another advantage of a scleroscope hardness test is that the hammer does not leave an impression in the surface of the material being tested. Highly polished and close tolerance surfaces can be checked without damage or introduction of notches that might contribute to a premature fatigue failure in service.

Small or thin specimens must be clamped firmly to the anvil of the scleroscope or to a large piece of metal to avoid inertia effects. As the size of specimen increases, clamping becomes unnecessary, and the test piece is merely placed on a very large piece of metal. Extremely large pieces are tested without any auxiliary backing metal. The surface to be tested must be located in a horizontal plane.

Tension Test

The tension test, as the name implies, is used to determine the properties of a material under tension. The properties determined are applicable when an applied load is in the direction perpendicular to the cross-sectional area carrying the load.

In this test, a suitable specimen is loaded to failure in tension between self-aligning grips of a tensile testing machine. Extensometers are generally attached to the specimen until the loading reaches a point that is just above the value of the yield stress. The extensometers are then removed from the test specimen. Observations of the applied load and the corresponding elongations, which are converted to stress and strain, respectively, provide the data for plotting a stress-strain diagram. Values for the various tensile properties are determined from the diagram by prescribed methods and from direct load and dimensional measurements. The properties most commonly determined are yield strength, tensile or ultimate strength, elongation, and reduction in area. The proportional limit, elastic limit, and modulus of elasticity are determined less frequently, because the other properties usually suffice, and they require less care and accuracy in their determination.

Elevated- and low-temperature tensile properties are determined by essentially the same method as those used at normal temperatures. The chief differences are the provisions for maintaining specimen temperature and the necessary modifications for measuring strains. An electrically heated furnace, mounted on the testing machine in a manner to enclose the specimen, provides elevated temperatures. An insulated container of coolant, mounted on the testing machine so that the specimen is on the coolant, provides low temperatures. Dry ice (solid carbon dioxide), acetone mixtures, and low-temperature boiling liquids, such as liquid nitrogen, are used as coolants. In all cases, means are taken to ensure uniform specimen temperature.

Strain measurements usually are made with an autographic-type extensometer having extension arms that transmit the strain to the autographic extensometer, which is outside the temperature-controlled chamber. These modifications permit the measurement of the tensile properties, elongation, reduction in area, ultimate strength, and yield strength without too much difficulty.

Compression Tests

Compressive strength is generally defined as the maximum stress in compression that a metal will withstand before rupture. However, when a metal fails in this manner, it is usually accompanied by shearing stress in a diagonal direction. In the case of a material that does not fail by fracture, the compressive stress is usually regarded as an arbitrary value that produces sufficient permanent distortion to make the material unusable. The values of yield point and elastic limit in compression are usually about 110-115% of their values in tension.

The compression test is used to determine the properties of materials under compression. The properties determined are applicable when the load is in a direction normal to the cross-sectional area carrying the load and tends to compress the material. In the test, a suitable specimen is loaded in compression between the platens of a universal testing machine. In most cases, the loading is generally not carried to complete failure of the specimen, owing to the ductility of most metals. Strain gages are attached to the specimen until the loading reaches a point just above the load that corresponds to the yield stress. The strain gages are then removed, and the loading is discontinued unless it is desired to load the specimen to failure. Observations of the applied load and the corresponding deformations converted to stress and strain, respectively, provide the necessary data to plot a stress-strain diagram. Values for the different compressive properties are then determined by prescribed methods from the stress-strain diagram. The properties most commonly determined are yield strength, proportional limit, and modulus of elasticity; compressive strength and elastic limit are seldom determined.

Although it would appear that compressive properties are no more difficult to determine than tensile properties, this is far from the fact. Parallelism of the testing machine platens and of specimen ends is a factor of great importance and is frequently overlooked or underestimated. If special care is not exercised to ensure a high degree of parallelism of the platens and specimen ends, uniform axial loading will not be obtained. The latter is necessary for reliable results. Self-aligning hemispherical or ball-mounted platens are desirable for such work.

Direct Shear Tests

Shear stresses result from the application of a load in the plane or line of the cross section bearing the load. Direct shear is present when one layer of a material is made to move on the adjacent layer in a linear direction. Transverse loading of a rivet or bolt in a plate produces shearing stresses in it. When the load is carried by one plane or cross section of the rivet, as in a single-lap riveted joint, it is called single shear. When the load is carried by two cross sections as in a double-lap riveted joint, it is called double shear. If the opposing forces producing shear do not act in the same plane or line, bending stresses are set up. Therefore, in a direct shear test it is important to have the opposing forces at the cross section, which transmits the load, act in the same plane or line, at least with reasonable precision.

A jig with a specimen in place is mounted between the platens of a universal testing machine and loaded

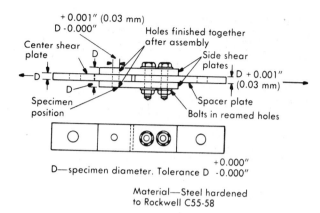

Figure 17-60   Shear jig for tensile loading in self-aligning fixtures

to failure of the specimen in shear. The tensile loading features of the testing machine, including self-aligning drawbars, are used with the jig shown in Fig. 17-60.

The shear strength is the maximum observed load divided by the cross-sectional area that is sheared. For example, the shear strength of a cylindrical specimen sheared in the jig shown in Fig. 17-60 is the maximum observed load up to failure divided by twice the cross-sectional area of the cylinder.

Torsion Tests

Torsion shear is produced by rotation or by torque. In this type of shear, one layer of a material is made to rotate on an adjacent layer. This type of shear is present in rotating shafts, such as crankshafts or driveshafts, when power is being transmitted.

In a torsion test, equal and opposing moments are applied at opposite ends of a suitable specimen in planes perpendicular to the specimen's longitudinal axis. When placing the specimen in the testing machine, it is important that the longitudinal axis of the specimen coincides with the common axis about which the heads of the testing machine rotate. The applied torque is generally increased until the specimen fractures. A device known as a troptometer is usually attached to the specimen to measure the amount of twist during the application of torque. Observations of the applied torque and corresponding twist of rotation, which are converted to stress in the outer fiber and strain in the outer fiber, respectively, provide the data for plotting a stress-strain diagram. The properties commonly determined are shear strength or modulus of rupture, yield strength, proportional limit, modulus of elasticity or modulus of rigidity, and angle of twist.

Notched-Bar Impact Tests

Notched-bar impact tests are commonly called impact tests, implying that the test results are applicable to problems involving shock loading or impact. Unfortunately, this is not the case because practically all specimens used in impact tests are notched. The type of specimen and the method of breaking it were originally designed and used to show a variation in notch sensitivity for steels that exhibit a ductile fracture in the tensile test. Impact tests are, in reality, notched-bar tests. There are true impact tests, such as ballistics tests, but these are performed infrequently.

Impact tests, such as the Charpy and Izod tests with notched specimens, measure the amount of energy absorbed in fracturing the specimen. The true worth of these values is to determine the relative notch toughness of two or more materials under the particular test conditions. Values determined under one set of test conditions are not convertible to values for other test conditions.

In the case of steels, the results of impact tests at various temperatures frequently show a relatively sudden drop in impact value accompanied by a change from a ductile to a brittle fracture. For many steels, this change occurs in the region not far above or below room temperature. Therefore, it is important to know the temperature sensitivity for many applications that involve atmospheric and subatmospheric temperatures. Standard tests show only the sensitivity that is developed by the particular bar and notch used in the test, and larger parts and structures with more severe notch conditions will show low-temperature brittleness at higher temperatures. In general, ductile nonferrous metals and alloys and austenitic steels retain notch toughness down to very low temperatures.

Fracture Toughness Tests

The linear elastic fracture mechanics approach to judging fracture toughness has been studied intensively for many years. It is appropriate for quantifying fracture and crack growth resistance of materials. Fracture mechanics leads to parametric values that can be used in design if careful consideration is given to differences between testing and service conditions.

Toughness tests based on fracture mechanics characterize strong materials on the basis of their tolerance for cracks and resistance to brittle fracture. It is based on the assumption and experience that cracks or flaws exist in materials and grow when the intensity of the stress field near the edge of the crack reaches a critical value. It is also assumed that the stress intensity is proportional to the square root of the crack parameter. The crack parameter is usually taken as half the crack length because the calculations are usually concerned with disc-like flaws growing to a free surface, such as through-thickness failures in plates. The fracture toughness value for quasi-plane strain, termed K_{IC}, is reported in units of kpsi $\sqrt{\text{inch}}$; higher values indicate better toughness.

The fracture toughness value is also known as the critical stress intensity factor for the opening mode of cracking in the stress state of quasi-plane-strain. The critical stress intensity factor characterizes the resistance of a material to fracture in the presence of a sharp crack under severe tensile constraint when the plastic region at the tip of the crack is small compared with the size of the crack and the specimen. The K_{IC} value is believed to represent a lower limiting value of fracture toughness; it varies with testing temperature and speed.

Conducting fracture toughness studies requires special equipment and careful measurements and techniques. The methods and precautions to use in determining K_{IC} values on specimens 0.25" (6.4 mm) thick or thicker are described in ASTM Standard E399. The specimens are notched and fatigue-cracked prior to testing. One type of specimen is single-edge-notched and loaded as a beam in three-point bending. The compact tension specimen is single-edge-notched and pin-loaded in tension. A variety of specimens are permitted by the standard because the appropriate dimensions increase with the square of the ratio of toughness to the yield strength of a material. If the stock available for testing is not of appropriate size, valid K_{IC} values cannot be determined by the standard method. Thinner materials can be tested by other types of specimens, if the materials are sufficiently brittle.

The stress intensity factor not only describes the instability of a crack in a material under load, but it also appears to describe the stable extension of a crack under cyclic loadings at stress intensity levels below those characteristic of conditions critical for fracture. Because fracture toughness evaluations are becoming increasingly important and experimental techniques and methods of data interpretation are changing rapidly, the reader is urged to consult current publications.

Fatigue Tests

Fatigue tests are concerned with the progressive failure of materials under repeated loading. Fatigue properties of a material are usually determined from a series of tests on a number of similar specimens. In one kind of test, a specimen is subjected to cycles of fully reversed (tension to equal compression) nominal stress and the number of cycles withstood to rupture is recorded. Then other specimens are subjected to cycles of other different stress ranges. A plot known as an S-N curve is then made of stress, S, against number of cycles, N, to failure (Fig. 17-61).

Usually S is plotted as the ordinate on either a Cartesian or a logarithmic scale and N as the abscissa on a logarithmic scale. Some materials (particularly steels) show curves that flatten out at large values of N. The stress level at which this occurs, and below which fatigue lifetime would presumably

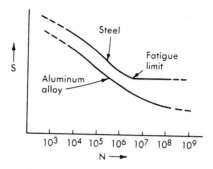

Figure 17-61 Typical endurance curves for aluminum

be infinite, is called a fatigue limit. Some materials may not exhibit well-defined fatigue limits; hence, the stress level at an arbitrary long lifetime (say, more than 10^7 cycles) is used as a design fatigue limit for such a material. It should be kept in mind that, in the presence of other deteriorating factors (such as corrosion and elevated temperature), a material may not have a fatigue limit.

Fatigue tests may, of course, be run under various kinds of loading such as rotating bending, plane bending, axial loading, and repeated torsion. In many of these (axial loading, for example), another parameter emerges. Tests may be run at a fixed value of mean load and an S-N curve obtained by plotting the maximum stress (or the stress amplitude) against N; other curves may be obtained at other values of mean stress. Thus a material may be characterized, not by a single fatigue value, but by many values.

Creep Tests

Creep is the continuing change in dimension with time of a material under stress. Materials exhibit creep, particularly at elevated temperatures, even at stresses below their short-time proportional limits.

Creep tests are usually made under a constant tensile load. A selected constant tensile load is applied to a specimen at a selected elevated temperature, and the resulting elongation is observed at sufficient intervals of time to define the relationship between elongation and time. When the observed data are plotted, elongation is usually made the ordinate and time the abscissa. Because the load is not applied until the specimen has reached temperature, there is an initial elastic elongation. If the load is above the proportional limit, the initial elongation will also include some plastic deformation. Some plots of creep-time-elongation data include the initial elongation that occurs on application of the load and some do not.

Fig. 17-62 shows two typical creep curves in which the initial elastic elongations are included. The lower curve in the figure illustrates the type of creep curve obtained when the combination of stress and temperature used in the test does not cause failure of the specimen during the test. The first stage of creep is evidenced by a high but decreasing rate of elongation. The second stage is characterized by an approximately constant rate of elongation. Usually a total test time in excess of 1000 hr is required to establish the approximately constant rate of elongation. The minimum creep rate is observed during the second stage. The upper curve of Fig. 17-62 illustrates the type of creep curve obtained when the

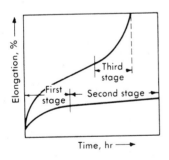

Figure 17-62 Typical creep curves

combination of stress and temperature used in the test produces failure of the specimen. This curve shows the third, or final, stage of creep, which is characterized by an increased rate of elongation. The time and elongation at which second-stage creep changes to the third stage of increasing creep rate is called the transition point.

Rapid Metal Identification Tests

Various tests, when applicable, are used as a rapid means of identifying a metal without resorting to methods of quantitative chemical analysis. They are often used to sort unidentified or mixed materials. Such a test does not determine the chemical composition, but determines whether or not a selected property of an unknown metal is the same as that of a known metal. Judgment must be exercised in identification testing because of the possibility that more than one material may have a particular value of a given property.

Rapid identification tests depend on different approaches: chemical behavior, visual observation of the color and luster of the material or the appearance of its chips or sparks, or instrumented measurements. The most useful tests are those that can be conducted in place without sampling in plant environments. Rapid identification tests should be reliable, portable, and inexpensive.

Magnetic Tests: Magnetic tests generally involve the comparison of a magnetic property of a known metal with that of an unknown metal. A permanent magnet is used to differentiate between magnetic and nonmagnetic metals. When both metals are magnetic, the comparison is made with special techniques and equipment.

Spark Tests: Spark testing consists of holding a piece of metal against a rotating grinding wheel and observing the characteristics of the sparks produced. Various grades of steel give sparks with typical patterns that serve as means of identification. Even small added quantities of some elements, such as aluminum and titanium, can be detected by experienced practitioners. With care and practice, spark testing can be a reliable and inexpensive method of rapid metal identification. Over the years, the industrial use of spark testing has declined, but the art is still being practiced.

Hardness-After-Quenching Test: The carbon content of a steel can be estimated by determining the R_C hardness of a small sample that has been water-quenched from its hardening temperature. Curves are available that show the relationship between maximum hardness and carbon content and may be used for converting the observed R_C hardness to approximate carbon content.

Thermoelectric Test: When the junction formed by two dissimilar metals in contact with each other is heated, an electromotive force is set up. If the two metals forming the junction are identical, the electromotive force is zero. A galvanometer connected across the ends of the two metals opposite the junction may be used to indicate the presence or absence of an electromotive force and hence the dissimilarity or identity, respectively, of the two metals forming the junction. Routine checking with this test method is generally done with special equipment.

Chemical Spot Tests: There are a number of chemical spot tests, each of which will indicate the presence or absence of an element in a metal. A chemical test generally consists of applying a few drops of one or more chemical reagents to a spot on the unknown metal and watching for some characteristic result, such as a particular color.

Stress Analysis

Experimental stress analysis is the term applied to the determination of the location, direction, and approximate intensity of stress in a part; no mechanical properties are determined. In practice, strains are measured and the corresponding stresses are obtained by multiplying the known modulus of elasticity of the material under test by the observed strains.

Practical stress analysis methods include photoelasticity, brittle coatings, resin-based coatings, ceramic-based coatings, and strain gages. These methods are generally applicable to parts of any size, shape, or material.

Photoelasticity: In the photoelastic method of stress analysis, a model of the part is made from a transparent plastic material and is loaded as in service. Polarized light is transmitted through the model and the stresses are calculated from the fringe pattern that is observed.

Brittle Coatings: Brittle coatings are applied to the entire surface of the structure. The coatings crack in response to strains within the material produced by external loads. When the strain has reached a certain value, fractures occur in the coating at right angles to the principal tension strains, so peak and localized stresses can be evaluated. These are the points of greatest tension stress; therefore, a direct correlation exists between the crack patterns in the coating and possible fatigue failure. Used quantitatively, the brittle coatings also measure the strain level within ± 10% accuracy. Another use of brittle coatings is to survey stresses over an entire structure. This overall stress picture shows how loads are carried by the parts and indicates how to obtain a proper and efficient distribution of material.

Resin-Based Coatings: Resin-based coatings are applicable to most stress problems and are supplied graded for threshold strain, temperature, and humidity. The strain range is from 0.0005 to 0.0030 in./in. (mm/mm); temperature range is from 10 to 120°F (-12 to 50°C); and the humidity range is from 0 to 100%. Before the coating is applied, the part surfaces must be degreased and sprayed with an aluminum undercoat. The part under test and the calibration bars are sprayed with a coating selected to meet the test conditions expected. Coatings are normally dried for about 16 hours, but drying can be done in six hours at slightly elevated temperatures.

Ceramic-Based Coatings: Ceramic-based coatings extend the temperature range of rapid metal tests and are graded for threshold strain and for the coefficient of thermal expansion of the metal involved. Normal range of strain is about 0.0003-0.0015 in./in. (mm/mm) and coatings are usable on metals with the coefficient of expansion ranging from 5×10^{-6} to about 9x10⁻⁶in./in./°F (2.8x10⁻⁶ to 5x10⁻⁶mm/mm/°C). Surfaces are prepared by sandblasting, and coatings are sprayed, air-dried, and fired at approximately 1000°F (540°C) for a certain length of time, depending on the size of the part. Ceramic-based coatings are calibrated similarly to resin-based coatings, but the calibration bars must be made of the same material as the test structure.

Bonded Strain Gages: The bonded, resistance strain gage is the most widely used strain measurement tool for experimental stress analysis. It consists of a grid of very fine wire or a thin metallic foil bonded to an insulating backing called a carrier matrix. The electrical resistance of this grid material varies linearly with strain. Strain gages are small and light, will operate over a wide temperature range, and can respond to both static and dynamic strains.

There are many types, shapes, and sizes of commercially made strain gages having gage lengths from 0.008 to 4.0″ (0.20 to 102 mm). Strain gage selection is based on the operating temperature, state of strain, and the stability requirements for the gage installation. It is recommended that the tester refer to the strain gage manufacturer for assistance in selecting the proper strain gages, adhesives, and protective coatings for a specific application. Adhesives are available for bonding these gages to surfaces for use at temperatures ranging from -320 to 1100°F (-196 to 595°C).

In use, the carrier matrix is attached with an adhesive to the part being tested. When the part is loaded, the strain on the surface is transmitted to the grid material by the adhesive and carrier matrix. The strain in the part is found by measuring the change in electrical resistance of the grid material.

Strain gages are generally attached to the part being tested in arrangements of two or four gages, following one of the three installation patterns shown in Fig. 17-63. The two strain gages, A and B, are installed to measure the moment, *M*, in the beam. Gages C and D (with C¹ and D¹ on the opposite side of the beam) will measure the force, *L*. Gages E and F (with E¹ and F¹ on the opposite side) will measure torque, *T*. Each set of gages is connected in a Wheatstone-bridge circuit.

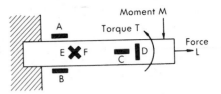

Figure 17-63   Beam gaged to measure force, moment, and torque components

Statistical Process Control (SPC)

The concepts of mass production and interchangeability of parts gave rise to the need for quality control. Prior to these concepts, manufactured items had been tailor-made one at a time. Eli Whitney is usually credited with making the first attempt at mass production through interchangeability of parts. In 1798 he was awarded a contract from the U.S. Government to produce 10,000 muskets; he proposed to complete the contract by manufacturing 10,000 stocks, 10,000 trigger mechanisms, 10,000 barrels, and so on, and then assembling the 10,000 muskets. The parts produced individually were intended to be interchangeable. It didn't work out this way, and Whitney had problems fulfilling the contract.

Eli Whitney learned about the need for quality control the hard way. Since the advent of mass production through interchangeable parts, quality control methods and processes have improved continually. It started out as a very simple process, which amounted to developing a written specification for a part and then ensuring that the manufactured part conformed to the specification. Early specifications usually related to such factors as material, dimension, and surface finish. Over the years as manufacturing materials, processes, and equipment became increasingly sophisticated, so did the methods and processes used for quality control. Many of those methods and processes have been covered in this chapter.

Eventually a variety of factors, such as large batches, made 100% inspection unfeasible. Manufacturing professionals also began to realize that quality control methods that focused only on after-the-fact evaluations of produced parts were no longer sufficient; greater emphasis was needed on the processes used to produce the parts so that corrections could be made before large volumes of unacceptable workpieces were produced. This led to the development of statistical quality control, or as it is now called, *statistical process control*. The original concept was developed by Dr. Walter A. Shewhart in an effort to improve the quality of manufactured products produced in large batches for the U.S. military. Shewhart was a physicist who specialized in the random behavior of small particles in a fluid caused by the collision of molecules; he used statistics to analyze the behavior of these particles. His methods eventually evolved into what is known today as *statistical process control*. It means using statistical principles to control the quality of manufacturing processes and, in turn, the products produced using these processes.

In order to understand statistical process control, it is necessary to understand several basic statistical concepts. These include *variability, central tendency, range and standard deviation, normal distribution,* and the *central limit theorem*.

Variability

In manufacturing, it is impossible to produce two or more parts that are exactly the same. Every successive part produced will vary from other parts to some degree. This is recognized in the design process when tolerances and allowances are built into the design of a part.

It is important for manufacturing personnel to understand the concept of variability and the causes of variability. All of the many causes of variability can be grouped into two broad categories: *common causes* and *assignable causes*.

Chance is a common cause of variability. For example, when tossing a coin, the result can be either heads or tails. If the coin is tossed enough times, the probability of coming up heads is equal to the probability of coming up tails. In other words, over an extended number of tosses, there is a 50% chance of the coin coming up heads and a 50% chance of the coin coming up tails. This translates to a probability of 0.5. *Probability* means the likelihood that a given occurrence will have a particular outcome. When the outcomes of a process such as a manufacturing process can be expressed in probabilities, and the distribution of outcomes is predictable, a *constant cause system* exists. If all things behaved perfectly in a manufacturing process, for example, if tool wear did not change the behavior of a given tool, all manufacturing processes would be constant cause systems. This would mean they could produce parts with the same degree of variation continually as long as the process was operating. Using statistics, variations attributable to common causes can be identified.

Variations applicable to specifically identifiable causes are called *assignable causes of variability;* these are causes that fall outside the realm of chance. In a manufacturing setting such causes could be tool wear, a new machine operator, improper setup, or a variety of causes that cannot be explained by statistics. Assignable causes of variation produce behavior that falls outside in a range established by statistical probability. By using control charts, manufacturing personnel can separate common causes of variability from assignable causes of variability or, in other words, separate predictable variability from unpredictable variability. There are a number of different types of control charts that can be used in statistical process control. All of them serve the purpose of charting the actual behavior of a given process in such a way as to show how it relates to an upper limit, lower limit, and mean. Figure 17-64 is an example of a control chart showing points plotted between a lower and upper limit; Figure 17-65 shows a simple manufactured part with a dimensional specification and plus and minus tolerances. By applying the tolerance it can be seen that the upper limit, or largest acceptable part, is one with a thickness of 1.280″; the lower limit, or smallest acceptable part, is one with a thickness of 1.220″. Any part produced within the range established by

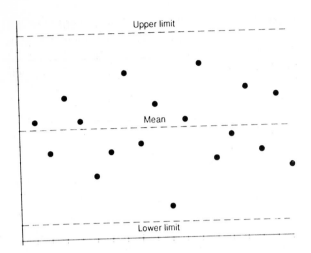

Figure 17-64 SPC chart

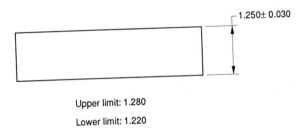

Figure 17-65 Upper and lower limits of a manufactured part

these upper and lower limits is an acceptable part. So long as only common causes of variability are acting on the process used to produce this part, parts produced will exhibit what is known as *central tendency*. This means they will tend to group in actual produced sizes around a given dimension.

Further, the tendency will be to group around the dimensions represented by the mean. The mean is represented by the symbol $\overline{X}$. The formula used to calculate the mean is:

$$\overline{X} = \frac{X1 + X2 + X3 + \ldots + X_n}{N}$$

Using the workpiece in Fig. 17-65 as an example, the dimensions for all produced parts would be added

together and divided by the number of parts in the batch to determine the mean dimension. In this example, all parts produced would tend to arrange themselves around or near the mean. However, that does not imply that parts with the mean dimension will be produced in greater numbers than those of other dimensions within the upper and lower limits; in fact, parts actually carrying the mean dimension may be the least number produced. It simply means that over the entire batch there will be a tendency for parts to arrange themselves around or near the mean.

Range and Standard Deviation

The concept of range has already been described as that area established by the upper and lower limits. Anything within the upper and lower limits falls within the established range. A related measure of dispersion is the *standard deviation*. A standard deviation can be a useful statistical tool because data charted can form graphs of radically different shapes that have the same range and the same mean. Standard deviation can be used to explain not just the range and the mean but the shape of the distribution of charted data. Standard deviation gives manufacturing personnel a measure of distance from the mean. This concept is illustrated in Fig. 17-66.

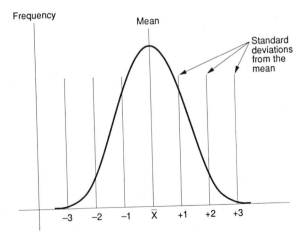

Figure 17-66 Bell-shaped curve

The vertical lines drawn upwards from the base that intersect the plotted curve represent standard deviations from the mean. Data that take the shape shown in Fig. 17-66 (bell-shaped curve) have what is known as a normal distribution. With a normal distribution, 68.25% of all data will fall between one standard deviation to the right and one standard deviation to the left of the mean; 95.46% of all data will fall between two standard deviations on the right and two standard deviations on the left of the mean; 99.73% of all data will fall between three standard deviations on the right and three standard deviations on the left of the mean.

Normal Distribution

Bell-shaped curves such as the one shown in Fig. 17-66 illustrate the normal distribution of data. Normal distribution charts can be valuable tools for manufacturing personnel. By charting the actual behavior of a given process and comparing it with a bell-shaped curve showing a normal distribution, manufacturing personnel can readily see the capability of a process. Such comparisons are only valid, though, if the behavior of the process has been monitored over a sufficient period of time. The behavior of the process is plotted on a control chart such as the one shown earlier in this chapter. Control charts such as this one are based on the central limit theorem.

Central Limit Theorem

When a large batch of manufactured parts is broken into subgroups, the averages of the subgroups will plot in the form of a normal distribution curve, provided the manufacturing process is a *constant cause system*. The averages of different size subgroups from the overall distribution will follow the central tendency theory. The variation of averages will follow a normal distribution curve. This is the *central limit theorem of statistics*. This theory allows manufacturing personnel to monitor a process over a given period of time by measuring

and averaging a standard subgroup of workpieces or parts. The frequency could be one measurement per hour, one measurement every two hours, or even one measurement per day, depending on the rate of output. The size of the subgroup can vary depending on the overall size of the distribution. As long as the process is a constant cause system, the averages taken will fall under a normal curve. So long as this is the case, the process can and will produce results that can be predicted statistically.

Collecting Statistical Data

There are a number of different types of data. An easy way to categorize data is by how they are collected. Using this method, there are two broad categories: *variable data* and *attribute data*. Variable data are any data that can be measured. Attribute data are any data that can be counted or grouped together based on common characteristics. Both types of data can be valuable in identifying quality problems. However, variable data are generally more useful for correcting problems and improving quality.

In order to use data to improve quality, it is necessary to know how to identify the characteristics of a part that relate to quality. Selecting characteristics of quality for a given part involves clearly delineating the purpose of the part and identifying its characteristics as being under variable or attribute data. Selecting characteristics is a critical part of the process in statistical process control because it determines what type of data will be collected, charted, and analyzed.

Data that are collected must be reported. The most common ways of recording data in statistical process control are check sheets, handheld data collectors, and fixed station data collectors. Figure 17-67 is an example of a check sheet for collecting data concerning the dimensions of a specific part. By examining this check sheet it can be seen that 56 produced parts were inspected; of those, only two fell outside of the specified range. Those two were produced above the limit established by the tolerance in the specification.

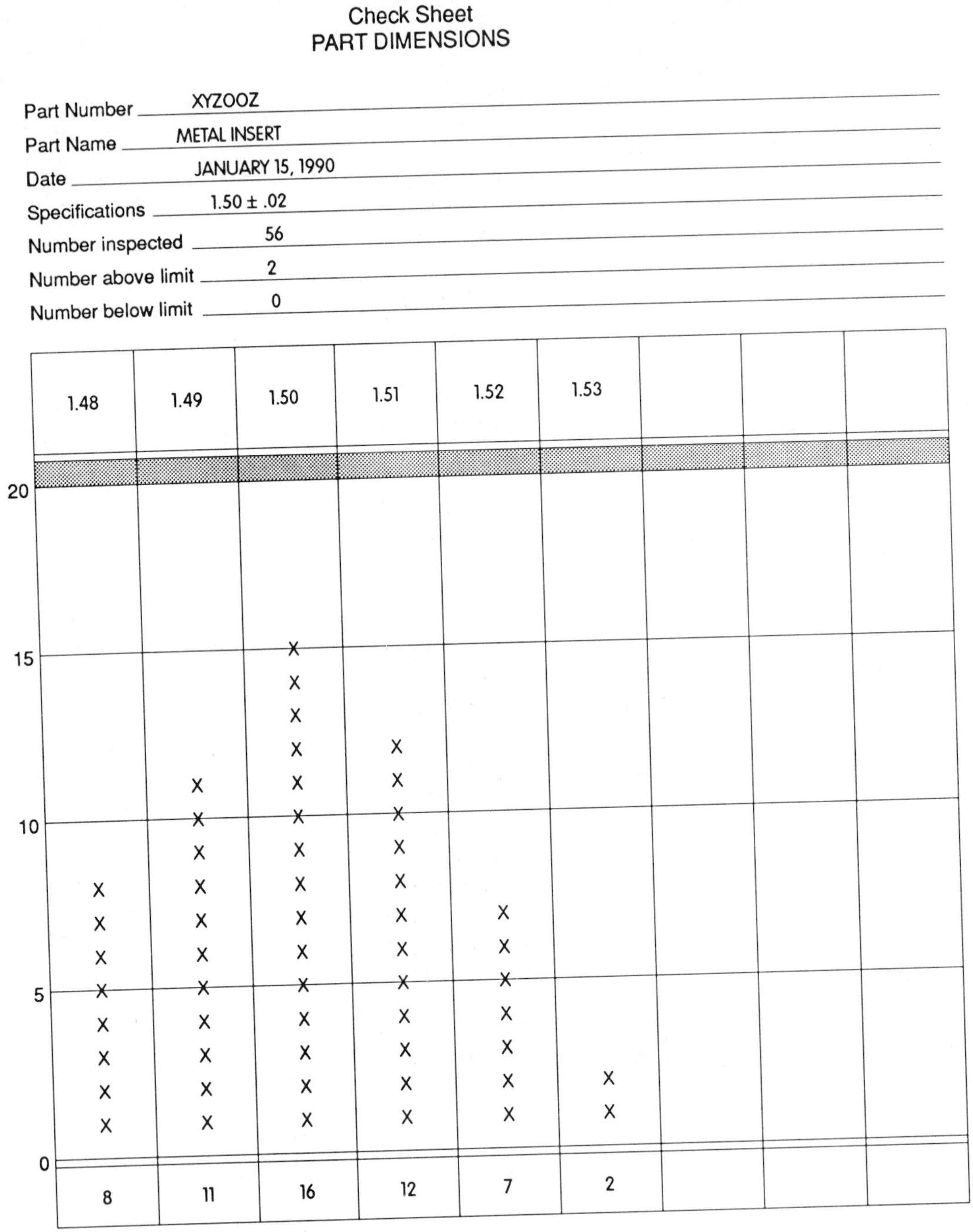

Check Sheet
PART DIMENSIONS

Part Number ____ XYZOOZ

Part Name ____ METAL INSERT

Date ____ JANUARY 15, 1990

Specifications ____ 1.50 ± .02

Number inspected ____ 56

Number above limit ____ 2

Number below limit ____ 0

1.48	1.49	1.50	1.51	1.52	1.53				
8	11	16	12	7	2				

Figure 17-67   Check sheet

Just-in-Time Manufacturing (JIT)

Manufacturing personnel tend to view just-in-time (JIT) as an innovative inventory and delivery system, which it is. But it is much more than just an approach to delivery and inventory. JIT is an innovative manufacturing strategy designed to make manufacturers more competitive and, in turn, more profitable.

The underlying principle of JIT is to purchase and/or manufacture only the exact amount of a supply or product needed to fill an order and to deliver it or have it delivered exactly when it is needed. In short, it means purchasing only what is needed and delivering only when it is needed.

When fully implemented, JIT can have a positive impact not just on competitiveness and profits, but also on quality. Advantages that can be gained from JIT include the following:

- Decrease in scrap, wasted material, and wasted labor.
- Easier identification of causes of mistakes and delays.
- Significantly less in-plant inventory.
- Improvement of quality.
- Improvement in productivity.
- Lower production costs.

The principal focus of JIT is to simplify and streamline the flow of materials into, and products out of, the manufacturing plant. JIT can be applied effectively in both a traditional and an automated environment.

Impact of JIT on Quality

The successful implementation of JIT depends on the delivery of defect-free materials; material defects will undermine a JIT system immediately. If four workpieces are delivered to a manufacturing cell and two of them have defects, production stops. Therefore, producing defect-free products is an essential ingredient of JIT. This contrasts with traditional batch manufacturing, in which numerous parts are delivered for every one needed. If a defective part is presented, it is tossed in a scrap bin and another part is presented. With traditional batch manufacturing techniques, scrap and waste are an accepted built-in element.

The dependence of JIT on defect-free parts means that this concept works best in manufacturing settings where statistical process control (SPC) is used. SPC allows manufacturers to monitor processes in such a way as to ensure defect-free parts.

With JIT, each person involved in the production of a product is personally responsible for a given piece of the process. Before presenting a part to the next station, it must be inspected to ensure it is defect-free. Direct responsibility on the part of production workers tends to promote defect-free parts throughout the manufacturing process. Contrast this with the traditional approach of tossing a finished workpiece into a bin along with numerous other workpieces. A worker who places just one more part in a bin is not likely to be as concerned about quality as one who passes just one single part on to the next person.

Establishing a JIT System

There are seven steps required in establishing a JIT system in a manufacturing company. Those steps can be summarized as follows:

- Reducing lot sizes.
- Reducing setup times on machines.
- Implementing total quality control.
- Implementing a *pull* system.
- Implementing a continuous flow approach.
- Elimination of buffer inventories.
- Simplification of purchasing processes.

Large lot sizes breed inefficiency and mitigate against productivity. Complicated materials handling systems are needed to move parts from storage bins to production stations. Such systems are expensive.

They also tend to hide defects, since it is difficult to identify defects in a part that is one of many in a bin. Correspondingly, this tends to increase the amount of waste.

With traditional manufacturing, the costs added from waste, materials handling, and defective parts are built in as fixed costs. When JIT is fully implemented, lot sizes can be reduced substantially with corresponding reductions in the fixed costs associated with traditional manufacturing.

In order to successfully reduce lot sizes, it is necessary to reduce setup times on machines. This is accomplished by investing time in the development of special jigs, fixtures, and conveyors. These special tools allow general-purpose machines to quickly become more like dedicated machines.

The traditional approach to manufacturing can be characterized as a *push* system. This means that parts are pushed through production. This approach can create bottlenecks as parts are pushed quickly through fast machines, and then back up when presented to slower machines.

Successful JIT requires an approach that can be characterized as a *pull* system. A pull system means that parts are pulled through production processes as needed by a *rope* represented by customer orders.

Total quality control means expanding quality measures beyond the realm of the production component to the entire company. In order for JIT to succeed, all components of a company must participate in assuring quality.

JIT works best when the production component is set up in manufacturing cells rather than in the traditional job-shop layout. In the latter approach, workers next to each other produce the same workpiece without seeing how and where they fit into the overall process; in the cellular format, workers are able to see the overall product production system and where they fit into it. The cellular approach also cuts down on the amount of complicated, sophisticated materials handling.

By eliminating buffer inventories, JIT forces manufacturing personnel to focus on the causes of delays and other factors which mitigate against efficient production. Without buffer inventory to fall back on, manufacturing personnel must continually improve production processes.

In order to successfully implement JIT, purchasing procedures must be simplified and streamlined. JIT eliminates the buffer inventory that is traditionally used to fall back on when purchasing glitches occur. This means more frequent deliveries of smaller numbers of parts. It also implies less steps in the process and less paperwork.

One of the traditional purchasing steps that may need to be eliminated with JIT is competitive bidding. With JIT, quality and dependability are more important than low bids. The bidding process is replaced with a vendor qualification process. A company sets up a set of specifications that vendors must comply with and standards they must meet in order to be a qualified vendor. Once a vendor is on the list of qualified suppliers, the focus switches to long-term relationships based on quality and dependability.

Total Quality Control

Total quality control is as much a philosophy as it is a quality control system. It involves including all components of a manufacturing firm in assuring quality. These components include design, finance, purchasing, marketing, production, and management.

All of these components must be structured in such a way as to promote rather than inhibit quality. In this way, the focus of a company changes from *detecting* defects to *preventing* defects. It involves a continual integrated effort to identify factors that promote quality while simultaneously identifying and eliminating factors that inhibit quality.

Implementing Total Quality Control

In a traditional manufacturing setting, costs are computed for and assigned to labor, material, and waste. With total quality control, cost computations are extended to quality. The cost of quality can be viewed as the cost of control added to the cost of problems. Problems occur during production or after a finished product has been delivered.

Problems that might occur during production include scrap, rework, design changes, and wasted time. Costs can be computed and assigned to these failures. Problems that might occur after production include in-field repairs, technical support, and lost orders. Costs for these problems can be computed and assigned.

Control involves both prevention and identification of defects. Prevention strategies include training, preventive maintenance, design reviews, and review of specifications; identification activities include inspection, testing, data collection, and data analysis. Costs can be computed and assigned for prevention and identification activities. These, when added to the cost of problems, equal the cost of quality.

This approach clearly identifies how and where money is being spent on quality, and it also allows manufacturing personnel to see exactly where money and effort should be focused in order to maximize improvements. This is why the total quality control approach to quality is so essential in a modern manufacturing environment.

KEY TERMS AND PHRASES

Acoustic emission testing
Autocollimator
Brinell hardness test
Calipers
Comparator charts
Compression test
Coordinate measuring machine
Creep
Cylindrical plug gages
Cylindrical ring gages
Direct shear

Eddy-current testing
Fatigue
Gage blocks
Gage transducers
Holographic testing
Impact fracture
Indicating gages
Interferometers
Laser triangulation
Leak testing
Liquid penetrant testing
Machine vision system
Magnetic particle testing
Micrometers
Neutron radiography testing
Nondestructive testing
Optical comparator
Overlay template
Process control
Quality
Quality assurance
Quality control
Quality improvement
Quality management
Quality system
Radiographic testing
Robotic inspection system
Rockwell hardness test
Sleroscope test
Sine bar
Snap gages
Spline gages
Stress analysis
Surface plates
Taper gages
Tension test
Thermal testing
Thread gages
Torsion
Toughness
Transverse bending
Ultrasonic testing
Vickers hardness test
Visual inspection testing

QUESTIONS FOR ADDITIONAL STUDY AND REVIEW _____

1. Define the term *quality*.

2. List six factors to be considered when developing a quality system.

3. Explain the concept of *quality improvement*.

4. List three commonly used graduated tools/ instruments.

5. What are the characteristics that have made electronic indicating gages popular?

6. What are *gage blocks*?

7. Explain the use of the following fixed functional gages:
   - Cylindrical plug gages
   - Cylindrical ring gages
   - Snap gages
   - Thread gages

8. Explain the use of *overlay templates*.

9. Explain the use of a *comparator chart*.

10. List four advantages of laser scanning instruments.

11. What is an *autocollimator*?

12. What is an *interferometer*?

13. Explain the term *process control*.

14. What is a *coordinate measuring machine*?

15. List five types of coordinate measuring machines.

16. What are the three main categories of industrial applications of machine vision systems?

17. List four application areas of robotic inspection systems.

18. Explain the following methods of nondestructive testing:
   - Liquid penetrant
   - Magnetic particle
   - Radiographic
   - Eddy-current
   - Thermal
   - Holographic

19. Explain the following mechanical testing methods:
   - Vickers hardness test
   - Tension testing
   - Compression testing
   - Toughness testing
   - Fatigue

20. Explain the concept of statistical process control (SPC).

CHAPTER 18

Flexible Manufacturing

MAJOR TOPICS COVERED

- Multifunction Machines
- Flexible Manufacturing Defined
- Overview of Flexible Manufacturing
- Historical Development of Flexible Manufacturing
- Rationale for Flexible Manufacturing
- Flexible Manufacturing System Components
- Flexible Manufacturing Cells
- Flexible Manufacturing and CIM

One of the benefits the computer has brought to manufacturing is the potential for ever-increasing degrees of flexibility. The concept of flexibility is not new in manufacturing. Manually operated machines have always been flexible, but only with piecework. Traditionally, large batches have meant a corresponding lack of flexibility. Even the smallest design change in a workpiece has traditionally meant time-consuming and expensive work stoppages. The modern concept of flexibility does not just mean the ability to produce parts with different design characteristics. It also means the ability to produce them quickly and competitively.

To understand the concept of flexibility, think of the leading fast food restaurant chains. They typically have a highly structured menu and a production

system set up to turn the product out fast. With some of these restaurants, requests for special changes to accommodate personal tastes—even minor changes—can result in major delays. They are not flexible. Other fast food restaurants are set up to accommodate individual differences in taste and do not prepare the product until it is ordered. Those that are able to do this without major sacrifices in time are *flexible*.

The same concept applies to manufacturing. Customers will frequently need a batch of workpieces, some of which will require minor variations. For example, a manufacturing company might receive an order for 3,000 metal plates of a specified size and material. Of the 3,000 total, 1,000 must have three holes drilled, 1,000 must have two holes and a notch, and 1,000 must have one hole and a slot.

All 3,000 of the plates are basically the same with only minor differences. In the modern world of manufacturing, companies must be able to accommodate such orders quickly, efficiently, and inexpensively.

The answer is flexible manufacturing. The first step toward flexible manufacturing was made with the advent of multifunction machines; the next step is the flexible manufacturing cell, Fig. 18-1; next is the flexible manufacturing system. Each of these concepts is dealt with in the sections which follow.

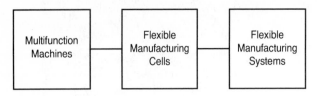

Figure 18-1   Steps to flexible manufacturing

Multifunction Machines

Multifunction machines can perform a number of operations simultaneously and/or consecutively, often permitting complete machining in one setup. There are many different types of multifunction machines. Those most widely used are:

- Single-spindle automatic lathes
- Single-spindle automatic screw machines
- Swiss-type automatic screw machines.
- Multiple-spindle automatic bar and chucking machines
- Center drilling and facing machines
- Horizontal boring machines
- Vertical boring machines and turret lathes
- Multiple-spindle vertical, automatic chucking machines
- Machining centers
- Head changing machines
- Automated and special-purpose machines
- Transfer machines

Single-Spindle Automatic Lathes

Features of single-spindle automatic lathes include: I) the capability to use multiple tools mounted on two or more independent synchronized slides; and 2) automatic cycling. The machines can be single-cycle automatic, with manual loading and unloading, or fully automatic.

A major advantage of single-spindle automatic lathes is high-speed production, resulting from having a number of tools cutting simultaneously with no time lost for tool indexing or positioning. Customarily, as many tools as possible are used without exceeding the power of the machine and within the rigidity constraints of the workpiece.

Single-spindle automatic lathes generally are best suited for high production requirements in turning and facing multiple-diameter or long workpieces. The more complete the setup, the longer the production run should be for minimum cost because setup and changeover are time-consuming.

When these machines are used for shorter production runs, consideration should be given to reducing the number of tools, thereby increasing the cycle time and increasing the setup time. Setup time can also be reduced by sequentially scheduling the production of families of parts, thus minimizing changeover time. Lathes and turning centers equipped with NC/CNC are being used extensively for short production runs and increased flexibility. Figure 18-2 shows examples of single-spindle automatic lathes.

Single-Spindle Automatic Screw Machines

The term *automatic screw machine* is not an exact, specific machine-tool classification. Use of the word *screw* originated from the initial use of these machines for producing screws. Now, these machines are employed to manufacture a wide variety of parts, but the word *screw* persists.

Automatic screw machines are designed to produce parts from bar or coil stock. With automatic operations taking place successively or simultaneously, using tools mounted on a turret and cross slides, these machines can complete workpieces at high production rates. Machines of this type have many tooling and operating principles similar to those for horizontal turret lathes, single-spindle automatic lathes, and multiple-spindle automatic bar and chucking machines.

Two major classifications for single-spindle automatic screw machines are *cam-controlled* and

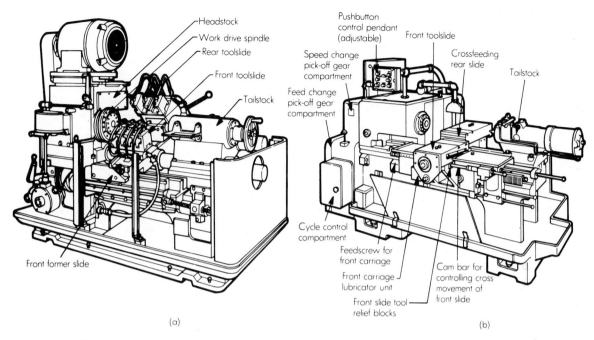

(a)

(b)

Figure 18-2   Single-spindle automatic lathes

programmable (camless) machines. Cam-controlled automatics, requiring cams and speed-change gears for specific applications, are used more extensively for the high-production requirements of a single part or family of parts. Camless automatics, programmed by CNC units, provide simpler setup, faster changeover, and increased flexibility for shorter run production. Figure 18-3 is an example of a single-spindle automatic screw machine. Figure 18-4 shows examples of the types of tools used with automatic screw machines.

Swiss-Type Automatic Screw Machines

The Swiss-type single-spindle automatic screw machine is not, strictly speaking, a screw machine, since it does not perform the ordinary screw jobs with the same facility as the conventional type of screw machine. Owing to the method by which the

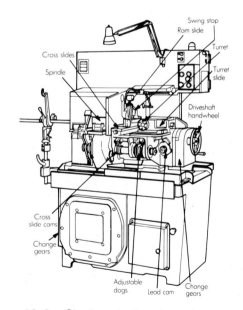

Figure 18-3   Single-spindle automatic screw machine with cam control *(Courtesy of Brown & Sharpe Manufacturing Company)*

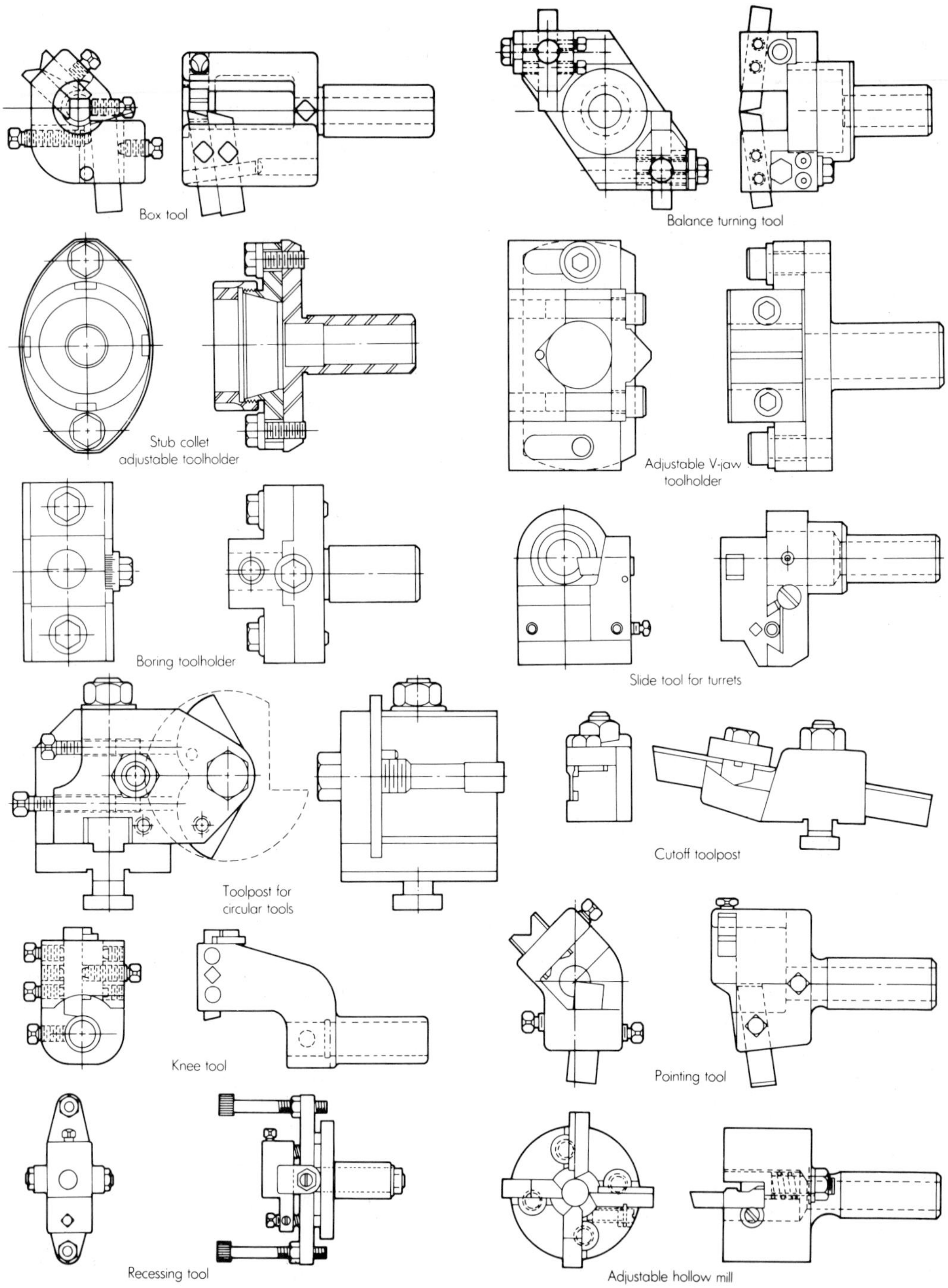

Box tool

Balance turning tool

Stub collet
adjustable toolholder

Adjustable V-jaw
toolholder

Boring toolholder

Slide tool for turrets

Toolpost for
circular tools

Cutoff toolpost

Knee tool

Pointing tool

Recessing tool

Adjustable hollow mill

Figure 18-4   Standard tools for automatic screw machines

stock is fed while rotating, by a sliding headstock through an adjustable carbide-lined guide bushing into the cutting tool, it should probably be known as a Swiss bushing-type or precision sliding-headstock automatic lathe. The Swiss-type automatic differs from the traditional automatic screw machine, which employs form tools, indexing turrets, and box tools, in that it uses single-point tools.

The Swiss-type automatic has distinct advantages over the conventional type of screw machine in that it is capable of producing long, slender, and complexly contoured parts with a high degree of accuracy. In the hands of a skilled operator, Swiss-type automatics have been known to repeat, over long periods of time, a total tolerance on diameters close to 0.0002″ (0.005 mm). Shoulder lengths have been held to a tolerance of 0.0005″ (0.013 mm); however, a tolerance of 0.0008″ (0.020 mm) is more practical.

A high quality of finish can be turned to a degree comparable to that of a ground finish using Swiss-type automatics. Therefore, the machines are invaluable when high-finish close-tolerance bearing surfaces are required on small shafts, such as those used in electric meters, watches, and clocks.

In addition to providing close tolerances and a high quality of finish, this class of machine is able to produce long, slender parts of extremely small diameters—ranging down to about 0.005″ (0.13 mm). This is possible because the guide bushing, through which the bar to be turned must pass while rotating, can be adjusted to practically eliminate all radial movement. Best results are obtained by using centerless-ground stocks as round as possible and uniform in their diameter throughout each bar length, although drawn wire to a total tolerance of 0.0003″ (0.008 mm) is usually sufficient for critical applications.

Cutting tools, almost without exception, are single-point carbide and positioned directly in front of the guide bushing. High-speed steel tools are used for some special applications. It is preferable that all tools be positioned just a few thousandths of an inch (about 0.05 mm) in front of the bushing. The bushing then relieves the turned portion, the tool load being almost entirely absorbed by the guide bushing. Optical machines with microscopes, as well as other machines, are available for presetting tools to reduce setup times.

The Swiss-type automatic is capable of completely machining certain kinds of parts that, if placed on a conventional screw machine, would require secondary and tertiary machining. The Swiss-type machine, however, does not equal the productivity of a conventional screw machine on straight screw jobs. When wide tolerances are permitted and better class 2 threads are not required, and when parts are not too long, the conventional screw machine exceeds Swiss-type machine production.

Swiss-type automatics are available with cam control or CNC units which eliminate the need for cams. Cam-controlled machines are lower in initial cost and are considered by many engineers to be the most efficient for high-volume production requirements. Machines with CNC, however, are being increasingly applied because of their short programming and setup times, which increase their flexibility. Figure 18-5 illustrates the movements of a Swiss-type automatic screw machine.

Multiple-Spindle Automatic Bar and Chucking Machines

The principal advantage of the multiple-spindle automatic over the single-spindle machine is the reduction in time required per piece. In contrast to the single-spindle machine, on which one turret face at a time is working on one spindle, the multiple-spindle machine has each turret or end-slide tool working on its respective spindle at the same time. On the single-spindle machine, the time required to complete one piece is a total of the time needed for each turret operation plus the time necessary to index the turret; on the multiple-spindle machine, the time necessary for one cycle is the time required only for the longest single cut plus idle time.

The range of work produced by a multiple-spindle machine is comparable to that produced by lathes, single-spindle bar machines, and turret lathes. Because of its longer setup time and increased tooling cost, the multiple-spindle machine is generally

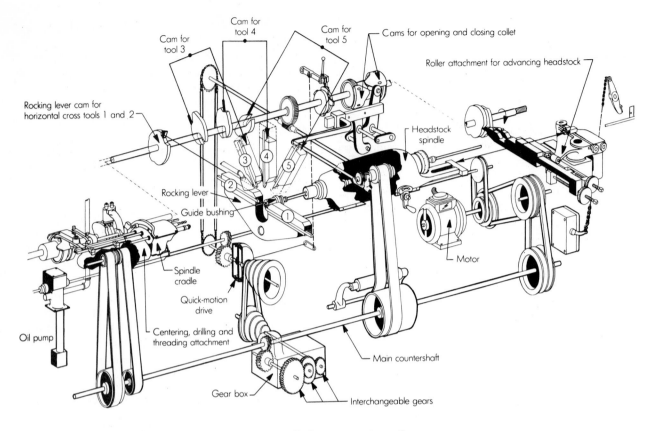

Figure 18-5   Movements on a cam-controlled Swiss-type automatic

less economical than the other three on short runs; however, it is more economical on long runs. Changeover time has been reduced on modern multiple-spindle automatics by features such as pre-set tooling, master collets and pushers that accept different stock sizes, magazine-fed bar feeders that feed stock into the reel tubes without stopping the machine, quadrant mechanisms that permit changing tooling strokes by adjustments instead of changing cams, and machine sequencing by programmable controller. Multiple-spindle machines lend them-selves well to the application of special fixtures and attachments that may eliminate secondary operations on the work. Figure 18-6 is an example of a six-spindle automatic bar machine.

Center Drilling and Facing Machines

The center drilling and facing machine is a multifunction machine now used extensively for shaft-type workpieces. The importance of center drilling is often overlooked, probably because the centers usually have no function once the workpieces are completed. Accuracy of the centers, however, has a major effect on tolerances that can be maintained in subsequent operations, such as turning, grinding, and hobbing, where the centers must be used for location.

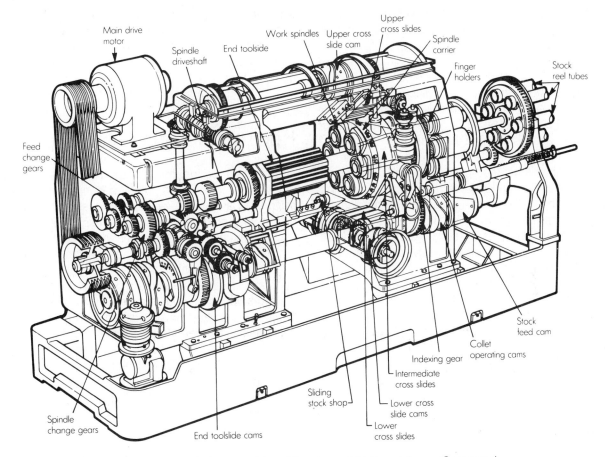

Figure 18-6 Six-spindle automatic bar machine *(Courtesy of National Acme Company)*

Historically, centers were usually produced in shafts, one end at a time, on engine lathes. This is a slow process and requires a skilled machinist to produce acceptable results. In an effort to speed the process, some manufacturers use a drill press equipped with a fixture. If the shafts are long, however, this method is cumbersome and the results are often unsatisfactory. Automatic machines now available can outproduce engine lathes and drill presses, and can center more accurately.

Most workpieces which require centering are repositioned, end-for-end, on centers when they are manufactured. For the features machined on both ends of the workpieces to be in proper relationship, the distance between centers must be maintained accurately. This dictates the use of a machine that drills both ends at once and consistently and accurately repeats the end-cutting operations.

Axes of the centers must be coincident, and the centers must be round and have a reasonably good finish; failure to achieve these conditions results in imperfect contact between the countersunk holes and the machine centers. Since heavy cuts are often taken over the tailstock center, the lack of good surface contact causes the countersunk holes to deform. This can cause chatter, inaccurate workpieces, and other problems.

Most product designs require that the ends of shaft-type components be machined to provide a reasonable tolerance on overall length and smooth finish.

Since facing to the tailstock center is difficult on a lathe, it is desirable to combine facing with the center drilling operation.

Plunge facing can be done with combination cutters consisting of a center drill with two or more facing blades mounted around the drill. Such tools are used in the spindles of centering machines. The diameter that can be plunge faced is primarily a function of the power available on the machine.

When the ends of the workpieces are smaller in diameter than the cutters, the entire ends are faced. When the shaft ends are larger in diameter, the cutters can be designed to spotface. Many shafts made from large-diameter bars have reduced diameters at their ends. In such cases, when stock is removed, the spotfaced surfaces cover the entire ends of the turned workpieces. When the turned surfaces are larger in diameter than the spotfaced surfaces, facing tools can be added to blend the spotfaced and faced surfaces.

Combination milling and centering machines are preferable to plunge facing and centering machines in the following cases: When the workpieces have ends with excessive stock, such as some forgings; when they have rough and/or out-of-square ends, such as sheared bars; or when they have large diameters for which continuous, flat end surfaces are required. Figure 18-7 is an example of a milling and centering machine.

Horizontal Boring Machines

Horizontal boring machines (HBMs) usually do many other operations besides boring, especially milling. As a result, they are often called horizontal boring mills or horizontal boring, milling, drilling, and tapping machines. These heavy-duty machines are employed extensively for large, complex castings, forgings, weldments, and similar workpieces. They perform different operations at various locations on the workpieces without the need for changing the basic setup, and they can maintain accurate relationships between the machined surfaces. These machines are not, however, high-production machines and are generally linked to low- to medium-size runs.

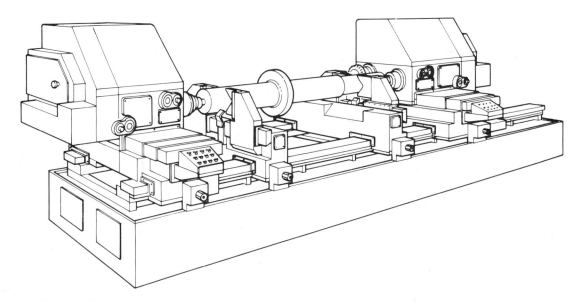

Figure 18-7   Milling and centering machine *(Courtesy of Seneca Falls Machine Company)*

Characteristic features of HBMs include the following:

1. Horizontal spindles that rotate the cutting tools.
2. Horizontal surfaces on which workpieces are mounted.
3. Power feed of the spindle to advance cutting tools into the workpieces.
4. Power-fed relative motion between the spindle and workpiece in at least two axes perpendicular to the spindle axis.
5. Power saddle feed parallel to the spindle axis.
6. Outboard supports on some machines, for the ends of line boring bars and arbor-mounted slotting cutters.

Horizontal boring machines are available in a wide range of capacities. The size of a machine is often identified by the diameter of its spindle, which generally varies from 3 to 10″ (76-254 mm). Spindle rigidity is directly related to the fourth power of its diameter. As a result, considerable additional cutting power is obtainable with larger spindle diameters. Main drive motors range from 15 to 75 hp (11.2-56 kW) or more. Figure 18-8 is an example of a horizontal boring machine.

Vertical Boring Machines and Turret Lathes

Vertical boring machines (VBMs) and vertical turret lathes (VTLs) are turning machines that in many ways are similar to conventional lathes turned on end. Workpieces are mounted on a horizontal table or chuck rotating about a vertical axis. Cutting tools, which are generally nonrotating, are fed horizontally or vertically into the workpieces.

Operations performed on a VBM or VTL are similar to those done on conventional lathes. They include turning, facing, boring, grooving, generating threads, and contouring. These machines are commonly used to make round parts having short lengths in relation to their diameters and to make large, heavy, and cumbersome parts.

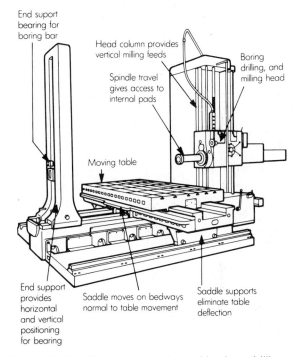

Figure 18-8 Table-type horizontal boring, drilling, and milling machine

Vertical boring machines (or mills) originally had one or two ram-type heads, while VTLs had a turret-type head. Since modern machines frequently combine the two types of heads and many ram heads now have indexable turrets, the historical distinction between the two machines has less validity than before. Also, the basic construction, tooling, workholding, controls, and operation of the machines are essentially the same. To avoid confusion, the term *vertical turning machine* is sometimes used for both machine types.

Some machine builders and users distinguish between a VBM and VTL based on machine size and, to a lesser extent, the volume of the production run. Loosely defined, a machine is called a VTL if it handles workpiece sizes of up to 100″ (2540 mm) in diameter; for workpieces above that diameter, the machine is designated a VBM. To some extent, VBMs are often characterized by one-of-a-kind and small-lot production requirements; but they can be tooled for long production runs. Figure 18-9 is an example of a vertical boring machine; Figure 18-10 is an example of a vertical turret lathe (CNC).

Figure 18-9 CNC Vertical Milling Center *(Courtesy of Cincinnati Milacron Marketing Company)*

Figure 18-10 CNC Turning Center *(Courtesy of Monarch Sidney)*

Multiple-Spindle Vertical, Automatic Chucking Machines

Various types of multiple-spindle vertical, automatic chucking machines are available. The machines consist of a carrier with six or eight equally spaced, vertical columns encircling a stationary column. On the column over each spindle, except at the loading station, are combination or multiple-tool heads.

Each spindle and head comprises a station or machining unit having independent feed and speed controls for maximum flexibility and efficiency. Each station is set up to perform specific operations in sequence with the next station, so that one carrier cycle around the column produces a finished workpiece. Since all stations of the machine are working simultaneously on various operations, each spindle successively transfers a finished workpiece as it indexes through the loading station.

For continuous or long production jobs, the standard design of the machine can be varied to suit the specific application. Dual spindles and heads can be used at each station, permitting duplicate or first and second chucking operations at each station. Production is also increased on simpler jobs that can be completely machined in half the cycle time by arranging two loading stations. Double indexing the spindle carrier has been used extensively where two chuckings or two sets of identical operations can be accomplished on the one machine.

Multiple-spindle vertical chucking machines have minimum floor space requirements and are easy to relocate to suit production-line manufacturing techniques. Figure 18-11 is an example of a multiple-spindle automatic chucker.

Machining Centers

Machining centers have been defined as multifunction CNC machines with automatic tool-changing capabilities and rotating cutting tools. Since their introduction in the late 1950s, they have become one of the most common of all cutting machines.

Figure 18-11   Milling machine capable of multiple cutting paths *(Courtesy of Cincinnati Milacron Marketing Company)*

Increased productivity and versatility are major advantages of machining centers. The ability to perform drilling, turning, reaming, boring, milling, contouring, and threading operations on a single machine eliminates the need for a number of individual machine tools, thus reducing capital equipment and labor requirements. One relatively unskilled operator can often attend two machining centers and sometimes more. Most workpieces can be completed on a single machining center, often with one setup.

Additional savings result from reduced materials handling, fixture costs, and floor space requirements. Substantial time conventionally spent moving work from machine to machine is saved, and throughput is much faster. Also, in-process inventory, represented by skids of workpieces normally seen at several machines, is replaced by work at only one machine.

Most machining centers maintain close, consistently repetitive tolerances, resulting in higher quality

parts, as well as reduced inspection costs and scrap. In particular, the relationship of machined features on the several faces of a workpiece are more easily held within tolerances. Changeover from the production of one workpiece to another can be done quickly.

Actual machining time on machining centers can be two or more times better than that of single-purpose, manually operated machine tools. Estimates of increases in productivity per man-hour range from 300 to 500% or more, especially on applications requiring many tools and frequent changeover.

While machining centers have a higher initial cost than many other machine tools, annual return on investment has been conservatively estimated to be about 30%. Smaller, compact models now available make these machines affordable even to small job shops. Accuracies that can be maintained and the reliability of the machines and their controls have been continuously improved. Figure 18-12 is an illustration of several different machining centers.

HB-4 MILLING CENTER

VB-2 MILLING CENTER

VB-2 MACHINING CENTER

VB-4 MACHINING CENTER

VB-4 MILLING CENTER

Figure 18-12 Machining centers *(Courtesy of Kearney & Trecker)*

Head-Changing Machines

Head-changing machines are a relatively new class of multifunction, numerically controlled machine tools. They differ from machining centers in that single or multiple-spindle heads, rather than tools, are transferred to a single workstation in proper sequence to perform the required series of operations. The single workstation is equipped with a spindle drive and slide feed unit; the workpiece remains in a fixed or indexable position. Additional workstations can be added on some machines if required.

Advantages of head-changing machines are similar to those of machine centers: increased productivity and versatility, reduced capital equipment and labor costs, and less materials handling. Head-

changing machines are generally used for larger lots of similar workpieces and for faster production requirements than are usually obtainable with machining centers. The use of modular heads and pallets on head-changing machines, however, permits quick changeover to suit various workpiece requirements. These machines are also being integrated with other NC machines in flexible machining systems, which are discussed later in this chapter.

On the machine shown in Fig. 18-13, standard-size, cubical machining heads, with single or multiple preset tools, are stored on a multilevel carousel alongside the traveling-column machine. On command of the machine controller, the proper head is automatically transferred, positioned, and clamped on the machine spindle. Multitooth couplings ensure accurate registration of toolheads and work pallets. The shuttle pallets on the machine table permit loading and unloading one workpiece while another is being machined. Programs and tooling can be stored in this system for a variety of workpieces. Some toolheads can be dedicated to operations performed on a specific workpiece, while others can be used on one or more operations common to several workpieces.

Automated and Special-Purpose Machines

Many of the standard machine tools already discussed in this volume are partially automated. In many cases, the addition of automatic feeding, loading/unloading, and gaging equipment can completely automate these standard machines, providing substantial production economies.

Standard machines and equipment should generally be used whenever possible because of their lower cost, quicker availability and, usually, proven performance. A possible disadvantage is that the use of such machines is usually a compromise of the ideal answer to specific automation requirements. The degree of compromise determines whether it is more economical to develop special-purpose machines and equipment that would better suit

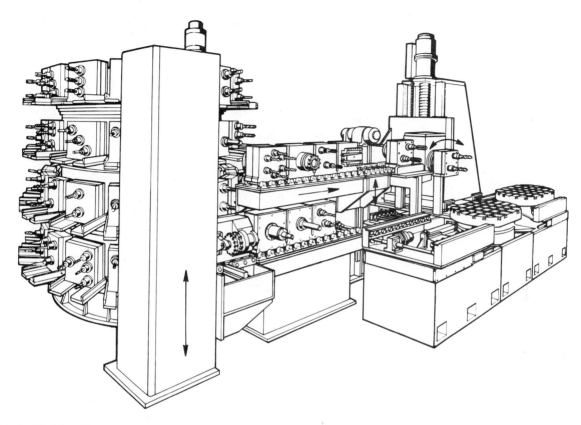

Figure 18-13 Machining heads stored on a multilevel carousel *(Courtesy of Cincinnati Milacron Marketing Company)*

present and future automation requirements than to use standard machines.

When it is impractical, impossible, or uneconomical to use standard machines for automation, special-purpose machines and equipment must be designed and built or purchased. Special machine tools often provide production economies because of built-in automation concepts that provide maximum efficiency in a minimum of floor space. Although they may not provide the inherent flexibility of standard machine tools, specials can have sufficient flexibility built in to produce a variety of related parts for medium or lower production if requirements are carefully planned in the design stages. If possible, continuous production should replace batch manufacturing methods. When quantities of identical parts are not

sufficient for continuous production, the use of more flexible automation equipment to handle families of parts (similar in size or shape) or similar operations should be considered.

When special-purpose equipment is considered, the possibility of combining several operations normally done on a number of individual machines should be investigated. As many operations as possible should be performed while the part is still located and clamped in the special machine. Cost savings resulting from eliminating the need for moving, relocating, and reclamping the workpieces can pay part of the development costs for the special machine. A variety of special-purpose machines have been developed. Figures 18-14 and 18-15 are examples of automated and special-purpose machines.

Figure 18-14   Automated/special purpose machine *(Courtesy of Cincinnati Milacron Marketing Company)*

Figure 18-15   Automated/special purpose machine *(Courtesy of Cincinnati Milacron Marketing Company)*

Transfer Machines

The highest degree of automation obtainable with special-purpose, multifunction machines is achieved by using transfer machines. Transfer machines are essentially a combination of individual workstations arranged in the required sequence, connected by work transfer devices, and integrated with interlocked controls. Workpieces are automatically transferred between the stations, which are equipped with horizontal, vertical, or angular units to perform machining, gaging, workpiece repositioning, assembling, washing, or other operations. The two major classes of transfer machines are *rotary* and *in-line* types.

An important advantage of transfer machines is that they permit the maximum number of operations to be performed simultaneously. There is relatively no limitation on the number of workpiece surfaces or planes that can be machined, since devices can be interposed in transfer machines at practically any point for inverting, rotating, or orienting the workpiece, so as to complete the machining operations. Work repositioning also minimizes the need for angular machining heads and allows operations to be performed in optimum time. Complete processing from rough castings or forgings to finished parts is often possible.

One or more finished parts are produced on a transfer machine with each index of the transfer system that moves the parts from station to station. Production efficiencies of such machines generally range from 50% for a machine producing a variety of different parts to 85% for a machine producing one part in high production, depending upon the workpiece and how the machine is operated (materials handling method, maintenance procedures, etc.)

All types of machining operations, such as drilling, tapping, reaming, boring, and milling, are economically combined on transfer machines. Lathe-type operations such as turning and facing are also being performed on in-line transfer machines, with the workpieces being rotated in selected machining stations. Turning operations are performed in lathe-type segments in which multiple toolholders are fed on slides mounted on tunnel-type bridge units. Workpieces are located on centers and rotated by chucks at each turning station. Turning stations with CNC are available for use on in-line transfer machines. The CNC units allow the machine cycles to be easily altered to accommodate changes in workpiece design and can also be used for automatic tool adjustments.

Maximum production economy on transfer lines is often achieved by assembling parts to the workpieces during their movement through the machine. Such items as bushings, seals, welch plugs, and heat tubes can be assembled and then machined or tested during the transfer machining sequence. Automatic nut torquing following the application of part subassemblies can also be carried out.

Gundrilling or reaming on transfer machines is an ideal application provided that proper machining units are employed and good bushing practices are followed. Contour boring and turning of spherical seats and other surfaces can be done with tracer-controlled single-point inserts, thus eliminating the need for costly special form tools. In-process gaging of reamed or bored holes and automatic tool setting are done on transfer machines to maintain close tolerances.

Less conventional operations sometimes performed on transfer machines include grinding, induction heating of ring gears for shrink-fit pressing on flywheels, induction hardening of valve seats, deep rolling to apply compressive preloads, and burnishing.

Transfer machines have long been used in the automotive industry for producing identical components at high production rates with a minimum of manual part handling. In addition to decreasing labor requirements, such machines ensure consistently uniform, high-quality parts at lower cost. They are no longer confined just to rough machining and now often eliminate the need for subsequent operations such as grinding and honing.

More recently, there has been an increasing demand for transfer machines to handle lower volumes of similar or even different parts in smaller sizes, with means for quick changeover between production runs. Built-in flexibility, the ability to rearrange and interchange machining units, and the provision of idle stations increases the cost of any transfer machine, but such features are economically feasible when product redesigns are common. Many such machines are now being used in nonautomotive applications for lower production requirements.

Special features now available to reduce the time required for part changeover include standardized dimensions, modular construction, interchangeable fixtures mounted on master pallets that remain on the machine, interchangeable fixture components, the ability to lock out certain stations for different parts by means of selector switches, and programmable controllers. Product design is also important, and common transfer and clamping surfaces should be provided on different parts whenever possible.

Flexible Manufacturing Defined

The evolution of manufacturing can be represented graphically as a continuum as shown in Fig. 18-16. As this figure shows, manufacturing processes and systems are in a state of transition from manual operation to the eventual realization of fully integrated manufacturing. The step preceding computer-integrated manufacturing is called *flexible manufacturing.*

Flexibility is an important characteristic in the modern manufacturing setting. It means that a manufacturing system is versatile and adaptable, while also capable of handling relatively high production runs. A flexible manufacturing system is versatile in that it can produce a variety of parts. It is adaptable because it can be quickly modified to produce a completely different line of parts. This flexibility can be the difference between success and failure in a competitive international marketplace.

It is a matter of balance. Stand-alone computer numerical control (CNC) machines have a high degree of flexibility, but are capable of relatively low-volume production runs. As the opposite end of the spectrum, transfer lines are capable of high-volume runs, but they are not very flexible. Flexible manufacturing is an attempt to use technology in such a way as to achieve the optimum balance between flexibility and production runs. These technologies include automated materials, handling, group technology, and computer and distributed numerical control.

A *flexible manufacturing system (FMS)* is an individual machine or group of machines served by an automated materials handling system that is computer controlled and has a tool handling capability. Because of its tool handling capability and computer control, such a system can be continually reconfigured to manufacture a wide variety of parts. This is why it is called a flexible manufacturing system.

The key elements necessary for a manufacturing system to qualify as an FMS are as follows:

1. Computer control.
2. Automated materials handling capability.
3. Tool handling capability.

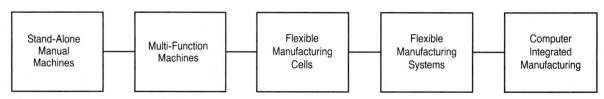

Figure 18-16   Manufacturing continuum

Flexible manufacturing represents a major step toward the goal of fully integrated manufacturing. It involves integration of automated production processes. In flexible manufacturing, the automated manufacturing machine (i.e., lathe, mill, drill) and the automated materials handling system share instantaneous communication via a computer network. This is integration on a small scale. Figure 18-17 is an example of a flexible manufacturing system.

Overview of Flexible Manufacturing

Flexible manufacturing takes a major step toward the goal of fully integrated manufacturing by integrating several automated manufacturing concepts:

1. Computer numerical control (CNC) of individual machine tools.

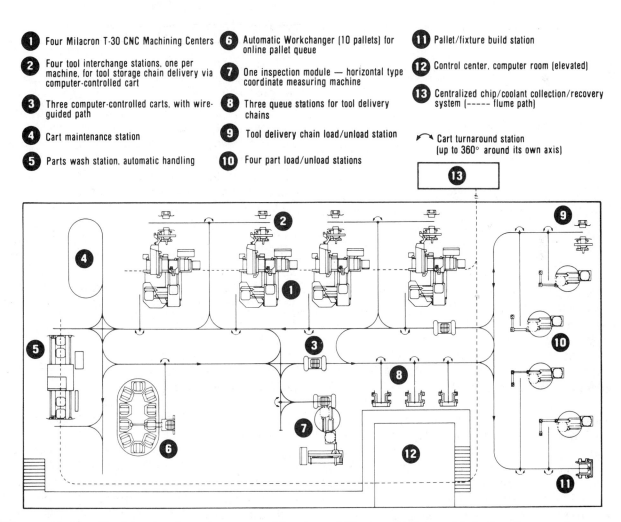

1 Four Milacron T-30 CNC Machining Centers

2 Four tool interchange stations, one per machine, for tool storage chain delivery via computer-controlled cart

3 Three computer-controlled carts, with wire-guided path

4 Cart maintenance station

5 Parts wash station, automatic handling

6 Automatic Workchanger (10 pallets) for online pallet queue

7 One inspection module — horizontal type coordinate measuring machine

8 Three queue stations for tool delivery chains

9 Tool delivery chain load/unload station

10 Four part load/unload stations

11 Pallet/fixture build station

12 Control center, computer room (elevated)

13 Centralized chip/coolant collection/recovery system (----- flume path)

Cart turnaround station (up to 360° around its own axis)

Figure 18-17 Flexible manufacturing system *(Courtesy of Cincinnati Milacron Marketing Company)*

2. Distributed numerical control (DNC) of manufacturing systems.
3. Automated materials handling systems.
4. Group technology (families of parts).

When these automated processes, machines, and concepts are brought together in one integrated system, an FMS is the result. Humans and computers play major roles in an FMS. The amount of human labor is much less than with a manually operated manufacturing system, of course. However, humans still play a vital role in the operation of an FMS. Human tasks include the following:

1. Equipment troubleshooting, maintenance, and repair.
2. Tool changing and setup.
3. Loading and unloading the system.
4. Data input.
5. Changing of parts programs.
6. Development of programs.

Flexible manufacturing system equipment, like all manufacturing equipment, must be monitored for *bugs*, malfunctions, and breakdowns. When a problem is discovered, a human troubleshooter must identify its source and prescribe corrective measures. Humans also undertake the prescribed measures to repair the malfunctioning equipment. Even when all systems are properly functioning, periodic maintenance is necessary.

Human operators also set up machines, change tools, and reconfigure systems as necessary. The tool handling capability of an FMS decreases, but does not eliminate, human involvement in tool changing and setup. The same is true of loading and unloading the FMS. Once raw material has been loaded onto the automated materials handling system, it is moved through the system in the prescribed manner. However, the original loading onto the materials handling system is still usually done by human operators, as is the unloading of finished products.

Humans are also needed for interaction with the computer. Humans develop parts programs that control the FMS via computers. They also change the programs as necessary when reconfiguring the FMS to produce another type of part or parts. Humans

play less labor-intensive roles in an FMS, but the roles are still critical.

Control at all levels in an FMS is provided by computers. Individual machine tools within an FMS are controlled by CNC. The overall system is controlled by DNC. The automated materials handling system is computer controlled, as are other functions including data collection, system monitoring, tool control, and traffic control. Human/computer interaction is the key to the flexibility of an FMS.

Historical Development of Flexible Manufacturing

Flexible manufacturing was born in the mid-1960s when the British firm Molins, Ltd. developed its System 24. System 24 was a real FMS. However, it was doomed from the outset because automation, integration, and computer control technology had not yet been developed to the point where they could properly support the system. The first FMS was a development that was ahead of its time. As such, it was eventually discarded as unworkable.

Flexible manufacturing remained an academic concept through the remainder of the 1960s and 1970s. However, with the emergence of sophisticated computer control technology in the late 1970s and early 1980s, flexible manufacturing became a viable concept. The first major users of flexible manufacturing in the United States were manufacturers of automobiles, trucks, and tractors.

Rationale for Flexible Manufacturing

In manufacturing there have always been tradeoffs between production rates and flexibility. At one end of the spectrum are transfer lines capable of high production rates, but low flexibility. At the other end of the spectrum are independent CNC machines that offer maximum flexibility, but are capable only of low production rates. Flexible manufacturing falls in the middle of the continuum. There has always been a need in manufacturing for a system that could produce higher volume and production runs than could independent machines, while still maintaining flexibility.

Transfer lines are capable of producing large volumes of parts at high production rates. The line takes a great deal of setup, but can turn out identical parts in large quantities. Its chief shortcoming is that even minor design changes in a part can cause the entire line to be shut down and reconfigured. This is a critical weakness because it means that transfer lines cannot produce different parts, even parts from within the same family, without costly and time-consuming shutdown and reconfiguration.

Traditionally, CNC machines have been used to produce small volumes of parts that differ slightly in design. Such machines are ideal for this purpose because they can be quickly reprogrammed to accommodate minor or even major design changes. However, as independent machines they cannot produce parts in large volumes or at high production rates.

An FMS can handle higher volumes and production rates than independent CNC machines. They cannot quite match such machines for flexibility, but they come close. What is particularly significant about the middle ground capabilities of flexible manufacturing is that most manufacturing situations require medium production rates to produce medium volumes with enough flexibility to quickly reconfigure to produce another part or product. Flexible manufacturing fills this long-standing void in manufacturing.

Flexible manufacturing, with its ground capabilities, offers a number of advantages for manufacturers:

1. Flexibility within a family of parts.
2. Random feeding of parts.
3. Simultaneous production of different parts.
4. Decreased setup time and lead time.
5. More efficient machine usage.
6. Decreased direct and indirect labor costs.
7. Ability to handle different materials.
8. Ability to continue some production if one machine breaks down.

Flexibility Within a Family of Parts: A family of parts is a group of parts that is similar enough in design to require similar production processes. An FMS is flexible enough that it can be quickly reconfigured to produce a wide variety of parts so long as they fall within the same family.

Random Feeding of Parts: An FMS can be set up and programmed to accommodate random feeding of parts within the family being produced. This involves ensuring that the necessary tooling is set up on the appropriate machines and the necessary controls are programmed in. With this done, parts may be introduced randomly by identifying each part to the controller as it is introduced into the system. The controller then routes the part to the appropriate machines in the processes within the FMS.

Simultaneous Production: In addition to its random capability, an FMS also has a simultaneous production capability. This means that different parts within a family of parts can be processed at the same time as the rest of the system. Again, this is due to the flexibility that comes from programmed operations. The key lies in effective production planning and programming.

Decreased Setup and Lead Time: An important advantage of flexible manufacturing is that it requires less setup time. This, in turn, means that an FMS requires less lead time. Setting up machines for manufacturing operations involves:

1. Outfitting them with the proper tools.
2. Placing raw materials into the fixtures and making the necessary adjustments.

Each time a setup operation is required, a traditional manufacturing system must be shut down. Tools must be retrieved from the tool crib, raw materials must be retrieved from storage, and machines must be reconfigured. Because of this, extensive lead time is often necessary.

With flexible manufacturing, tooling and raw stock can be set up off line. In this way, changing tools is just a matter of placing preset tools on the appropriate machines. An individual machine might be loaded with 50 or more different tools at once. Then, rather than changing tools, the system is simply programmed as to when it should use each tool. Hence, breakdown and resetup time are saved. Raw material is also provided off line, usually on pallets. The pallets are configured for the specific operations that will take place. The pallets contain all of the necessary fixtures. Again, this saves on breakdown and setup time.

More Efficient Machine Usage: The combined advantages of flexible manufacturing lead to another advantage: more efficient machine usage. In traditional manufacturing systems, individual machines are set up to perform specific operations. If a given part requires three different processes, two machines in a system are typically idle, waiting for processing on the other machines. Only the machine processing the current operation is normally in use. This results in inefficient usage.

Flexible manufacturing systems solve the problem. If that same part was produced on an FMS and 100 copies were to be produced, the system could be set up and programmed to produce the part simultaneously. While station 1 performs its processes on a group of workpieces, stations 2 and 3 would be performing all or some of their processes on other groups of workpieces. The workpiece then rotates through each station as needed. The result is more efficient use of machines.

Decreased Direct and Indirect Labor Costs: In traditional manufacturing systems and even with individual CNC machines, there is typically one human operator for each machine. Add to this the human labor involved in materials handling away from the machine and additional manufacturing systems, including CNC machines. The amount of on-line and off-line labor decreases with flexible manufacturing. This can be attributed to the following:

1. Automated as opposed to human materials handling with flexible manufacturing.
2. Automated as opposed to human control.
3. Off-line as opposed to on-line setup and tooling preparation.

Flexible Manufacturing System Components

An FMS has four major components:

1. Machine tools
2. Control system
3. Materials handling system
4. Human operators

Machine Tools: A flexible manufacturing system uses the same types of machine tools as any other manufacturing system, be it automated or manually operated. These include lathes, mills, drills, saws, and so on. The type of machine tools actually included in an FMS depends on the setting in which the machine will be used. Some FMSs are designed to meet a specific, well-defined need. In these cases, the machine tools included in the system will be only those necessary for the planned operations. Such a system would be known as a dedicated system.

In a job-shop setting, or any other setting in which the actual application is not known ahead of time or must necessarily include a wide range of possibilities, machines capable of performing at least the standard manufacturing operations would be included. Such systems are known as *general-purpose* systems.

Control System: The control system for an FMS serves a number of different control functions for the system:

1. Storage and distribution of parts programs.

2. Work flow control and monitoring.
3. Production control.
4. System/tool control/monitoring.

The control system for an FMS accepts, stores, and distributes parts programs. These are the CNC programs that guide the operation of individual machines and workstations within the system in performing the turning, cutting, drilling, and other processes necessary to produce parts.

Regulating the flow of workpieces from station to station for both primary and secondary materials handling systems and monitoring the locations of workpieces within the system are important control tasks. Different parts require different speeds and feed rates. These types of production-oriented controls represent another important control function in FMS.

The overall system must be monitored and controlled, as must individual tools within it. The control system must continually collect and store data that can periodically be output in the form of performance reports. The wear on individual tools should be monitored continually so that worn tools can be changed as needed and reports on the projected versus actual lives of tools can be produced. These are important functions of the control system.

Materials Handling System:
The automated materials handling system is a fundamental component that helps mold a group of independent CNC machines into a comprehensive FMS. The system must be capable of accepting workpieces mounted on pallets and moving them from workstation to workstation as needed. It must also be able to place workpieces *on hold* as they wait to be processed at a given workstation.

The materials handling system must be able to unload a workpiece at one station and load another for transport to the next station. It must accommodate computer control and be completely compatible in that regard with other components in the flexible manufacturing system. Finally, the materials handling system for an FMS must be able to withstand the rigors of a shop environment. Some FMSs are con-figured with automated guided vehicles (AGVs) as a principal means of materials handling.

Human Operators:
The final component in an FMS is the human component. Although flexible manufacturing as a concept decreases the amount of human involvement in manufacturing, it does not eliminate it completely. Further, the roles humans play in flexible manufacturing are critical. These include programming, operating, monitoring, controlling, and maintaining the system.

Flexible Manufacturing Cells

Flexible manufacturing cells (FMCs) are dedicated groups of workstations within a larger FMS. Such cells are segregated components of an FMS. The reasons for segregating within a system are varied:

1. Working with dangerous or hazardous materials.
2. Noise.
3. Different operator tasks required.
4. Different materials required.

The development of FMCs followed that of FMSs, although it might have worked better had the order been reversed. Flexible manufacturing cells are actually small FMSs. As such, they are less expensive to develop and implement and more likely to succeed. For this reason FMCs are growing in use more rapidly than the larger FMSs.

The FMC is actually the FMS concept in microcosm. As such, it offers several advantages over FMSs:

1. Less initial capital outlay.
2. Less sophisticated computer control.
3. Easy to learn to operate.
4. More easily understood by management and production personnel.

In its simplest form, an FMC is a group of related CNC machines with common computer control and a common materials handling system. Figure 18-18 is an example of an FMC.

Figure 18-18   Flexible manufacturing cell *(Courtesy of Amatrol)*

Flexible Manufacturing and CIM

Flexible manufacturing is a key step on the road to fully integrated manufacturing, or CIM (covered in the next chapter). CIM involves the automation and integration of all components of a manufacturing firm including management, design, planning/control, information resource management, finance, and production. Flexible manufacturing involves automating and integrating the production components.

Both flexible manufacturing cells and systems have automated and integrated machine tools, control systems, and material handling systems. In the evolution from manual manufacturing to CIM, flexible manufacturing is a step that should not be skipped. Manufacturing personnel who have successfully implemented flexible manufacturing will be much better prepared to deal successfully with a conversion to CIM than those who attempt to bypass this critical step.

KEY TERMS AND PHRASES _____

Automated and special-purpose machines
Automated guided vehicles
Automated materials handling
Batch manufacturing
Center drilling and facing machines
Computer control
Computer numerical control (CNC)
Distributed numerical control (DNC)
Families of parts
Flexible manufacturing
Flexible manufacturing cell
Flexible manufacturing system
Group technology
Head-changing machines
Horizontal boring machines
Lead time
Machining centers
Multifunction machines
Multiple-spindle automatic bar and chucking
  machines
Production control
Setup
Simultaneous production
Single-spindle automatic screw machines
Single-spindle automatic lathes
Swiss-type automatic screw machines
System 24
Tool handling
Transfer machines
Transfer line
Vertical boring machines and turret lathes

QUESTIONS FOR ADDITIONAL STUDY AND REVIEW _____

1. What is a *multifunction machine*? *P 530*

2. Explain the primary functions of the following multifunction machines:

   - Single-spindle automatic lathes
   - Center drilling and facing machines
   - Horizontal boring machines
   - Machining centers
   - Transfer machines

3. Define the term *flexible manufacturing*. *P 544*

4. What are the key elements of a flexible manu- *P544* facturing system?

5. List six key tasks performed by human workers *P 546* in a flexible manufacturing system.

6. Why did the original FMS, the System 24, ultimately fail?

7. Explain briefly the rationale for flexible manufacturing.

8. What is a transfer line?

9. Why is an independent CNC machine more flexible than a transfer line?

10. List five key advantages of flexible manufacturing.

11. List and briefly explain the four major components of an FMS.

12. What are four control functions of an FMS control system?

13. What is a flexible manufacturing cell?

14. How does an *FMC* differ from an FMS?

15. List four reasons for segregating an individual cell within an FMS.

16. List four advantages of an FMC over an FMS.

17. Explain how flexible manufacturing relates to CIM.

CHAPTER 19

Computer Integrated Manufacturing

MAJOR TOPICS COVERED

- CIM Defined
- Historical Development of CIM
- CIM Wheel
- Benefits of CIM
- CIM-Related Standards
- Group Technology and CIM
- Process Planning and CIM
- Manufacturing Resources Planning and CIM
- Just-in-Time and CIM
- Production Planning and Control and CIM
- Communication and CIM
- Materials Handling and CIM
- Artificial Intelligence and CIM
- Expert Systems and CIM
- Databases and CIM

CIM Defined

Computer integrated manufacturing (CIM) is the term used to describe the modern approach to manufacturing. Although CIM encompasses many of the other advanced manufacturing technologies such as computer numerical control (CNC), computer-aided design/computer-aided manufacturing (CAD/CAM),

robotics, and just-in-time delivery (JIT), it is more than a new technology or a new concept. Computer integrated manufacturing is an entirely new approach to manufacturing, a new way of doing business.

To understand CIM, it is necessary to begin with a comparison of modern and traditional manufacturing. Modern manufacturing encompasses all of the activities and processes necessary to convert raw materials into finished products, deliver them to the market, and support them in the field. These activities include the following:

1. Identifying a need for a product.
2. Designing a product to meet the needs.
3. Obtaining the raw materials needed to produce the product.
4. Applying appropriate processes to transform the raw materials into finished products.
5. Transporting products to the market.
6. Maintaining the product to ensure proper performance in the field.

This broad, modern view of manufacturing can be compared with the more limited traditional view that focused almost entirely on the conversion processes. The old approach excluded such critical preconversion elements as market analysis research, development, and design, as well as such after-conversion elements as product delivery and product maintenance. In other words, in the old approach to

552

manufacturing, only those processes that took place on the shop floor were considered manufacturing. This traditional approach of separating the overall concept into numerous stand-alone specialized elements was not fundamentally changed with the advent of automation.

With CIM, not only are the various elements automated, but the islands of automation are all linked together or integrated. *Integration* means that a system can provide complete and instantaneous sharing of information. In modern manufacturing, integration is accomplished by computers. CIM, then, is the *total integration of all components involved in converting raw materials into finished products and getting the products to the market*, Fig. 19-1.

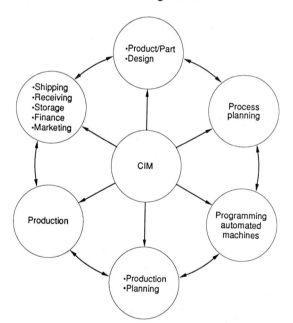

Figure 19-1   Major components of CIM

Historical Development of CIM

The term *computer integrated manufacturing* was developed in 1974 by Joseph Harrington as the title of a book he wrote about tying islands of automation together through the use of computers. It has taken many years for CIM to develop as a concept, but integrated manufacturing is not really new. In fact, integration is where manufacturing actually began. Manufacturing has evolved through four distinct stages:

- Manual manufacturing
- Mechanization/specialization
- Automation
- Integration

Manual Manufacturing

Manual manufacturing using simple hand tools was actually integrated manufacturing. All information needed to design, produce, and deliver a product was readily available because it resided in the mind of the one person who performed all of the necessary tasks. The tool of integration in the earliest years of manufacturing was the human mind of the craftsman who designed, produced, and delivered the product. An example of integrated manual manufacturing is the village blacksmith producing a special tool for a local farmer. The blacksmith would have in his mind all of the information needed to design, produce, and deliver the farmer's tools. In this example, all elements of manufacturing are integrated.

Mechanization/Specialization

With the advent of the industrial revolution, manufacturing processes became both specialized and mechanized. Instead of one person designing, producing, and delivering a product, workers and/or machines performed specialized tasks within each of these broad areas. Communication among these separate entities was achieved using drawings, specifications, job orders, process plans, and a variety of other communication aids. To ensure that the finished product matched the planned product, the concept of quality control was introduced.

The positive side of the mechanization/specialization stage was that it permitted mass production, interchangeability of parts, different levels of accuracy, and uniformity. The disadvantage is that the lack of integration led to a great deal of waste.

Automation

Automation improved the performance and enhanced the capabilities of both people and machines within specialized manufacturing components. For example, CAD enhanced the capability of designers and drafters. CNC enhanced the capabilities of machinists and computer-assisted planners. But the improvements brought on by automation were isolated within individual components or islands. Because of this, automation did not always live up to its potential.

To understand the limitations of automation with regard to overall productivity improvement, consider the following analogy. Suppose that various subsystems of an automobile (i.e., the engine, steering, brakes) were automated to make the driver's job easier. Automatic acceleration, deceleration, steering, and braking would certainly be more efficient than the manual versions. However, consider what would happen if these various automated subsystems were not tied together in a way that allowed them to communicate and share accurate, up-to-date information instantly and continually. One system might be attempting to accelerate the automobile while another system was attempting to apply the brakes. The same limitations apply in an automated manufacturing setting. These limitations are what led to the current stage in the development of manufacturing, *integration*.

Integration

With the advent of the computer age, manufacturing has developed full circle. It began as a totally integrated concept and, with CIM, has once again become one. However, there are major differences in the manufacturing integration of today and that of the manual era of the past. First, the instrument of integration in the manual era was the human

mind. The instrument of integration in modern manufacturing is the computer. Second, processes in the modern manufacturing setting are still specialized and automated.

Another way to view the historical development of CIM is by examining the ways in which some of the individual components of CIM have developed over the years. Such components as design, planning, and production have evolved both as processes and in the tools and equipment used to accomplish the processes.

Design has evolved from a manual process using such tools as slide rules, triangles, pencils, scales, and erasers into an automated process known as *computer-aided design* (CAD). Process planning has evolved from a manual process using planning tables, diagrams, and charts into an automated process known as *computer-aided process planning* (CAPP). Production has evolved from a manual process involving manually controlled machines into an automated process known as *computer-aided manufacturing* (CAM).

These individual components of manufacturing evolved over the years into separate islands of automation. However, communication among these islands was still handled manually. This limited the level of improvement in productivity that could be accomplished in the overall manufacturing process. When these islands and other automated components of manufacturing are linked together through computer networks, these limitations can be overcome.

The CIM Wheel

The Computer and Automated Systems Association (CASA) of the Society of Manufacturing Engineers (SME) developed the CIM wheel (Fig. 19-2) as a way to comprehensively but concisely illustrate the concept of CIM. The CASA/SME developed the CIM wheel to include several distinct components:

1. Manufacturing management/human resource management.

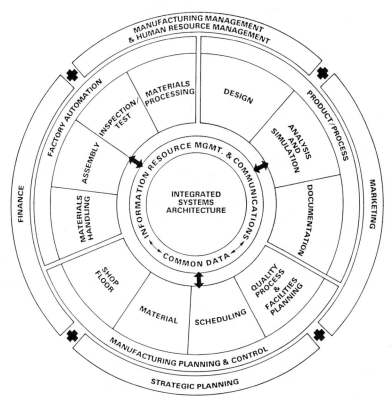

Figure 19-2 SME/CASA CIM Wheel

2. Marketing.
3. Strategic planning.
4. Finance.
5. Product/process design and planning.
6. Manufacturing planning and control.
7. Factory automation.

Benefits of CIM

Fully integrated manufacturing firms realize a number of benefits from CIM:

1. Product quality increases.
2. Lead times are reduced.
3. Direct labor costs are reduced.
4. Product development times are reduced.

5. Inventories are reduced.
6. Overall productivity increases.
7. Design quality increases.

CIM-Related Standards

Incompatibility is an inhibitor of the full development of CIM. Standards have been developed to help overcome the problem of incompatibility. Three in particular have had a positive impact:

1. Manufacturing automation protocol (MAP).
2. Technical and office protocol (TOP).
3. Initial graphics exchange specification (IGES).

Manufacturing Automation Protocol

Manufacturing automation protocol (MAP) is a communications standard developed to promote compatibility among automated manufacturing systems produced by different vendors. It allows different machines to *talk* to each other. It was originally developed by the General Motors Corporation to help them increase productivity so that they could be competitive with foreign automobile manufacturing firms. There are now international MAP user groups that have input into the ongoing development and improvement of MAP.

The first version of MAP was published in 1982 by the Advanced Product Manufacturing and Engineering Staff (APMES). Since that time it has been continually updated, improved, and revised. MAP is now being used by companies to integrate automated manufacturing systems produced by different vendors. MAP is based on the open systems interconnection (OSI) seven-layer model (Fig. 19-3). This model was adopted by General Motors Corporation because it already had achieved a high degree of acceptance worldwide. Having a broad base of support and acceptance is critical to the success of a proposed standard.

The overall goal of MAP is the total integration of islands of automation in manufacturing, regardless of the producer of the hardware and software used in the system. With MAP fully developed and in place, a user will have access to any computer within a manufacturing facility from any other computer within that facility, regardless of the make, model, or vendor of the computer.

MAP offers several benefits to manufacturers in a CIM environment. These include:

1. Better shop floor communication.
2. Decreased risk during installation.
3. Lower cost.
4. Decreased installation time.
5. Easier upkeep and expansion.

MAP SPECIFICATIONS BY LAYER		
Layer Number	Layer Description	Layer Function
7	Application	Provides all services directly understandable to application programs.
6	Presentation	Converts data to and from agreed to standardized formats.
5	Session	Synchronizes and manages data.
4	Transport	Provides transparent data transfer from end note to end note.
3	Network	Provides pocket routing for transferring data between nodes on different networks.
2	Data Link	Detects errors for messages transferred between nodes on the same networks.
1	Physical	Encodes bits and transfers them between adjacent nodes.

Figure 19-3   MAP Specifications *(Reprinted from ADVANCED MANUFACTURING TECHNOLOGY by David L. Goetsch, copyright 1990 by Delmar Publishers Inc.)*

Better Shop Floor Communication: MAP is an enabling tool. It allows machines and systems from different vendors to communicate without the need for customization of software. Without MAP, shop floor machines and systems cannot be fully integrated without difficult and expensive customization work, if then. With MAP, integration is possible which, in turn, leads to optimum machine use, faster responses to design and/or production changes, and continuous monitoring of product and process parameters.

Decreased Risk During Installation: There is always risk associated with the installation of a new technology. Without MAP, the greatest risk is that substantially customized and modified software may not work after installation. The downtime necessary to work the bugs out is costly, nonproductive time.

With MAP there is no such risk since standard hardware and software that have been tested and proven are used. The fact that it allows standard *off-the-shelf* hardware and software to be used in a CIM setting significantly decreases installation risk.

Lower Cost: MAP results in lower costs for several different reasons. It decreases the cost of the hardware and software needed to facilitate shop floor communications, operating costs, and support costs. Operating and support costs are lower primarily because customization of hardware and software is not necessary.

MAP also reduces developmental costs for vendors which, in turn, reduces costs to users. It does this by allowing vendors to spend their developmental resources on product functionability rather than all of the modifications that, without MAP, would be required to achieve compatibility.

Decreased Installation Time: In addition to decreasing the risk associated with a CIM installation, MAP decreases the amount of time required to accomplish an installation. The shorter time is attributable to the use of *off-the-shelf* hardware and software as opposed to heavily modified, customized hardware and software.

Easier Upkeep and Expansion: It is less difficult to maintain and expand off-the-shelf hardware and software than it is to maintain customized hardware and software. This is attributable to modularity and easier trouble shooting and repair.

In addition to these benefits, MAP also allows communication among systems at all levels within a factory. This is another advantage of MAP. Manufacturing companies arrange their functions in six separate levels. These levels can be viewed as a hierarchy represented by an inverted triangle, Fig. 19-4. The six levels from the lowest to highest (broadest) are:

1. Machine level
2. Station level
3. Cell level
4. Shop level
5. Facility level
6. Enterprise level

Communication at the machine level is accomplished by such devices as sensors, motor speed controllers, and limit switches. These devices are found on individual machines. Information from these devices must be communicated to the next level up in the hierarchy, the station level.

Communication at the station level is accomplished by such devices as programmable logic controllers (PLCs), microcomputer controllers, and vision systems such as those used in conjunction with robots. Information from these devices must be communicated down to the machine level and up to the cell level.

Communication at the cell level is accomplished by such devices as microcomputer controllers, PLCs, and minicomputer controllers. Vision systems such as those used in conjunction with robots are also used at the cell level. Information from these devices must be communicated down to the station level. For example, CNC programs are downloaded to machine

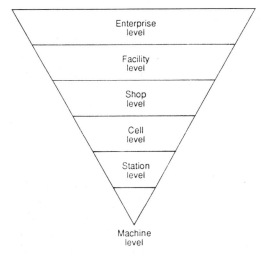

Figure 19-4   Manufacturing functions hierarchy

controllers. Information must also be communicated upward to the shop level. For example, production statistics are provided to shop level computers.

Communication at the shop level is accomplished primarily by minicomputers. Information from these devices must be communicated down to the cell level. For example, production scheduling information is downloaded to the cell level. Information needed by facility level personnel is communicated up. The shop level is the first level in the hierarchy that can operate with relative autonomy.

Communication at the facility level is accomplished by large minicomputer and mainframe computers. In those companies that have only one plant (facility), the facility and enterprise levels are the same. Process design, inventory management, and production control information must be communicated from the facility level down to the shop level and up to the enterprise level.

Communication at the enterprise level is accomplished primarily by mainframe computers. Information from this level must be passed down to the facility level. This information concerns product and process design, product analysis, production scheduling, manufacturing resource planning, marketing, and finance.

Communication up and down the hierarchy means that sensors, vision systems, PLCs, microcomputers, minicomputers, and mainframe computers must all talk to each other. MAP allows this communication to occur.

Technical and Office Protocol

Technical and office protocol (TOP) is a standard that was developed to promote integration within an office environment. While MAP is used to promote integration among manufacturing components, TOP was developed to promote integration among business and office components. Boeing has played the lead role in the development of TOP. The purpose of TOP is to allow islands of automation within the business components of the CIM wheel to interface and communicate, not just among themselves, but also between and among those islands contained

in the manufacturing components of the wheel. Technical and office protocol is also based on a seven-layer model, similar to the model illustrated in Fig. 19-4.

Technical and office protocol is being developed in three phases. The first phase includes standards for file transfer and, on a limited basis, file management. Phase two includes standards covering file access, message handling, and improved file management. The final phase included standards covering document revision, document exchange, directory services, graphics, and database management. In 1985 efforts began to merge MAP and TOP so that, eventually, they will become a single network.

Initial Graphics Exchange Specification

The initial graphics exchange specification (IGES) is much more limited than MAP or TOP. It was developed to promote communication between CAD systems manufactured by different vendors and is limited to the product and process definition component of the CIM wheel. The central technology of an IGES specification is a translator that is arranged between two CAD systems that are communicating. System A transfers the data that is to be moved to system B into this translator, where it is converted into the neutral IGES format. It then is converted from that format into the format understood by CAD system B (Fig. 19-5).

A key weakness of IGES is its inability to deal with three-dimensional solid models, electronic design, and nongraphic data management. The *National Institute of Standards and Technology* is currently

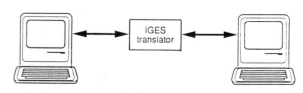

Figure 19-5   IGES

developing a new standard called the product data exchange standard (PDES) that will be able to handle solids modeling data, nongraphic data management, and electronic design.

Group Technology and CIM

Group technology is a concept at the very heart of CIM. CIM is supposed to give manufacturers the flexibility to produce customized products without sacrificing productivity. Group technology is a key ingredient in the larger formula of CIM that makes this possible. It amounts to making batch manufacturing economical.

Group technology involves grouping parts according to design characteristics, the processes used to produce them, or a combination of these. Fig. 19-6 is an example of similar parts grouped together on the basis of two design characteristics (shape and material). These similar parts fall into a *family* of parts. Families of parts can be produced using similar processes usually within a single flexible manufacturing cell (FMC).

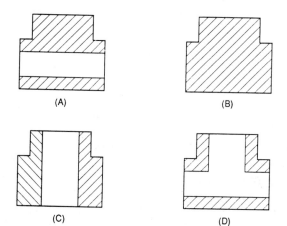

(A) (B)

(C) (D)

Figure 19-6 Parts with similar design characteristics

Historical Background of Group Technology

Ever since the industrial revolution, manufacturing and engineering personnel have searched for ways to optimize manufacturing processes. There have been numerous developments over the years since the industrial revolution mechanized production. Mass production and interchangeability of parts in the 1800s were major steps forward in optimizing manufacturing.

However, even with mass production and assembly lines, most manufacturing is done in small batches ranging from one workpiece to two or three thousand. Even today, over 70% of manufacturing involves batches of less than three thousand workpieces. Historically, less has been done to optimize small-batch production than has been done for assembly line work.

There have been attempts to standardize a variety of design tasks and some work in queuing and sequencing in manufacturing, but until recently, design and manufacturing in small-batch settings has been somewhat random.

The underlying problem that has historically prevented significant improvements to small-batch manufacturing is that any solution must apply broadly to general production processes and principles rather than a specific product. This is a difficult problem because the various workpieces in a small batch can be so random and different.

When manufacturing entered the age of automation and computerization, such developments as scheduling software, sequencing software, and material requirements planning (MRP) systems became available to improve production of both small and large batches. Even these developments have not optimized the production of small-batch manufacturing lots. The problem has become even more critical because, since the end of World War II, the trend has been toward more small-batch and less large-batch production.

In recent years, the problems of small-batch production have finally begun to receive the attention necessary to bring about improvements. A major step is the ongoing development of group technology.

Part Families

Parts may be similar in design and/or in the manufacturing processes used to produce them. A group of such parts is called a *part family*. It is possible for parts in the same family to be very similar in design yet radically different in the area of production requirements. The opposite may also be true.

Figure 19-7 contains examples of two parts from the same family. These parts were placed in the same family based on design characteristics. They have exactly the same shape and size. However, they differ in the area of production processes. Part 1, after it is drilled, will go to a painting station for two coats of primer. Its dimensions must be held to a tolerance of ± 0.125 inch. Part 2, after it is drilled, will go to a finishing station for sanding and buffing. Its dimensions require more restrictive tolerances of ± 0.003 inch. The parts differ in material: part 1 is cold-rolled steel and part 2 is aluminum.

Figure 19-8 contains examples of two parts from another family. Although the design characteristics of these two parts are drastically different, (i.e., different sizes and shapes), a close examination reveals that they are similar in the area of production processes. Part 1 is made of stainless steel. Its dimensions must be held to a tolerance of ± 0.003 inch, and three holes must be drilled through it. Part 2, in spite of the differences in size and shape, has exactly the same manufacturing characteristics.

The parts shown in Fig. 19-7, because of their similar design characteristics, are grouped in the same family. Such a family is referred to as a *design part family*. Those in Fig. 19-8 are grouped together because of similar manufacturing characteristics. Such a family is referred to as a *manufacturing part family*. The characteristics used in classifying parts are referred to as *attributes*.

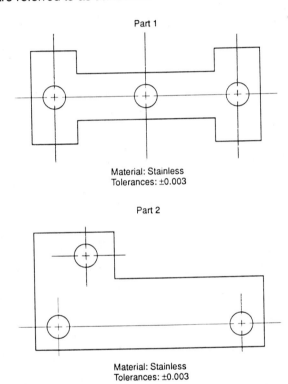

Part 1

Material: Stainless
Tolerances: ±0.003

Part 2

Material: Stainless
Tolerances: ±0.003

Figure 19-8 Similar parts in different part families

By grouping parts into families, manufacturing personnel can cut down significantly on the amount of materials handled and movement wasted in producing them. This is because manufacturing machines can be correspondingly grouped into specialized work cells instead of the traditional arrangement of machines according to function (i.e., mills together, lathes together, drills together, etc.). This becomes very important when configuring flexible manufacturing cells.

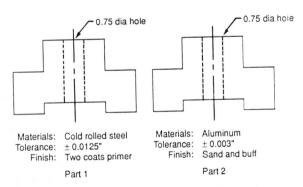

0.75 dia hole   0.75 dia hole

Materials: Cold rolled steel   Materials: Aluminum
Tolerance: ± 0.0125"   Tolerance: ± 0.003"
Finish: Two coats primer   Finish: Sand and buff

Part 1   Part 2

Figure 19-7 Parts in the same family based on design characteristics

Each work cell can be specially configured to produce a given family of parts. When this is done, the number of setups, the amount of material handling, the length of lead time, and the amount of in-process inventory are all reduced.

Grouping Parts into Families: Part grouping is not a simple process. You already know the criteria used: design similarities and manufacturing similarities. Three methods can be used to group parts into families:

1. Sight inspection
2. Route sheet inspection
3. Parts classification and coding

All three methods require the expertise of experienced manufacturing personnel. Sight inspection is the simplest, least sophisticated method. It involves looking at parts, photos of parts, or drawings of parts. Through such an examination, experienced personnel are able to identify similar characteristics and group the parts accordingly. This is the easiest approach, especially for grouping parts by design attributes, but it is also the least accurate of the three methods.

The second method involves route sheets that are used to route the parts through the various operations to be performed. This can be an effective way to group parts into manufacturing part families, provided the route sheets are correct. If they are, this method is more accurate than the sight inspection approach. This method is sometimes referred to as the production flow analysis (PFA) method.

The most widely used method for grouping parts is the third method: *parts classification and coding*. This is also the most sophisticated, most difficult, and most time-consuming method.

Parts Classification and Coding

Parts classification and coding is a method in which the various design and/or manufacturing characteristics for a part are identified, listed, and assigned a code number. Recall that these characteristics are referred to as attributes. This is a general approach used in classifying and coding parts. Many different systems have been developed to actually carry out the process, none of which has emerged as the standard.

The many different classification and coding systems that have been developed all fall into one of three groups:

1. Design attribute group
2. Manufacturing attribute group
3. Combined attribute group

Design attribute group. Classification and coding systems that use design attributes as the qualifying criteria fall into this group. Commonly used design attributes include:

- Dimensions
- Tolerances
- Shape
- Finish
- Material

Manufacturing attribute group. Classification and coding systems that use manufacturing attributes as the qualifying criteria fall into this group. Commonly used manufacturing attributes include the following:

- Production processes
- Operational sequence
- Production time
- Tools required
- Fixtures required
- Batch size

Combined attribute group. There are advantages in using design attributes and advantages in using manufacturing attributes. Systems that fall into the design attribute group are particularly advantageous if the goal is design retrieval. Those in the manufacturing group are better if the goal is a production-related function. However, there is a need for systems that combine the best characteristics of both. Such systems use both design and manufacturing attributes.

Group technology is an enabling technology. It allows design, manufacturing, and other descriptive data to be collected and communicated in a common language. Its applications in a CIM setting include design retrieval, process planning, numerical control, manufacturing resources planning, machine tool selection, and shop layout.

Process Planning and CIM

One of the most effective ways of increasing productivity is to reduce the amount of *in-process* time involved in manufacturing discrete parts. The consensus among manufacturing professionals is that, prior to CIM, the typical part would spend over 90% of its process time waiting between operations. Process planning is a systematic approach to reducing the time required to process parts.

The advent of flexible batch manufacturing through CIM has increased the complexity of the process planner's job several times over. Process planning involves scheduling jobs and the machines required to do the jobs. To understand how complex a task this can be, consider the following. A process planner with five jobs to run over six machines has almost three trillion scheduling possibilities, an impossible number to deal with. However, with CIM, the computer has reduced this to a manageable task. Use of the computer in process planning is called computer-aided process planning, or CAPP.

Computer-Aided Process Planning (CAPP)

Once a part is designed, the processes used to produce it must be planned. In a traditional manufacturing setting, a wide gap exists between the design and manufacturing components. Productivity and quality can be improved when the design component works with the manufacturing component from the beginning of the design through completion of the production of the part. Computer-aided process planning (CAPP) represents a major step toward bridging the gap between the design and manufacturing components.

As you have seen, once a product has been designed, there are many sequences that can be used within the various processes required to produce the part. In fact, the number of combinations of sequences is usually so large that, prior to computers, process planning was really just a guessing game. However, with the advent of CAPP, manufacturing personnel can easily determine the optimum sequence of operations for producing a part. CAPP systems are expert computer systems that collect and store all known information about a specific manufacturing setting, as well as numerous general manufacturing and engineering principles. They then use this information to determine the optimum plan for producing a given part. Such a plan will specify the machines to be used in producing the part, the sequence of operations, the tooling to be used, optimum speed and feed settings for the tools, and any other data needed to produce the part. Two key concepts in CAPP are *CAD* and *group technology*.

How CAPP Works: With CAPP, the part is designed on a CAD/CAM system. The mathematical model that describes the part is transferred electronically from the CAD/CAM system to the CAPP system. Using information stored in the CAPP system, the computer matches the characteristics of the part to the machines and processes available on the shop floor. The CAPP system prints out the process sheets and routing sheets that make up the process plan.

Two types of CAPP systems are available: the *variant system* and the *generative system*. The variant system is the more widely used of the two. The variant system is based on the concept of group technology. It develops a process plan for a new part based on the classification and coding of other similar parts that have already been produced. Variant planning involves identifying in the database the part produced in the past that is most similar to the new part to be produced. The process plan for the previously produced part is modified appropriately to produce a plan for the new part.

The generative process planning system starts from scratch each time. Such systems have a database that contains a wide variety of manufacturing specifications, standards, logic, and the capabilities of available machines and equipment. The part description and specifications are entered into the CAPP system. The system then develops the optimum plan for producing the part.

Manufacturing Resources Planning and CIM

Material requirements planning (MRP) is an important concept with a direct relationship to CIM. It is a process that can be used to calculate the amount of raw materials that must be obtained in order to manufacture a specified lot of a certain product. Material requirements planning involves using the bill of material, production schedule, and inventory record to produce a comprehensive, detailed schedule of the raw materials and components needed for a job.

As manufacturing technology has evolved from automation to integration, MRP has also evolved. The acronym MRP now means manufacturing resources planning. This broader concept goes beyond determining material requirements to also encompass financial tracking and accounting. The modern version of MRP is particularly well suited to the integrated approach represented by CIM. In this approach, MRP can be an effective inventory planning and control tool.

Key concepts relating to MRP include: a) independent and dependent demand; b) lead times; and c) common-use items. Independent demand resources are those that are not tied to any other resource.

They stand alone. Dependent demand resources are tied directly to other resources. Receiving a dependent resource without the other resources it requires does no good. In manufacturing, resources are more likely to be dependent than independent. Raw materials, in-progress parts, components, and subassemblies are all part of the overall manufacturing inventory.

Lead times are of two types: a) ordering lead time and b) manufacturing lead time. Ordering lead time is the total amount of time between initiating a purchase order and receiving the order. Manufacturing lead time is the total amount of time required to perform all the steps necessary to produce a given part.

Lead times are important because they are used in developing the schedules for ordering materials and producing products. They are also where MRP is most likely to break down. Resource planners depend on the lead times provided to them by other personnel. If these times are padded or inaccurate, the MRP results will be equally inaccurate. Common-use items are items used in producing more than just one product. For example, the same type of aluminum sheet might be used in producing several different parts. The integrated approach of MRP allows planners to identify common-use items for a number of different products and use this information to save money by ordering in quantity.

Manufacturing resources planning results in a variety of products of value to manufacturing managers in addition to the master schedule:

1. Release notices that notify the purchasing department to place orders.
2. Revise schedules showing updated due dates.
3. Cancellation notices that notify appropriate personnel of cancellations that result from changes to the master schedule.
4. Inventory status reports.

Manufacturing resources planning is the most appropriate planning approach for a CIM setting. When completely implemented it can result in a number of benefits:

1. Inventory reduction
2. Quicker response to demand changes

3. Reductions in setup costs
4. More efficient machine utilization
5. Quicker response to revisions to the master schedule

Just-in-Time and CIM

Just-in-time (JIT) is a concept closely associated with CIM. It is typically thought of as an inventory program. However, this is not a complete definition. Like CIM, JIT is actually more than just a system; it is a new operating philosophy. Although JIT is generally thought of as a modern concept, it was actually born in the 1920s at Ford Motor Company. The basic idea of JIT is the same now as it was then: to reduce production cycle time while eliminating waste.

At the heart of the JIT philosophy is the concept of *value added*. Anything that does not add value to a given product is considered waste. For example, large amounts of raw materials sitting in a warehouse does not add value to the finished product. With a JIT system, there is no large inventory of materials in warehouses. The materials needed are delivered where and when they are needed *just-in-time*. This is why so many people think of JIT as a new inventory control system.

The overall goal of a JIT system is to identify and eliminate any aspect of any process involved in producing a product that does not add value to the product. The essential benefits of JIT are summarized as follows:

1. Stable final assembly production
2. Limited batch production
3. Shorter supply lead time
4. Shorter production lead times
5. Better quality
6. Easily integrated with manufacturing resources planning (MRP)
7. Decreases the number of suppliers
8. Greater at-source control of quality
9. Improves documentation procedures

Production Planning and Control and CIM

Production planning and control in a CIM environment involves such tasks as bringing in production jobs, scheduling, planning processes, determining material requirements, allocating work to machines, planning transportation schemes, and a variety of other tasks. All of these tasks can be arranged in a planning and control hierarchy (Fig. 19-9) with the following elements:

1. Management control
2. Production control
3. Material control
4. Process control
5. Machine control

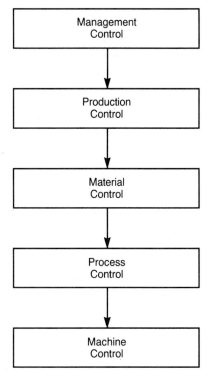

Figure 19-9 Production planning and control hierarchy

Management Control

This is the highest level in the hierarchy. It has four subcomponents: input, checking, process planning, and knowledge base, Fig. 19-10. Input involves providing information to the system that describes the part to be produced. Such information comes from the design database or CAD component.

Checking involves making sure the production system can handle the part before accepting it. This involves checking with factors as machine requirements, accuracy specifications, size limitations, and tool/fixture requirements.

Process planning involves determining all of the processes required to produce a part and ordering them sequentially. The knowledge base is a component of an expert system that serves all of the various elements displayed in the CIM wheel.

The knowledge base contains both part and procedural information. Part information contains all of the geometric data necessary to describe the part. Procedural information is data in the form of *if-then* statements. Procedural information includes both the conditional data for the *IF* side of the statement and action data for the *THEN* side.

Production Control

This component of the hierarchy has three subcomponents: work allocation system, a part programming system, and a material handling system, Fig. 19-11. Work allocation involves putting process plans into action according to the priorities established at the management level. Part programming involves producing the numerical control (NC) program. The material handling system must be set up to move workpieces from machine to machine in a manner that optimizes the amount of time devoted to workpiece movement, and minimize work-in-place inventory.

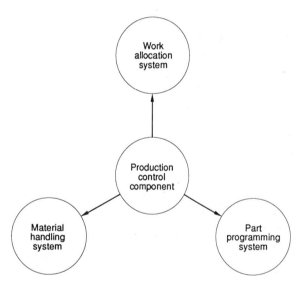

Figure 19-11   Production control component

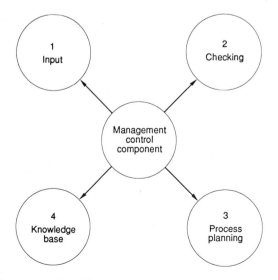

Figure 19-10   Management control component

Material Control

Material control involves identifying what will be needed and when and ensuring that needed materials arrive just-in-time. This component is where JIT (discussed earlier in this chapter) comes into play.

Process Control

Process control carries out direct numerical control or distributed numerical control (DNC). It is also set up to send feedback information up in the hierarchy. Information processed in this component includes tool wear, machine condition, inventory updates, material handling updates, production schedule updates, traffic control, fixture and pallet updates, and chip processing updates.

Machine Control

This component controls individual machines using NC programs sent down via DNC networks to programmable logic controllers (PLCs) or microcomputer controllers.

Communication and CIM

Communication is a particularly important concept in CIM. It means the movement of data among the various components of an overall CIM system. It is how data are extracted from the system as needed. Without communication, the individual components in a CIM setting are just *islands of automation.*

To understand communications as a concept one must first understand the difference between data and knowledge. Data represents the raw unorganized collection of information in a system. It becomes knowledge when it is organized and categorized by specified heuristic rules. Communication is the process by which data is reduced to knowledge and transmitted to the point of need.

In a CIM setting communication takes place via networks. It is important to understand that networks are not, in themselves, communication, just as roadways are not, in themselves, transportation. Rather, networks allow communication to take place.

Local Area Networks

A local area network, or LAN, is a dedicated data communication system covering a specific geographic area. LANs allow data to be communicated vertically and horizontally. One can think of a LAN in a CIM setting as a pipeline.

The actual physical structure of the pipeline can be twisted pair, coaxial, or fiber optic cable. Fiber optic cable has several advantages over the other two. It can carry over 50 megabits of data per second compared with 10 megabits per second with basebaud coaxial cable and 10 kilobits per second with twisted pair. It can carry voice, data, and video compared with just voice and data for basebaud coaxial cable and twisted pair. In addition, fiber optic cable is smaller, more secure, and immune to electromagnetic interference.

LANs can be configured in any one of several ways, Figs. 19-12 and 19-13. These configurations are

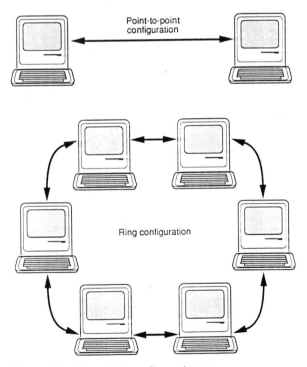

Figure 19-12　LAN configurations

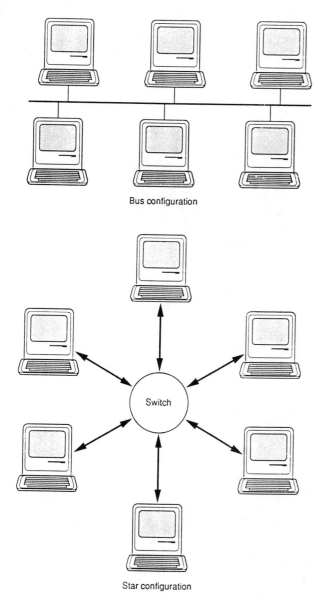

Bus configuration

Star configuration

Figure 19-13 LAN configurations

known as the point-to-point, ring, bus, and star configurations. Using such networks communication can occur between and among subsystems of a CIM system as diverse as a computer in accounting and an interactive graphics workstation in the design department or a word processing system in an office and a CNC machine tool on the shop floor.

Materials Handling and CIM

Materials handling is an important component in a CIM system. It is accomplished using one or more of the following technologies:

- Conveyor systems
- Monorails systems
- Automated guided vehicles
- Robots
- Automated storage and retrieval systems

Conveyor Systems

Conveyor systems are of two types: belt and roller. Both have their advantages and disadvantages. Neither is flexible enough for a CIM environment without special adaptations. Belt conveyors are limited to straight, round, or oval configurations; operate at a uniform speed; and operate in a continuous run format with only occasional stops. Roller conveyors are able to duplicate these capabilities. In addition, they can also be arranged in *T* or plus (+) shaped configurations and set up for periodic stops/starts.

Options added to conveyor systems in a CIM setting include gates to change the course of material being transported and computer control. Such systems are used primarily for moving workpieces from station to station. Figures 19-14 and 19-15 are examples of modern conveyor systems.

Monorail Systems

Monorails are a widely used material handling system in manufacturing. They can be configured so that the material load rides on top of the rail or suspended underneath. Monorails are particularly useful in settings where odd-shaped and bulky materials must be moved.

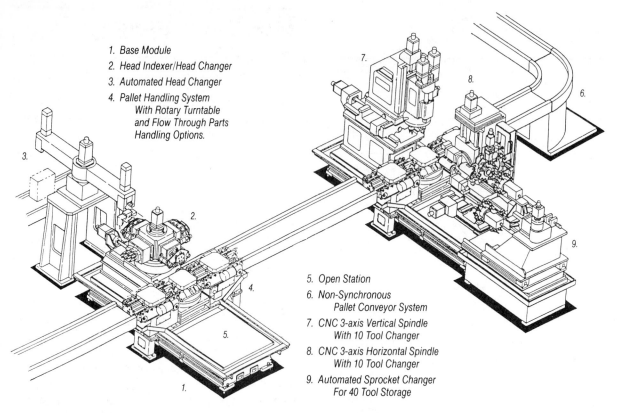

1. Base Module
2. Head Indexer/Head Changer
3. Automated Head Changer
4. Pallet Handling System
   With Rotary Turntable
   and Flow Through Parts
   Handling Options.

5. Open Station
6. Non-Synchronous
   Pallet Conveyor System
7. CNC 3-axis Vertical Spindle
   With 10 Tool Changer
8. CNC 3-axis Horizontal Spindle
   With 10 Tool Changer
9. Automated Sprocket Changer
   For 40 Tool Storage

Figure 19-14 Conveyor system *(Courtesy of Kingsbury Corporation)*

They are also useful for coordinating work-in-progress so that workpieces do not back up at workstations. This is accomplished by adding spurs to the monorail system that divert parts according to the production schedule in a coordinated manner systemwide. The pace of a monorail system can be changed at any time to accommodate the current level of activity on the shop floor. This flexibility makes the monorail a particularly effective material handling approach for CIM.

Automated Guided Vehicles

One advanced manufacturing technology seeing widescale use in CIM is the automated guided vehicle (AGV). As the world of manufacturing continues to evolve toward the fully automated factory, AGVs will play an increasingly important role.

An AGV is a computer-controlled, driverless vehicle used for transporting materials from point to point in a manufacturing setting. In any discussion of AGVs, three key terms are frequently used:

1. Guide path
2. Routing
3. Traffic management

The term *guide path* refers to the actual path the AGV follows in making its rounds through a manufacturing plant. The guide path can be one of two types. The first and oldest type is the embedded wire guide path. With this type, which has been in existence for over 20 years, the AGV follows a path dictated by a wire that is contained within a path

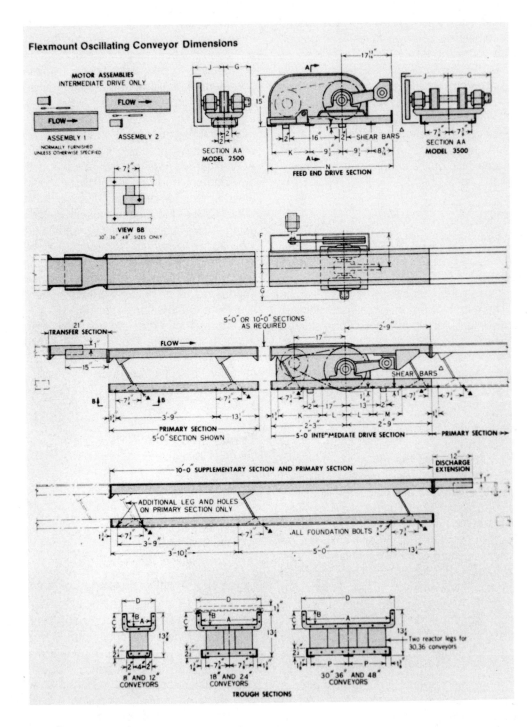

Figure 19-15 Conveyor system

that runs under the shop floor. This is why the earliest AGVs were sometimes referred to as *wire-guided vehicles*. The more modern AGVs are guided by optical devices.

The term *routing* is also used frequently in association with AGVs. Routing has to do with the AGV's ability to make decisions that allow it to select the appropriate route as it moves across the shop floor. The final term, *traffic management*, means exactly the same thing on the shop floor that it means on the highway.

Rationale for Using AGVs: The reasons AGVs are especially well suited to CIM are:

1. AGVs are flexible because they can be computer-controlled.
2. AGVs decrease labor costs by decreasing the amount of human involvement in material handling.
3. AGVs are compatible with production and storage equipment.
4. AGVs can operate in hazardous environments.
5. AGVs can handle and transport hazardous materials safely.

Flexibility is one of the keys to improved productivity in the modern manufacturing setting. It means the ability to adapt quickly to changes in products and processes brought about by the ever-changing demands of the marketplace. For a company to maximize its productivity and, thereby, its competitiveness, all manufacturing systems must be flexible. Computer control makes AGVs more flexible than traditional materials handling systems. Another factor that interests industrial engineers, manufacturing engineers, and manufacturing managers is the decreased amount of human involvement in materials handling that results with AGVs. Human involvement in materials handling adds significantly to the direct labor costs associated with manufactured products. It also increases indirect costs such as those associated with insurance and medical care necessary when human workers handle dangerous materials. By decreasing the amount of human involvement in materials handling, AGVs cut both direct and indirect costs.

Another key feature of AGVs is that they are easily interfaced with existing production and storage equipment. Because they are so versatile, they can be adapted to be compatible with most production and storage equipment that might exist in a typical manufacturing setting. The AGVs also appeal to industrial engineers, manufacturing engineers, and manufacturing managers responsible for producing products in hazardous or special environments. The AGVs that are designed to operate in a hazardous environment can be as tough and durable as the environment demands and they can transport heavy loads. One of the most frequently stated reasons for using AGVs in the modern manufacturing plant is their ability to handle hazardous material. Occupational safety and health regulations coupled with a concern for human workers have made it nearly impossible to handle hazardous materials productively in a manufacturing setting.

Of the various reasons frequently given for using AGVs, perhaps the two that are the most important to the future of manufacturing are flexibility and compatibility. Their flexibility and compatibility allow AGVs to fit in with trends in the world of manufacturing, including CIM.

Types of AGVs: There are six types of AGVs used in CIM settings:

1. Towing vehicles
2. Unit load vehicles
3. Pallet trucks
4. Fork trucks
5. Light load vehicles
6. Assembly line vehicles

Figure 19-16 contains examples of AGVs.

Monitoring of AGVs: One of the shortcomings of an automated materials handling system that relies principally on AGVs is that a malfunction of one vehicle can cause problems throughout the entire system. Therefore, it is important that AGV systems be monitored closely and continually. The ideal monitoring system is one that gives human operators instant, real-time feedback on the following:

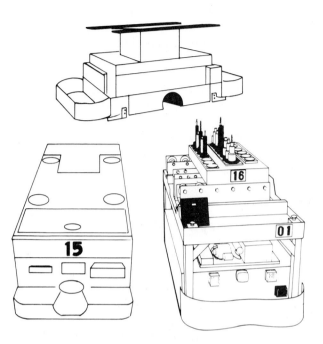

Figure 19-16   Sample of AGVs *(Courtesy of Society of Manufacturing Engineers)*

1. Location of all vehicles within the system.
2. Location of malfunctioning or inoperative vehicles.
3. Movement of vehicles.
4. Amount of time vehicles spend at each stop and en route between stops.
5. Status of all vehicles in the system, loaded or unloaded.
6. Destination of all vehicles within the system.
7. Status of the batteries in all vehicles within the system: charged, charging, or weak.

The sophistication of the monitoring system is dictated by the sophistication of the overall AGV system. For example, AGV systems that rely on simple dispatch methods such as onboard dispatch or offboard call system dispatch require little monitoring. This is because the human operators who use the onboard dispatch panel or offboard call box visually monitor routinely. However, AGV systems that use sophisticated central computer dispatch methods require very close and continual monitoring because

even the slightest programming error can cause problems throughout the entire AGV system.

Robots

Industrial robots play a major role in material handling in most CIM settings. The Robot Institute of America developed the following definition:

A robot is a reprogrammable multifunctional manipulator designed to move material, parts, tools, or specialized devices through variable programmed motions for the performance of a variety of tasks.

Figure 19-17 is an example of a modern industrial robot used for material handling.

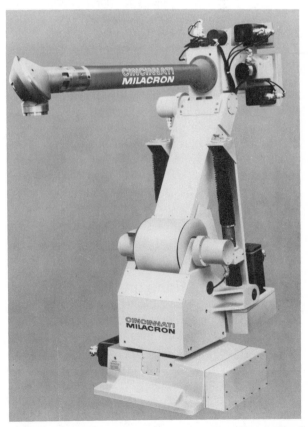

Figure 19-17   Modern industrial robot *(Courtesy of Cincinnati Milacron Marketing Company)*

The Robot System:

Work in a CIM setting is accomplished by a robot system. A robot system has four major components: the controller, the robot arm or manipulator, end-of-arm tools or end-effectors, and power sources. These components, coupled with the various other equipment and tools needed to perform the job for which a robot is programmed, are called the robot *work cell*. The work cell contains not just the robot system, but also an index table with an operator safety shield and special welding equipment.

The contents of a robot work cell vary according to the application of the robot. However, the one constant in a robot work cell is the robot system.

Robot Sensors:

Robots must be aware of their environment if they are to perform material handling tasks. Sensors are devices that make robots aware. There are three basic types of robot sensors: *contact, noncontact*, and *process-monitoring* sensors.

Robot sensors serve a variety of purposes, including locating and identifying parts to be handled, verification of the presence and the proper orientation of parts, determining forces, measuring temperatures, correction of errors in positioning, regulation of gripper pressure, protection against overloads, and calibration/recalibration of robots.

All of these purposes fall into one of four broad categories:

1. Monitoring
2. Detection
3. Analysis
4. Calibration

Robot Applications in Material Handling:

Handling of small, light parts is typically done by electrical robots. Electrical robots have a higher level of repeatability than hydraulically or pneumatically powered robots. This means they can more accurately return to a given position on a repeated basis than can hydraulic or pneumatic robots. However, a problem with electrical robots is they have a limited load capacity.

So material handling situations involving work too heavy for electrical robots require hydraulic or pneumatic robots. These types are less accurate, but have higher load capacities.

Robots are used in a variety of materials handling applications. They are particularly useful in settings where the materials to be handled are toxic, hot, or otherwise dangerous to humans. High repeatability and vision systems now allow robots to be used for presenting work to machine tools.

Automated Storage and Retrieval Systems

Storage of raw materials in warehouses has always been a problem. Often material is misplaced and, therefore, not available when needed. Getting material from the warehouse to the shop floor in a timely manner is a problem. Finally, there is seldom a match between what appears on an inventory record and what actually exists in the warehouse.

The problems associated with traditional storage and retrieval methods coupled with demands for warehousing efficiency brought by CIM led to the development of automated storage and retrieval systems (AS/RS), or computerized warehousing. AS/RS systems are the warehousing approach for CIM.

There are two broad types of AS/RS: *pallet load* and *box load*. In the former, material is stored in pallets that can be called up and brought to the shop floor in response to computer commands. In the latter, material is segregated in bins and brought to the shop floor in boxes. Both approaches can receive, segregate, store, and bring forth the material automatically. Such systems can be programmed according to a preset schedule or they can respond to individual commands sent via a computer terminal. In addition to receiving, storing, and retrieving materials, AS/RSs maintain continuously updated records of material on hand and available.

The movement of materials from the warehouse to the shop floor is typically handled by conveyor systems, AGVs, or both. Robots may be used for placing pallets or boxes on the conveyor or in an AGV and/or for unloading tasks.

Artificial Intelligence and CIM

A technology that will help in the full development of CIM is artificial intelligence. A most difficult problem to overcome in the factory automation component of CIM is the inability of production systems to mimic such basic human capabilities as adjusting appropriately to differences in the size, shape, and/or orientation of objects. Artificial intelligence will help solve this dilemma.

For example, in a traditional factory setting, an assembly worker whose job is to retrieve small parts from a feeder bin and insert them into the appropriate holes in a plate has many human attributes to assist him. These include: *sight, hand-eye coordination, reasoning abilities, logic, judgment*, and *experience*. If the assembly worker picks up a part that is not properly oriented or if on his first attempt to insert the part it does not properly seat, these human capabilities allow him to adjust appropriately. Even the most sophisticated automated assembly systems cannot completely mimic these capabilities. Artificial intelligence is an attempt to increase the number of human characteristics computers or computer-controlled systems can mimic.

Artificial Intelligence Defined

Artificial intelligence is the ability of a computer to imitate human intelligence and, thereby, make intelligent decisions. Computer-controlled systems that apply artificial intelligence to everyday settings are called *expert systems*. Such systems are discussed in the next major section.

In any discussion of artificial intelligence, there are several key words and phrases that are frequently used. Students of automated assembly should be familiar with at least the following artificial intelligence-related terms:

Algorithm: A special computer program that will solve selected problems within a given time frame.

Early vision: Computer calculations that allow systems to *see* by providing low-level data such as spatial and geometrical information.

Higher level vision: Computer calculations that allow systems to accomplish higher level tasks such as smart movement within an environment, object recognition, and reasoning about objects.

Knowledge engineering: A process through which knowledge is collected from experts in a given field and converted into a computable format.

Neurocomputing: An approach to performing calculations on a computer that is based on how the human nervous system operates.

Humans are able to make logical, reasoned adjustments in a work setting because they are able to quickly collect information, access it against the sum total of their human experience, and evaluate known relationships among various items of information. The science of artificial intelligence attempts to imitate this process with computers.

Humans attempt to create an experience in computers by feeding them all known information about a given subject. This information is then used by the computer in making decisions. This is why the concept is called *artificial intelligence*. The computer does not really think. Rather, it simply searches its memory for the appropriate information. If the information is there, the computer uses it in making logical decisions. The key is in feeding the computer enough relevant information.

Artificial Intelligence in CIM

Artificial intelligence has applications in a number of manufacturing settings, one of which is CIM. In such a setting, artificial intelligence can be used to allow automated systems such as robots to duplicate such human capabilities as vision and language processing. It can help improve the manufacturing skills of robots and other machines. Finally, artificial intelligence can improve the ability of information management systems used in CIM settings.

Expert Systems and CIM

CIM enables manufacturing firms to customize their products while maintaining both speed and flexibility. However, there is a downside that comes with these benefits. Customization greatly increases the amount of information that flows and must be collected, analyzed, synthesized, and acted on. The flexibility and speed requirements demand that this information be promptly dealt with. Expert systems have been developed to assist in the planning, implementation, and operation of CIM systems.

Expert systems are interactive computer systems that, through simulation, are able to play the roles of expert human beings in a specific area of expertise. Expert systems make information in a selected area of expertise available to people who are not experts in that area.

Expert systems have three basic components: 1) *a basic core of knowledge and rules*, 2) *people who interact with and operate the system*, and 3) *the system base*.

Human Rules Component

There is a fundamental knowledge base associated with any specific area of expertise. The principal element making up the knowledge base is a set of facts, figures, and hard data. Another element is a set of rules that can be applied to infer additional facts, figures, and data. This component is the nucleus of an expert system.

Operator/Interaction Component

The people who interact with an expert system make up another important component. They fall into three categories:

1. Experts
2. Knowledge engineers
3. Users

Experts are the people who provide the knowledge to the system. It is their expertise that is used to build the knowledge/rules component. They provide the facts and the rules of inference.

Users are the lay people in the subject area of expertise who use the system. In a CIM setting users may come to the system for manufacturing, management, or support assistance.

Knowledge engineers serve as a bridge between users and experts. They help experts properly code information that goes into the system and they structure simple nontechnical approaches to help lay people get information out of the system.

System Base Component

This component is the nucleus of the overall system. In addition to the knowledge/rules component, it houses six other subsystems:

1. Acquisition subsystem
2. Application subsystem
3. Explanation subsystem
4. Display subsystem
5. Edit subsystem
6. Validation subsystem

The acquisition subsystem gives the system the ability to acquire knowledge and rules from the experts through an interviewing process. The application subsystem tests input from users so that they receive the actual output they seek.

The explanation subsystem responds to queries concerning how information provided to users was actually derived. The display subsystem displays information called for in a format that is easy for the user to understand.

The edit subsystem allows knowledge in the system to be edited without losing, damaging, or violating the integrity of the original knowledge base. The validation subsystem allows the users to validate information by checking it against other known information.

Expert systems may be found in the production, management, and support components of a CIM setting. Figure 19-18 illustrates the various components of an expert system and how they relate to each other.

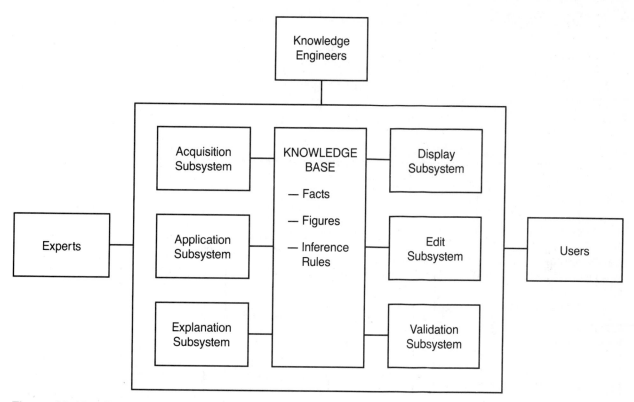

Figure 19-18   Expert systems in manufacturing

Databases and CIM

The potential for enhanced productivity through CIM is based on better management of information in all the components contained in the CIM wheel (see Figure 19-2). This is really the key to CIM: the integration of information from the management, finance, planning, design, and production components and better management of this information. The CIM database consists of data from several sources (Fig. 19-19):

1. Management
2. Marketing
3. Finance
4. Planning
5. Design
6. Production

All of this information must be continually processed and managed. CIM presented a new challenge to database management experts. It requires a more sophisticated system than those typically available off the shelf. CIM database applications are very different from business applications in that they: 1) must deal with geometric data; 2) must manage geometric data; 3) must understand relationships among various types of geometric data; and 4) must be able to deal with the concept of finite element analysis. Consequently, CIM database management systems must be intelligent systems with the ability to draw inferences and make deductions. The answer for database management with CIM was found by using expert systems for database management. The

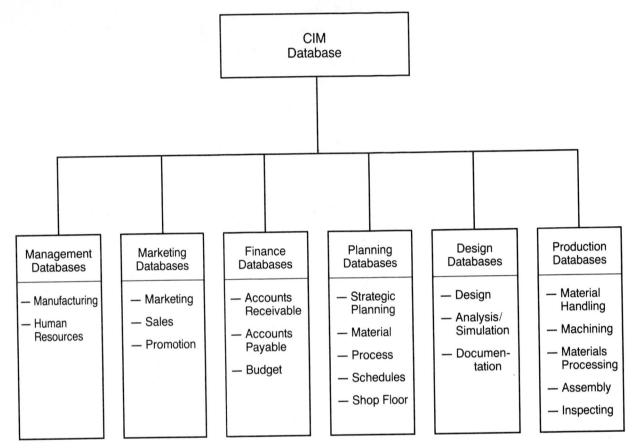

Figure 19-19   Components of a CIM database

result is known as *Engineering and Manufacturing Information Systems,* or *EMIS.*

Engineering and Manufacturing Information Systems

EMIS was developed to meet the database management challenge brought about by CIM. EMIS can be defined as:

A system which provides for the total integration of engineering and manufacturing processes and has the following attributes: 1) data manipulation and management; 2) the capabilities of an expert system; 3) a modeling capability for support of decision making; and 4) the ability to incorporate engineering data, geometric data, an engineering knowledge base, manufacturing data, and a manufacturing knowledge base.

EMIS must have a broad range of capabilities. These can be divided into four categories:

1. General capabilities
2. Database capabilities
3. Knowledge base capabilities
4. Miscellaneous capabilities

General capabilities of EMIS include deductive problem-solving, handling of incomplete information, distributed processing, and real-time processing. Database capabilities include manipulation of geometric data, handling of complex relationships, processing of long transactions, handling of different versions of data which represent different versions of a product, and simultaneous handling of both public (shared) data and private data.

Knowledge base capabilities include multiple knowledge representation, drawing inferences, and working cooperatively with other expert systems. The most important miscellaneous capability is management of decision making models.

KEY TERMS AND PHRASES

AGVs
Artificial intelligence
AS/RS
Automation
Batch manufacturing
CAD
CAPP
CIM
CNC
Conveyor systems
Databases
Design attributes
EMIS
Expert systems
Factory automation
Generative system
Group technology
IGES
Integration
Island of automation
Just-in-time (JIT)
Knowledge engineering
Local area network (LAN)
Manufacturing attributes
Manufacturing planning and control
MAP
Materials handling
MRP

National Institute of Standards and Technology
Neurocomputing
Part families
Parts classification and coding
Process planning
Production planning and control
TOP
Variant system

QUESTIONS FOR ADDITIONAL STUDY AND REVIEW

1. Define the term CIM.

2. List the various processes and activities necessary to convert raw materials to finished products and get them to their markets.

3. Explain the development of the term CIM.

4. List the four stages in the historical development of CIM.

5. List the various components of the CASA/SME *CIM Wheel.*

6. List the principal benefits of CIM.

7. Explain the following CIM-related standards:
   - MAP
   - TOP
   - IGES

8. Define the term *group technology.*

9. Define the term *part family* and explain how parts are grouped into families.

10. List four design attributes.

11. List four manufacturing attributes.

12. Explain the term *process planning.* 562

13. Define the term *CAPP*.

14. Explain the difference between variant and generative systems.

15. What is *MRP*?

16. List five benefits of MRP.

17. Define the term *JIT*.

18. List six benefits of JIT.

19. List and explain the five elements of *production planning and control*.

20. What is a *local area network?*

21. Explain the following materials handling technologies:
    - AGVs
    - AS/RS

22. List five advantages of using AGVs to handle materials.

23. What is *artificial intelligence?*

24. What is an *expert system?*

Glossary

abort A signal indicating that an action, operation, or procedure is to be terminated.

abrasive The material from which the grains in the wheel are made—usually crystalline aluminum oxide, silicon carbide, or diamond.

access time 1. The time interval between the instant at which data is requested from storage and the instant at which delivery is completed. 2. The time interval between the instant at which data is ready for storage and the instant at which storage is completed.

accumulator A register in the arithmetic logic unit of a computer in which the result of an arithmetic or logical operation is formed. Numbers may be totaled or manipulated, or they may be stored temporarily for transfers to and from memory or external devices.

active light A LED indicator which, when illuminated, indicates that communication exists between a module and the processor.

active storage Data storage locations which hold data being transformed into motion.

adaptive control (AC) A method using automatic means to change the type and/or influence of control parameters to achieve near optimum processing performance. Adaptive control is used to optimize independent parameters such as speeds and feeds to be consistent with processing constraints such as quality of surface finish and cutter life.

Adaptive Control Constrained (ACC) A control system in which improved machine productivity is obtained through in-process measurement by using limiting values for machine parameters such as torque or spindle deflection.

Adaptive Control Optimized (ACO) A control system in which optimum machine productivity is obtained through in-process measurement and adjustment of operating parameters.

address 1. A name, number, or label identifying a computer register, memory location, storage device, or any other computer data source or destination. 2. A symbol indicating the significance of information immediately following it.

air clamp An air-operated device for holding workparts against a nonmagnetic driver.

air lift hammer A gravity-drop forging hammer which uses air pressure to lift the hammer between strokes.

air orifice The air escape vent of an air gage which directs the air onto the work surface.

algorithm A finite set of rules or procedures for accomplishing a given result by proceeding on a logical step-by-step basis. Numerical control and computer programs are developed by this method.

alphanumeric code A coding system consisting of characters, including numbers, letters, punctuation marks, and such signs as $, ¢, and #. Also referred to as alphameric code.

American Standard Code for Information Interchange (ASCII) A data transmission code used for interchanging information among communication systems, data processing systems, and associated equipment. Seven bits represent each of the 128 characters in this code.

analog The use of physical variables, such as distance and rotation, to represent and correspond with numerical variables occurring in a computation. In NC, a system utilizing magnitudes of ratios of electrical voltages to represent physical axis positions.

anvil Large, heavy block of metal that supports structure of conventional forging hammers. Also, the block of metal on which hand forgings are made.

application A machine or process monitored by a processor-controller by means of a user program developed to accomplish a specific task.

arbor The spindle of a grinding machine on which the wheel is mounted.

architecture Preset, physical, and logical operating characteristics of a control system or control unit.

array A series of items or elements arranged in a meaningful pattern in one or more dimensions.

assembler A computer program that converts symbolic input into machine language and assigns memory locations for variables and constants. Also referred to as assembly program.

assembly language An operation language consisting of brief expressions. The language is translated by the assembler into machine language.

asynchronous A method of data transmission in which extra bits are transmitted with each character to identify the beginning and end of the character. The data bits within each character are transmitted in a definite time sequence, but the characters themselves are transmitted without a time relationship between one character and another.

automated process planning Creation of process plans, with partial or total computer assistance, for items in a particular family.

Automatically Programmed Tools (APT) A computer-assisted program system describing parts illustrated on a design and defining, in a sequence of statements, the part geometry, cutter operations, and machine tool capabilities. Used for turning, point-to-point work, and multiaxis milling.

automatic programming Digital computer transformation of instructions from a person into machine-oriented language used by the computer.

automatic size correction Automatic device for making corrections in the machine or the cycle in response to gage signals in order to correct drift.

balance (dynamic) A wheel in static balance is also in dynamic balance if, upon rotating, there is no vibration or whip due to unequal distribution of weight throughout its mass.

balance (static) A grinding wheel is in static balance when, centered on a frictionless horizontal arbor, it remains at rest in any position.

balancing Testing for balance; adding or subtracting weight to put a grinding wheel into either static or dynamic balance.

batch processing A manufacturing operation in which a designated quantity of material is treated in a series of steps. Also, a method of processing jobs so that each is completed before the next job is initialized.

baud A unit of signaling speed equal to the number of code elements (bits) per second. Normally one data bit per cycle is transmitted, but special equipment allows the transmittal of 2-4 bits per cycle in an octal train of signals.

bed The stationary, and usually horizontal, part of a press that serves as a table to which a bolster plate or lower die assembly is fastened.

bed The base of the machine on which most of the major components are mounted.

bed The stationary part of the shear frame that supports the material being sheared and the fixed blade.

Beginner's All-Purpose Symbolic Instruction Code (BASIC) A procedure-level computer language that is easy to learn and well suited for time-sharing communication via terminals connected with a remotely located computer.

binary A numerical system pertaining to characteristics involving a selection or condition in which two possibilities exist.

bit rate The rate at which binary digits, or the impulses representing them, pass a specific point in a communication line.

blank A piece of stock (also called a slug or multiple) from which a forging is to be made.

blister A defect caused by gas bubbles either on the surface or beneath the surface of the metal.

blocking A forging operation often used to impart an intermediate shape to a forging, preparatory to forging of the final shape in the finishing impression of the dies. Blocking can ensure proper "working" of the material and contribute to greater die life.

bloom Also called slab or billet, semifinished products of rectangular cross section with rounded corners, hot-rolled or forged. Blooms can also be circular forged sections. The cross-sectional area is usually larger for blooms than for billets.

blow The force delivered by one stroke of forging equipment.

blow hole A cavity produced by gas evolved during solidification of metal.

board hammer A type of gravity drop hammer which uses hardwood boards attached to the ram or hammer to raise the ram after the forging stroke.

bolster The plate secured to the bed of a press for locating and supporting the die assembly.

bond The material which cements the grains together making up the wheel. Bond may be rubber, shellac, resin, silicate, vitreous material, or metal, depending upon the abrasive material.

Boolean algebra A process of reasoning or a deduction system of theorems using symbolic logic and dealing with classes, propositions, yes/no criteria, etc., for variables rather than numeric quantities. Developed by George Boole, this algebra includes operators, such as AND, OR, NOT, EXCEPT, IF...THEN, that permit mathematical calculations.

boss A relatively short protrusion or projection on the surface of a forging, often cylindrical in shape.

brake A mechanism used to stop the motion of the shear ram and hold it in a stopped position when the clutch is disengaged.

buffer storage 1. A device for storing information for eventual transfer to active storage. It enables the control system to act on stored data without waiting for tape reading. 2. A register used for intermediate storage of data during the transfer of it from or to the computer's accumulators and a peripheral device. 3. A synchronizing element between two forms of storage; computation continues while information is transferred between the buffer storage device and the secondary storage device.

bug A flaw or defect in a program code or in the design of the computer rendering the program incapable of performing the objectives for which it was written.

burnishing The result of the movable blade rubbing against the edge of the sheared material due to a blade clearance that is adjusted too tight.

bus A conductor, or group of conductors considered as a single entity, which transfers signals or power between elements.

byte A sequence of binary digits operated upon as a single unit. A byte may be comprised of 8, 12, or 16 binary digits, depending upon the system.

camber Deviation from edge straightness, usually referring to the greatest deviation of a side edge from a straight line. Sometimes used to indicate crown or flat rolls.

camber The tendency of material being sheared from a sheet to bend away from the sheet in the same plane.

carbonitriding A surface hardening process consisting of heating ferrous metals in an atmosphere that permits absorption of both carbon and nitrogen into a shallow surface layer.

carburizing A process for introducing carbon into ferrous metals by heating above the transformation temperature while in contact with a carbonaceous medium (solid, liquid, gas, or plasma). Subsequent quenching produces a hardened surface. Homogeneous carburizing is the use of a carburizing process to convert a low-carbon ferrous alloy to one of uniform and higher carbon content throughout the section.

Cartesian coordinate system A system of two or three axes that intersect each other at right angles forming rectangles. Any point within the rectangular space can be identified by the distance and direction from any other point. Also known as rectangular coordinate system.

cathode ray tube (CRT) An electronic vacuum tube in which an electron beam can be focused on a small area of a luminescent screen and varied in position and intensity to form alphanumeric or graphic representations.

centerless grinding Grinding in which the workpiece is supported on its OD and rotated around an axis created by this reference surface. The workpiece is free to shift, and if the support surface is the one being ground, the axis of rotation also shifts.

centerline The axis of rotation.

centers Conical pins of a grinding machine upon which the work is centered, supported, and rotated during grinding.

center-type grinding Grinding by rotating the workpiece around a fixed centerline established by the chuck or centers in which it is held.

central processing unit (CPU) The portion of a computer that is the basic memory or logic. It includes the circuits controlling the interpretation and execution of instructions. Also known as the processor, frame, or main frame.

chatter A surface finish pattern caused by vibration of the wheel and/or work.

checks Very small, often microscopic, cracks.

chip 1. A small piece of semiconductor material on which electrical components are formed; an electronic circuit element prior to the addition of terminal connections and prior to being encased. 2. A piece of silicon cut from a slice by scribing or breaking, possibly containing one or more circuits but packaged as a unit. Also known as **die**.

chromizing A surface treatment at elevated temperature in which an alloy is formed by the diffusion of chromium into the base metal.

chuck A device attached to the work spindle that holds the workpiece for grinding, usually gripping it with jaws or fingers.

chuck jaws The actual gripping members in a chuck. Also referred to as fingers.

clearance The distance between the blades of a shear.

clutch An assembly that connects the flywheel to the driveshaft either directly or through a gear train to impart motion to the crosshead.

coaxial cable A two-conductor cable comprised of a wire centrally supported by insulators inside a flexible or nonflexible metal tube.

coding The preparation of a set of program instructions, by means of a specialized language, into an accurate representation of the program thereby allowing a given action to be taken or problem to be solved.

cogging The process of forging ingots to produce blooms or billets.

coining The process of applying necessary pressure to all or some portion of a forging's surface to obtain closer tolerances and smoother surfaces or to eliminate draft. Coining may be done while forgings are hot or cold and is usually performed on surfaces parallel with the parting line of the forging.

cold shut A defect characterized by a fissure or lap on a forging's surface which has been closed without fusion during the forging operation.

cold treatment Exposure to suitable subzero temperatures for the purpose of obtaining desired conditions or properties such as dimensional or microstructural stability.

command A signal from a machine control unit initiating a movement or function.

Common Business Oriented Language (COBOL) A programming language used mostly for business purposes. Most NC computer programs are written in FORTRAN (Formula Translation).

compatibility The degree to which tapes, languages, programming, and various specified units can be interchanged between various machine tools and various NC systems with minimal reduction in capability.

compiler A software program which translates symbolic operation codes into machine operation codes to produce an object language program.

Complementary Metal Oxide Semiconductor (CMOS) circuitry An integrated circuit family characterized by low power consumption.

compressive strength The maximum stress that a material subjected to compression can withstand when loaded without deformation or fracture.

computer An electronic device which uses programmed intructions to accept information in the form of signals or symbols, performing substantial computation, including arithmetic or logic operations, and supplying results of its performance without human operator intervention during the run.

Computer-Aided Design (CAD) The use of computers to aid in designing products.

Computer-Aided Manufacturing (CAM) The use of computers to aid in the various phases of manufacturing. Numerical Control (NC) is a subset of CAM.

computer graphics The process of communicating between a person and a computer in which the computer input and output are pictorial in nature, having the form of charts, drawings, or graphs. Cathode ray tubes, curve tracers, mechanical plotting boards, coordinate digitizers, and light pens are employed in the creation of the graphic design.

Computer Integrated Manufacturing System (CIMS) A multimachine manufacturing complex linked by a material handling system and including features such as toolchangers and load/unload stations. Under the control of a computer, various workpieces are introduced into the system, then randomly and simultaneously transported to the NC machine tools and other processing stations.

Computer Numerical Control (CNC) A self-contained NC system for a single machine tool utilizing a dedicated computer controlled by stored instructions to perform some or all of the basic NC functions. Punched tape and tape readers are not used except possibly as backup in the event of computer failure. Through a direct link to a central processor, the CNC system can become part of a Direct Numerical Control (DNC) system.

Computer Output Microfilm (COM) A microfilm printer that takes output directly from the computer, substituting for a line printer or tape output.

computer part programming The preparation of a manuscript, in an NC computer language, to define the necessary calculations to be performed by the computer.

computer program A detailed set or series of instructions or statements in a form acceptable as input to a computer to achieve a specific result.

continuous operation Uninterrupted multiple strokes of the crosshead without intervening stops at the end of individual strokes.

contouring control system An NC system that generates a contour by controlling a machine or cutting tool in a path resulting from the coordinated, simultaneous motion of two or more axes.

controller An apparatus through which commands are introduced and manipulated to compute, encode, and store data, produce readouts, and process computation and output. In NC, also known as machine control unit.

coping Shaping stone or other hard nonmetallic material with a grinding wheel.

core A ring of ferrite which can be magnetized either clockwise or counterclockwise to represent a binary digit 0 or 1.

core forging The process of displacing metal with a punch to fill a die cavity.

core memory A programmable high-speed random-access data storage device used to store information in ferrite cores. Usually employed as a working computer memory, the core memory retains information in the event of a power failure. Also referred to as magnetic core memory and magnetic core storage.

corner wear The tendency of a grinding wheel to wear on its corner so that it does not grind up to a shoulder without leaving a fillet.

counterblow equipment Equipment with two opposed rams that are activated simultaneously to strike repeated blows on the workpiece placed midway between them.

counterlock A jog in mating surfaces of dies to prevent lateral die shifting from side thrusts developed in forging irregular-shaped pieces.

creep Time-dependent strain occurring under stress. The resistance to creep, or creep strength, decreases with increasing temperature.

creep-feed grinding A technique of plunge grinding with special design in which the table speeds are kept very low and the wheel is fed down to full depth of cut in one or two passes.

critical speed That rotating speed beyond which the vibration of a spindle carrying an abrasive wheel or point would be hazardous.

critical (temperatures) Temperatures at which phase changes take place in metals.

crossfeed In surface grinding, the amount of horizontal feed of the wheel across the table, or of the table across the wheel.

cross forging Preliminary working of forging stock in flat dies so that the principal increase in dimension is in the transverse direction with respect to the original axis of the ingot.

cryogenics The area of technology that uses properties assumed by metals at extremely low temperatures.

cyaniding A surface hardening process consisting of heating ferrous metals to above their critical temperatures in molten salt containing cyanide, resulting in the simultaneous absorption of carbon and nitrogen. Subsequent quenching produces a hardened surface.

cybernetics The field of technology relating to the comparative study of the control and communication of information-handling machines and living organisms.

cylindrical gringing Grinding the outer surface of a part that rotates on centers or in a chuck.

data A representation of facts, instructions, concepts, numerical and alphabetical characters, etc., in a manner suitable for communicating, interpreting, and processing by humans or by automatic means such as NC systems.

debug The process of detecting, locating, and removing software errors and hardware problems causing malfunctions in a computer.

decarburization The loss of carbon from the surface of a ferrous metal as the result of heating in a medium, such as air, that reacts with the carbon.

deflection Bending or displacement of the wheel, wheelshaft, workpiece, or a machine member from its normal position. Usually refers to the wheel and wheelshaft.

diamond tool The diamond crystal and nib into which it is set.

diamond turner A device for holding the diamond and which provides a means of indexing the diamond easily without loosening the nib. Indexing can be either automatic or manual, and it allows dressing with a new face on the diamond.

die forging 1. Compression in a closed impression die. 2. A product of such an operation.

die match The condition in which dies, after having been set up in the forging equipment, are in proper alignment relative to each other.

digital Information and values expressed in discrete terms such as numbers. All information stored, transferred, or processed by dual-state conditions can be expressed by a combination of binary on/off or positive/negative signals. Contrasted with analog in which fluctuating signal strength determines the fluctuations of values.

digital computer A computer that can accept, store, and operate on symbols representing data by performing arithmetic and logic processes on the data.

Direct Numerical Control (DNC) The use of a shared computer to program, service, and log a process such as a machine tool cutting operation. Part program data is distributed via data lines to the machine tools.

disc grinder A machine on which abrasive discs are used.

discrete component circuit An electrical circuit implemented with individual components such as transistors, resistors, diodes, or capacitors.

disc wheel A grinding wheel shaped like a straight wheel, but usually mounted on a plate for grinding on the side of the wheel. Also referred to as abrasive disc.

dish wheel A ginding wheel shaped like a dish.

disk A flat rotating circular plate with a magnetizable surface on which information may be stored as a pattern of polarized portions on concentric recording tracks. Also spelled disc and known as magnetic disk.

disk storage A means of storing binary digits in the form of magnetized spots on thin circular metal plates coated with magnetizable material. Data is stored and retrieved by heads positioned over the disk surfaces. Also known as magnetic disk storage.

display The lights, annunciators, numerical indicators, or other operator output devices on the control console of computer, NC control, or programmable controller, etc., by which operations, commands, or data may be shown electrically to assist the operator.

documentation Manuals and other printed materials, such as tables, tape, listings, and diagrams, which provide instructive information regarding the operation, installation, and maintenance of a manufactured product.

dog A machine tool attached to the workpiece by means of which the work is revolved. A trigger which limits the advance of a traversing table.

dopant An impurity added to semiconductor materials to change the electrical characteristics of the material.

downfeed In surface grinding, the rate at which the grinding wheel is fed into the work.

downtime The time period in which a system or machine tool is not available for use due to failure or routine maintenance. Also known as cumulative lost time.

drawing out Stretching by a series of upsets along the length of the workpiece.

dressing Resharpening and renewing the cutting face of the wheel by removing or severing dull grains with a diamond or other type of dressing tool. Also referred to as trueing.

drop forging A forging produced in impression dies with a drop hammer.

dynamic storage Storage in which data is permitted to move or vary with time in such a way that it is not always instantly available for recovery; for example, storage in a magnetic drum or acoustic delay.

eccentric The offset portion of the driveshaft that governs the stroke or distance the crosshead moves on a mechanically or manually powered shear.

Erasable Programmable Read-Only Memory (EPROM) A read-only memory in which stored data can be erased and reprogrammed with voltage pulses.

error The discrepancy between a computed or measured value and an actual, specified, or theoretically correct value.

even parity check A parity check in which the sum of the 0's or 1's in a binary word is expected to be even.

external storage A storage medium or unit, such as a floppy disk or punched tape, that is not an internal part of the computer.

extrusion forging 1. Forcing metal into or through a die opening by restricting flow in other directions. 2. A part made by the operation.

feed Controlled movement of the wheel toward or away from the work surface.

feedback A unit for evaluating gage signals and sending them to the automatic size-correction device.

feedback The signal or data sent back to a commanding unit from a controlled machine or process for use as input in subsequent operations.

feedback device The element of a control system that converts linear or rotary motion to an electrical signal for subsequent comparison to an input signal.

feedback loop The portion of a closed-loop system that provides controlled response information enabling a comparison of the information with a referenced command.

feed rate The rate of movement between a machine element and a workpiece in the direction of cutting. Expressed as a unit of distance relative to time; a machine function such as spindle rotation or table stroke.

feed rate The rate of advance, usually expressed in thousandths of an inch (millimeters) (or smaller increments) per revolution of workpiece.

ferrite-core memory A storage device using a ferrimagnetic core for information storage. The core consists of a matrix of tiny toroidal cores molded from a square-loop ferrite through which the pulse-carrying wires and sense wire are threaded.

finishing The final cuts taken with a grinding wheel to obtain the accuracy and surface finish desired.

firmware A series of program instructions used so frequently that they are stored in a read-only memory instead of being handled by software.

first-generation computer The computer design of the early 1960s characterized by vacuum tubes, electronics, off-line storage on drum or disc, and programming in machine language.

fishtails Short, comet-like scratches caused by loose grains, or grains in the coolant, which are carried around by the wheel for only part of a revolution.

flame hardening A surface hardening process consisting of heating ferrous metals with a flame to above the Ac_3 temperature, followed by quenching.

flanges The circular metal plates which retain and drive a grinding wheel.

flash Excess metal that is pushed out of the die cavity.

floppy disk A flexible, magnetic-based disk used to store data input to NC machine control units.

flowchart A graphical representation of a problem or system, in which interconnected symbols signify operations, data flow, equipment, etc. It is used in defining, analyzing, or solving a problem.

flow lines Patterns resulting from elongation of the nonhomogeneities present in the ingot in the direction that the metal flows during working. Flow lines are usually revealed in cross sections of forgings by macroetching or sulfur printing.

forgeability The relative ability of material to deform without rupture.

forging (1)The process of deforming to the desired shape by forming in presses, hammers, rolls, upsetters, and related machinery. (2)The product resulting from this deformation process.

forging machine (upsetter or header) A type of forging equipment, related to the mechanical press, in which the main forming energy is applied horizontally to the workpiece, which is gripped and held by prior action of the dies.

forging stresses Elastic stresses induced by forging or cooling from the forging temperature; sometimes erroneously referred to as forging strains.

Formula Translation (FORTRAN) Any of a family of universal procedure-oriented languages used to describe numeric processes in such a way that both humans and computers can understand them.

fourth generation In the NC industry, the change in technology of control logic so that computer architecture and core memory are included.

frequency The number of cycles per second (Hz) occurring in various electronic devices.

friability The ability of abrasive grains to shatter under pressure.

front-gage Same as back-gage except that the locating fingers or surfaces are in front of the shear bed blade.

full-revolution clutch A type of clutch that, when tripped, cannot be disengaged until the crosshead has completed a full cycle.

gap An opening or recess in the housings to permit shearing or slitting material longer than the width of the shear. Also referred to as a throat.

gap frame Frame with a cutout to allow slitting or notching.

gaging Checking the workpiece for size with gages.

garbage Erroneous, unwanted, meaningless, or extraneous data in a computer or NC program.

gate A circuit, device, or element which blocks or passes a signal depending on one or more specified inputs.

G code A preparatory numerical code in a program addressed by the letter G indicating a special function or cycle type in an NC system. Also known as G function.

general-purpose computer A computer not dedicated to a specific task by a design.

glazed wheel A wheel with a cutting surface too smooth (or dull) to grind efficiently. Glazing is caused by worn or improperly dressed grains.

grade The strength of bonding of a grinding wheel; sometimes referred to as hardness.

grain The tiny particles of abrasive which, with the bond, make up the wheel. Grains do the actual cutting. Also referred to as grit.

grain flow Fiberlike lines caused by orientation of the constituents of the metal in the direction of working; can be visible on etched sections.

graphic input Input of symbols to NC systems that comes from lines drawn on a cathode ray tube or information obtained from drawings by a scanner.

gravity hammer A type of forging hammer that obtains energy for forging by the mass and velocity of a free-falling ram or hammer.

grinding Removing material from a workpiece with a grinding wheel or coated abrasives.

group technology 1. The classification and coding of parts on the basis of similarity of parts. 2. The grouping of parts based on processing similarities so that they can be processed together. 3. The grouping of various machines to produce a family of parts.

hard-acting wheel Grinding wheel that retains its dull abrasive grains or is less friable.

hard copy Any visually readable form of data output produced by a computer. For example, a printed listing, punched cards, or paper tape.

hardenability Comparative ability of metals to be hardened. For steels, hardenability refers specifically to the ability of martensite to be formed to a certain depth.

hardware The physical equipment of a system, as opposed to software; the mechanical, electrical, magnetic features of a system that are permanent components.

hard-wired system An NC system with a fixed wired program built in when manufactured and not subject to changes by programming. Changes are possible only through altering the physical components or interconnections.

heuristic method An exploratory method of problem solving in which various types of solutions that may or may not work are systematically applied and evaluated until a solution is found.

hierarchy A group or series classified and arranged in rank order.

high-level language Computer language which uses readily understood symbols and command statements. Each statement typically represents a series of computer instructions. Examples of high-level languages are BASIC, FORTRAN, and APT.

histogram A computer feature allowing the display or printing of ON/OFF times (measured in seconds) for any data table bit, whether an image table bit, a storage bit, or a bit associated with a times or counter instruction.

hold-down The mechanism used to clamp the workpiece to the bed so that it does not move during shearing.

hold-down beam A full-length member extending between the endframes on which hold-downs are mounted.

Hollerith A 12-bit code representing letters, numbers, or special symbols punched in 80-column cards with 12 rows per column.

home position The fixed location in the basic coordinate axes of the machine tool. Usually the point in the work process in which tools are fully retracted permitting any necessary changes.

homogenizing A high-temperature heat treatment process to decrease or eliminate chemical segregation by diffusion.

honing An abrasive process, usually performed on internal cylindrical surfaces, which employs bonded abrasive stones in a special holder to remove stock and improve surface finish.

host computer A main computer which monitors and controls other computers.

hot working The mechanical working of metal at a temperature above its recrystallization point, a temperature high enough to prevent strain hardening.

hydraulic hammer A gravity drop forging hammer which uses hydraulic pressure to lift the hammer between strokes.

hydraulic shear A shear with its crosshead actuated by hydraulic cylinders.

immediate access The ability to obtain data directly from a storage device or to place data directly in a storage device in a relatively short period of time and without serial delay due to other units of data.

impedance The total opposition a circuit offers to the flow of alternating current, including resistance and reactance.

impression A cavity machined into a forging die to produce a desired configuration in the workpiece during forging.

impression-die forging A forging that is formed to the required shape and size by machined impressions in specially prepared dies which exert three-dimensional control on the workpiece.

incremental coordinates Coordinates measured from the preceding value in a sequence of values.

incremental dimension The dimension from one point of departure to the next. In an NC program, if the entire job is incrementally dimensioned and the tool programmed to return to its start point, the algebraic sum of all the intervening plus and minus motion is zero.

index feed In cylindrical grinding, an arrangement by which the amount of infeed is indicated on a dial. On most machines, the reference is to the diameter of the work; on a few machines, the reference is to the radius.

induction hardening A surface hardening process consisting of heating ferrous metals by electromagnetic induction to above the Ac_3 temperature, followed by immediate quenching.

infeed The advance of the wheel toward and into the material (stock) to be ground away.

initialize To cause a program or hardware circuit to return a program, system, or harware device to an original state or to selected points by setting counters, addresses, or switches to zero or a selected starting value.

in-process gaging Continuous gaging of the part while being ground.

input 1. The transfer of external information by an appropriate medium into a computer or machine control unit. 2. Information transferred into main memory from terminals, buffer storage, or auxiliary storage.

input/output (I/O) The transfer of information into or out of a computer. Refer also to input and output.

input/output device Equipment such as limit switches, pressure switches, and pushbuttons, used to communicate with a control system.

instruction A set of bits which cause a computer to perform a specific prescribed operation and which may also indicate the values or locations of its operands.

integrated circuit (IC) A combination of passive and active circuit elements that are interconnected and incorporated on or within a continuous substrate.

interface A hardware circuit or medium by which two separate pieces of electrical equipment having separate functions, such as a machine control unit and a machine tool, may be linked.

interferometer An instrument that uses light interference phenomena to precisely determine wave length, spectral fine structure, indexes of refraction, and small linear displacements.

internal grinding Grinding the surface of a hole in the workpiece.

internal storage The total memory or storage that is directly controlled by the central processing unit of a computer.

interpolation A function of control enabling data points to be generated between specific coordinate positions to allow simultaneous movement of two or more axes of motion in a defined geometric pattern. For example, in NC, curved sections can be approximated by a series of straight lines or parabolic segments. Also known as linear interpolation.

interpolator A device that defines the path and rate of travel of a cutting tool when provided with a coded mathematical description of the path. All points between programmed end points are defined resulting in smooth curves or straight lines.

interrupt A break in the normal process of a system or program that enables high-priority work to be done and then normal processing resumed.

isothermal forging A forging operation performed on a workpiece during which the temperature remains constant and uniform. Generally used when aluminum, nickel, or titanium is being forged.

job control statement Computer statement used in identifying the job in a job stream and in describing the job's requirements to the operating system of the computer.

Karnaugh map Used to design logic, this map is a truth table rearranged to show a geometrical pattern of functional relationships for gating configurations. It facilitiates recognizing essential gating requirements by detailing similar, logical expressions and thereby allowing duplicate logical functions to be combined.

kilo (k) A prefix used in decimal notation to designate quantities 1000 times as great, as in kilowatt or kilovolt.

language A set of symbols combined with specific rules necessary for their interpretation.

language translator Any assembler, compiler, or routine that converts statements from one language into equivalent statements in a different language.

large scale integration (LSI) Any integrated circuits having more than 100 interconnected individual devices, such as gates and transistors, manufactured into a single semiconductor chip.

LED display An illuminated visual display composed of LED alphanumeric characters.

ledeburite The eutectic of the iron-carbon system, the constituents being austenite and cementite.

Light-Emitting Diode (LED) A semiconductor diode that converts electric energy into visible wavelengths.

limit switch A switch activated by a part or motion of a machine to change the electrical circuit associated with it.

lobiness From one to three high (or low) points around the circumference of a workpiece.

logic family A group of digital integrated circuits sharing a basic circuit design having standardized I/O characteristics.

loop The repeated execution of a series of instructions for a variable number of times, but usually with address modifications changing the operands of each iteration, until a terminating condition is completed.

machine language A language written in symbols, bits, characters, signs, or a series of bits to convey to a computer instructions or information to be processed.

machining center A machine tool, usually numerically controlled, that can automatically drill, ream, tap, mill, and bore workpieces. It is often equipped with a system for automatic toolchanging.

macro 1. A powerful computer instruction from which a string of micro instructions can be called as a unit. 2. A source language instruction from which many instructions can be generated. Also known as macro instruction, macro program, or macro routine.

magnetic core A ferrous element for switching or storing a binary bit of information in a computer.

magnetic disk A rotating circular plate that is coated or permeated with magnetic material on which information is recorded and stored for subsequent use.

magnetic tape A plastic, metal, or paper tape that is coated or permeated with magnetic material. It is capable of storing data by selective polarization of portions of the surface.

malfunction Any incorrect functioning within hardware.

Management Information System (MIS) An information feedback system in which data is recorded and processed for use by management personnel in decision making.

manipulation The controlling and monitoring of selected data upon which action can be taken to vary application functions.

manual data input (MDI) A means of manually inserting commands and other data into an NC control.

manual part programming The preparation of a manuscript in machine control language and format to define a sequence of commands required to accomplish a given task on an NC machine.

mechanical shear A shear with its crosshead driven by an eccentric which is engaged by a flywheel-clutch combination.

memory Any grouping of circuit elements having data storage and retrieval capability.

metal oxide semiconductor (MOS) 1. A metal insulator semiconductor structure in which the insulating layer is an oxide of the base material. 2. An electronic circuit in which the active region consists of an insulating oxide layer and a substrate. The oxide layer acts as the insulator between the metal gate and the conducting channel.

M function A function which controls a miscellaneous machine tool function, such as operating power clamps or turning coolant on or off.

microcomputer A computer constructed with a microprocessor as the basic element.

microelectronics The technology of constructing circuits and devices in miniaturized components. Refer to chip.

microprocessor A basic element of a central processing unit manufactured on relatively few integrated-circuit chips. It has a limited instruction set that is expandable by means of microprogramming.

microprogramming A programming technique in which each instruction begins execution of a sequence of microinstructions to obtain greater speed and more efficient use of memory.

mnemonic A combination of letters, numbers, pictures, or words that aids in recalling a memory location or computer operation.

mnemonic code A programming code that facilitates recall because it is written as meaningful notation resembling the original words. For example, MPY signifies multiply.

modulation The process or result of an operation by which a characteristic of a signal is varied in accordance with another signal.

modulator/demodulator (MODEM) A device used to convert binary digital data to audio tone signals for transmitting and receiving. Also known as data set.

module An interchangeable hardware subassembly containing electronic components that can be combined with other inerchangeable subassemblies to form a complete unit.

monitor To observe a program and supervise its execution to ensure that it is operating correctly.

monitoring controller A controller used in an application to continually check a process and alert an operator to application malfunctions.

monolithic integrated circuit An integrated circuit with at least one element formed within a silicon substrate.

mounted wheels Small bonded abrasive wheels permanently mounted on shafts.

movable blade A blade having one or more cutting edges that is attached to the crosshead.

nesting A programming technique in which a segment of a larger program is executed iteratively (looping) until a specific data condition is detected, or until a predetermined number of interactions has been performed. The nesting technique allows a program segment to be nested within a larger segment and that segment to be nested within an even larger segment.

network A collection of logic elements connected to perform a specific function.

neutral hardening The heat treatment of steel parts without affecting their surfaces with respect to carburization or decarburization.

new wheel A wheel that has not been trued.

nitriding A surface hardening process consisting of heating a ferrous alloy to a subcritical temperature in an atmosphere of ammonia or in contact with nitrogenous material. Hardening is attained by the formation of nitrides. Quenching is not required.

node A junction point in a network. Power can be received from the left as input, or power flow can be provided to the right as output.

noise 1. Unwanted and interfering signals in an electrical circuit. 2. Extra bits or words which serve no purpose and must be ignored or removed when data is being used.

normalizing A heat treatment process for ferrous metals consisting of heating to a temperature above the transformation range and then cooling in air. The process refines the microstructure and provides a carbide size and distribution favorable for subsequent heat treatment. Normalizing is also frequently used to treat large sections to provide a moderate increase in strength without an undue increase in stress and is often followed by tempering to reduce stresses further and to slightly modify the mechanical properties.

numerical control (NC) A technique for controlling actions of machine tools and similar equipment by the direct insertion of numerical data at a given point. Data is automatically interpreted.

numerical data Data in which a set of numbers or symbols that assume definite discrete values is used to express information.

object deck A set of cards containing machine-readable, condensed, computer instructions compiled for handling a specific general processor.

object program A fully compiled or assembled program, which is the output of an automatic coding system, that is ready for loading onto a computer.

odd parity Condition resulting when the sum of 1's in a binary word is odd.

offhand grinding Grinding work that is held in the operator's hand; also known as freehand grinding.

offset In centerless grinding, the displacement of the work center from the driver center.

on-line Operation of peripheral equipment that is under direct control of a central processor.

open-die forging Hot mechanical forming of metals between flat or shaped dies where metal flow is not completely restricted. Also known as hand or smith forging.

open-ended A process or system that can be augmented to permit an expansion, extension, or increase in capability.

open-loop system A control system that is incapable of comparing output with input for control purposes; that is, no feedback is obtainable.

operating system A group of programs and/or routines that guide a computer and assist it in accomplishing tasks.

operation code A recognizable alphanumeric code which is the part of a program instruction designating an operation to be performed.

optimize The rearrangement of instructions or data in NC or computer applications to obtain the best set of operating conditions.

organic bond A bond consisting of an organic material such as rubber, synthetic resin, or shellac.

oscillation A reciprocating grinding stroke.

out-of-round Having some points on the profile not equidistant from the common center (see roughness).

out-of-square More or less than 90 from the reference surface.

out-of-true Rotating eccentrically.

output 1. Printed or recorded data resulting from computed source programs. 2. Data transferred from internal storage to output devices or external storage.

output devices Devices which convey data from a computer to an external device.

parting line The line or plane along which the dies separate, sometimes called flash line or split line.

parting plane The plane which includes the principal die face and which is perpendicular to the direction of the ram travel. When parting surfaces of the dies are flat, the parting plane coincides with the parting line. Also referred to as the forging plane.

parity A means of testing the accuracy of binary numbers used in transmitted, recorded, or received data. A self-checking code is used in which the total number of 1's or 0's is always even or odd.

parity bit An additional nondata bit appended to an array of bits to make the sum of all 1's in a word always even or odd.

parity check A check to determine errors in a group of bits. The number of 1's or 0's in an array of binary digits should always be even or odd.

park A programmed instruction for moving a tool to a location at which tool and workpiece inspection is safe.

part program A complete set of data and instructions written in source languages for computer processing or written in machine language for manual programming for the manufacturing of parts on an NC machine.

part-revolution clutch A type of clutch that may be engaged or disengaged during any part of the cycle.

penetration The actual percentage of total material thickness that the blade has to enter to shear the material.

peripheral equipment Auxiliary machines and storage devices which may be placed under control of a central computer and used on- or off-line to provide a system with outside communication; for example, tape readers, high-speed printers, CRTs, magnetic tape feeds, and magnetic drums or disks.

photo-optic memory A memory which uses an optical medium for storage; for example, a laser used to record on photographic film.

pin gaging A variation of front-gaging in which the sheet is accurately positioned over pins by means of prepunched holes.

plotter 1. A device which will draw a facsimile of coded data input, such as the cutter path of an NC program. 2. A visual display or board on which a dependent variable can be drawn automatically as a function of one or more variables.

point-to-point control system An NC system which controls motion only to move from one point to another without exercising path control during the transition from one end point to the next.

polar axes The fixed lines from which the angles made by radius vectors are measured in a polar coordinates system.

polar coordinates A mathematical system of coordinates for locating a point in a plane by the length of the plane's radius vector and the angle the vector makes with a fixed line.

port 1. An entrance or exit of an electrical network. 2. A connecting unit between a data link and a device; for example, between an I/O channel, data bus, or interface module and a computer, data terminal, or CRT.

positioning/contouring system An NC system that is able to contour in two axes, without buffer storage, and position in a third axis for operations such as drilling, tapping, and boring.

postprocessor A computer program which converts generalized or centerline output, obtained from the general purpose processor and all other programming instructions for a machine and control, into a form that can be correctly interpreted by the machine control.

preparatory function An NC command on the input tape that changes the mode of control operation; usually referred to as G function because it is noted at the beginning of a block with the letter character G plus a 2-digit number.

preset tool A cutting tool placed in a holder so that a predetermined geometrical relationship exists with a gage point.

press forging Mechanical forming of metals by means of a press. The action is that of kneading the metal by relatively slow application of a force as compared with the action of hammering.

printed circuit A circuit for electronic components which is made by depositing conductive material in predetermined continuous paths from terminal to terminal on the surface of an insulating base.

printed circuit board A board on which a predetermined conductive pattern, which may or may not include printed components, has been formed.

printer An output device that prints or types characters in parallel or serial entry.

printout A printed output of a system giving all data that has been processed by a program.

Profilometer An instrument for measuring the degree of surface roughness in microinches or micrometers.

program A set of instructions that is expressed in a language suitable for computer input and that defines a desired sequence of conditions for a process as well as the operations required between the conditions.

programmable controller (PC) A solid-state industrial control system with a memory which can be set to operate in a specified manner to store instructions that implement functions such as I/O control logic, timing, counting, arithmetic, and data manipulation.

Programmable Read-Only Memory (PROM) A memory that is programmed only by special routines. Once programmed with permanent data, such as a mathematical formula, it becomes a Read-Only Memory (ROM).

programmable gaging Back-gaging in which the gage bar is driven by an encoder signal or servomotor that can be programmed by the operator.

protocol A formal agreement between two communicating devices. It defines how data is formatted, what the control signals mean, how error checking is performed, and the order and priority of various types of messages.

quenching Rapid coooling after heating by contact with liquids, gases, or solids.

rake The inclination of one blade with respect to the other in the shearing plane.

ram The moving part of a forging hammer, forging machine, or press, to which one of the tools is fastened.

random access memory (RAM) A type of memory that can be accessed (read from) independent of the time of the last access or the location of the most recently accessed data.

random tool selection A feature allowing the next tool to be loaded from any position in an automatic toolchanger rather than from the next location in the changer.

rapid traverse Tool movement at a maximum feed rate from one cutting operation to another.

read-only memory (ROM) Digital storage device that can be read from but cannot be written into by the computer.

read/write memory A memory in which data can be placed or accessed. When the data is placed, it destroys previous data. Stored data is not altered when accessed.

real time The ability of a computer to function and control a process as the process occurs.

remote access Access to a data processing facility enabling communication by one or more stations that are distant from the facility.

remote input/output The capability to position a portion of a controller's I/O (usually one channel) a distance from the processor, with communication from the I/O to the processor provided by means of two twin-axial cables.

repeatability Closeness of agreement among repeated measurements of the same characteristics by the same method under identical conditions. Also known as reproducibility.

resistivity A factor used in expressing the ability of a material to pass an electrical current through its bulk or on the surface.

resistor A device having electrical resistance and used in an electric circuit for protection, operation, or current control.

resistor-capacitor-transistor logic (RCTL) Logic performed by several resistors, a transistor, and a diode. Transistors are used to produce an inverted output; capacitors are used to enhance switching speed.

resistor-transistor logic (RTL) Logic performed by resistors, with transistors used to produce an inverted output.

resolution 1. A measure of the smallest distinguishable increment of change in the variable output of a device. 2. The minimum positioning motion that can be specified by an NC system.

restriking Striking a trimmed forging an additional blow in the dies to align or size its several components or sections. The operation can be performed hot or cold.

retrofit Modification of a machine originally operated by manual or tracer control to one that operates by NC controls.

roll forging The process of shaping stock between power-driven rolls bearing contoured dies, usually used for preforming. Roll forging is often employed to reduce thickness and increase length of stock.

roll grinding machine A special type of cylindrical grinding machine for grinding cylindrical rolls to be used for rolling metals, paper, or rubber.

rotary blade A shearing tool whose cutting edge makes a complete revolution about a fixed axis.

rough feed Feeding with relatively large increments. Usually done early in the cycle for fast stock removal.

roughness Surface finish characterized by sharp, closely spaced high and low spots.

round Having a curved profile, all points of which are equidistant from a common center.

routine A series of computer instructions which performs a specific application function.

RS-232C Electronic Institute of America (EIA) standard for data communications, RS-232 type C. Data is provided at various rates, 8 data bits per character.

rubber bond A bonding material whose principal constituent is natural or synthetic rubber.

rung A grouping of PC instructions controlling one output or storage bit. This is represented as one section of a logic ladder diagram.

scleroscope An instrument for determining the relative hardness of materials by a drop-and-rebound method.

scratches Annular marks on the surface usually caused by the wheel.

segmental wheel A wheel composed of segments assembled by the manufacturer to form a complete wheel.

seam A crack or inclusion on the surface of forging stock which may carry through forging and appear on the finished product.

secondary shear The condition occurring on material when the blades are too tight.

second generation In NC, the period of technology associated with transistors.

sensor A transducer or other device whose input is a quantitative measurement of an external physical phenomenon and whose output can be monitored by a computer or other control system.

servomechanism A power device for effecting machine motion. It embodies a closed-loop system in which the controlled variable is mechanical position and velocity.

sharp wheel A wheel that has just been dressed properly.

shearing The parting of material resulting when one blade forces the material past an opposing blade.

shear lance gaging Gaging by means of reference points made during punching.

shoe A nonrotating work rest with attached wear pad for supporting a cylindrical workpiece during grinding.

short stroke In plunge grinding, a slight grinding stroke imparted to the wheel (by a special device) to improve surface finish and geometry.

silica Silicon dioxide, SiO_2.

silicon carbide An abrasive made in the electric furnace from coke and silica, SiC.

silicon controlled rectifier (SCR) An electronic device generally used in control systems for high-power loads. It is an electrical "value" that can be turned on by a signal and will turn off when the power is removed or reverses direction.

simulation 1. The representation of physical systems and phenomena by computers or other equipment. 2. The technique of setting up a routine for one computer to make it operate like another computer.

sintering A heat treatment process by which the adjacent surfaces of powder metal particles in a compacted part are bonded to develop strength and adhesion.

sizing plug In the plug sizing method, the plug gage which is used to measure the bore.

skip dress Grinding more than one workpiece for each wheel dressing.

slideway A member that guides the crosshead downward during the shearing cycle.

slippage The constant sliding of the workpiece, on the driver face, as it seats itself in the shoes.

small scale integration (SSI) Any integrated circuit having fewer than 12 equivalent gates.

snagging Grinding which removes relatively large amounts of material without regard to finish; typically the removal of gates, tins, sprues, and parting lines from castings, surface defects from billets, and excess metal from welds.

soaking Holding a load of parts in a furnace at a fixed temperature for sufficient time to allow equalization of the temperature throughout the load.

soft-acting wheel Grinding wheel that loses its abrasive grains before they are dull.

software All programs, routines, and documents associated with a computer.

softwired A system in which a computer generates control logic, as determined by a software program.

solid state Pertaining to an electrical circuit having no moving parts, relays, vacuum tubes, or gaseous tube components.

solution heat treatment A treatment in which an alloy is heated to a suitable temperature and held at this temperature for a sufficient length of time to allow a desired constituent to enter into solid solution, followed by rapid cooling to hold the constituent in solution.

source language A computer input language comprised of statements and formulas used to specify computer processing. It is translated into object language by an assembler, compiler, or an interpreter.

source program 1. A program written in a symbolic language designed for ease of expression by humans. 2. The input program to be processed.

special-purpose logic Those proprietary features of a controller which allow it to do things not normally found in relay ladder logic.

stand-alone system A complete operational system that does not require support from other devices or systems.

statement A meaningful expression or generalized instruction in a source language.

steam hammer A type of drop hammer in which the ram is actuated for each stroke by a double-action steam cylinder.

stock Material to be ground from the workpiece to produce the required diameter.

storage medium Any device or recording medium on which data can be stored for subsequent retrieval.

stored-field read-only alterable memory Memories, generally read-only in nature, which may be reprogrammed in a limited fashion.

stored program numerical control The same as CNC except that it features an internal memory which can be altered by receiving new instructions.

straight-cut system A system which has feed rate control only along the axes and controlled cutting action that occurs only along a path parallel to the linear (or circular) machine ways.

straight dress Trueing a wheel to a cylindrical shape.

straight wheel A grinding wheel of any dimensions which has straight sides and a straight face and is not recessed, grooved, dovetailed, or rendered otherwise than cylindrical.

stress relieving A process to reduce internal residual stresses in metal parts by heating the parts to a suitable temperature, holding for a proper time at that temperature, and then cooling slowly to minimize the development of new residual stresses.

stroke position Axial position of grinding stroke relative to workpiece.

stroke positioning knob Control for positioning the grinding stroke relative to the work.

subroutine A portion of an NC program, stored in memory and capable of being called up to accomplish a particular operation. It reverts to the master routine upon completion.

surface finish The quality of the surface with respect to smoothness. Also referred to as surface texture.

surface grinding Grinding a plane surface.

surface hardening Various processes for producing surface layers on ferrous alloys that are harder or more wear resistant than the softer, tougher cores.

swage (swedge) Reducing or changing the cross-sectional area of the stock, usually by revolving the work between rapid impact blows.

swarf Accumulated chips, wheel particles, and other debris produced by grinding.

swarf cut The removal of a section of material such as clamping lugs from a part by cutting with a profiling cutter pass.

swing beam A shear design in which the crosshead swings from a bearing point to the rear of the shear.

symbolic coding Coding in which instructions are written in nonmachine language.

synchronous A method of data communication in which the data characters are transmitted one after another in a steady bit stream. A special "sync" character synchronizes the sending and receiving ends of groups of characters. In continuous data flow it is sent and sensed at the reveiving end to assure synchronization between sending and receiving ends.

taper Condition in a hole when the sides are not parallel.

temper brittleness Loss of notch toughness that results when certain steels are held within, or cooled slowly through, a specific range of temperatures below the transformation range, usually 600-950°F (315-510 C).

tempering Reheating of previously hardened or normalized material for the purpose of decreasing the hardness, minimizing stresses, improving ductility, and increasing toughness.

terminal A point in a system or communication network at which data can either enter or leave.

T function A code identifying a tool select command on a program tape.

thermocouple A pair of dissimilar metals in contact forming a thermojunction at which voltage is generated when the junction is heated.

third generation 1. In NC, the period of technology associated with integrated circuits. 2. In computer design, the period of technology utilizing integrated circuits, core memory, advanced programming concepts, advanced subroutines, time sharing, and fast core access.

time sharing The interleaved use of a device to provide apparently simultaneous service.

tool assembly A complete assembly usually consisting of the toolholder with collet, etc., where necessary, the cutter, and if applicable, the tool insert. The toolholder fits directly into the spindle nose of the machine.

tool function A command identifying a tool and calling for its selection.

tooling A set of required standard or special tools needed to produce a particular part, including jigs, fixtures, gages, and cutting tools but excluding machine tools.

tool offset An incremental displacement correction for tool position parallel to a controlled axis. 2. The ability to reset tool position manually to compensate for tool wear, finish cuts, and tool exchange.

transducer 1. A device for converting energy from one form to another. 2. In NC, a device for measuring output and converting it into a signal acceptable to an error detector.

transfer line A manufacturing system in which individual stations are used for dedicated purposes.

transformer coupling A method of isolating I/O devices from a controller.

transistor A device consisting of a small block of semiconductor material that has three or more electrodes and controls the flow of current.

transistor-transistor logic (TTL) A logic system evolving from DTL wherein the multiple diode cluster is replaced by a multiple emitter transistor, but is commonly applied to a circuit that has a multiple emitter input and an active pullup network.

trimming The process of removing flash or excess metal from a forging.

trueing Shaping the cutting surface of the wheel to the required form and bringing it into concentricity (making it true) with the axis of rotation (see dressing).

turning center A lathe-type NC machine tool capable of automatically boring, turning outer and inner diameters, threading, and facing parts. It is often equipped with a system for automatically changing or indexing cutting tools.

turn key system An NC or computer system installed by a supplier who has total responsibility for building, installing, and testing the system.

twist The tendency of material (strip) that is being sheared off to curve about a central longitudinal axis.

universal grinding machine A machine on which cylindrical, taper, internal, or face grinding can be done as required in toolrooms and machine shops.

unloading arm On some machines, an arm that unloads the workpart.

unloading chute A discharge chute for finished workparts.

upsetting Working metal in such a manner that the cross-sectional area of a portion or all of the stock is increased.

uptime The percentage of total working time in which a machine is in operating condition.

UV erasable PROM An erasable PROM that can be cleared by exposure to ultraviolet light. It can then be reprogrammed.

variable data Numerical information that can be changed during application operation.

vector A quantity that has magnitude and direction and is usually represented by a directed line segment whose length represents the magnitude and whose orientation in space represents the direction.

vector feed rate The resultant rate of feed at which a tool moves with respect to the work surface. Individual slides may move at a rate other than the programmed rate, but resultant movement is equal to the programmed rate.

verify To check, usually by automatic means, one typing or recording of data against another to minimize the number of errors in the data transcription.

vibration test A test used to determine a device's ability to withstand physical oscillations of specified frequency, duration, and magnitude.

vitrified wheel A grinding wheel made with a vitrified ceramic bond.

virtual memory A combination of core memory and secondary memory that can be treated as a single memory, thereby giving the "virtual" appearance of a larger core memory to the programmer.

volatile storage A memory in which data is retained only while power is applied.

wheel A grinding wheel; a straight or formed abrasive tool which is rotated to remove metal during the grinding process.

wheel breakthrough The distance the edge of the wheel projects beyond the edge of the bore at each end of the stroke.

wheel form The shape created on the wheel during trueing and dressing.

wheelhead Unit comprised of the wheel shaft and bearing assembly and the housing.

wheelhead axis The centerline around which the wheel revolves.

wheel path The imaginary line a wheel travels during one wheel slide stroke.

wheel shaft The shaft on which the wheel is mounted. Also called quill projection and wheel spindle.

wheel slide The slide that holds the wheelhead and gives the wheel its traversing or longitudinal motion.

wheel slide cam Cam governing the wheel slide traverse.

wheel slide cylinder The hydraulic cylinder that provides the traverse stroke.

wheel slide housing The housing containing the cross slide—wheel slide assembly.

wheel slide stroke Total axial travel of the wheel slide, including grinding, dressing, and loading stroke.

wheel speed Rotary speed of the wheel in sfm (m/s).

wheel structure The character of the wheel as determined by the proportion and arrangement of the grains and bond composing it.

windup Lost motion in a mechanical system that is proportional to the applied force or torque.

wire gauge One of many standard systems for identifying wire sizes.

word Any characters in logical sequence on a program tape sufficient to initiate a specific machine tool action.

word address format An NC tape format in which each word in a block is identified by one or more preceding characters.

word length The number of bits or characters in a word.

work The workpiece or workpart.

work area Central area between the workhead and the wheelhead in which the loading, grinding, and dressing are done.

work axis The centerline around which the workpiece revolve.

work drive The means of rotating the work spindle.

work holder The chuck collet or arbor attached to the work spindle which holds and may also rotate the workpart. On a shoe centerless machine the shoe holder and shoes.

workpiece program A program that provides instructions for machining a specific workpiece.

work speed Rotary speed of the work in sfm (m/s).

work spindle Spindle within the workhead which rotates the workpiece.

work surface That part of the work being ground.

worn diamond A diamond worn too flat on its exposed face to properly dress the wheel. Also referred to as dull diamond.

worn wheel A wheel worn or dressed down too small to be useable.

XTABL The APT vocabulary table containing the code numbers which are used to represent the vocabulary words of the APT language, as used internally by APT and passed along to the postprocessor.

Z axis The axis of motion that is parallel to the principal spindle of the machine.

zero offset A characteristic of an NC machine which permits the zero point on an axis to be shifted readily over a specified range.

zero synchronization A technique permitting automatic recovery of a precise position after the machine axis has been approximately positioned by manual control.

References

"What's New in Machinery and Equipment," *Adhesives Age* (May 1979), pp. 38-43; (May 1980), pp. 16-22; (May 1981), pp. 24-29; (May 1982), pp. 23-29.

Metalcutting: Today's Techniques for Engineers and Shop Personnel, the editors of *American Machinist* (New York: McGraw-Hill, 1979), p. 82.

"Markings for Indentifying Grinding Wheels and Other Bonded Abrasives," ANSI Standard B74.13—1977, American National Standards Institute, New York, p. 6.

"Specifications for Shapes and Sizes of Grinding Wheels, and Identification of Mounted Wheels," ANSI Standard B74.2—1974, American National Standards Institute, New York.

"Safety Requirements for the Construction, Care and Use of Grinding Machines," ANSI Standard B11.9—1975, American National Standards Institute, New York.

National Electrical Code, ANSI Standard C1—1975, American National Standards Institute, New York.

American National Standard for the Safe Use of Lasers, ANSI Standard Z136.1—1980, American National Standards Institute, New York.

"Quality Systems Terminology," ANSI/ASQC A3 (Milwaukee: American Society for Quality Control, 1978).

A.G. Bachmann, "Aerobic Acrylic Adhesives," *Adhesives Age* (August 1982), pp. 19-23.

John E. Barger, *Plasma Arc Cutting*, SME Technical Paper MR76-712, 1976, p. 2.

J.C. Bolger, *Treatise of Adhesion and Adhesives*, ed. R.L. Patrick (New York: Marcel Dekker, 1973), vol. 3, chap. 1, pp. 31-50.

Terry Bryce, *Wire EDM in Manufacturing Today*, SME Technical Paper MR79-990, 1979, p. 4.

C.V. Cagle, *Adhesive Bonding Techniques and Applications* (New York: McGraw-Hill Book Co., 1968), p. 71.

Carboloy Systems Dept., *Milling Handbook of High-Efficiency Metal Cutting* (Detroit: General Electric Co., 1980).

Carboloy Systems Dept., *Turning Handbook of High-Efficiency Metal Cutting* (Detroit: General Electric Co., 1980).

L.V. Colwell, J.R. Frederick, and L.J. Quackenbush, "Research in Support of Numerical and Adaptive Control in Manufacturing," The University of Michigan, Ann Arbor, MI, 1969.

Janet Devine, "Ultrasonically Assisted Machining," *The Carbide and Tool Journal* (September-October 1980), pp. 26, 28.

R.D. Dexheimer and L.R. Vertnik, *Adhesives in Manufacturing*, ed. G.L. Schneberger (New York: Marcel Dekker, 1983), chap. 13, pp. 325-352.

Thomas C. Doud, "Collets: An Effective Slant on Workholding," *Machine and Tool Blue Book* (November 1980).

J.F. Engelberger, *Robotics in Practice* (New York: AMACOM, 1980).

A.V. Feigenbaum, "Quality: Managing the Modern Company," *Quality Progress* (March 1985).

Bernard Feinberg, "Adaptive Control: Trainability Adds a New Dimension," *Manufacturing Engineering Management* (December 1971), pp. 18-22.

David L. Goetsch, *Advanced Manufacturing Technology* (Albany, New York: Delmar Publishers Inc., 1990), chap. 8.

M.P. Groover, *A Definition and Survey of Adaptive Control Machining*, SME Technical Paper MS70-561, 1970.

J.W. Hagan and K.C. Steuben, *Adhesives in Manufacturing*, ed. G.L. Schneberger (New York: Marcel Dekker, 1983), chap. 14, pp. 353-386.

M. Hauser and G.S Haviland, *Adhesives in Manufacturing*, ed. G.L. Schneberger (New York: Marcel Dekker, 1983), chap. 11, pp. 269-303.

G.S. Haviland, *Machinery Adhesives for Locking, Retaining and Sealing* (New York: Marcel Dekker, 1986).

F.C. Herot, "What You Should Know About Engineered Dispensing Stations for Adhesives," *Adhesives Age* (May 1980), pp. 23-28.

D.J. Hines, "Testing and Performance of Hot-Melt Adhesives," *Adhesives Age* (June 1980), pp. 27-32.

Lowell Holmes, "Hard Facts About Soft-Wired NC," *American Machinist* (July 1973).

"Quality-Vocabulary," ISO 8402—1986, American National Standards Institute, New York.

"Quality Management and Quality Assurance Standards—Guidelines for Selection and Use," ISO 9000—1987, American National Standards Institute, New York.

K.A. Jacobs, "Adhesive Application Equipment for Two-Part Reactive Materials," *Adhesives Age* (May 1982), pp. 35-39.

J. Llewell Jessup, *What Price Ultra-Precision Machining?*, SME Technical Paper MR78-954, 1978.

Theodore W. Judson, *Product Design for Turning and Milling*, SME Technical Paper MR76-902, 1976.

D.H. Kaelble, *Physical Chemistry of Adhesion* (New York: John Wiley & Sons, 1971).

R. Kardashian and S.V. Nablo, "Electron Beam Curing Equipment," *Adhesives Age* (December 1982).

M.E. Kimball, "Polyurethane Adhesives: Properties and Bonding Procedures," *Adhesives Age* (June 1981), pp. 21-26.

Eric R. Kline, *End Milling Experience with Adaptive Control*, SME Technical Paper MR69-208.

Jack D. Lane, *Automated Assembly*, 2nd ed. (Dearborn, MI: Society of Manufacturing Engineers, 1986), p. 127.

Paul D. Larson, "Ultrasonics—Machining the Unmachinable," *Automation* (now *Production Engineering*) (February 1975), p. 62.

A.F. Lewis and R. Saxon, *Epoxy Resins*, ed. H. Kawichi (New York: Marcel Dekker, 1969), chap. 10.

J.V. Lindyberg, *Adhesives in Manufacturing*, ed. G.L. Schneberger (New York: Marcel Dekker, 1983), chap. 15, pp. 387-406.

Machinability Data Center, *Machining Data Handbook*, Volume I, 3rd ed. (Cincinnati: Metcut Research Associates Inc., 1980).

"Lasers," *Machine Design* (November 19, 1978), p. 110.

Machine Vision Systems: A Summary and Forecast, 2nd ed. (Lake Geneva, WI: Tech Tran Consultants, 1985), pp. 1, 26-27, 29-66.

R.A. Mathias, *An Effective System for Adaptive Control of the Milling Process*, SME Technical Paper MS68-202, 1968.

J.D. Minford, *Durability of Structural Adhesives*, ed. A.J. Kinloch (London: Applied Science Publishers, 1983), chap. 4, pp. 173-200.

J.D. Minford, F.R. Hoch, and E.M. Vader, *Weldbond and Its Performance in Aluminum Automotive Body Sheet*, Paper No. 750462, SAE Congress and Exposition, Held February 1975, Detroit (Warrendale, PA: Society of Automotive Engineers, 1975).

J.D. Minford and E.M. Vader, *Adhesive Bonding of Aluminum Automotive Body Sheet*, Paper No. 740078, SAE Congress and Exposition, held February 1974, Detroit (Warrendale, PA: Society of Automotive Engineers, 1974).

Karl K. Moltrecht, *Calculating Machining Power*, SME Technical Paper MR77-974, 1977.

K. Nielsen, S. Locke, and J. Green, "New Developments in Electromechanical Machining," *Modern Machine Shop* (February 1977), p. 90.

Arne Novak, "Survey of AC Sensors," State of the Art Briefing on Adaptive Control, June 21, 1977, University of Michigan, Ann Arbor, MI.

Amir Novini, "Fundamentals of Machine Vision Lighting," *Vision* (May 1986), pp. 18-20.

W.A. Pletcher and E.J. Yaroch, *Adhesives in Manufacturing*, ed. G.L. Schneberger (New York: Marcel Dekker, 1983), chap. 16. pp. 407-423.

T. Pryor and W. Pastorius, *Applications of Machine Vision to Parts Inspection and Machine Control in the Piece Part Manufacturing Industries*, SME Technical Paper MS83-312 (Dearborn, MI: Society of Manufacturing Engineers, 1983).

E.A. Randlett, Jr., and Myron P. Ellis, *Electrochemical Honing—ECH*, SME Technical Paper MR68-815, 1968, p. 9.

E. Salje, H. Mushardt, and E. Scherf, "Measurement of Roughness for Control and Optimization of External Cylindrical Grinding," *Proceedings: Fifteenth Annual Abrasive Engineering Society Conference, May 1977*, Abrasive Engineering Society, Plymouth, MI.

George Schaffer, "Taking the Measure of CMMs," *American Machinist* (October 1982), pp. 146-147.

I. Skeist, *Handbook of Adhesives*, 2nd ed. (New York: Van Nostrand Reinhold, 1977).

Dr. Walter A. Specht, *Laser Safety Hazards—Problems but Solvable*, SME Technical Paper MR79-402, 1979, p. 5.

Norman E. Terrell, *Laser Precision Small Hole Drilling*, SME Technical Paper MR80-849, 1980, p. 6.

William F. Thomsen, *Adhesives in Manufacturing*, ed. G.L. Schneberger (New York: Marcel Dekker, 1983), chap. 12, pp. 305-323.

W. Tyrrell, *Rotary Ultrasonic Machining*, SME Technical Paper MR70-516, 1970.

Lawrence J. Utzig, "Quality Reputation—A Precious Asset," *34th Annual Quality Congress Transactions* (Milwaukee: American Society for Quality Control, 1980).

P. Villers, *Recent Proliferation of Industrial Artificial Vision Applications*, SME Technical Paper MS83-311 (Dearborn, MI: Society of Manufacturing Engineers, 1983).

W.G. Voorhees, *Electrochemical Discharge Machining*, SME Technical Paper MR67-165, 1967, p. 1.

P. Guenther Werner, *Application and Technological Fundamentals of Deep and Creep Feed Grinding*, SME Technical Paper MR79-319, 1979.

Charles Wick, "Automatic Adaptive Control of Machine Tools," *Manufacturing Engineering* (September 1977), p. 43.

William O. Winchell, "Assuring Quality in Strategic Business Units," *38th Annual Quality Congress Transactions* (Milwaukee: American Society for Quality Control, 1985).

D.J. Zalucha, "New Acrylics Structurally Bond Unprepared Metals," *Adhesives Age* (February 1972), p. 21.

A. Zawilinski, "Formulation and Performance of Water-Based PSA's," *Adhesives Age* (September 1984), pp. 29-34.

Index

NOW!

MANUFACTURING INSIGHTS VIDEO SERIES
Order Form (0979D)

Complete your instructional program with these quality videotapes from the Society of Manufacturing Engineers. Each tape conforms directly to a chapter in the text and supports the educational process by providing a visual explanation of the featured concept and its application.

You won't want to miss this valuable opportunity—order your videos TODAY! (Quantity Discounts Available)

☐ Yes! I need the information contained in these **Manufacturing Insights** videotapes. Please send me the title(s) indicated below. (Prices include UPS shipping and handling.)

Qty.	Order No.	Tape	Price Each	*Quantity Discount	Total
	CAD, CAM, CIM _____				
_____	VT252-0979D	CAD/CAM (VHS)	$200.00	$160.00	_____
_____	VT252U-0979D	CAD/CAM (U-Matic)	200.00	160.00	_____
_____	VT282-0979D	CAD/CAM Networking (VHS)	200.00	160.00	_____
_____	VT282U-0979D	CAD/CAM Networking (U-Matic)	200.00	160.00	_____
_____	VT250-0979D	Personal Computers in Manufacturing (VHS)	200.00	160.00	_____
_____	VT250U-0979D	Personal Computers in Manufacturing (U-Matic)	200.00	160.00	_____
_____	VT253-0979D	Simulation (VHS)	200.00	160.00	_____
_____	VT253U-0979D	Simulation (U-Matic)	200.00	160.00	_____
	Metalworking and Control _____				
_____	VT254-0979D	Programmable Controllers (VHS)	200.00	160.00	_____
_____	VT254U-0979D	Programmable Controllers (U-Matic)	200.00	160.00	_____
_____	VT239-0979D	Adaptive Control (VHS)	200.00	160.00	_____
_____	VT239U-0979D	Adaptive Control (U-Matic)	200.00	160.00	_____
_____	VT249-0979D	Cutting Tools (VHS)	200.00	160.00	_____
_____	VT249U-0979D	Cutting Tools (U-Matic)	200.00	160.00	_____
_____	VT256-0979D	Flexible Manufacturing Cells (VHS)	200.00	160.00	_____
_____	VT256U-0979D	Flexible Manufacturing Cells (U-Matic)	200.00	160.00	_____
_____	VT237-0979D	Flexible Manufacturing Systems (VHS)	200.00	160.00	_____
_____	VT237U-0979D	Flexible Manufacturing Systems (U-Matic)	200.00	160.00	_____
	Composites _____				
_____	VT248-0979D	Composites in Manufacturing (VHS)	200.00	160.00	_____
_____	VT248U-0979D	Composites in Manufacturing (U-Matic)	200.00	160.00	_____
	Automation _____				
_____	VT251-0979D	Automated Material Handling (VHS)	200.00	160.00	_____
_____	VT251U-0979D	Automated Material Handling (U-Matic)	200.00	160.00	_____
_____	VT255-0979D	Automated Assembly (VHS)	200.00	160.00	_____
_____	VT255U-0979D	Automated Assembly (U-Matic)	200.00	160.00	_____
_____	VT281-0979D	Automated Inspection/Non-Destructive Testing (VHS)	200.00	160.00	_____
_____	VT281U-0979D	Automated Inspection/Non-Destructive Testing (U-Matic)	200.00	160.00	_____
	Vision, Lasers, Sensors _____				
_____	VT240-0979D	Machine Vision (VHS)	200.00	160.00	_____
_____	VT240U-0979D	Machine Vision (U-Matic)	200.00	160.00	_____
_____	VT242-0979D	Lasers In Manufacturing (VHS)	200.00	160.00	_____
_____	VT242U-0979D	Lasers In Manufacturing (U-Matic)	200.00	160.00	_____
_____	VT280-0979D	Lasers In Manufacturing—A New Look (VHS)	200.00	160.00	_____
_____	VT280U-0979D	Lasers In Manufacturing—A New Look (U-Matic)	200.00	160.00	_____
_____	VT257-0979D	Sensors (VHS)	200.00	160.00	_____
_____	VT257U-0979D	Sensors (U-Matic)	200.00	160.00	_____
	Robotics _____				
_____	VT238-0979D	Robots in Assembly and Packaging (VHS)	200.00	160.00	_____
_____	VT238U-0979D	Robots in Assembly and Packaging (U-Matic)	200.00	160.00	_____
_____	VT241-0979D	Robots in Welding and Painting (VHS)	200.00	160.00	_____
_____	VT241U-0979D	Robots in Welding and Painting (U-Matic)	200.00	160.00	_____

The following tapes are also available from SME but were not used in the development of the text.

Qty.	Order No.	Tape	Price Each	*Quantity Discount	Total
_____	VT290-0979D	CAD/CAM Workstations (VHS)	$200.00	$160.00	_____
_____	VT290U-0979D	CAD/CAM Workstations (U-Matic)	$200.00	$160.00	_____
_____	VT286-0979D	Simultaneous Engineering (VHS)	$200.00	$160.00	_____
_____	VT286U-0979D	Simultaneous Engineering (U-Matic)	$200.00	$160.00	_____
_____	VT284-0979D	Implementing Just-In-Time (VHS)	$200.00	$160.00	_____
_____	VT284U-0979D	Implementing Just-In-Time (U-Matic)	$200.00	$160.00	_____
_____	VT287-0979D	Factory Data Collection (VHS)	$200.00	$160.00	_____
_____	VT287U-0979D	Factory Data Collection (U-Matic)	$200.00	$160.00	_____
_____	VT291-0979D	Advances in CNC (VHS)	$200.00	$160.00	_____
_____	VT291U-0979D	Advances in CNC (U-Matic)	$200.00	$160.00	_____
_____	VT288-0979D	Tooling for Plastics and Composites (VHS)	$200.00	$160.00	_____
_____	VT288U-0979D	Tooling for Plastics and Composites (U-Matic)	$200.00	$160.00	_____
_____	VT285-0979D	Machine Vision—A New Look (VHS)	$200.00	$160.00	_____
_____	VT285U-0979D	Machine Vision—A New Look (U-Matic)	$200.00	$160.00	_____
_____	VT289-0979D	Robotics in Circuit Board Assembly (VHS)	$200.00	$160.00	_____
_____	VT289U-0979D	Robotics in Circuit Board Assembly (U-Matic)	$200.00	$160.00	_____
_____	VT283-0979D	Robotics in Surface Preparation (VHS)	$200.00	$160.00	_____
_____	VT283U-0979D	Robotics in Surface Preparation (U-Matic)	$200.00	$160.00	_____
			Total Enclosed		$ _____

*Quantity Discounts Available! Order six or more of these informative videotapes and save 20%! Each tape will cost you only $160.00. Order yours and save today!

Your Choice of 3 Options:

☐ Payment Enclosed
☐ Purchase Order Enclosed
☐ Credit Card (Circle One)　　MasterCard　　　　American Express　　　　VISA

Account Number　　　　　　　　　　　　Expiration Date

Signature

Ship to: (Please Print or Type)

Name

Title

School/Company

Address

City

State/Zip

Phone (　　) _____
(In case there's a question about your order.)

Mail order to: Delmar Publishers Inc.
2 Computer Drive, West
Box 15015
Albany, New York 12212-5015

Order by phone with your credit card.
Call 1-800-347-7707.

Note: Your order must be accompanied by full payment, purchase order, or credit card information. Prices subject to change without notice. Sorry, videotapes are not available for rent. All videotape sales are final.

Preview Policy: To discuss preview arrangements, please contact Kim Harris at 1-800-347-7707.